CALCULUS

CALCULUS
ONE AND SEVERAL VARIABLES

SATURNINO L. SALAS
UNIVERSITY OF CONNECTICUT

EINAR HILLE
UNIVERSITY OF NEW MEXICO

XEROX COLLEGE PUBLISHING

LEXINGTON, MASSACHUSETTS | TORONTO

CONSULTING EDITOR | George Springer, Indiana University

ISB Number: 0-536-00650-4   (Domestic)
ISB Number: 0-536-00701-2   (International)
Library of Congress Catalog Card Number: 74-141896

Printed in the United States of America.

PREFACE

Preliminary versions of this text have been used in a three semester calculus sequence at the University of Connecticut:

Chapters 1–9, plus excerpts from 10, during the first two semesters;
Chapters 12–15, plus excerpts from 10 and 11, during the third semester.

We have deliberately avoided the exotic and stayed within the main stream of calculus. We have done this in the belief that the so-called standard material is the most important, the most useful, and the most interesting. What we have tried to do here is present the standard material in a congenial manner.

S.L.S.

E.H.

ACKNOWLEDGMENTS

To Judith E. Salas and Dagmar Noll for their sustained and sustaining assistance. To George Springer, J. P. King, Louis J. DeLuca, Donald R. Kerr, Jr., Donald R. Wilken, and Norton Starr for their many suggestions. To Xerox College Publishing for permission to include exercises from Granville, Smith, and Longley's celebrated *Elements of Calculus*.

THE GREEK ALPHABET

A	α	alpha
B	β	beta
Γ	γ	gamma
Δ	δ	delta
E	ϵ	epsilon
Z	ζ	zeta
H	η	eta
Θ	θ ϑ	theta
I	ι	iota
K	κ	kappa
Λ	λ	lambda
M	μ	mu
N	ν	nu
Ξ	ξ	xi
O	o	omicron
Π	π ϖ	pi
P	ρ	rho
Σ	σ ς	sigma
T	τ	tau
Υ	υ	upsilon
Φ	ϕ φ	phi
X	χ	chi
Ψ	ψ	psi
Ω	ω	omega

CONTENTS

4   INTEGRATION

5   THE LOGARITHM AND EXPONENTIAL FUNCTIONS

6   THE TRIGONOMETRIC AND HYPERBOLIC FUNCTIONS

11   L'HOSPITAL'S RULE; IMPROPER INTEGRALS

12   VECTORS

13   VECTOR CALCULUS

14   FUNCTIONS OF SEVERAL VARIABLES

15   MULTIPLE INTEGRALS

APPENDIX

CALCULUS

This book is available both as a complete volume and in two parts. The complete volume is intended for three semesters. In the two-part version, Part I can be used for a two-semester course and deals with functions of one variable, analytic geometry, and infinite series (Chapters 1–11 of the complete volume). Part II contains infinite series, vectors, and functions of several variables (Chapters 10–15 of the complete volume).

INTRODUCTION

1.1 What is Calculus?

To a Roman in the days of the empire a "calculus" was a little pebble that he used in counting and in gambling. Centuries later the verb "calculare" came to mean "to compute," "to reckon," "to figure out." To the engineer and mathematician of today calculus is the branch of mathematics that takes in elementary algebra and geometry and adds one more ingredient: *the limit process.*

Calculus begins where elementary mathematics leaves off. It takes ideas from elementary mathematics and extends them to a much more general situation. Here are some examples. On the left-hand side you will find an idea from elementary mathematics; on the right, this same idea as enriched by calculus.

Elementary Mathematics	*Calculus*
slope of a line $y = mx + b$	slope of a curve $y = f(x)$
tangent line to a circle	tangent line to a more general curve

average velocity, average acceleration	instantaneous velocity, instantaneous acceleration
distance moved under a constant velocity	distance moved under varying velocity
area of a region bounded by line segments	area of a region bounded by curves
sum of a finite collection of numbers $a_1 + a_2 + \cdots + a_n$	sum of an infinite series $a_1 + a_2 + \cdots + a_n + \cdots$
average of a finite collection of numbers	average value of a function on an interval
length of a line segment	length of a curve
center of a circle	center of gravity of a region
volume of a rectangular solid	volume of a solid with a curved boundary

surface area of
a cylinder

surface area of
a more general solid

tangent plane to
a sphere

tangent plane to
a more general surface

work done by
a constant force

work done by
a varying force

mass of an object
of constant density

mass of an object
of varying density

center of a sphere

center of gravity of
a more general solid

1.2   Notions and formulas from elementary mathematics

The following outline is presented for review and easy reference.

I Sets

the object x is in the set A: $x \in A$
(x is an element of A)
the object x is not in the set A: $x \notin A$
containment: $A \subseteq B$
union: $A \cup B$
intersection: $A \cap B$
empty set: a set with no elements

(These are the only notions from set theory that you will need for this book. If you
are not familiar with them, see Section 1 of the appendix.)

II Real Numbers

(1) CLASSIFICATION

integers: $0, 1, -1, 2, -2, 3, -3,$ etc.

rational numbers: $\dfrac{p}{q}$ where p and q are integers, $q \neq 0$

irrational numbers: real numbers which are not rational; for example, $\sqrt{2}, \pi$.

(2) ORDER PROPERTIES

  (i) $a < b, b < a,$ or $a = b$

  (ii) if $a < b$ and $b < c,$ then $a < c$

  (iii) if $a < b,$ then $a + c < b + c$ for all real numbers c

  (iv) if $a < b$ and $c > 0,$ then $ac < bc$

     if $a < b$ and $c < 0,$ then $ac > bc$

(3) DENSITY

Between any two numbers there is a rational number and an irrational number.

(4) ABSOLUTE VALUE

$$|a| = \sqrt{a^2}; \ |a| = \max \{a, -a\}; \ |a| = \begin{cases} a, & \text{if } a \geq 0 \\ -a, & \text{if } a \leq 0 \end{cases}$$

geometric interpretation: $|a| = $ distance between a and 0

                               $|a - c| = $ distance between a and c

properties: (i) $|a| = 0$ iff $a = 0$†

           (ii) $|-a| = |a|$

           (iii) $|ab| = |a|\,|b|$

           (iv) $|a + b| \leq |a| + |b|$ (the triangle inequality)

           (v) $\big||a| - |b|\big| \leq |a - b|$ (alternate form of the triangle inequality)

(5) INTERVALS

The notation

$$\{x: (\quad)\}$$

is used to denote the set of all x such that ( ). Suppose now that $a < b$. The *open interval* (a, b) is the set of all numbers between a and b:

$$(a, b) = \{x: a < x < b\}.$$

The *closed interval* $[a, b]$ is the open interval (a, b) plus the end points

$$[a, b] = \{x: a \leq x \leq b\}.$$

---

† By "iff" we mean "if and only if." This expression is used so often in mathematics that it is convenient to have an abbreviation for it.

There are seven other types of intervals:

$$(a, b] = \{x: a < x \leq b\}, \qquad [a, b) = \{x: a \leq x < b\},$$
$$(a, \infty) = \{x: a < x\}, \qquad [a, \infty) = \{x: a \leq x\},$$
$$(-\infty, b) = \{x: x < b\}, \qquad (-\infty, b] = \{x: x \leq b\},$$
$$(-\infty, \infty) = \mathbf{R} = \text{set of real numbers}$$

(6) BOUNDEDNESS

A set S of real numbers is said to be

(i) *bounded above* iff there exists a real number M such that

$$x \leq M \qquad \text{for all} \quad x \in S.$$

(M is called an *upper bound* for S)

(ii) *bounded below* iff there exists a real number m such that

$$m \leq x \qquad \text{for all} \quad x \in S.$$

(m is called a *lower bound* for S)

(iii) *bounded* iff it is bounded above and below.

Example. The intervals $(-\infty, 2]$ and $(-\infty, 2)$ are bounded above but not below.

Example. The set of positive integers is bounded below but not above.

Example. The intervals $[0, 1]$, $(0, 1)$, and $(0, 1]$ are bounded (both above and below).

III Algebra and Geometry

(1) GENERAL QUADRATIC FORMULA

The quadratic equation

$$ax^2 + bx + c = 0, \qquad a \neq 0$$

has solutions

$$x = \frac{-b \pm \sqrt{b^2 - 4ac}}{2a}.$$

(2) FACTORIALS

$$0! = 1$$
$$1! = 1$$
$$2! = 2 \cdot 1$$
$$3! = 3 \cdot 2 \cdot 1$$
$$\cdot$$
$$\cdot$$
$$\cdot$$
$$n! = n(n - 1) \cdots (2)(1).$$

(3) ELEMENTARY FIGURES

circle: area $= \pi r^2$; circumference $= 2\pi r$;

            area of sector $= \frac{1}{2}r^2\theta$, where θ is the central angle measured in radians;

            length of circular arc $= r\theta$, where θ is the central angle measured in radians

right circular cylinder: volume $= \pi r^2 h$; lateral area $= 2\pi rh$;

                       total surface area $= 2\pi r(r + h)$

cone: volume $= \frac{1}{3}\pi r^2 h$; lateral area $= \pi r\sqrt{r^2 + h^2}$;

          total surface area $= \pi r(r + \sqrt{r^2 + h^2})$

sphere: volume $= \frac{4}{3}\pi r^3$; surface area $= 4\pi r^2$

IV *Analytic Geometry*

(1) ABSCISSA AND ORDINATE

The x-coordinate of a point is called the *abscissa*; the y-coordinate is called the *ordinate*.

(2) DISTANCE BETWEEN TWO POINTS $P(x_0, y_0)$ AND $P(x_1, y_1)$:

$$d = \sqrt{(x_1 - x_0)^2 + (y_1 - y_0)^2}.$$

(3) LINES

(i) slope of a line $= \dfrac{\text{rise}}{\text{run}} = \tan \alpha$, where α is the angle of inclination

(ii) equations for lines

general form: $Ax + By + C = 0$, A and B not both 0

vertical line: $x = a$

slope-intercept form: $y = mx + b$

point-slope form: $y - y_0 = m(x - x_0)$

two-point form: $y - y_0 = \dfrac{y_1 - y_0}{x_1 - x_0}(x - x_0)$

two-intercept form: $\dfrac{x}{a} + \dfrac{y}{b} = 1$

(iii) angle between two nonvertical lines

$$\tan \theta = \frac{m_1 - m_0}{1 + m_1 m_0}$$

(iv) perpendicular lines

$$m_1 = -\frac{1}{m_0}$$

(4) EQUATIONS OF CONIC SECTIONS

circle of radius r centered at the origin: $x^2 + y^2 = r^2$

circle of radius r centered at $P(x_0, y_0)$: $(x - x_0)^2 + (y - y_0)^2 = r^2$

parabolas: $y = 4cx^2$, $x = 4cy^2$

ellipse: $\dfrac{x^2}{a^2} + \dfrac{y^2}{b^2} = 1$

hyperbolas: $\dfrac{x^2}{a^2} - \dfrac{y^2}{b^2} = 1, \quad xy = c$

[The conic sections are discussed in detail in Chapter 7.]

V Trigonometry

(1) ANGLE MEASUREMENT

2π radians = 360 degrees = one complete revolution

one radian = $\dfrac{180}{\pi}$ degrees

(2) SECTORS

length of subtended arc = $r\theta$, where θ is the central angle measured in radians
area of sector = $\frac{1}{2}r^2\theta$, where θ is the central angle measured in radians
$= \frac{1}{2}r \cdot$ length of subtended arc.

(3) SINE AND COSINE

Take θ between 0 and 2π. In the unit circle (Figure 1.2.2) mark off the sector OAP that has central angle θ radians:

$$\cos\theta = x\text{-coordinate of } P, \quad \sin\theta = y\text{-coordinate of } P$$

These definitions are then extended periodically:

$$\cos\theta = \cos(\theta + 2n\pi), \quad \sin\theta = \sin(\theta + 2n\pi).$$

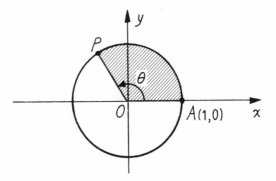

FIGURE 1.2.1   FIGURE 1.2.2

(4) OTHER TRIGONOMETRIC FUNCTIONS

$$\tan\theta = \frac{\sin\theta}{\cos\theta} \qquad \cot\theta = \frac{\cos\theta}{\sin\theta}$$

$$\sec\theta = \frac{1}{\cos\theta} \qquad \operatorname{cosec}\theta = \frac{1}{\sin\theta}$$

(5) IN TERMS OF A RIGHT TRIANGLE

For θ between 0 and $\dfrac{\pi}{2}$,

$$\sin \theta = \frac{\text{opposite side}}{\text{hypotenuse}} \qquad \cos \theta = \frac{\text{adjacent side}}{\text{hypotenuse}}$$

$$\tan \theta = \frac{\text{opposite side}}{\text{adjacent side}} \qquad \cot \theta = \frac{\text{adjacent side}}{\text{opposite side}}$$

$$\sec \theta = \frac{\text{hypotenuse}}{\text{adjacent side}} \qquad \operatorname{cosec} \theta = \frac{\text{hypotenuse}}{\text{opposite side}}$$

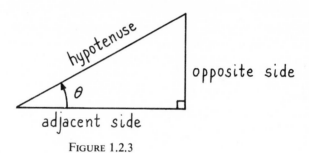

FIGURE 1.2.3

(6) ODDNESS AND EVENNESS
cosine function is even: $\cos(-\theta) = \cos \theta$ (graph symmetric with respect to the y-axis)
sine and tangent functions are odd: $\sin(-\theta) = -\sin \theta$, $\tan(-\theta) = -\tan \theta$ (graph symmetric with respect to the origin)

(7) IDENTITIES
(i) $\cos^2 \theta + \sin^2 \theta = 1$, $\tan^2 \theta + 1 = \sec^2 \theta$, $\cot^2 \theta + 1 = \operatorname{cosec}^2 \theta$
(ii) $\sin(\theta_1 + \theta_2) = \sin \theta_1 \cos \theta_2 + \cos \theta_1 \sin \theta_2$
      $\sin(\theta_1 - \theta_2) = \sin \theta_1 \cos \theta_2 - \cos \theta_1 \sin \theta_2$
      $\cos(\theta_1 + \theta_2) = \cos \theta_1 \cos \theta_2 - \sin \theta_1 \sin \theta_2$
      $\cos(\theta_1 - \theta_2) = \cos \theta_1 \cos \theta_2 + \sin \theta_1 \sin \theta_2$
(iii) $\sin 2\theta = 2 \sin \theta \cos \theta$, $\cos 2\theta = \cos^2 \theta - \sin^2 \theta$
(iv) $\sin^2 \theta = \dfrac{1 - \cos 2\theta}{2}$, $\cos^2 \theta = \dfrac{1 + \cos 2\theta}{2}$

(8) IN AN ARBITRARY TRIANGLE

law of sines: $\dfrac{\sin A}{a} = \dfrac{\sin B}{b} = \dfrac{\sin C}{c}$

law of cosines: $a^2 = b^2 + c^2 - 2bc \cos A$
[The calculus of the trigonometric functions is discussed in Chapter 6.]

VI Induction

Axiom: Let S be a set of integers. If

(A) 1 is in S and   (B) k is in S implies $k + 1$ is in S,

then all the positive integers are in S.

In general, we use induction when we want to prove that a certain proposition is true for all positive integers n. To do this, first we prove that the proposition is true for $n = 1$. Then we prove that, if it is true for $n = k$, then it is true for $n = k + 1$. It follows then from the axiom that the proposition is true for all positive integers n. We will use induction only sparingly. For a discussion of it we refer you to Section 2 of the appendix.

1.3 Inequalities; absolute value; boundedness

To solve an inequality is to find the set of numbers that satisfy it. Inequalities play such an important role in calculus, that it is probably a good idea to refresh your memory on the subject. Here are some sample problems.

Problem.   Solve the inequality

$$3(1 - x) \leq 6.$$

SOLUTION

$$3(1 - x) \leq 6$$

$$\begin{aligned}
1 - x &\leq 2 &&\text{(we divided by 3)} \\
-x &\leq 1 &&\text{(subtracted 1)} \\
x &\geq -1 &&\text{(multiplied by } -1)
\end{aligned}$$

As a solution we have the interval $[-1, \infty)$.   □

Problem.   Solve the inequality

$$\frac{(x^2 - 4x + 3)}{5} > 0.$$

SOLUTION

$$\frac{(x^2 - 4x + 3)}{5} > 0$$

$$\begin{aligned}
x^2 - 4x + 3 &> 0 &&\text{(multiplied by 5)} \\
(x - 1)(x - 3) &> 0. &&\text{(factored)}
\end{aligned}$$

The product $(x - 1)(x - 3)$ is positive iff both factors are negative:

$$x - 1 < 0, \quad x - 3 < 0,$$

or both factors are positive:

$$x - 1 > 0, \quad x - 3 > 0.$$

The first situation arises when

$$x < 1$$

and the second situation arises when

$$x > 3.$$

As the solution we have

$$\{x: x < 1 \text{ or } x > 3\} = (-\infty, 1) \cup (3, \infty). \quad \square$$

Problem.   Solve the inequality

$$\frac{x+2}{1-x} > 1.$$

SOLUTION.   Since division by 0 is not defined, $1 - x$ cannot be 0 and therefore x cannot be 1. To clear fractions we will have to multiply by $1 - x$. It is therefore important to keep track of the sign of $1 - x$.

Let's assume first that

$$1 - x > 0, \qquad \text{or equivalently, that} \qquad x < 1.$$

In this situation

$$\frac{x+2}{1-x} > 1$$

gives

$$\begin{aligned}
x + 2 &> 1 - x \\
x &> -1 - x \\
2x &> -1 \\
x &> -\tfrac{1}{2}.
\end{aligned}$$

This means that, of all the numbers x that are less than 1, the only ones that satisfy the initial inequality are those that are greater than $-\tfrac{1}{2}$. The set $(-\tfrac{1}{2}, 1)$ is therefore at least a partial solution.

Let's assume now that

$$1 - x < 0, \qquad \text{or equivalently, that} \qquad x > 1.$$

In this situation,

$$\frac{x+2}{1-x} > 1$$

gives

$$\begin{aligned}
x + 2 &< 1 - x \\
x &< -1 - x \\
2x &< -1 \\
x &< -\tfrac{1}{2}.
\end{aligned}$$

This means that, of all the numbers that are greater than 1, the only ones that satisfy the initial inequality are those that are less than $-\tfrac{1}{2}$. There are no such numbers.

The set $(-\tfrac{1}{2}, 1)$, which we obtained in the first case, is therefore the total solution. $\square$

We come now to some inequalities that involve absolute values. We begin with the inequality

$$|x| < d.$$

The easiest way to handle this inequality is to think of $|x|$ as the distance between 0 and x. It then becomes immediately obvious that

$$\boxed{|x| < d \quad \text{iff} \quad -d < x < d.}$$

The inequality

$$|x - c| < d$$

can be handled with similar ease. The number $|x - c|$ represents the distance between c and x. It is therefore obvious that

$$\boxed{|x - c| < d \quad \text{iff} \quad c - d < x < c + d}$$

We illustrate the boxed-in assertions in Figure 1.3.1.

FIGURE 1.3.1

As another example of this type we take the inequality

$$0 < |x - c| < d.$$

Here we have the inequality

$$|x - c| < d$$

with the additional requirement that x cannot be c. Consequently we have

$$0 < |x - c| < d \quad \text{iff} \quad c - d < x < c \quad \text{or} \quad c < x < c + d.$$

One of the fundamental inequalities of calculus is the triangle inequality

$$\boxed{|a + b| \leq |a| + |b|.}$$

Problem. Prove the validity of the triangle inequality

$$|a + b| \leq |a| + |b|.$$

PROOF. The proof is easy if you think of $|x|$ as $\sqrt{x^2}$. We begin by noting that

$$(a + b)^2 = a^2 + 2ab + b^2 \leq |a|^2 + 2|a||b| + |b|^2 = (|a| + |b|)^2.$$

Comparing the extremes of the inequality and taking square roots, we get

$$\sqrt{(a + b)^2} \leq |a| + |b|.$$

The result follows from observing that

$$\sqrt{(a + b)^2} = |a + b|. \quad \square$$

Here is another inequality that comes up in calculus:

$$\boxed{||x| - |c|| \le |x - c|.}$$

Problem.   Prove that

$$||x| - |c|| \le |x - c|.$$

PROOF.   Once again we begin by squaring.

$$\begin{aligned}
||x| - |c||^2 = (|x| - |c|)^2 &= |x|^2 - 2|x||c| + |c|^2 \\
&= x^2 - 2|x||c| + c^2 \\
&\le x^2 - 2xc + c^2 \quad \text{(Why?)} \\
&= (x - c)^2
\end{aligned}$$

Comparing extremes we get

$$||x| - |c||^2 \le (x - c)^2.$$

Now we take square roots:

$$||x| - |c|| \le \sqrt{(x - c)^2} = |x - c|. \quad \square$$

Exercises †

Solve the following equations and inequalities.

1.* $|x - 2| = 0.$	8. $4(1 - 2x) < 5.$	15.* $|x - 2| < x.$
2. $|3x - 5| = 0.$	9.* $(x - 1)(x + 1) < 0.$	16.* $(x - 1)(x + 1) \le 3.$
3.* $|(x - a)(x - b)| = 0.$	10.* $x \le |x|.$	17. $\dfrac{1}{x} < x.$
4.* $|x - 2| < 1.$	11. $x - 2 = |2 - x|.$	18.* $x + \dfrac{1}{x} \ge 1.$
5. $|x - 2| \le 1.$	12.* $|x| \le x.$	19.* $\dfrac{x}{x - 5} \ge 0.$
6.* $|x - 2| > 1.$	13.* $x^3 + x < 0.$	20. $|2x - 3| < \dfrac{1}{2}.$
7.* $4x - 1 < x.$	14. $x^4 - 3x^3 + 2x^2 > 0.$	21.* $\dfrac{1}{|2x - 3|} < 1.$

---

† The starred exercises have answers at the back of the book.

1.4 Some comments on functions

As the last step of our review of elementary mathematics we single out for special attention some properties of functions. In particular we go over some terminology.

Domain and Range

The *domain* of a function is the set of numbers for which it is defined. The *range* of a function is the set of values that it takes on. In the case of the squaring function

$$f(x) = x^2, \qquad x \text{ real}$$

the domain is the set of real numbers but the range is only $[0, \infty)$. In abbreviated form we can write

$$\operatorname{dom}(f) = (-\infty, \infty) \qquad \text{and} \qquad \operatorname{ran}(f) = [0, \infty).$$

In the case of

$$g(x) = \sqrt{1 - x^2}, \qquad x \in [-1, 1]$$

the domain is the closed interval $[-1, 1]$ and the range is the closed interval $[0, 1]$:

$$\operatorname{dom}(g) = [-1, 1] \qquad \text{and} \qquad \operatorname{ran}(g) = [0, 1].$$

The graph of f is the parabola of Figure 1.4.1. The graph of g is the semicircular arc depicted in Figure 1.4.2.

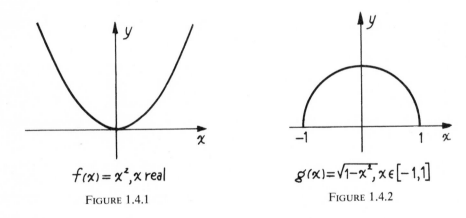

$$f(x) = x^2, x \text{ real} \qquad\qquad g(x) = \sqrt{1-x^2}, x \in [-1,1]$$

FIGURE 1.4.1   FIGURE 1.4.2

Sometimes the domain is not explicitly given. For example, we might write

$$F(x) = x^3 \qquad \text{and} \qquad G(x) = \sqrt{x}. \qquad\qquad \text{(Figures 1.4.3 and 1.4.4)}$$

In such cases you can take as the domain the maximal set for which the definition makes sense. For the examples just given you can take

$$\operatorname{dom}(F) = (-\infty, \infty) \qquad \text{and} \qquad \operatorname{dom}(G) = [0, \infty).$$

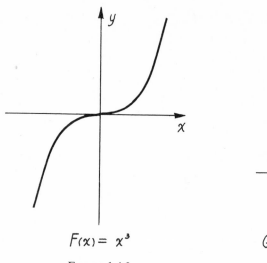

$$F(x) = x^3$$

FIGURE 1.4.3

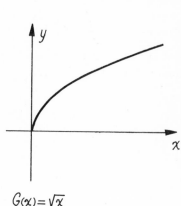

$$G(x) = \sqrt{x}$$

FIGURE 1.4.4

One-to-Oneness

A function can take on the same value at different points of its domain. Thus, for example, the squaring function takes on the same value at $-c$ as it does at c. In the case of

$$f(x) = (x - 3)(x - 5)$$

we have not only

$$f(3) = 0 \quad \text{but also} \quad f(5) = 0.$$

Functions for which this kind of repetition does not occur are called *one-to-one*.

Definition of One-to-Oneness

A function is said to be *one-to-one* iff there are no two points at which it takes on the same value.

As examples we can take

$$f(x) = x^3 \quad \text{and} \quad g(x) = \sqrt{x}.$$

The cubing function is one-to-one because no two numbers have the same cube. The square root function is one-to-one because no two numbers have the same square root.

Combining Functions

Functions with a common domain can be added and subtracted:

$$(f \pm g)(x) = f(x) \pm g(x).$$

They can be multiplied:

$$(fg)(x) = f(x)g(x).$$

They can be divided:

$$\frac{f}{g}(x) = \frac{f(x)}{g(x)}, \qquad \text{provided that} \quad g(x) \neq 0.$$

They can also be multiplied by a scalar (a real number) α:

$$(\alpha f)(x) = \alpha f(x).$$

Example. With

$$f(x) = |2 - x| \qquad \text{and} \qquad g(x) = x^2 + 1$$

we have

$$(f + g)(x) = f(x) + g(x) = |2 - x| + x^2 + 1$$

$$(f - g)(x) = f(x) - g(x) = |2 - x| - (x^2 + 1)$$

$$(fg)(x) = f(x)g(x) = |2 - x|(x^2 + 1)$$

$$\frac{f}{g}(x) = \frac{f(x)}{g(x)} = \frac{|2 - x|}{x^2 + 1}$$

$$(2f)(x) = 2f(x) = 2|2 - x|. \quad \square$$

The arithmetical operations just described present no difficulties. There is another way of combining functions on which we want to refresh your memory. To describe it, we begin with two functions f and g and a number x in the domain of g. By applying g to x, we get the number $g(x)$. If $g(x)$ is in the domain of f, then we can apply f to $g(x)$ and thereby obtain the number $f(g(x))$. If we can do this with each number in the domain of g, then we can create a new function in this manner.

Definition of Composition

Suppose that the range of g is contained in the domain of f. That is, suppose that f is defined at $g(x)$ for each x in the domain of g. The composition $f \circ g$ (read "f circle g") is the function defined on the domain of g by setting

$$(f \circ g)(x) = f(g(x)).$$

To apply $f \circ g$ we first apply g, then f. Here are some examples.

Examples

(1) If

$$f(x) = -(x^3 + 1) \qquad \text{and} \qquad g(x) = \sqrt{x}$$

then

$$(f \circ g)(x) = f(g(x)) = -([g(x)]^3 + 1) = -(x\sqrt{x} + 1).$$

(2) If

$$f(x) = \frac{1}{x} \quad \text{and} \quad g(x) = x^2 + 1$$

then

$$(f \circ g)(x) = f(g(x)) = \frac{1}{g(x)} = \frac{1}{x^2 + 1}$$

and

$$(g \circ f)(x) = g(f(x)) = [f(x)]^2 + 1 = \frac{1}{x^2} + 1. \quad \square$$

Inverses

If f is a one-to-one function then f^{-1}, read "f inverse" and called the inverse of f, is the function defined on the range of f by setting

$$f^{-1}(f(x)) = x.$$

In simple language we can characterize f^{-1} as the function that "undoes" the work of f. If f has the value $f(x)$ at x, then f^{-1} has the value x at $f(x)$. If you think of f as taking x to $f(x)$, then you can think of f^{-1} as taking $f(x)$ back to x. More briefly,

(1.4.1)   if $\quad y = f(x) \quad$ then $\quad x = f^{-1}(y)$.

Geometrically the situation is pictured in Figure 1.4.5. The graph of f^{-1} is the reflection of the graph of f in the line $y = x$. Corresponding to the point $(x, f(x))$ on the graph of f is the point $(f(x), x)$ on the graph of f^{-1}.

An easy way to find the inverse of a given function is to use (1.4.1). Set $y = f(x)$ and solve for x in terms of y. The resulting expression is then $f^{-1}(y)$.

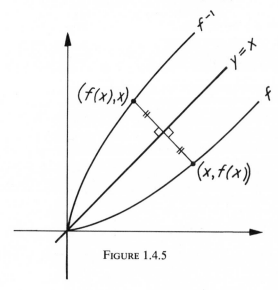

FIGURE 1.4.5

Example. To find the inverse of the cubing function

$$f(x) = x^3$$

we set

$$y = x^3.$$

Solving this equation for x in terms of y, we get

$$x = y^{1/3}.$$

This tells us that

$$f^{-1}(y) = y^{1/3}. \quad \square$$

Example. To find the inverse of

$$f(x) = (1 - x^3)^{1/5} + 2$$

we set

$$y = (1 - x^3)^{1/5} + 2$$

and once again solve for x:

$$y = (1 - x^3)^{1/5} + 2$$
$$y - 2 = (1 - x^3)^{1/5}$$
$$(y - 2)^5 = 1 - x^3$$
$$x^3 = 1 - (y - 2)^5$$
$$x = [1 - (y - 2)^5]^{1/3}.$$

In this case,

$$f^{-1}(y) = [1 - (y - 2)^5]^{1/3}. \quad \square$$

Exercises

Find the domain and the range.

1.* $f(x) = |x|$.

5.* $f(x) = \dfrac{1}{x}$.

2. $g(x) = x^2 - 1$.

6. $g(y) = \sqrt{1 - y^2} - 1$.

3.* $F(t) = 2t - 1$.

7.* $F(x) = \dfrac{1}{\sqrt{1 - x^2}}$.

4. $G(z) = \sqrt{z} - 1$.

8. $H(t) = \sqrt{t} + \sqrt{t + 1}$.

Determine whether the given function is one-to-one.

9.* $f(x) = 3 - x$.

12. $g(x) = x|x|$.

10. $g(x) = x^2 - 3x + 2$.

13.* $f(x) = \sqrt{x - 1}$.

11.* $f(x) = x^{1/3} - 1$.

14. $g(x) = \sqrt{x^2 - 1}$.

Define the composition $f \circ g$.

15.* $f(x) = \sqrt{x}, \quad g(x) = x^2 + 5$.

16. $f(x) = x^2, \quad g(x) = \dfrac{1}{x - 1}$.

17.* $f(x) = x - 1, \quad g(x) = \dfrac{1}{x}$.

18. $f(x) = |x^2 - 1|, \quad g(x) = x(x - 1)$.

19.* $f(x) = \dfrac{1}{\sqrt{x} - 1}, \quad g(x) = x^4 + 4x^2 + 4$.

20. $f(x) = \dfrac{1}{x} - \dfrac{1}{x + 1}, \quad g(x) = \dfrac{1}{x^2}$.

Find the inverse.

21.* $f(x) = x^{3/5}$.

22. $f(x) = 1 + x^5$.

23.* $f(x) = (1 - x^3)^5$.

24. $f(x) = 1 - (x - 2)^{1/3}$.

25.* $f(x) = \dfrac{1}{x}$.

26. $f(x) = \dfrac{1}{1 - x}$.

27.* $f(x) = \dfrac{1}{x^3 + 1}$.

28. $f(x) = \dfrac{1}{1 - x} - 1$.

A function f is called *even* iff

$$f(-x) = f(x) \qquad \text{for all } x \in \text{dom } (f).$$

It is called *odd* iff

$$f(-x) = -f(x) \qquad \text{for all } x \in \text{dom } (f).$$

Test each of the functions below for evenness and oddness.

29.* $f(x) = x^3$.

30. $f(x) = x^2$.

31.* $g(x) = x(x - 1)$.

32. $g(x) = x(x^2 + 1)$.

33.* $f(x) = |x|$.

34. $f(x) = x + \dfrac{1}{x}$.

35.* What can you conclude about the product of two odd functions?

36.* What can you conclude about the product of two even functions?

37.* What can you conclude about the product of an odd function and an even function?

38.* What is the characteristic feature of the graph of an even function?

39.* What is the characteristic feature of the graph of an odd function?

LIMITS AND CONTINUITY

2.1. The idea of limit

We start with a number l and a function f defined near the number c but not necessarily at c. A rough translation of

$$\lim_{x \to c} f(x) = l$$

might read

> as x approaches c, $f(x)$ approaches l

or

> for x close to c, $f(x)$ is close to l

or still

> if x is approximately equal to c,
> then $f(x)$ is approximately equal to l.

We can illustrate this idea with some figures. In each case the "curve" represents the graph of the function in question. The functions depicted in Figures 2.1.1 and 2.1.2 both satisfy

$$\lim_{x \to c} f(x) = l$$

since as x approaches c, $f(x)$ approaches l. (See Figures 2.1.3 and 2.1.4)

In taking the limit as x approaches c it does not matter whether or not f is defined at c and, if so, how it is defined there. The only thing that matters is how f is defined *near c*.

FIGURE 2.1.1

FIGURE 2.1.2

FIGURE 2.1.3

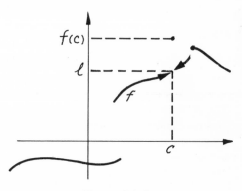

FIGURE 2.1.4

For example, in Figure 2.1.5, the graph of f is a broken curve defined peculiarly at c and yet

$$\lim_{x \to c} f(x) = l$$

because, as suggested in Figure 2.1.6,

as x approaches c, $f(x)$ approaches l.

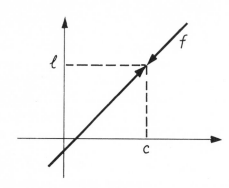

FIGURE 2.1.5

FIGURE 2.1.6

A different situation arises in the case of the function

$$f(x) = \begin{cases} 1, & x > c \\ -1, & x < c \end{cases}.$$ (Figure 2.1.7)

As x approaches c from the left (Figure 2.1.8), $f(x)$ approaches -1. But as x approaches c from the right, $f(x)$ approaches 1. There is no *one* number that $f(x)$ approaches as x approaches c; namely,

$$\lim_{x \to c} f(x) \qquad \text{does not exist.}$$

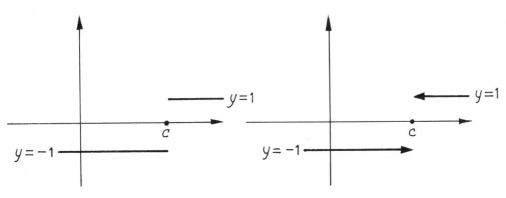

FIGURE 2.1.7   FIGURE 2.1.8

Other instances in which

$$\lim_{x \to c} f(x) \qquad \text{does not exist}$$

are given by

$$f(x) = \frac{1}{x - c}, \quad f(x) = \frac{1}{|x - c|}, \quad \text{and} \quad f(x) = \begin{cases} 1, & x \text{ rational} \\ 0, & x \text{ irrational} \end{cases}.$$

We begin with

$$f(x) = \frac{1}{x - c}.$$

The graph is displayed in Figure 2.1.9. As x approaches c from the right, $f(x)$ becomes arbitrarily large; as x approaches c from the left, $f(x)$ becomes arbitrarily large negative. Clearly there is no number l that $f(x)$ approaches. A slightly different situation occurs in the case of

$$f(x) = \frac{1}{|x - c|}.$$ (Figure 2.1.10)

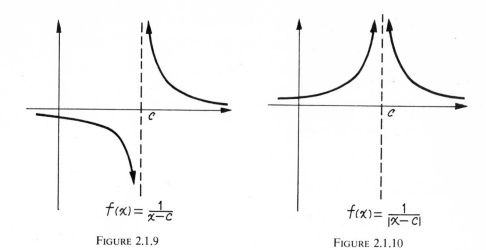

$$f(x) = \frac{1}{x-c}$$

FIGURE 2.1.9

$$f(x) = \frac{1}{|x-c|}$$

FIGURE 2.1.10

Here, as x approaches c from either side, $f(x)$ becomes arbitrarily large. Becoming arbitrarily large, $f(x)$ cannot stay close to a fixed number l. The final example

$$f(x) = \begin{cases} 1, & x \text{ rational} \\ 0, & x \text{ irrational} \end{cases} \qquad \text{(See Figure 2.1.11)}$$

is probably the most interesting. As x approaches c, x passes through both rational and irrational numbers. As this happens, $f(x)$ jumps wildly back and forth between 0 and 1, and cannot stay close to any fixed number l.

FIGURE 2.1.11

2.2 Definition of limit

In Section 2.1 we tried to convey the idea of limit in an intuitive manner. Our remarks, however, were too vague to be called mathematics. In this section we shall be more precise. To say that

$$\lim_{x \to c} f(x) = l$$

is to say that the *difference between $f(x)$ and l can be made arbitrarily small (as small as we wish) simply by requiring that x be sufficiently close to c.*

Think of a positive number and call it ϵ (epsilon). If it is true that

$$\lim_{x \to c} f(x) = l,$$

then you can be sure that

$$|f(x) - l| < \epsilon \qquad \text{for all } x \text{ sufficiently close to } c;$$

namely, you can be sure that there exists a positive number δ (delta) such that

$$\text{if } \ 0 < |x - c| < \delta, \qquad \text{then} \quad |f(x) - l| < \epsilon.$$

Definition of Limit

$$\lim_{x \to c} f(x) = l \quad \text{iff} \quad \begin{cases} \text{for each } \epsilon > 0 \text{ there exists } \delta > 0 \text{ such that} \\ \text{if } \ 0 < |x - c| < \delta, \qquad \text{then} \quad |f(x) - l| < \epsilon. \end{cases}$$

To illustrate this definition we begin with a number c which we picture on the x-axis and a number l which we picture on the y-axis (Figure 2.2.1).

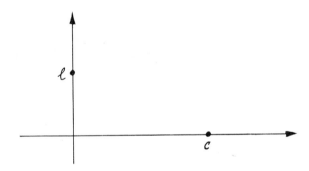

FIGURE 2.2.1

For each $\epsilon > 0$ (Figure 2.2.2),

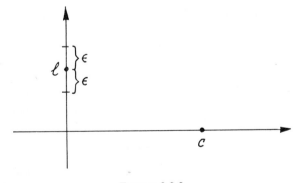

FIGURE 2.2.2

there exists $\delta > 0$ (Figure 2.2.3)

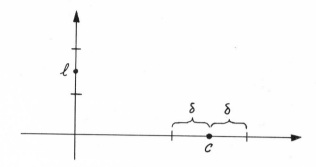

FIGURE 2.2.3

such that

$$\text{if} \quad 0 < |x - c| < \delta, \qquad \text{(Figure 2.2.4)}$$

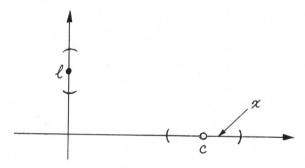

FIGURE 2.2.4

(if x is different from c but within δ of c) then

$$|f(x) - l| < \epsilon. \qquad \text{(Figure 2.2.5)}$$

($f(x)$ is within ϵ of l).

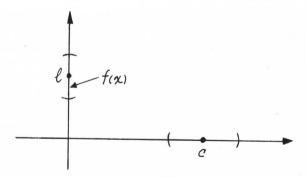

FIGURE 2.2.5

REMARK 1.   Note that for f to have a limit at c it must be defined at all numbers sufficiently close to c, but it need not be defined at c. Even if it is defined at c, its value there
is immaterial.

REMARK 2.   In general, the choice of δ depends upon the previous choice of ϵ. We do
not require that there exist a number δ which "works" for *all* ϵ but, rather, that for *each* ϵ
there exist a δ which "works" for it.

In Figure 2.2.6, we give two choices of ϵ and for each we display a suitable δ.

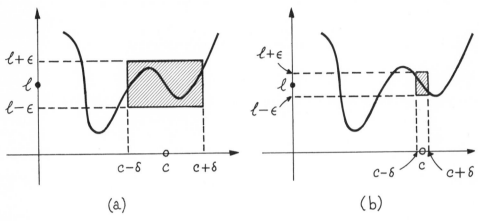

(a)   (b)

FIGURE 2.2.6

Below we apply the ϵ, δ definition of limit to a wide variety of functions. If you have
never run across ϵ, δ arguments before, you may find them confusing at first. It usually
takes a little while for the ϵ, δ idea to take hold.

Example

$$\lim_{x \to 2} (2x - 1) = 3. \qquad \text{(Figure 2.2.7)}$$

PROOF.   Let $\epsilon > 0$. We must show that there exists $\delta > 0$ such that

$$\text{if} \quad 0 < |x - 2| < \delta, \quad \text{then} \quad |(2x - 1) - 3| < \epsilon.$$

Since

$$|(2x - 1) - 3| = |2x - 4| = 2|x - 2|,$$

we can choose

$$\delta = \frac{\epsilon}{2}.$$

To see this, suppose that

$$0 < |x - 2| < \frac{\epsilon}{2}.$$

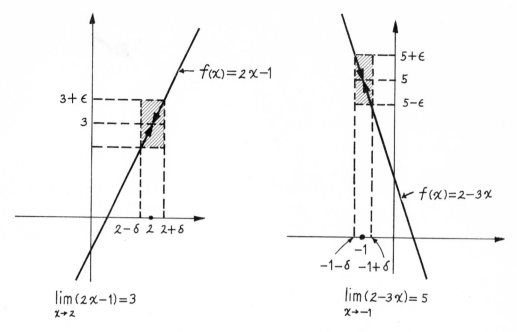

$$\lim_{x \to 2}(2x-1)=3$$

$$\lim_{x \to -1}(2-3x)=5$$

FIGURE 2.2.7

FIGURE 2.2.8

This gives

$$2|x - 2| < \epsilon$$

and thus

$$|(2x - 1) - 3| < \epsilon. \quad \square$$

Example

$$\lim_{x \to -1} (2 - 3x) = 5. \qquad \text{(Figure 2.2.8)}$$

PROOF.   Let $\epsilon > 0$. We must show that there exists $\delta > 0$ such that

if $0 < |x - (-1)| < \delta$,   then $|(2 - 3x) - 5| < \epsilon$.

Since

$$|x - (-1)| = |x + 1|$$

and

$$|(2 - 3x) - 5| = |-3x - 3| = 3|-x - 1| = 3|x + 1|,$$

we can choose

$$\delta = \frac{\epsilon}{3}.$$

To see this, suppose that

$$0 < |x - (-1)| < \frac{\epsilon}{3}.$$

This gives

$$|x + 1| < \frac{\epsilon}{3}, \qquad 3|x + 1| < \epsilon,$$

and thus

$$|(2 - 3x) - 5| < \epsilon. \quad \square$$

Example

(2.2.1) $$\boxed{\lim_{x \to c} |x| = |c|.}$$ (Figure 2.2.9)

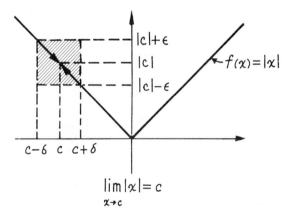

FIGURE 2.2.9

PROOF.   Let $\epsilon > 0$. We seek $\delta > 0$ such that

$$\text{if} \quad 0 < |x - c| < \delta, \quad \text{then} \quad \big||x| - |c|\big| < \epsilon.$$

Since

$$\big||x| - |c|\big| \le |x - c|$$

we can choose $\delta = \epsilon$; for

$$\text{if} \quad 0 < |x - c| < \epsilon, \quad \text{then} \quad \big||x| - |c|\big| < \epsilon. \quad \square$$

Example

$$\lim_{x \to 4} \sqrt{x} = 2.$$ (Figure 2.2.10)

$$\lim_{x \to 4} \sqrt{x} = 2$$

FIGURE 2.2.10

PROOF.   Let $\epsilon > 0$. As we shall see, δ can be chosen to be any positive number which satisfies

$$\delta < 4 \qquad \text{and} \qquad \delta < 2\epsilon;$$

namely, for such a number δ, we have:

$$\text{if} \quad 0 < |x - 4| < \delta, \qquad \text{then} \quad |\sqrt{x} - 2| < \epsilon.$$

To see this, we suppose that

$$0 < |x - 4| < \delta.$$

Since $\delta < 4$, we see that $x > 0$. Thus we can form $\sqrt{x}$ and write

$$x - 4 = (\sqrt{x} + 2)(\sqrt{x} - 2).$$

This means that we have

$$|\sqrt{x} + 2| \, |\sqrt{x} - 2| < \delta.$$

Since

$$2 < |\sqrt{x} + 2|,$$

we have

$$2|\sqrt{x} - 2| < \delta$$

and thus

$$|\sqrt{x} - 2| < \frac{\delta}{2}.$$

With $\delta/2 < \epsilon$, we have $|\sqrt{x} - 2| < \epsilon$.   □

Example

$$\text{If} \quad c \neq 0, \quad \text{then} \quad \lim_{x \to c} \frac{1}{x} = \frac{1}{c}. \qquad \text{(Figure 2.2.11)}$$

PROOF.   Let $\epsilon > 0$. Our task is to show that there exists $\delta > 0$ such that

$$\text{if} \quad 0 < |x - c| < \delta, \quad \text{then} \quad \left| \frac{1}{x} - \frac{1}{c} \right| < \epsilon.$$

Note that, for $x \neq 0$,

$$\left| \frac{1}{x} - \frac{1}{c} \right| = \left| \frac{x - c}{xc} \right| = \frac{|x - c|}{|x||c|}.$$

Let δ be any positive number satisfying

$$\delta < \frac{|c|}{2} \quad \text{and} \quad \delta < \frac{|c|^2}{2} \epsilon.$$

(Why this choice of δ is made will be clear as we go on.) Now if

$$0 < |x - c| < \delta,$$

then

$$|x| > \frac{|c|}{2} \quad \text{and} \quad |x - c| < \frac{|c|^2}{2} \epsilon. \qquad \text{(Explain)}$$

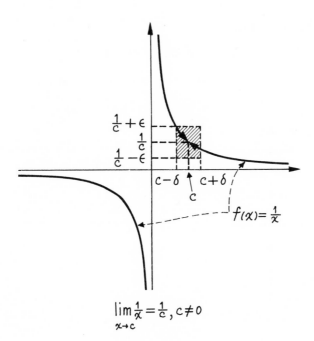

$$\lim_{x \to c} \frac{1}{x} = \frac{1}{c}, c \neq 0$$

FIGURE 2.2.11

This means that we have

$$\frac{|x - c|}{|c/2|\,|c|} < \epsilon \quad \text{and} \quad |x| > \frac{|c|}{2}\,.$$

Consequently,

$$\frac{|x - c|}{|x|\,|c|} < \epsilon.$$

Since, for such x,

$$\left|\frac{1}{x} - \frac{1}{c}\right| = \frac{|x - c|}{|x|\,|c|}\,,$$

we obtain the desired

$$\left|\frac{1}{x} - \frac{1}{c}\right| < \epsilon. \quad \square$$

Example

(2.2.2) $$\lim_{x \to c} x = c.$$ (Figure 2.2.12)

PROOF.   Let $\epsilon > 0$. Here we must find $\delta > 0$ such that

$$\text{if} \quad 0 < |x - c| < \delta, \quad \text{then} \quad |x - c| < \epsilon.$$

Obviously we can choose $\delta = \epsilon$. $\square$

Example

(2.2.3) $$\lim_{x \to c} a = a.$$ (Figure 2.2.13)

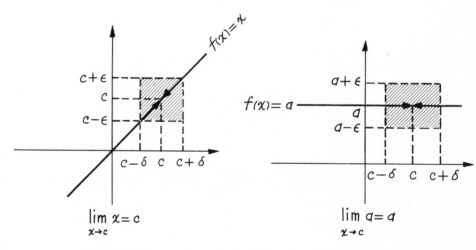

FIGURE 2.2.12   FIGURE 2.2.13

PROOF. Here we are dealing with the constant function

$$f(x) = a.$$

Let $\epsilon > 0$. We must find $\delta > 0$ such that

$$\text{if}\quad 0 < |x - c| < \delta, \qquad \text{then}\quad |a - a| < \epsilon.$$

Since

$$|a - a| = 0,$$

we always have

$$|a - a| < \epsilon$$

no matter how δ is chosen; in short any positive number will do for δ. $\square$

Example 2.2.4

If

$$h(x) = \begin{cases} 1, & x > 0 \\ -1, & x < 0 \end{cases}, \qquad\qquad \text{(Figure 2.2.14)}$$

then

$$\lim_{x \to 0} h(x) \quad \text{does not exist.}$$

PROOF. Suppose on the contrary that

$$\lim_{x \to 0} h(x) = l.$$

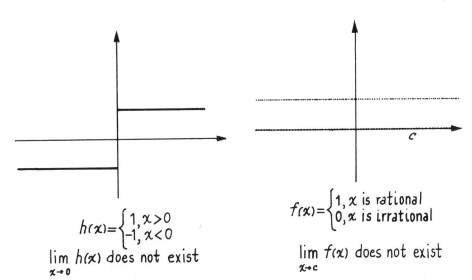

$$h(x) = \begin{cases} 1, & x > 0 \\ -1, & x < 0 \end{cases}$$

$$\lim_{x \to 0} h(x) \text{ does not exist}$$

FIGURE 2.2.14

$$f(x) = \begin{cases} 1, & x \text{ is rational} \\ 0, & x \text{ is irrational} \end{cases}$$

$$\lim_{x \to c} f(x) \text{ does not exist}$$

FIGURE 2.2.15

Then there must exist $\delta > 0$ such that

$$\text{if} \quad 0 < |x - 0| < \delta, \quad \text{then} \quad |h(x) - l| < 1. \qquad \text{(Take } \epsilon = 1)$$

Since

$$0 < \left|\frac{\delta}{2} - 0\right| < \delta \quad \text{and} \quad h\left(\frac{\delta}{2}\right) = 1,$$

we must have

$$|1 - l| < 1.$$

Since

$$0 < \left|-\frac{\delta}{2} - 0\right| < \delta \quad \text{and} \quad h\left(-\frac{\delta}{2}\right) = -1,$$

we must have

$$|-1 - l| < 1.$$

From $|1 - l| < 1$ we conclude that $l > 0$. From $|-1 - l| < 1$ we conclude that $l < 0$. Clearly no such number l exists. $\square$

Example 2.2.5 If f is the Dirichlet function, that is, if

$$f(x) = \begin{cases} 1, & x \text{ rational} \\ 0, & x \text{ irrational} \end{cases}, \qquad \text{(Figure 2.2.15)}$$

then for each real number c

$$\lim_{x \to c} f(x) \qquad \text{does not exist.}$$

PROOF. Suppose, on the contrary, that

$$\lim_{x \to c} f(x) = l.$$

Taking $\epsilon = \frac{1}{2}$, there must exist $\delta > 0$ such that,

$$\text{if} \quad 0 < |x - c| < \delta, \quad \text{then} \quad |f(x) - l| < \tfrac{1}{2}.$$

Let x_1 be a rational number satisfying

$$0 < |x_1 - c| < \delta$$

and x_2 an irrational number satisfying

$$0 < |x_2 - c| < \delta.$$

(That such numbers exist follows from the fact that every interval contains both rational and irrational numbers.) Now

$$f(x_1) = 1 \quad \text{and} \quad f(x_2) = 0.$$

Thus we must have both

$$|1 - l| < \tfrac{1}{2} \quad \text{and} \quad |0 - l| < \tfrac{1}{2}.$$

From the first inequality we conclude that $l > \tfrac{1}{2}$. From the second one we conclude that $l < \tfrac{1}{2}$. Clearly no such number l exists. □

Example 2.2.6

If

$$g(x) = \begin{cases} x, & x \text{ rational} \\ 0, & x \text{ irrational} \end{cases}, \qquad \text{(Figure 2.2.16)}$$

then

$$\lim_{x \to 0} g(x) = 0.$$

PROOF. Let $\epsilon > 0$. We shall show that we can use ϵ itself as δ; namely, we shall show that

$$\text{if} \quad 0 < |x - 0| < \epsilon, \quad \text{then} \quad |g(x) - 0| < \epsilon.$$

For suppose that

$$0 < |x - 0| < \epsilon.$$

If x is rational, then $g(x) = x$. If x is irrational, then $g(x) = 0$. In either case,

$$|g(x) - 0| < \epsilon. \quad □$$

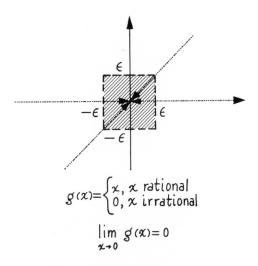

$$g(x) = \begin{cases} x, & x \text{ rational} \\ 0, & x \text{ irrational} \end{cases}$$

$$\lim_{x \to 0} g(x) = 0$$

FIGURE 2.2.16

Exercises

For exercises 1–20, draw the graph and determine whether or not the indicated limit exists. Evaluate the limits which do exist.

1.* $\lim\limits_{x \to 1} 2x$.

2. $\lim\limits_{x \to 0} (3x - 5)$.

3.* $\lim\limits_{x \to -1} (2 - 5x)$.

4. $\lim\limits_{x \to 2} (x^2 - 1)$.

5.* $\lim\limits_{x \to 1} (1 - 2x^2)$.

6. $\lim\limits_{x \to 3} |x - 2|$.

7.* $\lim\limits_{x \to 2} |x - 2|$.

8. $\lim\limits_{x \to 2} \dfrac{x - 2}{x - 2}$.

9.* $\lim\limits_{x \to 2} \dfrac{(x - 2)^2}{x - 2}$.

10. $\lim\limits_{x \to 2} \dfrac{x - 2}{(x - 2)^2}$.

11.* $\lim\limits_{x \to 3} \dfrac{|x|}{x}$.

12. $\lim\limits_{x \to 0} \dfrac{|x|}{x}$.

13.* $\lim\limits_{x \to 1} \dfrac{1 - x^2}{1 - x}$.

14. $\lim\limits_{x \to 1} \dfrac{1 + x^2}{1 - x}$.

15.* $\lim\limits_{x \to 0} f(x)$ if $f(x) = \begin{cases} -5, & x = 0 \\ 2x, & x \neq 0 \end{cases}$.

16.* $\lim\limits_{x \to 0} f(x)$ if $f(x) = \begin{cases} x, & x \text{ rational} \\ -x, & x \text{ irrational} \end{cases}$.

17.* $\lim\limits_{x \to 1} f(x)$ if $f(x) = \begin{cases} x, & x > 1 \\ x^2, & x < 1 \end{cases}$.

18.* $\lim\limits_{x \to 2} f(x)$ if $f(x) = \begin{cases} x^2, & x > 1 \\ x, & x < 1 \end{cases}$.

19.* $\lim\limits_{x \to c} f(x)$ if $f(x) = \begin{cases} 2, & x > c \\ -2, & x < c \end{cases}$.

20.* $\lim\limits_{x \to c} f(x)$ if $f(x) = \begin{cases} 0, & x > c \\ x - c, & x < c \end{cases}$.

Give an ϵ, δ proof of the following limits.

21. $\lim\limits_{x \to 4} (x - 3) = 1$.

22. $\lim\limits_{x \to 2} (3x - 1) = 5$.

23. $\lim\limits_{x \to 0} (2 - 5x) = 0$.

24. $\lim\limits_{x \to 3} (6x - 7) = 11$.

25. $\lim\limits_{x \to 2} |x - 2| = 0$.

26. $\lim\limits_{x \to 9} \sqrt{x} = 3$.

27. $\lim\limits_{x \to 1} \sqrt{x} = 1$.

28. $\lim\limits_{x \to 10} \sqrt{x - 1} = 3$.

29. (*Optional*) $\lim\limits_{x \to 2} x^2 = 4$.

30. (*Optional*) $\lim\limits_{x \to 3} x^2 = 9$.

2.3 Some limit theorems

As you saw in the last section it can be rather tedious to apply the ϵ, δ limit test to individual functions. By proving some general theorems about limits we can avoid some of this repetitive work. The theorems themselves of course (at least the first ones) will have to be proved by ϵ, δ methods.

We begin by showing that if a limit exists, it is unique.

Uniqueness Theorem

If

$$\lim_{x \to c} f(x) = l \quad \text{and} \quad \lim_{x \to c} f(x) = m,$$

then

$$l = m.$$

PROOF. We shall show that $l = m$ by proving that the assumption $l \neq m$ leads to the absurd result $|l - m| < |l - m|$.

Let us assume that $l \neq m$. It follows that $|l - m|/2 > 0$. Since

$$\lim_{x \to c} f(x) = l,$$

we know that there exists $\delta_1 > 0$ such that,

$$\text{if} \quad 0 < |x - c| < \delta_1, \quad \text{then} \quad |f(x) - l| < \frac{|l - m|}{2}.$$

Since

$$\lim_{x \to c} f(x) = m,$$

we know that there exists $\delta_2 > 0$ such that

$$\text{if} \quad 0 < |x - c| < \delta_2, \quad \text{then} \quad |f(x) - m| < \frac{|l - m|}{2}.$$

For x_1 satisfying

$$0 < |x_1 - c| < \text{minimum of} \quad \delta_1 \quad \text{and} \quad \delta_2,$$

we find that

$$|f(x_1) - l| < \frac{|l - m|}{2} \quad \text{and} \quad |f(x_1) - m| < \frac{|l - m|}{2},$$

which for convenience we rewrite as

$$|l - f(x_1)| < \frac{|l - m|}{2} \quad \text{and} \quad |f(x_1) - m| < \frac{|l - m|}{2}.$$

It follows now that

$$|l - m| = |[l - f(x_1)] + [f(x_1) - m]| \le |l - f(x_1)| + |f(x_1) - m|$$
$$< \frac{|l - m|}{2} + \frac{|l - m|}{2} = |l - m|.$$

In short, we have arrived at the absurdity

$$|l - m| < |l - m|. \quad \square$$

Theorem 2.3.1

If

$$\lim_{x \to c} f(x) = l \quad \text{and} \quad \lim_{x \to c} g(x) = m,$$

then

(i) $$\lim_{x \to c} [f(x) + g(x)] = l + m$$

(ii) $$\lim_{x \to c} [\alpha f(x)] = \alpha l \quad \text{for each real } \alpha$$

(iii) $$\lim_{x \to c} [f(x)g(x)] = lm.$$

PROOF. Let $\epsilon > 0$. To prove (i) we must show that there exists $\delta > 0$ such that

$$\text{if} \quad 0 < |x - c| < \delta, \quad \text{then} \quad |[f(x) + g(x)] - [l + m]| < \epsilon.$$

Note that

(2.3.2) $$|[f(x) + g(x)] - [l + m]| = |[f(x) - l] + [g(x) - m]|$$
$$\le |f(x) - l| + |g(x) - m|.$$

We will make

$$|[f(x) + g(x)] - [l + m]|$$

less than ϵ by making

$$|f(x) - l| \quad \text{and} \quad |g(x) - m|$$

each less than $\epsilon/2$. Since $\epsilon > 0$, we know that $\epsilon/2 > 0$. Since

$$\lim_{x \to c} f(x) = l \quad \text{and} \quad \lim_{x \to c} g(x) = m,$$

we know that there exist positive numbers δ_1 and δ_2 such that

$$\text{if} \quad 0 < |x - c| < \delta_1, \quad \text{then} \quad |f(x) - l| < \frac{\epsilon}{2},$$

and

$$\text{if} \quad 0 < |x - c| < \delta_2, \quad \text{then} \quad |g(x) - m| < \frac{\epsilon}{2}.$$

Now we set

$$\delta = \text{minimum of } \delta_1 \text{ and } \delta_2$$

and note that,

$$\text{if } 0 < |x - c| < \delta, \quad \text{then } |f(x) - l| < \frac{\epsilon}{2} \text{ and } |g(x) - m| < \frac{\epsilon}{2},$$

and thus by (2.3.2)

$$|[f(x) + g(x)] - [l + m]| < \epsilon.$$

In summary, by setting $\delta = \min \{\delta_1, \delta_2\}$, we found that,

$$\text{if } \quad 0 < |x - c| < \delta, \quad \text{then} \quad |[f(x) + g(x)] - [l + m]| < \epsilon.$$

Thus (i) is proved.

To prove (ii) we consider two cases: $\alpha \neq 0$, and $\alpha = 0$. If $\alpha \neq 0$, then $\epsilon/|\alpha| > 0$ and since

$$\lim_{x \to c} f(x) = l,$$

we know that there exists $\delta > 0$ such that,

$$\text{if } \quad 0 < |x - c| < \delta, \quad \text{then} \quad |f(x) - l| < \frac{\epsilon}{|\alpha|} \cdot$$

From the last inequality we obtain

$$|\alpha||f(x) - l| < \epsilon,$$

and thus

$$|\alpha f(x) - \alpha l| < \epsilon.$$

The case $\alpha = 0$ was treated before in (2.2.3). For a proof of (iii), see the supplement to this section. □

The results of Theorem 2.3.1 are easily extended to apply to any finite number of functions; namely, if

$$\lim_{x \to c} f_1(x) = l_1, \lim_{x \to c} f_2(x) = l_2, \ldots, \lim_{x \to c} f_n(x) = l_n$$

then

(2.3.3) $$\lim_{x \to c} [\alpha_1 f_1(x) + \alpha_2 f_2(x) + \cdots + \alpha_n f_n(x)] = \alpha_1 l_1 + \alpha_2 l_2 + \cdots + \alpha_n l_n$$

and

(2.3.4) $$\lim_{x \to c} [f_1(x) f_2(x) \cdots f_n(x)] = l_1 l_2 \cdots l_n.$$

From this it is easy to see that every polynomial

$$P(x) = \alpha_n x^n + \cdots + \alpha_1 x + \alpha_0$$

satisfies

$$\lim_{x \to c} P(x) = P(c).$$

PROOF.   We already know that

$$\lim_{x \to c} x = c.$$

Applying (2.3.4) we have

$$\lim_{x \to c} x^k = c^k \qquad \text{for each positive integer } k.$$

We also know that

$$\lim_{x \to c} \alpha_0 = \alpha_0.$$

It follows now from (2.3.3) that

$$\lim_{x \to c} (\alpha_n x^n + \cdots + \alpha_1 x + \alpha_0) = \alpha_n c^n + \cdots + \alpha_1 c + \alpha_0;$$

that is,

$$\lim_{x \to c} P(x) = P(c). \quad \square$$

Examples

$$\lim_{x \to 1} (5x^2 - 12x + 2) = 5(1)^2 - 12(1) + 2 = -5$$

$$\lim_{x \to 0} (14x^5 - 7x^2 + 2x + 8) = 8$$

$$\lim_{x \to -1} (2x^3 + x^2 - 2x - 3) = 2(-1)^3 + (-1)^2 - 2(-1) - 3 = -2. \quad \square$$

We come now to reciprocals and quotients.

Theorem 2.3.5

If

$$\lim_{x \to c} g(x) = m \text{ and } m \neq 0, \qquad \text{then} \qquad \lim_{x \to c} \frac{1}{g(x)} = \frac{1}{m}.$$

PROOF.   See the supplement to this section. $\square$

Once you know that reciprocals present no trouble, quotients become easy to handle.

Theorem

If
$$\lim_{x \to c} f(x) = l, \qquad \lim_{x \to c} g(x) = m, \qquad \text{and} \qquad m \neq 0,$$

then
$$\lim_{x \to c} \frac{f(x)}{g(x)} = \frac{l}{m}.$$

PROOF.   The key here is to observe that the quotient can be written as a product

$$\frac{f(x)}{g(x)} = f(x) \frac{1}{g(x)}.$$

With

$$\lim_{x \to c} f(x) = l \qquad \text{and} \qquad \lim_{x \to c} \frac{1}{g(x)} = \frac{1}{m},$$

the product rule [part iii of Theorem 2.3.1] gives

$$\lim_{x \to c} \frac{f(x)}{g(x)} = l \frac{1}{m} = \frac{l}{m}. \qquad \square$$

As an immediate consequence to this theorem on quotients you can see that, if P and Q are polynomials and $Q(c) \neq 0$, then

$$\lim_{x \to c} \frac{P(x)}{Q(x)} = \frac{P(c)}{Q(c)}.$$

Examples

$$\lim_{x \to 2} \frac{3x - 5}{x^2 + 1} = \frac{6 - 5}{4 + 1} = \frac{1}{5}, \qquad \lim_{x \to -3} \left(x + \frac{1}{x} \right) = -3 + \frac{1}{-3} = -3\frac{1}{3},$$

$$\lim_{x \to 3} \frac{x^3 - 3x^2}{1 - x^2} = \frac{27 - 27}{1 - 9} = 0.$$

There is no point looking for a limit that does not exist. The last theorem of this section gives a condition under which a quotient does not have a limit.

Theorem 2.3.6

If
$$\lim_{x \to c} f(x) = l \qquad \text{with} \qquad l \neq 0, \qquad \text{and} \qquad \lim_{x \to c} g(x) = 0,$$

then
$$\lim_{x \to c} \frac{f(x)}{g(x)} \qquad \text{does not exist.}$$

PROOF. Suppose on the contrary that there exists a real number L such that

$$\lim_{x \to c} \frac{f(x)}{g(x)} = L.$$

Then

$$l = \lim_{x \to c} f(x) = \lim_{x \to c} \left[g(x) \cdot \frac{f(x)}{g(x)} \right] = \lim_{x \to c} g(x) \cdot \lim_{x \to c} \frac{f(x)}{g(x)} = 0 \cdot L = 0,$$

which contradicts our assumption that $l \neq 0$. □

Examples. Applying Theorem 2.3.6, we see that

$$\lim_{x \to 1} \frac{x^2}{x - 1}, \qquad \lim_{x \to 2} \frac{3x - 7}{x^2 - 4}, \qquad \text{and} \qquad \lim_{x \to 0} \frac{5}{x}$$

all fail to exist. □

Exercises

1. Evaluate the limits that exist:

(a) $\lim\limits_{x \to 2} \dfrac{x^2 + x + 1}{x^2 + 2x}$.

(b)* $\lim\limits_{x \to 2} \dfrac{x - 2}{x^2 - 4}$.

(c)* $\lim\limits_{x \to 2} \dfrac{x^2 - 4}{x - 2}$.

(d) $\lim\limits_{x \to -1} (\sqrt{2x} - 6x + 1)$.

(e)* $\lim\limits_{x \to 0} \left(x - \dfrac{4}{x} \right)$.

(f) $\lim\limits_{x \to -1} \dfrac{|x| - x^2}{(3x - 1)(x^4 - 2)}$.

(g) $\lim\limits_{x \to 5} \dfrac{2 - x^2}{4x}$.

(h)* $\lim\limits_{x \to 1} \dfrac{x - x^2}{1 - x}$.

2. Evaluate the limits that exist:

(a) $\lim\limits_{x \to -3} \dfrac{5x + 15}{x^3 + 3x^2 - x - 3}$.

(b)* $\lim\limits_{x \to -4} \left(\dfrac{2x}{x + 4} + \dfrac{8}{x + 4} \right)$.

(c)* $\lim\limits_{t \to 1} \dfrac{t}{t^2 - 1}$.

(d) $\lim\limits_{h \to 0} |h - |h||$.

3. Given that

$$\lim_{x \to c} f(x) = 2, \qquad \lim_{x \to c} g(x) = -1, \qquad \text{and} \qquad \lim_{x \to c} h(x) = 0,$$

evaluate the limits that exist.

(a)* $\lim\limits_{x \to c} [f(x) - g(x)]$.

(b) $\lim\limits_{x \to c} [f(x)]^2$.

(c) $\lim\limits_{x \to c} \dfrac{f(x)}{g(x)}$.

(d)* $\lim\limits_{x \to c} \dfrac{h(x)}{f(x)}$.

(e)* $\lim\limits_{x \to c} \dfrac{f(x)}{h(x)}$.

(f) $\lim\limits_{x \to c} \dfrac{1}{f(x) - g(x)}$.

4. Given that $f(x) = x^3$, evaluate the limits that exist.

(a)* $\lim\limits_{x \to 3} \dfrac{f(x) - f(3)}{x - 3}$.

(c)* $\lim\limits_{x \to 3} \dfrac{f(x) - f(3)}{x - 2}$.

(b) $\lim\limits_{x \to 3} \dfrac{f(x) - f(2)}{x - 3}$.

(d) $\lim\limits_{x \to 1} \dfrac{f(x) - f(1)}{x - 1}$.

5. Given that

$$\lim\limits_{x \to c} g(x) = 0 \quad \text{and} \quad f(x)g(x) = 1 \text{ for all real } x,$$

prove that $\lim\limits_{x \to c} f(x)$ does not exist.

SUPPLEMENT TO SECTION 2.3

PROOF OF THEOREM 2.3.1 (iii)

$$|f(x)g(x) - lm| \leq |f(x)g(x) - f(x)m| + |f(x)m - lm|$$
$$= |f(x)||g(x) - m| + |m||f(x) - l|$$
$$\leq |f(x)||g(x) - m| + (1 + |m|)|f(x) - l|.$$

Let $\epsilon > 0$. Since

$$\lim\limits_{x \to c} f(x) = l \quad \text{and} \quad \lim\limits_{x \to c} g(x) = m,$$

we know

(1) that there exists $\delta_1 > 0$ such that, if $0 < |x - c| < \delta_1$, then

$$|f(x) - l| < 1 \quad \text{and thus} \quad |f(x)| < 1 + |l|;$$

(2) that there exists $\delta_2 > 0$ such that

$$\text{if} \quad 0 < |x - c| < \delta_2, \quad \text{then} \quad |g(x) - m| < \frac{\epsilon}{2}\left(\frac{1}{1 + |l|}\right);$$

(3) that there exists $\delta_3 > 0$ such that

$$\text{if} \quad 0 < |x - c| < \delta_3, \quad \text{then} \quad |f(x) - l| < \frac{\epsilon}{2}\left(\frac{1}{1 + |m|}\right).$$

We can now set $\delta = \min\{\delta_1, \delta_2, \delta_3\}$ and observe that if $0 < |x - c| < \delta$, then

$$|f(x)g(x) - lm| < (1 + |l|)\frac{\epsilon}{2}\left(\frac{1}{1 + |l|}\right) + (1 + |m|)\frac{\epsilon}{2}\left(\frac{1}{1 + |m|}\right) = \epsilon. \quad \square$$

PROOF OF THEOREM 2.3.5. For $g(x) \neq 0$,

$$\left|\frac{1}{g(x)} - \frac{1}{m}\right| = \frac{|g(x) - m|}{|m||g(x)|}.$$

Choose $\delta_1 > 0$ such that

$$\text{if} \quad 0 < |x - c| < \delta_1, \quad \text{then} \quad |g(x) - m| < \frac{|m|}{2}.$$

For such x,

$$|g(x) > \frac{|m|}{2}$$

and thus

$$\left| \frac{1}{g(x)} - \frac{1}{m} \right| \leq \frac{2}{|m|^2} |g(x) - m|.$$

Now let $\epsilon > 0$ and choose $\delta_2 > 0$ such that

$$\text{if} \quad 0 < |x - c| < \delta_2, \quad \text{then} \quad |g(x) - m| < \frac{|m|^2}{2} \epsilon.$$

Setting $\delta = \min \{\delta_1, \delta_2\}$, we find that

$$\text{if} \quad 0 < |x - c| < \delta, \quad \text{then} \quad \left| \frac{1}{g(x)} - \frac{1}{m} \right| < \epsilon. \quad \square$$

2.4 More on limits

As we have indicated before, whether or not

$$\lim_{x \to c} f(x)$$

exists and, if so, what it is, depends only on the behavior of f for x close to c. If, for x close to c, f is trapped between two functions both of which tend to the same limit l (see Figure 2.4.1), then $f(x)$ must also tend to 1. This idea is the substance of what we call the "pinching theorem."

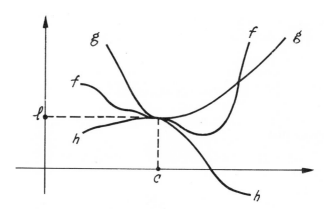

FIGURE 2.4.1

The Pinching Theorem 2.4.1

Suppose that there exists a number $p > 0$ such that

$$h(x) \leq f(x) \leq g(x) \qquad \text{for all } x \text{ satisfying } 0 < |x - c| < p.$$

If

$$\lim_{x \to c} h(x) = l \qquad \text{and} \qquad \lim_{x \to c} g(x) = l,$$

then

$$\lim_{x \to c} f(x) = l.$$

PROOF.   Let $\epsilon > 0$. Let $p > 0$ be such that,

$$\text{if} \quad 0 < |x - c| < p, \qquad \text{then} \quad h(x) \leq f(x) \leq g(x).$$

Choose $\delta_1 > 0$ such that

$$\text{if} \quad 0 < |x - c| < \delta_1, \qquad \text{then} \quad l - \epsilon < h(x) < l + \epsilon.$$

Choose $\delta_2 > 0$ such that

$$\text{if} \quad 0 < |x - c| < \delta_2, \qquad \text{then} \quad l - \epsilon < g(x) < l + \epsilon.$$

Let $\delta = \min(p, \delta_1, \delta_2)$. For x satisfying $0 < |x - c| < \delta$, we have

$$l - \epsilon < h(x) \leq f(x) \leq g(x) < l + \epsilon$$

and thus

$$|f(x) - l| < \epsilon. \quad \square$$

Example.   Suppose that

$$-x^2 \leq f(x) \leq x^2 \qquad \text{for all } x \neq 0.$$

Since

$$\lim_{x \to 0} -x^2 = 0 \qquad \text{and} \qquad \lim_{x \to 0} x^2 = 0,$$

we know that

$$\lim_{x \to 0} f(x) = 0. \quad \square$$

Example.   Suppose that

$$x^2 + 12x - 9 \leq f(x) \leq 5x^2 \qquad \text{for all } x \neq 3/2.$$

Since

$$\lim_{x \to 3/2} (x^2 + 12x - 9) = \left(\frac{3}{2}\right)^2 + 12\left(\frac{3}{2}\right) - 9 = \frac{45}{4}$$

and

$$\lim_{x \to 3/2} 5x^2 = 5 \left(\frac{3}{2}\right)^2 = \frac{45}{4}$$

we know that

$$\lim_{x \to 3/2} f(x) = \frac{45}{4}. \quad \square$$

Example. If

$$f(x) = \begin{cases} x^2, & x \text{ rational} \\ x^4, & x \text{ irrational} \end{cases},$$

then

$$\lim_{x \to 0} f(x) = 0.$$

To verify this, we note that for each x satisfying $|x| < 1$, we have

$$0 \le f(x) \le x^2. \qquad \text{[Explain]}$$

Since

$$\lim_{x \to 0} x^2 = 0, \qquad (\text{and, of course, } \lim_{x \to 0} 0 = 0)$$

the pinching theorem gives us

$$\lim_{x \to 0} f(x) = 0. \quad \square$$

There are many different ways of formulating the same limit statement. Sometimes one formulation is more convenient, sometimes another. In any case, it is useful to recognize that the following are equivalent:

(2.4.2)

(i) $\lim_{x \to c} f(x) = l.$ (iii) $\lim_{x \to c} |f(x) - l| = 0.$

(ii) $\lim_{x \to c} (f(x) - l) = 0.$ (iv) $\lim_{h \to c} f(c + h) = l.$

The equivalence of these four statements is obvious. It is, however, a good exercise in ϵ, δ technique to show that (i) is equivalent to (iv).

Example. For $f(x) = x^3$, we have

$$\lim_{x \to 2} x^3 = 8 \qquad\qquad \lim_{x \to 2} |x^3 - 8| = 0$$

$$\lim_{x \to 2} (x^3 - 8) = 0 \qquad \lim_{h \to 0} (2 + h)^3 = 8. \quad \square$$

While we are on the subject of equivalent statements, note that

$$\lim_{x \to c} f(x) = l \qquad \text{and} \qquad \lim_{x \to c} |f(x)| = |l|$$

are *not* equivalent. While

$$\lim_{x \to c} f(x) = l \qquad \text{implies} \qquad \lim_{x \to c} f(x) = |l|, \qquad \text{(Exercise 2)}$$

the converse is false. There are instances in which

$$\lim_{x \to c} |f(x)| \text{ exists,} \qquad \text{but} \qquad \lim_{x \to c} f(x) \text{ does not.} \qquad \text{(Exercise 3)}$$

Exercises

1. Find the limits that exist.

(a)* $\lim_{x \to 0} f(x)$ if $-|x| \le f(x) \le |x|$ for $x \ne 0$.

(b) $\lim_{x \to 3} f(x)$ if $1 \le f(x) \le (x - 3)^2 + 1$ for $x \ne 3$.

(c)* $\lim_{x \to 2} f(x)$ if $-(x - 2)^2 \le f(x) \le 0$ for $x \ne 2$.

(d) $\lim_{x \to 5} f(x)$ if $5 + x \le f(x) \le x^2 - 9x + 30$ for $x \ne 5$.

(e)* $\lim_{x \to 0} f(x)$ if $\left| \dfrac{f(x)}{x} \right| \le 1$ for $x \ne 0$.

(f) $\lim_{h \to 0} (3 + h)^2$.

(g) $\lim_{h \to 0} h \left(1 + \dfrac{1}{h} \right)$.

(h)* $\lim_{h \to 0} h \left(1 + \dfrac{1}{h^2} \right)$.

(i) $\lim_{h \to 1} \dfrac{h}{|h - 1|}$.

(j)* $\lim_{h \to 0} \dfrac{1 - 1/h}{1 + 1/h}$.

(k) $\lim_{h \to 0} \dfrac{1 - 1/h^2}{1 - 1/h}$.

(l)* $\lim_{x \to 1} \left(1 - \dfrac{1}{x} \right) \left(\dfrac{1}{x - 1} \right)$.

(m) $\lim_{x \to c} \dfrac{x - c}{|x - c|}$.

2. Show that

$$\text{if} \quad \lim_{x \to c} f(x) = l \qquad \text{then} \quad \lim_{x \to c} |f(x)| = |l|.$$

3.* Given that

$$f(x) = \begin{cases} 1, & x > 0 \\ -1, & x < 0 \end{cases}$$

find

(a) $\lim_{x \to 0} f(x)$ and   (b) $\lim_{x \to 0} |f(x)|$.

4. Show that, for each $c > 0$

$$\lim_{x \to c} \sqrt{x} = \sqrt{c}.$$

HINT: If x and c are positive, then

$$0 \le |\sqrt{x} - \sqrt{c}| = \frac{|x - c|}{\sqrt{x} + \sqrt{c}} \le \frac{1}{\sqrt{c}} |x - c|.$$

5.   (a)   Verify that

$$\max \{f(x), g(x)\} = \tfrac{1}{2}\{[f(x) + g(x)] + |f(x) - g(x)|\}.$$

(b)* Find a similar expression for

$$\min \{f(x), g(x)\}.$$

6.   Let

$$h(x) = \min \{f(x), g(x)\} \qquad \text{and} \qquad H(x) = \max \{f(x), g(x)\}.$$

Show that if

$$\lim_{x \to c} f(x) = l \qquad \text{and} \qquad \lim_{x \to c} g(x) = l$$

then

$$\lim_{x \to c} h(x) = l \qquad \text{and} \qquad \lim_{x \to c} H(x) = l.$$

[HINT: Use Exercise 5.]

7.   (*Optional*)   Give an ϵ, δ proof that statement (i) of 2.4.2 is equivalent to statement (iv).

2.5   One-sided limits

Whether or not $\lim_{x \to c} f(x)$ exists, and, if so, what it is, depends on the behavior of f on both sides of c. The situation is simpler in the case of one-sided limits: the *right-hand* limit [denoted by $\lim_{x \downarrow c} f(x)$] and the *left-hand* limit [denoted by $\lim_{x \uparrow c} f(x)$].
   Roughly speaking, the right-hand limit

$$\lim_{x \downarrow c} f(x)$$

is the number that $f(x)$ approaches as x comes into c from the right, and the left-hand limit

$$\lim_{x \uparrow c} f(x)$$

is the number that $f(x)$ approaches as x comes into c from the left.

Definition of Right-Hand Limit

Let f be a function defined at least on an interval of the form (c, d).

$$\lim_{x \downarrow c} f(x) = l \qquad \text{iff} \qquad \begin{cases} \text{for each } \epsilon > 0 \text{ there exists } \delta > 0 \text{ such that} \\ \text{if } c < x < c + \delta, \qquad \text{then} \quad |f(x) - l| < \epsilon. \end{cases}$$

Definition of Left-Hand Limit

Let f be a function defined at least on an interval of the form (a, c).

$$\lim_{x \uparrow c} f(x) = l \quad \text{iff} \quad \begin{cases} \text{for each } \epsilon > 0 \text{ there exists } \delta > 0 \text{ such that} \\ \text{if } c - \delta < x < c, \quad \text{then} \quad |f(x) - l| < \epsilon. \end{cases}$$

Example. If

$$h(x) = \begin{cases} 1, & x > 0 \\ -1, & x < 0 \end{cases}, \qquad \text{(see Figure 2.5.1)}$$

then

$$\lim_{x \downarrow 0} h(x) = 1 \quad \text{and} \quad \lim_{x \uparrow 0} h(x) = -1$$

although, as you saw before,

$$\lim_{x \to 0} h(x)$$

does not exist.   □

Example. Since the square-root function is not defined on both sides of 0, we cannot consider

$$\lim_{x \to 0} \sqrt{x}.$$

However, it is true that

$$\lim_{x \downarrow 0} \sqrt{x} = 0. \qquad \text{(see Figure 2.5.2)}$$

To see this, we let $\epsilon > 0$ and note that

$$|\sqrt{x} - 0| = \sqrt{x} < \epsilon \quad \text{if} \quad 0 < x < \epsilon^2.$$

Similarly, you can verify that

$$\lim_{x \uparrow 0} \sqrt{-x} = 0. \quad \square$$

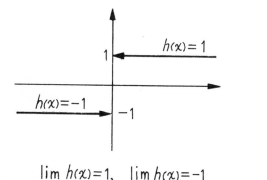

$$\lim_{x \downarrow 0} h(x) = 1, \quad \lim_{x \uparrow 0} h(x) = -1$$

FIGURE 2.5.1

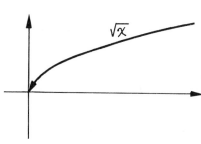

$$\lim_{x \downarrow 0} \sqrt{x} = 0$$

FIGURE 2.5.2

Example. An interesting function to look at when dealing with one-sided limits is the *greatest-integer function*:

(2.5.1)

$$\boxed{[x] = \text{greatest integer} \leq x.}$$

For the graph we refer to Figure 2.5.3. At 0 the function is 0 and it remains 0 throughout the interval $[0, 1)$. At 1 the function jumps up to 1 and it remains 1 throughout the interval $[1, 2)$. At 2 the function jumps up to 2 and so on. It is easy to see that for each integer n,

$$\lim_{x \downarrow n} [x] = n \qquad \text{and} \qquad \lim_{x \uparrow n} [x] = n - 1.$$

[For example, $\lim_{x \downarrow 2} [x] = 2$ and $\lim_{x \uparrow 2} [x] = 1$].

If c is a number which is not an integer, then c lies between consecutive integers n and $n + 1$. For such c, we have both

$$\lim_{x \downarrow c} [x] = n \qquad \text{and} \qquad \lim_{x \uparrow c} [x] = n.$$

[For example, $\lim_{x \downarrow 3/2} [x] = 1$ and $\lim_{x \uparrow 3/2} [x] = 1$.] □

Results analogous to those proved in Sections 2.3 and 2.4 hold for one-sided limits. Thus, for instance, if

$$\lim_{x \uparrow c} f(x) = l \qquad \text{and} \qquad \lim_{x \uparrow c} g(x) = m,$$

then

$$\lim_{x \uparrow c} [f(x) + g(x)] = l + m$$

$$\lim_{x \uparrow c} [\alpha f(x)] = \alpha l$$

$$\lim_{x \uparrow c} [f(x)g(x)] = lm.$$

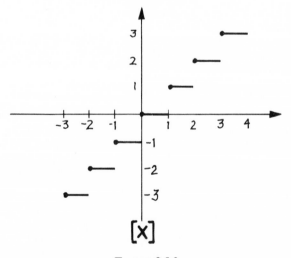

FIGURE 2.5.3

Moreover, if $m \neq 0$, then

$$\lim_{x \uparrow c} \frac{1}{g(x)} = \frac{1}{m} \quad \text{and} \quad \lim_{x \uparrow c} \frac{f(x)}{g(x)} = \frac{l}{m}.$$

Similar results hold for right-hand limits. Proofs can be obtained by mimicking the proofs given before.

One-sided limits give us a simple criterion for determining whether or not a (two-sided) limit exists:

(2.5.2)
$$\boxed{\lim_{x \to c} f(x) = l \quad \text{iff} \quad \lim_{x \uparrow c} f(x) = l \quad \text{and} \quad \lim_{x \downarrow c} f(x) = l.}$$

The proof is left as an exercise. It is easy because any δ that "works" for the limit will work for the two one-sided limits and any δ that works for the two one-sided limits will work for the limit.

We illustrate the effectiveness of (2.5.2) by some examples.

Example. For

$$h(x) = \begin{cases} 1, & x > 0 \\ -1, & x < 0 \end{cases}$$

we have

$$\lim_{x \downarrow 0} h(x) = 1 \quad \text{and} \quad \lim_{x \uparrow 0} h(x) = -1.$$

Since the two are not equal,

$$\lim_{x \to 0} h(x) \text{ does not exist.} \quad \square$$

Example. With

$$g(x) = \begin{cases} x^2, & x < 0 \\ \sqrt{x}, & x > 0 \end{cases}$$

we have both

$$\lim_{x \uparrow 0} g(x) = 0 \quad \text{and} \quad \lim_{x \downarrow 0} g(x) = 0.$$

Consequently,

$$\lim_{x \to 0} g(x) = 0. \quad \square$$

Example. Set

$$k(x) = \begin{cases} 0, & x < 0, \ x \text{ irrational} \\ 1, & x < 0, \ x \text{ rational} \\ x, & x > 0 \end{cases} \cdot$$

Here

$$\lim_{x \uparrow 0} k(x) \quad \text{does not exist}$$

and therefore

$$\lim_{x \to 0} k(x) \quad \text{does not exist either.} \quad \square$$

Exercises

1. Evaluate the limits which exist.

(a)* $\displaystyle\lim_{x \uparrow 2} \frac{x^2}{x + 2}$.

(b) $\displaystyle\lim_{x \downarrow 2} \frac{x^2}{x + 2}$.

(c)* $\displaystyle\lim_{x \uparrow 2} \frac{x - 2}{|x - 2|}$.

(d) $\displaystyle\lim_{x \downarrow 2} \frac{x - 2}{|x - 2|}$.

(e)* $\displaystyle\lim_{x \to 1} \frac{x^3 - 1}{|x^3 - 1|}$.

(f) $\displaystyle\lim_{x \downarrow 0} \frac{1 + \sqrt{x}}{1 - \sqrt{x}}$.

(g)* $\displaystyle\lim_{x \uparrow 1} \sqrt{|x| - x}$.

(h) $\displaystyle\lim_{x \downarrow 1} \sqrt{|x| - x}$.

(i)* $\displaystyle\lim_{x \uparrow 1} \sqrt{x - [x]}$.

(j) $\displaystyle\lim_{x \downarrow 1} \sqrt{x - [x]}$.

(k)* $\displaystyle\lim_{x \downarrow 0} \frac{[x] - x}{x}$.

(l) $\displaystyle\lim_{x \uparrow 1} (x^2 + 2)^{[x]}$.

(m)* $\displaystyle\lim_{x \uparrow 2} \left(\frac{1}{x - 2} - \frac{1}{|x - 2|} \right)$.

(n) $\displaystyle\lim_{x \downarrow 2} \left(\frac{1}{x - 2} - \frac{1}{|x - 2|} \right)$.

2. (a) Sketch the graph of

$$f(x) = [2x].$$

(b) Evaluate the limits that exist.

(i)* $\displaystyle\lim_{x \uparrow 1/2} [2x]$.

(ii)* $\displaystyle\lim_{x \downarrow 1/2} [2x]$.

(iii)* $\displaystyle\lim_{x \uparrow 3/4} [2x]$.

(iv)* $\displaystyle\lim_{x \downarrow 3/4} [2x]$.

(v)* $\displaystyle\lim_{x \to 1/2} [2x]$.

(vi)* $\displaystyle\lim_{x \to 3/4} [2x]$.

3. Give an ϵ, δ proof of (2.5.2).

4. (*Optional*) Give an ϵ, δ proof that

(a) $\displaystyle\lim_{x \uparrow c} f(x) = l$ iff $\displaystyle\lim_{h \to 0} f(c - |h|) = l$.

(b) $\displaystyle\lim_{x \downarrow c} f(x) = l$ iff $\displaystyle\lim_{h \to 0} f(c + |h|) = l$.

5. (*Optional*) Evaluate the limits that exist.

(a)* $\displaystyle\lim_{x\to 1} [2x](x-1).$

(c)* $\displaystyle\lim_{x\to 0} x[1/x].$

(b) $\displaystyle\lim_{x\to 0} [x][x+1].$

(d) $\displaystyle\lim_{x\to 0} x^2[1/x].$

[HINT: For (c) and (d) note that $t-1 \le [t] \le t.$]

2.6 Continuity

In ordinary language, to say that a certain process is "continuous" is to say that it goes on without interruption and without abrupt changes. In mathematics the word "continuous" has much the same meaning.

The idea of continuity is so important to calculus that we will have to discuss it with some care. First we introduce the idea of continuity at a point (or number) c and then we will talk about continuity on an interval.

Continuity At a Point

> **Definition**
>
> A function f is said to be *continuous* at c iff $\displaystyle\lim_{x\to c} f(x) = f(c).$

If c is in the domain of f, then f can fail to be continuous at c only for one of two reasons: either $f(x)$ does not have a limit as x tends to c, or it does have a limit, but the limit is not $f(c)$. These possibilities are illustrated in Figures 2.6.1, 2.6.2, and 2.6.3.

The function depicted in Figure 2.6.1 does not have a limit at c, and hence is not continuous at c. In Figure 2.6.2 we have tried to suggest the Dirichlet function

$$f(x) = \begin{cases} 1, & x\,\text{rational} \\ 0, & x\,\text{irrational} \end{cases}.$$

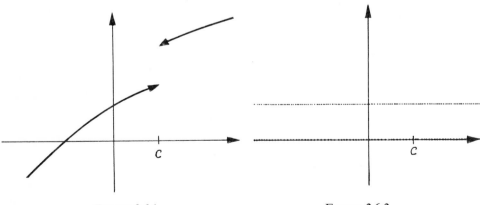

FIGURE 2.6.1   FIGURE 2.6.2

At no point c does f have a limit. It is therefore everywhere discontinuous. The function depicted in Figure 2.6.3 does have a limit at c. It is discontinuous at c because the limit at c is not the value at c.

The discontinuity displayed in Figure 2.6.3 is not serious in the sense that it can be removed simply by redefining the function at c (by lowering the dot into place). See Figure 2.6.4.

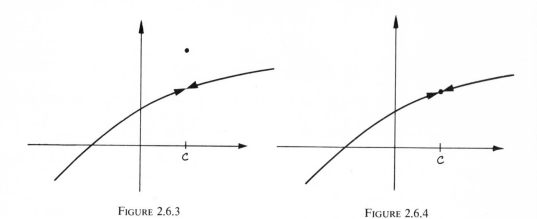

FIGURE 2.6.3   FIGURE 2.6.4

Most of the functions that you have encountered so far are continuous at each point of their domains. In particular, this is true for polynomials,

$$\left[\lim_{x \to c} P(x) = P(c) \right]$$

for rational functions, by which we mean quotients of polynomials,

$$\left[\lim_{x \to c} \frac{P(x)}{Q(x)} = \frac{P(c)}{Q(c)} \quad \text{if} \quad Q(c) \neq 0 \right]$$

and for the absolute-value function,

$$\left[\lim_{x \to c} |x| = |c| \right].$$

In one of the exercises you showed (or at least were asked to show) that

$$\lim_{x \to c} \sqrt{x} = \sqrt{c} \quad \text{for each } c > 0.$$

This makes the square-root function continuous at each positive number. What happens at 0, we discuss later.

With f and g continuous at c, we have

$$\lim_{x \to c} f(x) = f(c), \qquad \lim_{x \to c} g(x) = g(c)$$

and thus, by the limit theorem,

$$\lim_{x \to c} [f(x) + g(x)] = f(c) + g(c)$$

$$\lim_{x \to c} [\alpha f(x)] = \alpha f(c)$$

$$\lim_{x \to c} [f(x)g(x)] = f(c)g(c)$$

and, if $g(c) \neq 0$,

$$\lim_{x \to c} \frac{f(x)}{g(x)} = \frac{f(c)}{g(c)} \, .$$

This tells us that

> if f and g are continuous at c, then $f + g$, αf, and fg are continuous at c; moreover, if $g(c) \neq 0$, then the quotient f/g is also continuous at c.

These results can obviously be extended to any finite number of functions.

Our next topic is the continuity of composite functions. Before getting into this, however, let's take a look at continuity in terms of ϵ, δ. A direct translation of

$$\lim_{x \to c} f(x) = f(c)$$

into ϵ, δ terms reads like this:

> for each $\epsilon > 0$ there exists $\delta > 0$ such that
> if $\quad 0 < |x - c| < \delta, \qquad$ then $\quad |f(x) - f(c)| < \epsilon.$

Here, however, the restriction

$$0 < |x - c|$$

is unnecessary; namely, we can allow $|x - c| = 0$. We can allow it because, if $|x - c| = 0$, then $x = c$ and $f(x) = f(c)$ and thus $|f(x) - f(c)| = 0$. Being 0, $|f(x) - f(c)|$ is certainly less than ϵ.

In summary, an ϵ, δ characterization of continuity at c reads as follows:

> f is continuous at c $\qquad$ iff $\qquad$ $\begin{cases} \text{for each } \epsilon > 0 \text{ there exists } \delta > 0 \text{ such that} \\ \text{if } |x - c| < \delta \quad \text{then } |f(x) - f(c)| < \epsilon. \end{cases}$

In simple intuitive language

> f is continuous at c $\qquad$ iff $\qquad$ for x close to c, $f(x)$ is close to $f(c)$.

We are now ready to take up the continuity of composites.

> **Theorem**
>
> If g is continuous at c and f is continuous at $g(c)$ then the composition $f \circ g$ is continuous at c.

The idea here is simple:
with g continuous at c, we know that

$$\text{for } x \text{ close to } c, \, g(x) \text{ is close to } g(c);$$

from the continuity of f at $g(c)$, we know that

$$\text{with } g(x) \text{ close to } g(c), f(g(x)) \text{ is close to } f(g(c)).$$

In summary,

$$\text{with } x \text{ close to } c, f(g(x)) \text{ is close to } f(g(c)). \quad \square$$

The argument we just gave is too vague to be a proof. Here in contrast is a proof:

We begin with $\epsilon > 0$ and must show that there exists some number $\delta > 0$ such that

$$\text{if } |x - c| < \delta, \quad \text{then } |f(g(x)) - f(g(c))| < \epsilon.$$

In the first place, we observe that since f is continuous at $g(c)$ there does exist a number $\delta_1 > 0$ such that

$$\text{if } |t - g(c)| < \delta_1, \quad \text{then } |f(t) - f(g(c))| < \epsilon.$$

With $\delta_1 > 0$ we know from the continuity of g at c that there exists a number $\delta > 0$ such that

$$\text{if } |x - c| < \delta, \quad \text{then } |g(x) - g(c)| < \delta_1.$$

Putting these two statements together, we see that

$$\text{if } |x - c| < \delta, \quad \text{then } |g(x) - g(c)| < \delta_1$$

and thus

$$|f(g(x)) - f(g(c))| < \epsilon. \quad \square$$

It is time to look at some examples.

Example. The function

$$F(x) = \sqrt{x^2 + 1}$$

is everywhere continuous. To see this, note that

$$F = f \circ g,$$

where

$$g(x) = x^2 + 1 \quad \text{and} \quad f(x) = \sqrt{x}. \quad \square$$

Example.   The function
$$F(x) = \left| \frac{x^2 + 1}{(x - 8)^4} \right|$$
is continuous on its domain. This of course excludes $x = 8$. To see this, note that
$$F = f \circ g,$$
where
$$g(x) = \frac{x^2 + 1}{(x - 8)^4} \quad \text{and} \quad f(x) = |x|. \quad \square$$

The continuity of composites holds for any finite number of functions. The only requirement is that each function be continuous *where it is applied.*

Example.   The function
$$F(x) = \frac{1}{5 - \sqrt{x^2 + 16}}$$
is continuous everywhere except at $x = \pm 3$, where it is not defined. To see this, note that
$$F = f \circ g \circ k \circ h,$$
where
$$f(x) = \frac{1}{x}, \quad g(x) = 5 - x, \quad k(x) = \sqrt{x}, \quad h(x) = x^2 + 16$$
and observe that each of these functions is being applied only where it is continuous. In particular f is being applied only on nonzero numbers and k is being applied only on positive numbers. $\square$

Just as we considered one-sided limits, we can consider one-sided continuity.

Definition of One-Sided Continuity
A function f is called
$\qquad$ *continuous from the left* at c $\quad$ iff $\quad \lim\limits_{x \uparrow c} f(x) = f(c).$
It is called
$\qquad$ *continuous from the right* at c $\quad$ iff $\quad \lim\limits_{x \downarrow c} f(x) = f(c).$

It is clear from (2.5.2) that a function f is continuous at c iff it is continuous there from both sides.

At each integer the greatest-integer function
$$f(x) = [x] \qquad\qquad\qquad \text{(Figure 2.6.5)}$$
is continuous from the right but discontinuous from the left. This situation is reversed in the case of
$$g(x) = [x] = \text{greatest integer less than } x.$$

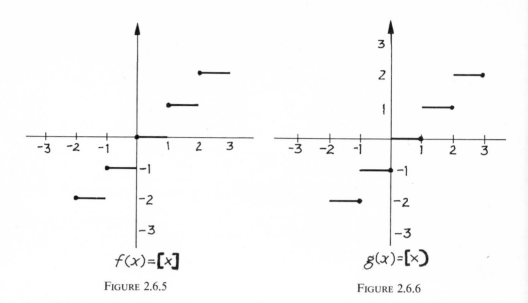

FIGURE 2.6.5

FIGURE 2.6.6

For the graph, see Figure 2.6.6. At each integer, g is continuous from the left but discontinuous from the right.

For more examples of one-sided continuity we refer to Figures 2.6.7 and 2.6.8. In Figure 2.6.7 we have continuity from the right at 0. In Figure 2.6.8 we have continuity from the left at 0.

Continuity on $[a,b]$

From a function defined on a closed interval $[a, b]$ the most continuity that we can possibly expect is

(1) continuity at each point c of the open interval (a, b)
(2) continuity from the right at a, and
(3) continuity from the left at b.

FIGURE 2.6.7

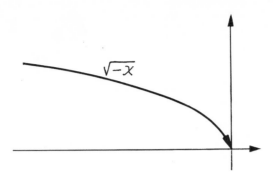

FIGURE 2.6.8

Any function f that fulfills these requirements is called *continuous* on $[a, b]$.

As an example we take the function

$$f(x) = \sqrt{1 - x^2}.$$

Its graph is the semicircle displayed in Figure 2.6.9. The function is continuous on $[-1, 1]$ because it is continuous at each number c in $(-1, 1)$, continuous from the right at -1 and continuous from the left at 1.

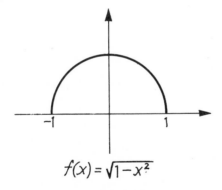

FIGURE 2.6.9

Functions which are continuous on a closed interval $[a, b]$ have special properties that, in general, discontinuous functions do not have. We close this section by emphasizing two of these properties.

In the first place, a function which is continuous on an interval does not "skip" any values and thus its graph is an "unbroken curve." There are no "holes" in it and no "gaps." This is the idea behind the *intermediate-value theorem*.

The Intermediate-Value Theorem 2.6.1

If f is continuous on $[a, b]$ and C is a number between $f(a)$ and $f(b)$, then there is at least one number c between a and b such that $f(c) = C$.

FIGURE 2.6.10   FIGURE 2.6.11

We illustrate the theorem in Figure 2.6.10. What can happen in the discontinuous case is illustrated in Figure 2.6.11. There the number C has been "skipped."

We come now to the maximum-minimum property of continuous functions.

Maximum-Minimum Theorem 2.6.2

If f is continuous on $[a, b]$ then, somewhere on $[a, b]$, f takes on a maximum value M and a minimum value m.

The situation is illustrated in Figure 2.6.12. The maximum value M is taken on at the point marked x_2 and the minimum value m is taken on at the point marked x_1.

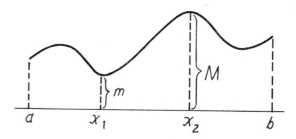

FIGURE 2.6.12

It is interesting to note that in the maximum-minimum theorem the full hypothesis is needed. If we drop the continuity requirement, the conclusion does not follow. As an example, we can take the function

$$f(x) = \begin{cases} \dfrac{a + b}{2}, & x = a \\ x, & a < x < b. \\ \dfrac{a + b}{2}, & x = b \end{cases}$$

The graph of this function is pictured in Figure 2.6.13. The function is defined on $[a, b]$ but it takes on neither a maximum nor a minimum value. If, instead of dropping the continuity requirement, we drop the requirement that the interval be of the form $[a, b]$, then again the result fails. For example, in the case of

$$g(x) = x \qquad \text{for } x \in (a, b),$$

g is continuous at each point of (a, b) but again there is no maximum value and no minimum value. See Figure 2.6.14. [For proofs of the intermediate-value theorem and the maximum-minimum theorem see the appendix at the end of the book.]

FIGURE 2.6.13

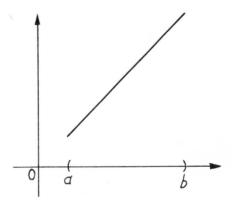

FIGURE 2.6.14

Exercises

1.* In each case, state whether or not the function is continuous at 2.

(a) $f(x) = 6x^7 - 100x + 1$.

(b) $g(x) = \sqrt{(x - 2)^3 + 5}$.

(c) $h(x) = \begin{cases} x^3, & x \geq 2 \\ x^2 + 4, & x < 2 \end{cases}$.

(d) $l(x) = \sqrt{1 - x}$.

(e) $m(x) = (x - 2)[x]$.

(f) $n(x) = \begin{cases} \dfrac{1}{x - 2}, & x \neq 2 \\ 0, & x = 2 \end{cases}$.

(g) $v(x) = \dfrac{\sqrt{x^3 - 1} - x^4}{x}$.

(h) $w(x) = \begin{cases} 0, & 1.99 < x < 2.001 \\ -1, & x \notin (1.99, 2.001) \end{cases}$.

(i) $z(x) = \begin{cases} 0, & x < 2 \\ 0.01, & x \geq 2 \end{cases}$.

(j) $q(x) = [2x]$.

2.* For each of the following functions sketch the graph and find the discontinuities (if any).

(a) $f(x) = |x^2 - 1|$.

(b) $f(x) = |6 - x|$.

(c) $f(x) = \begin{cases} 2x - 1, & x < 1 \\ x^2, & x \geq 1 \end{cases}$.

(d) $f(x) = \max \{x, x^2\}$.

(e) $f(x) = \dfrac{1}{x^2 + 5}$.

(f) $f(x) = \begin{cases} -1, & x < 2 \\ x/2, & 2 \leq x < 3 \\ x^{1/2}, & x > 3 \end{cases}$.

3. Find a function which is defined everywhere and discontinuous
   (a) only at 0,
   (b) only at 0 and 1,
   (c) from the left only at 0,
   (d) from the right only at 0.

4. At what points (if any) are the following functions continuous?

(a)* $f(x) = \begin{cases} 1, & x \text{ rational} \\ 0, & x \text{ irrational} \end{cases}$.

(b)* $g(x) = \begin{cases} x, & x \text{ rational} \\ 0, & x \text{ irrational} \end{cases}$.

5. Find a function which is continuous on the open interval $(0, 1)$ and has
   (a) no maximum value there,
   (b) a maximum value there.

6. Prove that there exists a real number x_0 such that

$$x_0^5 - 4x_0 + 1 = 7.21.$$

[HINT: Apply the intermediate-value theorem to the polynomial $P(x) = x^5 - 4x + 1$.]

7. Let n be a positive integer.
   (a) Prove that, if $0 \leq a < b$, then $a^n < b^n$.
   (b) Prove that every nonnegative real number x has a unique nonnegative nth root $x^{1/n}$. [HINT: The existence of $x^{1/n}$ can be seen by applying the intermediate-value theorem to the function $f(t) = t^n$ for $t \geq 0$. The uniqueness follows from part (a).]

8. Prove that f is continuous at c iff $\lim_{h \to 0} f(c + h) = f(c)$.

9. Let f and g be continuous at c. Prove that if
   (a) $f(c) > 0$, then there exists $\delta > 0$ such that

$$f(x) > 0 \qquad \text{for all } x \in (c - \delta, c + \delta).$$

   (b) $f(c) < 0$, then there exists $\delta > 0$ such that

$$f(x) < 0 \qquad \text{for all } x \in (c - \delta, c + \delta).$$

   (c) $f(c) < g(c)$, then there exists $\delta > 0$ such that

$$f(x) < g(x) \qquad \text{for all } x \in (c - \delta, c + \delta).$$

DIFFERENTIATION

3.1 The idea of derivative

Informal Beginnings

We begin with a function f and on its graph choose a point $(x, f(x))$. See Figure 3.1.1. Through the point $(x, f(x))$ we mark the line which to the naked eye seems to best approximate the graph of f at the chosen point. We call this line the *tangent line* at $(x, f(x))$. Our question is this: How can we determine the tangent line analytically?

We already know that the tangent line passes through $(x, f(x))$ and hence all we need to determine is the slope. To do this, we choose a small number $h \neq 0$ and on the graph of f mark the point $(x + h, f(x + h))$. See Figure 3.1.2. The secant line that passes through $(x, f(x))$ and $(x + h, f(x + h))$ has slope

$$\frac{f(x + h) - f(x)}{h}.$$

This is certainly not the slope of the tangent line but it is an approximation to it. To get the slope of the tangent line we will let h tend to zero. If all goes well, (this is all very informal), as h tends to 0, the point $(x + h, f(x + h))$ will slide along the curve toward the point $(x, f(x))$ and, as this happens, the secant line will have the tangent as a limiting position. With

$$\frac{f(x + h) - f(x)}{h} \qquad \text{as the slope of the secant line}$$

we can view

$$\lim_{h \to 0} \frac{f(x + h) - f(x)}{h} \qquad \text{as the slope of the tangent line.}$$

This in fact is how the slope of the tangent line will be defined.

FIGURE 3.1.1

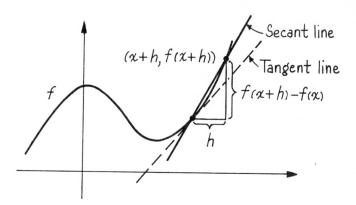

FIGURE 3.1.2

Definitions and Examples

Not all functions possess limits of the form

$$\lim_{h \to 0} \frac{f(x+h) - f(x)}{h} \, .$$

Those which do are called *differentiable*.

Definition of Derivative

A function f is said to be *differentiable* at x iff

$$\lim_{h \to 0} \frac{f(x+h) - f(x)}{h} \qquad \text{exists.}$$

If this limit exists, it is called the *derivative* of f at x and is denoted by $f'(x)$.†

---

† This prime notation goes back to the French mathematician Joseph Louis Lagrange (1736–1813). Another will be introduced later.

The number

$$f'(x) = \lim_{h \to 0} \frac{f(x + h) - f(x)}{h}$$

can be interpreted as the *slope* of the graph of f at the point $(x, f(x))$. The line through $(x, f(x))$ which has this slope is called the *tangent line* at $(x, f(x))$.

It is time we looked at some examples.

Example.   We begin with the squaring function

$$f(x) = x^2.$$

To find $f'(x)$ we form the *difference quotient*

$$\frac{f(x + h) - f(x)}{h} = \frac{(x + h)^2 - x^2}{h}.$$ (See Figure 3.1.3)

Since

$$\frac{(x + h)^2 - x^2}{h} = \frac{x^2 + 2xh + h^2 - x^2}{h} = \frac{2xh + h^2}{h} = 2x + h$$

we have

$$\frac{f(x + h) - f(x)}{h} = 2x + h.$$

Obviously then

$$f'(x) = \lim_{h \to 0} \frac{f(x + h) - f(x)}{h} = 2x. \quad \square$$

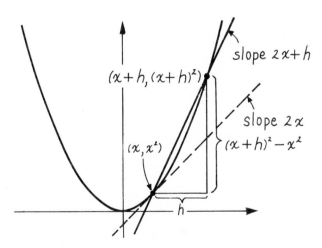

FIGURE 3.1.3

Example.   In the case of a linear function

$$f(x) = mx + b$$

we have

$$f'(x) = m$$

(and thus the graph is its own tangent line).

To see this, note that

$$\frac{f(x + h) - f(x)}{h} = \frac{[m(x + h) + b] - [mx + b]}{h} = \frac{mh}{h} = m.$$

It follows that

$$f'(x) = \lim_{h \to 0} \frac{f(x + h) - f(x)}{h} = m. \quad \square$$

The derivative

$$f'(x) = \lim_{h \to 0} \frac{f(x + h) - f(x)}{h}$$

is a two-sided limit. It can therefore not be taken at an end point of the domain. In our next example we will be dealing with the square-root function. Although this is defined for all $x \geq 0$, you can expect a derivative only for $x > 0$.

Example.   The square-root function

$$f(x) = \sqrt{x}, \qquad x \geq 0$$

satisfies

$$f'(x) = \frac{1}{2\sqrt{x}}, \qquad \text{for } x > 0.$$

To verify this, we begin with $x > 0$ and form the difference quotient

$$\frac{f(x + h) - f(x)}{h} = \frac{\sqrt{x + h} - \sqrt{x}}{h}.$$

To remove the radicals from the numerator we multiply both the numerator and the denominator by $\sqrt{x + h} + \sqrt{x}$. This gives

$$\frac{f(x + h) - f(x)}{h} = \left(\frac{\sqrt{x + h} - \sqrt{x}}{h} \right) \left(\frac{\sqrt{x + h} + \sqrt{x}}{\sqrt{x + h} + \sqrt{x}} \right) = \frac{1}{\sqrt{x + h} + \sqrt{x}}$$

and thus

$$f'(x) = \lim_{h \to 0} \frac{f(x + h) - f(x)}{h} = \frac{1}{2\sqrt{x}}. \quad \square$$

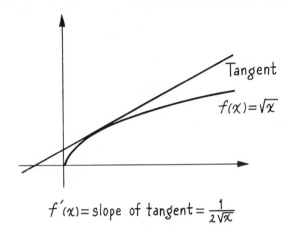

$$f'(x) = \text{slope of tangent} = \frac{1}{2\sqrt{x}}$$

FIGURE 3.1.4

Example.   Here we differentiate the function

$$f(x) = \sqrt{1 - x^2}.$$

The domain of f is the closed interval $[-1, 1]$ but we can expect differentiability at most on the open interval $(-1, 1)$. For x in $(-1, 1)$ we form the difference quotient

$$\frac{f(x + h) - f(x)}{h} = \frac{\sqrt{1 - (x + h)^2} - \sqrt{1 - x^2}}{h}.$$

Once again we remove the radicals from the numerator, this time by multiplying both numerator and denominator by

$$\sqrt{1 - (x + h)^2} + \sqrt{1 - x^2}.$$

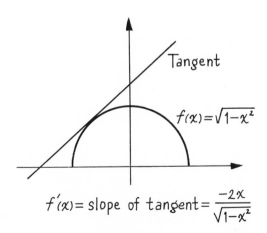

$$f'(x) = \text{slope of tangent} = \frac{-2x}{\sqrt{1 - x^2}}$$

FIGURE 3.1.5

After simplification these calculations yield

$$\frac{f(x+h)-f(x)}{h} = \frac{-2x-h}{\sqrt{1-(x+h)^2}+\sqrt{1-x^2}}$$

and thus

$$f'(x) = \lim_{h\to0}\frac{f(x+h)-f(x)}{h} = \frac{-x}{\sqrt{1-x^2}}. \quad \square$$

Differentiability vs. Continuity

A function can be continuous at some number x without being differentiable there. For example, the absolute-value function

$$f(x) = |x|$$

is continuous at 0 (it is everywhere continuous) but it is not differentiable at 0:

$$\frac{f(0+h)-f(0)}{h} = \frac{|0+h|-|0|}{h} = \frac{|h|}{h} = \begin{cases} 1, & h > 0 \\ -1, & h < 0 \end{cases}$$

so that

$$\lim_{h\to0}\frac{f(0+h)-f(0)}{h} \quad \text{does not exist.}$$

The failure of the absolute-value function to be differentiable at 0 is reflected by its graph. (Figure 3.1.6). At $(0, 0)$, the graph comes to a sharp point and there is no tangent line. A similar situation occurs with

$$f(x) = |x^2 - 1|. \quad \text{(Figure 3.1.7)}$$

No derivative at 0

FIGURE 3.1.6

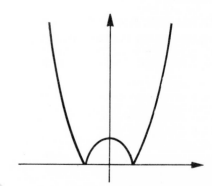

No derivative at −1; no derivative at 1

FIGURE 3.1.7

In this case the graph comes to a sharp point at $(-1, 0)$ and $(1, 0)$. The function is differentiable everywhere except at -1 and 1.

Although not every continuous function is differentiable, every differentiable function is continuous. In particular,

(3.1.1) | if f is differentiable at x,   then f is continuous at x. |

To prove this, we need only observe that for $h \neq 0$ and $x + h$ in the domain of f,

$$f(x + h) - f(x) = \frac{f(x + h) - f(x)}{h} \cdot h.$$

With f differentiable at x,

$$\lim_{h \to 0} \frac{f(x + h) - f(x)}{h} = f'(x).$$

Since

$$\lim_{h \to 0} h = 0,$$

we have

$$\lim_{h \to 0} [f(x + h) - f(x)] = \left[\lim_{h \to 0} \frac{f(x + h) - f(x)}{h} \right] \cdot \left[\lim_{h \to 0} h \right] = f'(x) \cdot 0 = 0.$$

This tells us that

$$\lim_{h \to 0} f(x + h) = f(x)$$

and thus (by Exercise 8, section 2.6) that f is continuous at x.   □

Exercises

Differentiate each of the following functions by forming a suitable difference quotient and taking the limit as h tends to 0.

1.* $f(x) = \alpha$.
2. $f(x) = 3x$.
3.* $f(x) = 3x + 5$.
4. $f(x) = mx + b$.
5.* $f(x) = 1/x$.

6. $f(x) = 1/x^2$.
7.* $f(x) = \frac{1}{2}x^2$.
8. $f(x) = -x^2$.
9.* $f(x) = 2x^3$.
10. $f(x) = x^4$.

11.* $f(x) = (x - 1)^2$.
12. $f(x) = (2x - 3)^2$.
13.* $f(x) = 1/\sqrt{x}$.
14. $f(x) = \sqrt{x - 1}$.
15.* $f(x) = 1/\sqrt{x - 1}$.

Draw the graph of each of the following functions and indicate where it is not differentiable.

16.* $f(x) = |x - 1|$.

17.* $f(x) = |x^2 - 4|$.

18.* $f(x) = \begin{cases} \sqrt{x}, & x \geq 0 \\ \sqrt{-x}, & x \leq 0 \end{cases}$.

19*. $f(x) = |2x - 5|$.

3.2   Some differentiation formulas

Calculating the derivative of

$$f(x) = (x^3 - 2)(x - 1) \quad \text{or} \quad f(x) = \frac{6x^2 - 1}{x^4 + 5x + 1}$$

by forming the proper difference quotient

$$\frac{f(x + h) - f(x)}{h}$$

and then taking the limit as h tends to 0 is rather tedious. Here we derive some general formulas which make such calculations quite simple.

For future reference we first point out that the constant functions have derivative 0:

$$\text{if} \quad f(x) = \alpha, \quad \text{then} \quad f'(x) = 0$$

and the identity function has derivative 1:

$$\text{if} \quad f(x) = x, \quad \text{then} \quad f'(x) = 1.$$

PROOF.   For $f(x) = \alpha$,

$$\frac{f(x + h) - f(x)}{h} = \frac{\alpha - \alpha}{h} = 0 \quad \text{and thus} \quad f'(x) = 0.$$

For $f(x) = x$,

$$\frac{f(x + h) - f(x)}{h} = \frac{(x + h) - x}{h} = \frac{h}{h} = 1 \quad \text{and thus} \quad f'(x) = 1. \quad \square$$

Theorem 3.2.1

Let α be a real number. If f and g are differentiable at x, then $f + g$ and αf are differentiable at x. Moreover,

$$\text{(i)} \quad (f + g)'(x) = f'(x) + g'(x),$$
$$\text{(ii)} \quad (\alpha f)'(x) = \alpha f'(x).$$

PROOF.   To prove (i) we note that

$$\frac{(f + g)(x + h) - (f + g)(x)}{h} = \frac{[f(x + h) + g(x + h)] - [f(x) + g(x)]}{h}$$

$$= \frac{f(x + h) - f(x)}{h} + \frac{g(x + h) - g(x)}{h}.$$

By definition,

$$\lim_{h \to 0} \frac{f(x + h) - f(x)}{h} = f'(x), \quad \lim_{h \to 0} \frac{g(x + h) - g(x)}{h} = g'(x).$$

Thus

$$\lim_{h \to 0} \frac{(f+g)(x+h) - (f+g)(x)}{h} = f'(x) + g'(x),$$

which means that

$$(f+g)'(x) = f'(x) + g'(x).$$

To show that (ii) holds we must show that

$$\lim_{h \to 0} \frac{(\alpha f)(x+h) - (\alpha f)(x)}{h} = \alpha f'(x).$$

This follows directly from

$$\frac{(\alpha f)(x+h) - (\alpha f)(x)}{h} = \alpha \left[\frac{f(x+h) - f(x)}{h} \right]. \quad \Box$$

Theorem 3.2.2

If f and g are differentiable at x, then so is their product and
$$(fg)'(x) = f(x)g'(x) + g(x)f'(x).$$

PROOF.   In the first place

$$\frac{(fg)(x+h) - (fg)(x)}{h} = \frac{f(x+h)g(x+h) - f(x)g(x)}{h}.$$

Subtracting and adding $f(x+h)g(x)$ to the numerator, we can rewrite the above difference quotient as

$$f(x+h) \left[\frac{g(x+h) - g(x)}{h} \right] + g(x) \left[\frac{f(x+h) - f(x)}{h} \right].$$

Since f is differentiable at x, we know that f is continuous at x (3.1.1) and thus that

$$\lim_{h \to 0} f(x+h) = f(x).$$

Since

$$\lim_{h \to 0} \frac{g(x+h) - g(x)}{h} = g'(x) \quad \text{and} \quad \lim_{h \to 0} \frac{f(x+h) - f(x)}{h} = f'(x),$$

we obtain

$$\lim_{h \to 0} \frac{(fg)(x+h) - (fg)(x)}{h} = f(x)g'(x) + g(x)f'(x). \quad \Box$$

Using Theorem 3.2.2 it is not hard to prove that

(3.2.3)

if n is a positive integer then the function $p(x) = x^n$ satisfies $p'(x) = nx^{n-1}$.

In particular

$$p(x) = x \quad \text{satisfies} \quad p'(x) = 1 \cdot x^0 = 1,$$
$$p(x) = x^2 \quad \text{satisfies} \quad p'(x) = 2x,$$
$$p(x) = x^3 \quad \text{satisfies} \quad p'(x) = 3x^2$$
$$p(x) = x^4 \quad \text{satisfies} \quad p'(x) = 4x^3,$$

and so on.

PROOF OF (3.2.3).   We proceed by induction on n. If $n = 1$, then we have the identity function

$$p(x) = x,$$

which we know satisfies

$$p'(x) = 1 = 1 \cdot x^0.$$

This means that the formula holds for $n = 1$.

We suppose now that the result holds for $n = k$, and show that it holds for $n = k + 1$. We let

$$p(x) = x^{k+1}$$

and note that

$$p(x) = x \cdot x^k.$$

Applying the product formula derived in Theorem 3.2.2 and our inductive hypothesis, we obtain

$$p'(x) = x \cdot kx^{k-1} + 1 \cdot x^k = (k + 1)x^k,$$

which shows that the formula holds for $k + 1$. $\square$

The formula for differentiating polynomials should now be obvious:

$$\text{if} \quad P(x) = a_n x^n + a_{n-1}x^{n-1} + \cdots + a_1 x + a_0$$
$$\text{then} \quad P'(x) = na_n x^{n-1} + (n - 1)a_{n-1}x^{n-2} + \cdots + a_1.$$

For example,

$$P(x) = 12x^3 - 6x - 2 \quad \text{satisfies} \quad P'(x) = 36x^2 - 6,$$

and

$$P(x) = \tfrac{1}{4}x^4 - 2x^2 + x + 5 \quad \text{satisfies} \quad P'(x) = x^3 - 4x + 1.$$

We turn now to the differentiability of reciprocals and quotients.

Theorem 3.2.4

If g is differentiable at x and $g(x) \neq 0$, then $1/g$ is differentiable at x and

$$\left(\frac{1}{g}\right)'(x) = -\frac{g'(x)}{[g(x)]^2}.$$

PROOF. Since g is differentiable at x, g is continuous at x (by 3.1.1). Since $g(x) \neq 0$, we know that $1/g$ is continuous at x, and thus

$$\lim_{h \to 0} \frac{1}{g(x+h)} = \frac{1}{g(x)} .$$

Let $h \neq 0$. If $g(x + h) \neq 0$, then

$$\frac{1}{h} \left[\frac{1}{g(x+h)} - \frac{1}{g(x)} \right] = - \left[\frac{g(x+h) - g(x)}{h} \right] \frac{1}{g(x+h)} \frac{1}{g(x)} .$$

Taking the limit as h tends to zero, we see that the right-hand side (and thus the left) tends to

$$- \frac{g'(x)}{[g(x)]^2} . \quad \square$$

From this last result it is easy to see that the formula for the derivative of a power, x^n, also applies to negative powers; namely,

(3.2.5)
> if n is a negative integer, then the function
> $p(x) = x^n$, $x \neq 0$ satisfies $p'(x) = nx^{n-1}$, $x \neq 0$.

The exclusion of zero is necessary since at zero the negative powers of x are not defined. To illustrate (3.2.5), we note that

$$p(x) = x^{-1} \quad \text{satisfies} \quad p'(x) = (-1)x^{-2} = -x^{-2}$$
$$p(x) = x^{-2} \quad \text{satisfies} \quad p'(x) = -2x^{-3}$$
$$p(x) = x^{-3} \quad \text{satisfies} \quad p'(x) = -3x^{-4}$$

and so on.

PROOF OF (3.2.5). For $x \neq 0$,

$$p(x) = \frac{1}{g(x)} , \quad \text{where} \quad g(x) = x^{-n}.$$

Thus

$$p'(x) = - \frac{g'(x)}{[g(x)]^2} = -g'(x)x^{2n}.$$

Since $-n$ is a positive integer,

$$g'(x) = -nx^{-n-1}.$$

It follows that

$$p'(x) = nx^{-n-1}x^{2n} = nx^{n-1}. \quad \square$$

Theorem 3.2.6

If f and g are differentiable at x and $g(x) \neq 0$, then the quotient f/g is differentiable at x and

$$\left(\frac{f}{g}\right)'(x) = \frac{g(x)f'(x) - f(x)g'(x)}{[g(x)]^2}.$$

The proof is left to you. [HINT: $f/g = f \cdot 1/g$.]

From this last theorem you can see that all rational functions (quotients of polynomials) are differentiable wherever they are defined.

Example. If $f(x) = 5x^2 - 6/x$, then we can write

$$f(x) = 5x^2 - 6x^{-1},$$

so that

$$f'(x) = 10x + 6x^{-2}. \quad \square$$

Example. If $f(x) = (x^3 - 2)(x - 1)$, then, applying the product formula, we get

$$f'(x) = (x^3 - 2) \cdot 1 + (x - 1)3x^2 = 4x^3 - 3x^2 - 2.$$

Instead of using the product formula we can multiply $x^3 - 2$ by $x - 1$ and thus obtain

$$f(x) = x^4 - x^3 - 2x + 2,$$

which (as one would expect) again yields

$$f'(x) = 4x^3 - 3x^2 - 2. \quad \square$$

Example. Here we find $f'(0), f'(1)$, and $f'(2)$ for the function

$$f(x) = \frac{5x}{1 + x}.$$

To do this we first find a general expression for $f'(x)$ and then evaluate it at 0, 1, and 2. Using the quotient formula, we get

$$f'(x) = \frac{(1 + x)5 - 5x(1)}{(1 + x)^2} = \frac{5}{(1 + x)^2}.$$

This gives

$$f'(0) = \frac{5}{(1 + 0)^2} = 5, \quad f'(1) = \frac{5}{(1 + 1)^2} = \frac{5}{4},$$

$$f'(2) = \frac{5}{(1 + 2)^2} = \frac{5}{9}. \quad \square$$

Example. Here we find $g'(-1), g'(0)$, and $g'(1)$ for the function

$$g(x) = \frac{6x^2 - 1}{x^4 + 5x + 1}.$$

The quotient formula gives

$$g'(x) = \frac{(x^4 + 5x + 1)12x - (6x^2 - 1)(4x^3 + 5)}{(x^4 + 5x + 1)^2}$$

which can be simplified to

$$g'(x) = -\frac{12x^5 - 30x^2 - 4x^3 - 12x - 5}{(x^4 + 5x + 1)^2}.$$

Substituting in turn -1, 0, and 1 into this expression for $g'(x)$ we get

$$g'(-1) = -\frac{12(-1)^5 - 30(-1)^2 - 4(-1)^3 - 12(-1) - 5}{[(-1)^4 + 5(-1) + 1]^2} = \frac{31}{9}$$

$$g'(0) = 5$$

$$g'(1) = -\frac{12(1)^5 - 30(1)^2 - 4(1)^3 - 12(1) - 5}{[1^4 + 5(1) + 1]^2} = \frac{39}{49}. \quad \square$$

Exercises

Differentiate the following functions.

1.* $f(x) = 1 - x$.

2. $f(x) = 2(1 - x)$.

3.* $f(x) = 11x^5 - 6x^3 + 8$.

4. $f(x) = \dfrac{x^4}{4} + \dfrac{x^3}{3} + \dfrac{x^2}{2} + \dfrac{x}{1}$.

5.* $f(x) = ax^2 + bx + c$.

6. $f(x) = \dfrac{3}{x}$.

7.* $f(x) = -\dfrac{1}{x^2}$.

8. $f(x) = \dfrac{(x^2 - 1)}{x^3}$.

9.* $f(x) = \dfrac{(x - 2)(x - 3)}{x - 1}$.

10. $f(x) = \left(x - \dfrac{1}{x}\right)^2$.

11.* $f(x) = \dfrac{x^3}{1 - x}(3x^2 + 2)$.

12. $f(x) = (x^2 + 1)^2$.

13.* $f(x) = (x^2 - 1)(x - 3)$.

14. $f(x) = \dfrac{7x^4 - 11}{x + 1}$.

15.* $f(x) = (x - 1)(x - 2)(x - 3)$.

16. $f(x) = \dfrac{2x - 1}{x - 2}$.

17.* $f(x) = \dfrac{6 - 1/x}{x - 2}$.

18. $f(x) = \dfrac{1 - x^4}{x^2}$.

19.* $f(x) = (9x^8 - 8x^9)\left(x + \dfrac{1}{x}\right)$.

20. $f(x) = \left(1 - \dfrac{1}{x}\right)^{-2}$.

Find $f'(0)$ and $f'(1)$.

21.* $f(x) = \dfrac{1}{x - 2}$.

22. $f(x) = x^2(x - 1)$.

23.* $f(x) = \dfrac{1 - x^2}{1 + x^2}$.

24. $f(x) = \dfrac{2x^2 + x - 1}{x^2 + x + 1}$.

25.* $f(x) = \dfrac{ax + b}{cx + d}$.

26. $f(x) = \dfrac{ax^2 + bx + c}{x^2 + x + 1}$.

Given that $h(0) = 2$ and $h'(0) = 1$, find $f'(0)$.

27.* $f(x) = xh(x)$.

28. $f(x) = 3[h(x)]^2 - 5x$.

30. $f(x) = h(x) - \dfrac{1}{h(x)}$.

29.* $f(x) = \dfrac{1}{[h(x)]^2}$.

31. Prove Theorem 3.2.6.

3.3   The $\dfrac{d}{dx}$ notation

So far we have indicated the derivative by a prime but there are other notations which are widely used. The most popular of these is the double-d notation of Leibniz.† In the Leibniz notation the derivative of a function y is indicated by writing

$$\frac{dy}{dx}, \quad \frac{dy}{dt}, \quad \text{or} \quad \frac{dy}{dz}, \quad \text{etc.,}$$

depending upon whether the letter x, t, or z, etc., is being used for the elements of the domain of y. For instance, if y is initially defined by

$$y(x) = x^3,$$

then the Leibniz notation gives

$$\frac{dy}{dx}(x) = 3x^2.$$

Usually writers drop the x on the left and simply write

$$y = x^3$$

and

$$\frac{dy}{dx} = 3x^2.$$

The symbols

$$\frac{d}{dx}, \frac{d}{dt}, \frac{d}{dz}, \quad \text{etc.,}$$

are also used as prefixes before expressions to be differentiated. For example,

$$\frac{d}{dx}(x^3 - 4x) = 3x^2 - 4, \quad \frac{d}{dt}(t^2 + 3t + 1) = 2t + 3, \quad \frac{d}{dz}(z^5 - 1) = 5z^4.$$

In the Leibniz notation the differentiation formulas of the last section look like this:

I $$\frac{d}{dx}[f(x) + g(x)] = \frac{d}{dx}[f(x)] + \frac{d}{dx}[g(x)]$$

---

† Gottfried Wilhelm Leibniz (1646–1716), a German, and Sir Isaac Newton (1642–1727), an Englishman, are the two men who are generally credited with the invention of calculus.

II
$$\frac{d}{dx}[\alpha f(x)] = \alpha \frac{d}{dx}[f(x)]$$

III
$$\frac{d}{dx}[f(x)g(x)] = f(x)\frac{d}{dx}[g(x)] + g(x)\frac{d}{dx}[f(x)]$$

IV
$$\frac{d}{dx}\left[\frac{1}{g(x)}\right] = -\frac{1}{[g(x)]^2}\frac{d}{dx}[g(x)]$$

V
$$\frac{d}{dx}\left[\frac{f(x)}{g(x)}\right] = \frac{g(x)\frac{d}{dx}[f(x)] - f(x)\frac{d}{dx}[g(x)]}{[g(x)]^2}$$

VI
$$\frac{d}{dx}(\alpha) = 0 \quad \text{(constant function)}$$

VII
$$\frac{d}{dx}(x^n) = nx^{n-1}$$

VIII $\dfrac{d}{dx}(a_n x^n + a_{n-1}x^{n-1} + \cdots + a_1 x + a_0)$

$$= na_n x^{n-1} + (n-1)a_{n-1}x^{n-2} + \cdots + a_1.$$

Often the functions f and g are replaced by u and v and the x is left out altogether. Formulas I–V then look like this:

I
$$\frac{d(u+v)}{dx} = \frac{du}{dx} + \frac{dv}{dx}$$

II
$$\frac{d(\alpha u)}{dx} = \alpha\frac{du}{dx}$$

III
$$\frac{d(uv)}{dx} = u\frac{dv}{dx} + v\frac{du}{dx}$$

IV
$$\frac{d(1/v)}{dx} = -\frac{dv/dx}{v^2}$$

V
$$\frac{d\left(\dfrac{u}{v}\right)}{dx} = \frac{v\left(\dfrac{du}{dx}\right) - u\left(\dfrac{dv}{dx}\right)}{v^2}.$$

Probably the only way to develop a feeling for this new notation is to use it. Below we work out some practice problems.

Problem. Find

$$\frac{dy}{dx} \quad \text{if} \quad y = \frac{x-1}{x+2}.$$

SOLUTION.   Here we use the quotient rule (V):

$$\frac{dy}{dx} = \frac{(x+2)\dfrac{d}{dx}(x-1) - (x-1)\dfrac{d}{dx}(x+2)}{(x+2)^2}$$

$$= \frac{(x+2) - (x-1)}{(x+2)^2}$$

$$= \frac{3}{(x+2)^2} \cdot \quad \square$$

Problem.   Find

$$\frac{dy}{dx} \quad \text{if} \quad y = (x^3 + 1)(3x^5 + 2x - 1).$$

SOLUTION.   Here we can use the product rule III.

$$\frac{dy}{dx} = (x^3 + 1)\frac{d}{dx}(3x^5 + 2x - 1) + (3x^5 + 2x - 1)\frac{d}{dx}(x^3 + 1)$$

$$= (x^3 + 1)(15x^4 + 2) + (3x^5 + 2x - 1)(3x^2)$$

$$= (15x^7 + 15x^4 + 2x^3 + 2) + (9x^7 + 6x^3 - 3x^2)$$

$$= 24x^7 + 15x^4 + 8x^3 - 3x^2 + 2.$$

We could have achieved the same result by carrying out the initial multiplication

$$y = (x^3 + 1)(3x^5 + 2x - 1)$$

$$= (3x^8 + 2x^4 - x^3) + (3x^5 + 2x - 1)$$

$$= 3x^8 + 3x^5 + 2x^4 - x^3 + 2x - 1,$$

and then differentiating,

$$\frac{dy}{dx} = 24x^7 + 15x^4 + 8x^3 - 3x^2 + 2. \quad \square$$

Problem.   Find

$$\frac{d}{dt}\left(t^3 - \frac{t}{t^2 - 1}\right).$$

SOLUTION

$$\frac{d}{dt}\left(t^3 - \frac{t}{t^2 - 1}\right) = \frac{d}{dt}(t^3) - \frac{d}{dt}\left(\frac{t}{t^2 - 1}\right)$$

$$= 3t^2 - \left[\frac{(t^2 - 1)\cdot 1 - t(2t)}{(t^2 - 1)^2}\right]$$

$$= 3t^2 + \frac{t^2 + 1}{(t^2 - 1)^2} \cdot \quad \square$$

Problem.   Find

$$\frac{du}{dx} \quad \text{if} \quad u = \frac{ax + b}{cx + d} - \frac{cx + d}{ax + b}.$$

SOLUTION

$$\frac{du}{dx} = \frac{d}{dx}\left(\frac{ax + b}{cx + d}\right) - \frac{d}{dx}\left(\frac{cx + d}{ax + b}\right)$$

$$= \frac{(cx + d)a - (ax + b)c}{(cx + d)^2} - \frac{(ax + b)c - (cx + d)a}{(ax + b)^2}$$

$$= \frac{ad - bc}{(cx + d)^2} - \frac{bc - ad}{(ax + b)^2}$$

$$= (ad - bc)\left[\frac{1}{(cx + d)^2} + \frac{1}{(ax + b)^2}\right]. \quad \square$$

Problem.   Evaluate

$$\frac{dy}{dx} \quad \text{at } x = 0 \quad \text{and} \quad x = 1 \quad \text{if} \quad y = \frac{x^2}{x^2 - 4}.$$

SOLUTION

$$\frac{dy}{dx} = \frac{(x^2 - 4)2x - x^2(2x)}{(x^2 - 4)^2} = -\frac{8x}{(x^2 - 4)^2}.$$

At $x = 0$, $dy/dx = 0$; at $x = 1$, $dy/dx = -8/9$. $\square$

Exercises

Find dy/dx.

1.* $y = 3x^4 - x^2 + 1.$

2. $y = x^2 - 2x^{-4}.$

3.* $y = x - \dfrac{1}{x}.$

4. $y = \dfrac{2x}{1 + x}.$

5.* $y = \dfrac{x}{1 + x^2}.$

6. $y = x(x - 1)(x + 1).$

7.* $y = \dfrac{x^2}{1 - x}.$

8. $y = \left(\dfrac{x}{1 - x}\right)\left(\dfrac{2 - x}{3}\right).$

9.* $y = \dfrac{x^3 + 1}{x^3 - 1}.$

10. $y = \dfrac{x^2}{1 - 2x + x^2}.$

Find the indicated derivative.

11.* $\dfrac{d}{dx}(2x - 5)$.

19.* $\dfrac{d}{du}\left(\dfrac{2u}{1 - 2u}\right)$.

12. $\dfrac{d}{dx}(5x - 2)$.

20. $\dfrac{d}{du}\left(\dfrac{u^2}{u^3 - 1}\right)$.

13.* $\dfrac{d}{dx}(7x^3 - 1)$.

21.* $\dfrac{d}{du}\left(\dfrac{u}{u - 1} - \dfrac{u}{u + 1}\right)$.

14. $\dfrac{d}{dx}[(1 - x)(1 + x)]$.

22. $\dfrac{d}{du}[u^2(1 - u^2)(1 - u^3)]$.

15.* $\dfrac{d}{dt}\left(\dfrac{t^2 + 1}{t^2 - 1}\right)$.

23.* $\dfrac{d}{dx}\left(\dfrac{x^2}{1 - x^2} - \dfrac{1 - x^2}{x^2}\right)$.

16. $\dfrac{d}{dt}\left(\dfrac{2t^3 - 1}{t^4}\right)$.

24. $\dfrac{d}{dx}\left(\dfrac{3x^4 - 2x + 1}{x^4 - x - 1}\right)$.

17.* $\dfrac{d}{dt}\left(\dfrac{t^4}{2t^3 - 1}\right)$.

25.* $\dfrac{d}{dx}\left(\dfrac{x^3 + x^2 + x + 1}{x^3 - x^2 + x - 1}\right)$.

18. $\dfrac{d}{dt}\left[\dfrac{t}{(1 - t)^2}\right]$.

26. $\dfrac{d}{dx}\left(\dfrac{x^3 - x^2 + x - 1}{x^3 + x^2 + x + 1}\right)$.

Evaluate dy/dx at $x = 2$.

27.* $y = (x + 1)(x + 2)(x + 3)$.

29.* $y = \dfrac{(x - 1)(x - 2)}{(x + 2)}$.

28. $y = (x^2 + 1)(x^2 + 2)(x^2 + 3)$.

30. $y = \dfrac{(x^2 - 1)(x^2 - 2)}{x^2 + 2}$.

3.4 The derivative as a rate of change

In the case of a linear function

$$y = mx + b$$

the graph is a straight line and the slope m gives the rate of change of y with respect to x:

$$m = \frac{\text{change in } y}{\text{change in } x}.$$ (Figure 3.4.1)

In other words, on a line of slope m, y changes m times as fast as x. Throughout such a line, a change in abscissa from x to $x + h$ produces a change in ordinate from y to $y + mh$. (Figure 3.4.2)

In the more general case of a differentiable function

$$y = f(x)$$

the graph is a curve. The slope

$$\frac{dy}{dx} = f'(x)$$

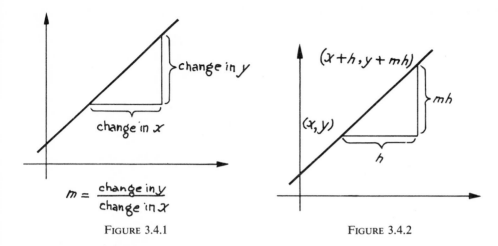

FIGURE 3.4.1   FIGURE 3.4.2

still gives the *rate of change of y with respect to x* but this rate can vary from point to point. At x_1 (see Figure 3.4.3) the rate of change is $f'(x_1)$; at x_2, the rate of change is $f'(x_2)$; at x_3, the rate of change is $f'(x_3)$.

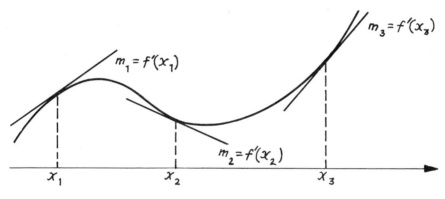

FIGURE 3.4.3

This rate of change idea is one of the fundamental ideas of the calculus. Keep it in mind whenever you see a derivative.

Problem. Find the rate of change of the area of a circle with respect to its radius r. Evaluate this rate of change when $r = 2$.

SOLUTION. Since

$$A = \pi r^2$$

the rate of change of A with respect to r is given by

$$\frac{dA}{dr} = 2\pi r,$$

which, by the way, is the circumference. When $r = 2$, the rate of change is 4π. This means that when the radius is 2, the area is changing 4π times as fast as the radius. □

Problem. Find the rate of change of the area of an equilateral triangle with respect to the length of a side. Evaluate this rate of change when the side has length $\sqrt{3}$.

SOLUTION.   If the side has length s, the area is given by the formula

$$A = \frac{1}{2} \,(\text{base})\,(\text{height}) = \frac{1}{2}\,(s)\left(\frac{\sqrt{3}}{2}\,s\right) = \frac{\sqrt{3}}{4}\,s^2.$$

The rate of change is therefore

$$\frac{dA}{ds} = \frac{\sqrt{3}}{2}\,s.$$

When $s = \sqrt{3}$, the rate of change is $\frac{3}{2}$. In other words, when the side has length $\sqrt{3}$, the area is changing $\frac{3}{2}$ times as fast as the length of the side. □

Problem.   The volume of a cylinder of height h and base radius r is given by the formula

$$V = \pi r^2 h.$$

Find the rate of change of h with respect to r if V is to remain constant as r increases.

SOLUTION.   Applying the product rule to

$$V = \pi r^2 h$$

we get

$$\frac{dV}{dr} = \pi r^2 \frac{dh}{dr} + h \frac{d}{dr}\,(\pi r^2) = \pi r^2 \frac{dh}{dr} + 2\pi rh.$$

Since V is to remain constant,

$$\frac{dV}{dr} = 0$$

and so

$$\pi r^2 \frac{dh}{dr} + 2\pi rh = 0.$$

Dividing through by πr, we get

$$r \frac{dh}{dr} + 2h = 0$$

and thus

$$\frac{dh}{dr} = -\frac{2h}{r}.$$

For the volume to remain constant, h must decrease $2h/r$ times as fast as r increases.

Exercises

1.* Find the rate of change of the area of a square with respect to the length s of one of its sides. Evaluate this rate of change when $s = 4$.

2. Find the rate of change of the volume of a cube with respect to the length s of one of its sides. Evaluate this rate of change when $s = 4$.

3.* Find the rate of change of the area of a square with respect to the length z of its diagonals. Evaluate this rate of change when $z = 4$.

4. Find the rate of change of

$$y = \frac{1}{x}$$

with respect to x when $x = -1$.

5.* Find the rate of change of

$$y = \frac{1}{x(x + 1)}$$

with respect to x when $x = 2$.

6. Find the rate of change of the volume of a ball with respect to its radius, given that $V = \frac{4}{3}\pi r^3$.

7.* Find the rate of change of the surface area of a ball with respect to its radius given that $A = 4\pi r^2$. What is this rate of change when $r = r_0$? How must r_0 be chosen so that the rate of change is 1?

8. Find x_0 given that the rate of change of

$$y = 2x^2 + x - 1$$

with respect to x is 4 when $x = x_0$.

9.* The dimensions of a rectangle are changing in such a way that the area of the rectangle remains constant. Find the rate of change of the height h with respect to the base b.

10. For what value of x is the rate of change of

$$y = ax^2 + bx + c \qquad \text{with respect to } x$$

the same as the rate of change of

$$z = bx^2 + ax + c \qquad \text{with respect to } x?$$

Assume $a \neq b$.

11.* Find the rate of change of the product $f(x)g(x)h(x)$ with respect to x when $x = 1$ given that

$$f(1) = 0, \quad g(1) = 2, \quad h(1) = -2, \quad f'(1) = 1, \quad g'(1) = -1, \quad h'(1) = 0.$$

3.5   The chain rule

Here we take up the differentiation of composite functions. As usual we begin informally.

Assume for the moment that the composition of differentiable functions is differentiable. Knowing the derivative of f and the derivative of g, how can we find the derivative of $f \circ g$? That is, how can we find $\dfrac{d}{dx}[f(g(x))]$?

The key to answering this question lies in the following two ideas:
The first idea is that for any differentiable function h

I $h(t)$ changes $h'(t)$ times as fast as t.

(This comes from $h'(t)$ being the rate of change of $h(t)$ with respect to t.)
The second idea is that

II   if A changes m times as fast as B
                      and B changes n times as fast as C,
                      then A changes mn times as fast as C.

Once you accept I and II the computation of $\dfrac{d}{dx}[f(g(x))]$ is easy. By I,

$f(g(x))$ changes $f'(g(x))$ times as fast as $g(x)$

and

$g(x)$ changes $g'(x)$ times as fast as x.

It follows by II that

$f(g(x))$ changes $f'(g(x))g'(x)$ times as fast as x.

This makes

$f'(g(x))g'(x)$ the rate of change of $f(g(x))$ with respect to x,

which means that

(3.5.1)
$$\frac{d}{dx}[f(g(x))] = f'(g(x))g'(x).\dagger$$

Formula (3.5.1) is called the *chain rule*. The name is particularly appropriate when three or more functions are involved. For the composition of three differentiable functions we have

$$\frac{d}{dx}[f(g(h(x)))] = f'(g(h(x))g'(h(x))h'(x).$$

If four functions are involved then a new link is added to the chain. The pattern must be obvious.

---

† If you wish to use the prime notation throughout, then the left-hand side becomes $(f \circ g)'(x)$ and the formula reads

$$(f \circ g)'(x) = f'(g(x))g'(x).$$

As an application of the chain rule we show how to differentiate integral powers of a differentiable function. The formula is this:

(3.5.2)
$$\frac{d}{dx}[g(x)]^n = n[g(x)]^{n-1}g'(x).$$

To derive this formula we set

$$f(x) = x^n$$

so that

$$\frac{d}{dx}[g(x)]^n \qquad \text{becomes} \qquad \frac{d}{dx}[f(g(x))].$$

The chain rule now gives

(1)
$$\frac{d}{dx}[g(x)]^n = f'(g(x))g'(x).$$

Since

$$f(x) = x^n \qquad \text{satisfies} \qquad f'(x) = nx^{n-1}$$

we have

$$f'(g(x)) = n[g(x)]^{(n-1)}.$$

Substituting this into (1), we get the desired formula. □

Formula (3.5.2) can also be written

(3.5.3)
$$\frac{d}{dx}[g(x)]^n = n[g(x)]^{(n-1)}\frac{d}{dx}[g(x)].$$

Example

$$\frac{d}{dx}(x^2 + 1)^3 = 3(x^2 + 1)^2\frac{d}{dx}(x^2 + 1)$$

$$= 3(x^2 + 1)^2 2x$$

$$= 6x(x^2 + 1)^2. □$$

Example

$$\frac{d}{dx}\left[\left(x + \frac{1}{x}\right)^{-3}\right] = -3\left(x + \frac{1}{x}\right)^{-4}\frac{d}{dx}\left(x + \frac{1}{x}\right)$$

$$= -3\left(x + \frac{1}{x}\right)^{-4}\left(1 - \frac{1}{x^2}\right). □$$

Example

$$\frac{d}{dx}[1 - (2 + 3x)^2]^3 = 3[1 - (2 + 3x)^2]^2 \frac{d}{dx}[1 - (2 + 3x)^2].$$

Since

$$\frac{d}{dx}[1 - (2 + 3x)^2] = -2(2 + 3x)\frac{d}{dx}(3x) = -6(2 + 3x),$$

we have

$$\frac{d}{dx}[1 - (2 + 3x)^2]^3 = -18(2 + 3x)[1 - (2 + 3x)^2]^2. \quad \square$$

Another Formulation of the Chain Rule

If y is expressed in terms of u:

$$y = f(u),$$

and u is expressed in terms of x:

$$u = g(x),$$

then y can be expressed in terms of x:

$$y = f(u) = f(g(x)).$$

In this situation we have

$$\frac{d}{dx}[f(g(x))] = \frac{dy}{dx}$$

$$f'(g(x)) = f'(u) = \frac{dy}{du}$$

$$g'(x) = \frac{du}{dx}$$

so that Formula 3.5.1 becomes

(3.5.4)
$$\boxed{\frac{dy}{dx} = \frac{dy}{du}\frac{du}{dx}.}$$

This formulation of the chain rule is particularly easy to understand. It simply points out that

$$\text{with } y \text{ changing } \frac{dy}{du} \text{ times as fast as } u,$$

$$\text{and } u \text{ changing } \frac{du}{dx} \text{ times as fast as } x,$$

$$y \text{ must change } \frac{dy}{du}\frac{du}{dx} \text{ times as fast as } x.$$

Problem. Find dy/dx given that

$$y = 3u^2 + 2 \qquad \text{and} \qquad u = \frac{1}{x-1} \cdot$$

SOLUTION

$$\frac{dy}{du} = 6u = \frac{6}{x-1} \cdot \qquad \frac{du}{dx} = -\frac{1}{(x-1)^2}$$

so that

$$\frac{dy}{dx} = \frac{dy}{du}\frac{du}{dx} = \frac{6}{x-1}\left(-\frac{1}{(x-1)^2}\right) = -\frac{6}{(x-1)^3} \cdot \quad \square$$

ALTERNATE SOLUTION. We can achieve the same result by first expressing y in terms of x and then differentiating. With

$$y = 3u^2 + 2 \qquad \text{and} \qquad u = \frac{1}{x-1}$$

we have

$$y = \frac{3}{(x-1)^2} + 2$$

so that

$$\frac{dy}{dx} = -\frac{6}{(x-1)^3} \cdot$$

Problem. Find dy/dx for $x = 2$ given that

$$y = \frac{u-1}{u+1} \qquad \text{and} \qquad u = x^2.$$

SOLUTION

$$\frac{dy}{du} = \frac{(u+1)1 - (u-1)1}{(u+1)^2} = \frac{2}{(u+1)^2} = \frac{2}{(x^2+1)^2} \qquad \text{and} \qquad \frac{du}{dx} = 2x$$

so that

$$\frac{dy}{dx} = \frac{dy}{du}\frac{du}{dx} = \frac{2}{(x^2+1)^2}(2x) = \frac{4x}{(x^2+1)^2} \cdot$$

At $x = 2$,

$$\frac{dy}{dx} = \frac{4(2)}{(2^2+1)^2} = \frac{8}{25} \cdot \quad \square$$

ALTERNATE SOLUTION.   With

$$y = \frac{u-1}{u+1} \qquad \text{and} \qquad u = x^2$$

we have

$$y = \frac{x^2-1}{x^2+1}$$

so that

$$\frac{dy}{dx} = \frac{(x^2+1)2x - (x^2-1)2x}{(x^2+1)^2} = \frac{4x}{(x^2+1)^2}.$$

At $x = 2$,

$$\frac{dy}{dx} = \frac{4(2)}{(2^2+1)^2} = \frac{8}{25}. \quad \square$$

The formula

$$\frac{dy}{dx} = \frac{dy}{du}\frac{du}{dx}$$

can easily be extended to more variables. For example, if x itself depends on s, then we have

$$\boxed{\frac{dy}{ds} = \frac{dy}{du}\frac{du}{dx}\frac{dx}{ds}.}$$

If, in addition, s depends on t, then

$$\boxed{\frac{dy}{dt} = \frac{dy}{du}\frac{du}{dx}\frac{dx}{ds}\frac{ds}{dt}}$$

and so on. Each new dependence adds a new link to the chain.

A More Rigorous Approach

The great advantage of looking at the chain rule from the rate of change point of view is that the chain rule becomes easy to understand. In fact, it becomes obvious. The disadvantage of this point of view is that it does not lend itself to a very rigorous treatment. A more rigorous treatment can be based on the following theorem.

Theorem 3.5.5

If g is differentiable at x and f is differentiable at $g(x)$, then the composition $f \circ g$ is differentiable at x and

$$(f \circ g)'(x) = f'(g(x))g'(x).$$

The advantage of phrasing the chain rule in this careful way is that the only assumptions which are needed (namely the differentiability of g at x and that of f at $g(x)$) are made explicit. Moreover, the differentiability of the composite function is not being assumed but has to be proven. If you would like to see a complete proof of this theorem look at the supplement to this section.

Exercises

Differentiate.

1.* $f(x) = (1 - 2x)^{-1}$.

2. $f(x) = (1 - 2x)^5$.

3.* $f(x) = (x^5 - x^{10})^{20}$.

4. $f(x) = \left(x^2 - \dfrac{1}{x^2}\right)^3$.

5.* $f(x) = x - \dfrac{1}{x}$.

6. $f(x) = \left(x - \dfrac{1}{x}\right)^3$.

7.* $f(x) = (x - x^3 - x^5)^4$.

8. $f(t) = \left(\dfrac{1}{1 + t}\right)^4$.

9.* $f(t) = (t^2 - 1)^{100}$.

10. $f(t) = (6 + t^2)^3$.

11.* $f(t) = (t^{-1} + t^{-2})^4$.

12. $f(x) = \left(\dfrac{ax + b}{cx + d}\right)^{-3}$.

13.* $f(x) = \left(\dfrac{3x}{x^2 + 1}\right)^4$.

14. $f(x) = [(2x + 1)^2 - (x + 1)^2]^3$.

15.* $f(x) = (x^4 + x^2 + x)^2$.

16. $f(x) = (x^2 + x + 1)^3$.

17.* $f(x) = \left(\dfrac{x^3}{3} + \dfrac{x^2}{2} + \dfrac{x}{1}\right)^{-1}$.

18. $f(x) = \left(\dfrac{x^2 - 1}{x^2 + 1}\right)^5$.

19.* $f(x) = \left(\dfrac{1}{x + 2} - \dfrac{1}{x - 2}\right)^3$.

20. $f(x) = [(6x - x^5)^{-1} + x]^2$.

Find dy/dx.

21.* $y = \dfrac{1}{1 + u^2}$, $u = 2x + 1$.

22. $y = u + \dfrac{1}{u}$, $u = (3x + 1)^4$.

23.* $y = \dfrac{2u}{1 - 4u}$, $u = (5x^2 + 1)^4$.

24. $y = u^3 + u + 1$, $u = \dfrac{1 - x}{1 + x}$.

Find dy/dt.

25. $y = \dfrac{1 - 7u}{1 + u^2}$, $u = 1 - x^2$, $x = 2t - 5$.

26. $y = 1 - u^2$, $u = \dfrac{1 - 7x}{1 + x^2}$, $x = 5t - 2$.

Given that

$$f(0) = 1, \quad f'(0) = 2, \quad f(1) = 0, \quad f'(1) = 1, \quad f(2) = 1, \quad f'(2) = 1,$$
$$g(0) = 2, \quad g'(0) = 1, \quad g(1) = 1, \quad g'(1) = 0, \quad g(2) = 2, \quad g'(2) = 1,$$
$$h(0) = 1, \quad h'(0) = 2, \quad h(1) = 2, \quad h'(1) = 1, \quad h(2) = 0, \quad h'(2) = 2,$$

evaluate the following.

27.* $(f \circ g)'(0)$.   31.* $(g \circ f)'(1)$.   35.* $(h \circ f)'(0)$.
28. $(f \circ g)'(1)$.   32. $(g \circ f)'(2)$.   36. $(f \circ h \circ g)'(1)$.
29.* $(f \circ g)'(2)$.   33.* $(f \circ h)'(0)$.   37.* $(g \circ f \circ h)'(2)$.
30. $(g \circ f)'(0)$.   34. $(h \circ f)'(1)$.   38. $(g \circ h \circ f)'(0)$.

SUPPLEMENT TO SECTION 3.5

To prove Theorem 3.5.5 it is convenient to use a slightly different formulation of derivative.

Theorem 3.5.6

The function f is differentiable at x iff

$$\lim_{t \to x} \frac{f(t) - f(x)}{t - x} \quad \text{exists.}$$

If this limit exists, it is $f'(x)$.

PROOF.   For each t in the domain of f, $t \neq x$, define

$$G(t) = \frac{f(t) - f(x)}{t - x}.$$

The theorem follows from noting that f is differentiable at x iff

$$\lim_{h \to 0} G(x + h) \quad \text{exists,}$$

and recalling that

$$\lim_{h \to 0} G(x + h) = l \quad \text{iff} \quad \lim_{t \to x} G(t) = l. \tag{2.4.2} \quad \square$$

PROOF OF THEOREM 3.5.5.   By Theorem 3.5.6 it is enough to show that

$$\lim_{t \to x} \frac{f(g(t)) - f(g(x))}{t - x} = f'(g(x))g'(x).$$

We begin by defining an auxiliary function F on the domain of f by

$$F(y) = \begin{cases} \dfrac{f(y) - f(g(x))}{y - g(x)}, & y \neq g(x) \\ f'(g(x)), & y = g(x) \end{cases}.$$

F is continuous at $g(x)$ since

$$\lim_{y \to g(x)} F(y) = \lim_{y \to g(x)} \frac{f(y) - f(g(x))}{y - g(x)},$$

and the right-hand side is, by Theorem 3.5.6, $f'(g(x))$, which is the value of F at $g(x)$. For $t \neq x$,

$$(1) \qquad \frac{f(g(t)) - f(g(x))}{t - x} = F(g(t)) \cdot \frac{g(t) - g(x)}{t - x}.$$

To see this we note that if $g(t) = g(x)$, then both sides are 0. If $g(t) \neq g(x)$, then

$$F(g(t)) = \frac{f(g(t)) - f(g(x))}{g(t) - g(x)},$$

so that again we have equality.

Since g, being differentiable at x, is continuous at x and since F is continuous at $g(x)$, we know that the composition $F \circ g$ is continuous at x. Thus

$$\lim_{t \to x} F(g(t)) = F(g(x)) = f'(g(x)).$$

This, together with Equation (1), gives

$$\lim_{t \to x} \frac{f(g(t)) - f(g(x))}{t - x} = f'(g(x))g'(x). \quad \square$$

3.6 Derivatives of higher order

If a function f is differentiable, then we can form a new function f'. If f' is itself differentiable, then we can form its derivative, called the *second derivative of f*, and denoted by f''. So long as we have differentiability, we can continue in this manner, forming f''', etc. The prime notation is not used beyond the third order. For the fourth derivative we write

$$f^{(4)}$$

and, more generally, for the nth derivative

$$f^{(n)}.$$

As an example, we can take

$$f(x) = x^3 - 5x^2 + 3x - 7$$

for which

$$f'(x) = 3x^2 - 10x + 3 \quad \text{and} \quad f''(x) = 6x - 10.$$

There is a third derivative

$$f'''(x) = 6,$$

and all higher derivatives are identically zero.

Since the derivative of a polynomial is again a polynomial and since the derivative of a rational function is again a rational function, you can see that polynomials and rational functions have derivatives of all orders. In the case of a polynomial, the derivatives of order greater than the degree of the polynomial are all identically zero. (Explain.)

In the Leibniz notation the derivatives of higher order are written

$$\frac{d^2y}{dx^2} = \frac{d}{dx}\left(\frac{dy}{dx}\right), \frac{d^3y}{dx^3} = \frac{d}{dx}\left(\frac{d^2y}{dx^2}\right), \ldots, \frac{d^ny}{dx^n} = \frac{d}{dx}\left(\frac{d^{n-1}y}{dx^{n-1}}\right), \ldots$$

or

$$\frac{d^2}{dx^2}[f(x)] = \frac{d}{dx}\left[\frac{d}{dx}[f(x)]\right], \frac{d^3}{dx^3}[f(x)] = \frac{d}{dx}\left[\frac{d^2}{dx^2}[f(x)]\right], \ldots,$$

$$\frac{d^n}{dx^n}[f(x)] = \frac{d}{dx}\left[\frac{d^{n-1}}{dx^{n-1}}[f(x)]\right], \ldots.$$

Below we work out some examples.

Example. If

$$y = x^{-1}$$

then

$$\frac{dy}{dx} = -x^{-2}, \quad \frac{d^2y}{dx^2} = 2x^{-3}, \quad \frac{d^3y}{dx^3} = -6x^{-4}, \quad \frac{d^4y}{dx^4} = 24x^{-5}. \quad \square$$

Example

$$\frac{d}{dx}\left(\frac{x}{1+x}\right) = \frac{(1+x)(1) - x(1)}{(1+x)^2} = \frac{1}{(1+x)^2}$$

so that

$$\frac{d^2}{dx^2}\left(\frac{x}{1+x}\right) = \frac{d}{dx}\left(\frac{1}{(1+x)^2}\right) = -\frac{2}{(1+x)^3}$$

and

$$\frac{d^3}{dx^3}\left(\frac{x}{1+x}\right) = \frac{d}{dx}\left(-\frac{2}{(1+x)^3}\right) = \frac{6}{(1+x)^4}. \quad \square$$

Example. If

$$f(x) = \frac{3x^2}{1+x^2}$$

then

$$f'(x) = \frac{(1+x^2)6x - 3x^2(2x)}{(1+x^2)^2} = \frac{6x}{(1+x^2)^2}$$

and

$$f''(x) = \frac{(1+x^2)^2 6 - 6x(2)(1+x^2)2x}{(1+x^2)^4} = \frac{(1+x^2)(6 - 24x^2)}{(1+x^2)^4} = \frac{6(1 - 4x^2)}{(1+x^2)^3}. \quad \square$$

Exercises

Find the following derivatives.

1.* $f''(x)$ for $f(x) = 7x^3 - 6x^5$.

2. $f''(x)$ for $f(x) = \dfrac{x}{1-x}$.

3.* $\dfrac{d^2y}{dx^2}$ for $y = x^2 - \dfrac{1}{x^2}$.

4. $\dfrac{d^4y}{dx^4}$ for $y = x^4$.

5.* $\dfrac{d^3y}{dx^3}$ for $y = (1 + 2x)^3$.

6. $\dfrac{d^3y}{dx^3}$ for $y = (1 + 3x)^2$.

7.* $\dfrac{d^2}{dx^2}\left(\dfrac{1-x}{1+x}\right)$.

14. $\dfrac{d^5}{dx^5}(x^5)$.

8. $\dfrac{d^2}{dx^2}\left(x^3 - \dfrac{1}{x^3}\right)$.

15.* $f'''(x)$ for $f(x) = \dfrac{x^3}{3} + \dfrac{x^2}{2} + \dfrac{x}{1} + 1$.

9.* $\dfrac{d^2}{dx^2}\left(\dfrac{ax+b}{cx+d}\right)$.

16. $f'''(x)$ for $f(x) = (7x^2 - 1)^{-1}$.

10. $\dfrac{d}{dx}\left[x\dfrac{d}{dx}(1-x^2)\right]$.

17.* $\dfrac{d^2}{dx^2}\left[\left(\dfrac{6-x}{x^2-1}\right)^2\right]$.

11.* $\dfrac{d}{dx}\left[x\dfrac{d^2}{dx^2}\left(\dfrac{1}{1+x}\right)\right]$.

18. $\dfrac{d^4}{dx^4}[(1+x)^4]$.

12. $\dfrac{d^2}{dx^2}\left[\dfrac{ax^2+b}{cx^2+d}\right]$.

19.* $\dfrac{d^n y}{dx^n}$ for $y = (1+x)^n$.

13.* $\dfrac{d^{100}}{dx^{100}}(x^9 - 20x^7 + x^5 + 1)$.

20. $\dfrac{d^n y}{dx^n}$ for $y = x^{-1}$.

3.7 Differentiating inverses

An Informal Approach

If f is a one-to-one function, then f has an inverse and the equation

$$y = f(x)$$

can be solved for x by setting

$$x = f^{-1}(y).$$

We begin with the following question: Knowing

$$\frac{dy}{dx} = \frac{d}{dx}[f(x)],$$

how can we determine

$$\frac{dx}{dy} = \frac{d}{dy}[f^{-1}(y)]?$$

If we approach this question from the rate of change point of view, the answer becomes obvious:

since y changes dy/dx times as fast as x,

x must change $\dfrac{1}{dy/dx}$ times as fast as y

and therefore we must have

(3.7.1)

$$\boxed{\frac{dx}{dy} = \frac{1}{dy/dx}.}$$

This formula of course makes no sense if $dy/dx = 0$.

nth Roots

We can use (3.7.1) to figure out

$$\frac{d}{dy}[y^{1/n}].$$

We initially restrict ourselves to $y > 0$.

If n is a positive integer, the equation

$$y = x^n, \qquad x > 0$$

is solved by setting $x = y^{1/n}$. With

$$y = x^n \quad \text{satisfying} \quad \frac{dy}{dx} = nx^{n-1},$$

we see from (3.7.1) that

$$\frac{dx}{dy} = \frac{1}{dy/dx} = \frac{1}{nx^{n-1}} = \frac{1}{n}x^{1-n}.$$

Since $x = y^{1/n}$, the left-hand side becomes

$$\frac{d}{dy}[y^{1/n}]$$

and the right-hand side becomes

$$\frac{1}{n}(y^{1/n})^{1-n} = \frac{1}{n}y^{(1/n)-1}.$$

In short we have found that

(3.7.2)
$$\boxed{\frac{d}{dy}[y^{1/n}] = \frac{1}{n}y^{1/n-1}.}$$

We derived (3.7.2) only for $y > 0$. If n is odd, the formula also holds for $y < 0$. (Same argument.) Under no condition does the formula hold for $y = 0$. (Explain.)

In writing Formula (3.7.2) there is no reason to tie ourselves to the letter y. In fact, since our other differentiation formulas have been expressed in terms of x rather than y, we may as well use x here too and write

(3.7.3)
$$\boxed{\frac{d}{dx}[x^{1/n}] = \frac{1}{n}x^{1/n-1}.}$$

As simple examples, we have

$$\frac{d}{dx}[x^{1/2}] = \frac{1}{2}x^{-1/2}, \quad \frac{d}{dx}[x^{1/3}] = \frac{1}{3}x^{-2/3}, \quad \frac{d}{dx}[x^{1/4}] = \frac{1}{4}x^{-3/4}.$$

Rational Powers

We come now to rational exponents p/q. No matter what sign p/q has, we can take q as positive. (Explain.) By definition

$$x^{p/q} = (x^{1/q})^p,$$

so that

$$\frac{d}{dx}[x^{p/q}] = \frac{d}{dx}[(x^{1/q})^p].$$

From the power formula

$$\frac{d}{dx}[(g(x))^p] = p[g(x)]^{p-1}\frac{d}{dx}[g(x)],$$

we see that

$$\frac{d}{dx}[(x^{1/q})^p] = p(x^{1/q})^{p-1}\frac{d}{dx}[x^{1/q}].$$

Since

$$\frac{d}{dx}[x^{1/q}] = \frac{1}{q}x^{(1/q)-1}, \qquad \text{(Formula 3.7.3)}$$

we have

$$\frac{d}{dx}[x^{p/q}] = \frac{d}{dx}[(x^{1/q})^p] = p(x^{1/q})^{p-1}\frac{1}{q}x^{(1/q)-1} = \frac{p}{q}x^{(p/q)-1}.$$

In short

(3.7.4)
$$\boxed{\frac{d}{dx}[x^{p/q}] = \frac{p}{q}x^{(p/q)-1}.}$$

Here are some simple examples:

$$\frac{d}{dx}[x^{2/3}] = \frac{2}{3}x^{-1/3}, \quad \frac{d}{dx}[x^{5/2}] = \frac{5}{2}x^{3/2}, \quad \frac{d}{dx}[x^{-7/9}] = -\frac{7}{9}x^{-16/9}. \quad \square$$

It is easy to go from (3.7.4) to

(3.7.5)
$$\boxed{\frac{d}{dx}[g(x)]^{p/q} = \frac{p}{q}[g(x)]^{(p/q)-1}\frac{d}{dx}[g(x)].}$$

To do this, set

$$f(x) = x^{p/q}$$

and apply the chain rule to

$$f(g(x)) = [g(x)]^{p/q}.$$

The details are left as an exercise. $\square$

The question of the applicability of (3.7.5) remains. If q is odd, then (3.7.5) is valid for all $g(x) \neq 0$. If q is even, then (3.7.5) holds only for $g(x) > 0$. In both instances of course g must be differentiable. It is time for some examples.

Example

$$\frac{d}{dx}(x^2 + 1)^{1/5} = \frac{1}{5}(x^2 + 1)^{-4/5} \cdot 2x = \frac{2}{5}x(x^2 + 1)^{-4/5}. \quad \square$$

Example

$$\frac{d}{dx}\sqrt[3]{3x^2 + 7} = \frac{d}{dx}(3x^2 + 7)^{1/3}$$

$$= \frac{1}{3}(3x^2 + 7)^{-2/3} \cdot 6x$$

$$= \frac{2x}{\sqrt[3]{(3x^2 + 7)^2}} \cdot \quad \square$$

Example

$$\frac{d}{dx}\sqrt{\frac{x^2}{1 + x^2}} = \frac{d}{dx}\left(\frac{x^2}{1 + x^2}\right)^{1/2}$$

$$= \frac{1}{2}\left(\frac{x^2}{1 + x^2}\right)^{-1/2}\frac{d}{dx}\left(\frac{x^2}{1 + x^2}\right)$$

$$= \frac{1}{2}\left(\frac{x^2}{1 + x^2}\right)^{-1/2}\frac{(1 + x^2)2x - x^2(2x)}{(1 + x^2)^2}$$

$$= \frac{1}{2}\left(\frac{1 + x^2}{x^2}\right)^{1/2}\frac{2x}{(1 + x^2)^2}$$

$$= \frac{x}{(1 + x^2)^2}\sqrt{\frac{1 + x^2}{x^2}} \cdot \quad \square$$

Some Further Comments

There are other approaches to the differentiation of inverse functions. If we begin with a differentiable function f which is one-to-one on its domain, then we can write

(3.7.6) $f^{-1}(f(x)) = x$ for all x in the domain of f.

If we assume now that f^{-1} is differentiable, then we can apply the chain rule to (3.7.6) and thereby obtain

$$(f^{-1})'(f(x))f'(x) = 1.$$

For $f'(x) \neq 0$, this gives

(3.7.7)
$$\boxed{(f^{-1})'(f(x)) = \frac{1}{f'(x)} \cdot}$$

In other words, the derivative of f^{-1} evaluated at $f(x)$ is the reciprocal of the derivative of f evaluated at x.

This is simply a more precise statement of what we had before. You can reduce it to the form

$$\frac{dx}{dy} = \frac{1}{dy/dx}$$

simply by setting

$$y = f(x).$$

A brief comment on our derivation of (3.7.7) seems in order. So as to apply the chain rule to

$$f^{-1}(f(x)) = x$$

we *assumed* that f^{-1} was differentiable. This need not be assumed. It can be proved from the assumption that $f'(x)$ exists and is not 0.

Another way to approach the differentiation of inverse functions is to look at the problem geometrically. In Figure 3.7.1 we display the graph of a function f and that of its inverse f^{-1}. Since the graph of f^{-1} is the mirror image of the graph of f (the line $y = x$

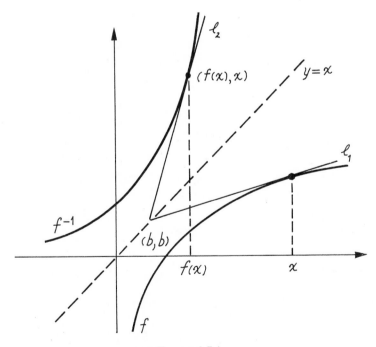

FIGURE 3.7.1

being the mirror) we can expect the tangent line l_2 to be the mirror image of the tangent line l_1. With

$$\text{slope of } l_1 = \frac{f(x) - b}{x - b} \qquad \text{and} \qquad \text{slope of } l_2 = \frac{x - b}{f(x) - b}$$

we see that

$$\text{slope of } l_2 = \frac{1}{\text{slope of } l_1} .$$

With

$$\text{slope of } l_1 = f'(x) \qquad \text{and} \qquad \text{slope of } l_2 = (f^{-1})'(f(x))$$

we have

$$(f^{-1})'(f(x)) = \frac{1}{f'(x)} .$$

This argument breaks down if $f'(x) = 0$. It also breaks down if $f'(x) = 1$, but in that case an even simpler argument can be used. (Exercise 23.)

Exercises

Find dy/dx.

1.* $y = \sqrt{x^3 + 1}$.

2. $y = (x^2 + 3)^{1/3}$.

3.* $y = x \sqrt{x^2 + 1}$.

4. $y = \sqrt{x^2 + 1}$.

5.* $y = \dfrac{x}{\sqrt{x^2 + 1}}$.

6. $y = \sqrt{\dfrac{2x + 1}{3x + 5}}$.

7.* $y = \sqrt[4]{2x^2 + 1}$.

8. $y = \sqrt{x} + \dfrac{1}{\sqrt{x}}$.

9.* $y = \sqrt[3]{x} + \dfrac{1}{\sqrt[3]{x}}$.

10. $y = \sqrt{1 + \sqrt{x^4 + 1}}$.

11.* $y = \sqrt[3]{(2x^3 - x + 1)^2}$.

12. $y = \sqrt{2 - x} \sqrt{3 - x}$.

13.* $y = \sqrt{2 - x^2} \sqrt{3 - x^2}$.

14. $y = \sqrt{(x^4 - x + 1)^3}$.

15.* $y = (2x + 3)^2 \sqrt{x^2 + 1}$.

16. $y = \sqrt[3]{x^2 + 1} \sqrt[4]{x^2 + 2}$.

17.* Find $f'(x)$ for $f(x) = |x^2 - 1|$.

[HINT: $|x^2 - 1| = \sqrt{(x^2 - 1)^2}$.]

18. Find $\dfrac{d}{dx} |f(x)|$. $\left[\text{HINT: } |f(x)| = \sqrt{[f(x)]^2}. \right]$

Find the following derivatives.

19.* $\dfrac{d}{dx} [f(x^2 + 1)]$.

20. $\dfrac{d}{dx} \sqrt{[f(x)]^2 + 1}$.

21.* $\dfrac{d}{dx} \sqrt{f(x^2 + 1)}$.

22. $\dfrac{d}{dx} [f(\sqrt{x^2 + 1})]$.

23.   Give a geometric argument for

$$(f^{-1})'(f(x)) = \frac{1}{f'(x)}$$

which will work if $f'(x) = 1$.

3.8   Some tangent-line problems

In the case of a differentiable function f, the tangent to the graph of f at the point $(x_0, f(x_0))$ has slope

$$m = f'(x_0).$$

To get an equation for this tangent line we use the point slope formula

$$y - y_0 = m(x - x_0).$$

Using

$$(x_0, f(x_0)) \quad \text{for} \quad (x_0, y_0)$$

and

$$f'(x_0) \quad \text{for} \quad m$$

we get the equation

$$\boxed{y - f(x_0) = f'(x_0)(x - x_0).}$$

Problem.   Find an equation for the line tangent to the graph of $f(x) = x^2$ at the points $(3, 9)$ and $(0, 0)$.

SOLUTION.   With $f(x) = x^2$ we have $f'(x) = 2x$. At $(3, 9)$, the slope of the tangent is $f'(3) = 6$. As an equation for the tangent line we have

$$y - 9 = 6(x - 3).$$

This simplifies to

$$y = 6x - 9.$$

At $(0, 0)$, the slope is $f'(0) = 0$. The tangent line is given by

$$y - 0 = 0(x - 0),$$

which we can simplify to

$$y = 0. \quad \square$$

Problem.   Find an equation for the line tangent to the circle

$$x^2 + y^2 = 25$$

at the point $(3, 4)$.

SOLUTION.   The point $(3, 4)$ lies on the upper semicircle

$$y = \sqrt{25 - x^2}.$$

In general

$$\frac{dy}{dx} = \frac{d}{dx} \sqrt{25 - x^2}$$

$$= \frac{d}{dx} (25 - x^2)^{1/2}$$

$$= \frac{1}{2} (25 - x^2)^{-1/2}(-2x)$$

$$= -\frac{x}{\sqrt{25 - x^2}}.$$

The slope m at $(3, 4)$ is dy/dx evaluated at $x = 3$.
With

$$m = -\frac{3}{\sqrt{25 - 9}} = -\frac{3}{4},$$

the tangent line has equation

$$y - 4 = -\frac{3}{4}(x - 3).$$

Multiplying both sides by 4 and collecting terms, we get

$$3x + 4y - 25 = 0. \quad \square$$

If $f'(x_0) = 0$, then the tangent at $(x_0, f(x_0))$ has slope 0. This means that it is horizontal. In Figure 3.8.1 we present several instances of a horizontal tangent. In each case the tangent line is the x-axis, and the point of tangency is the origin.

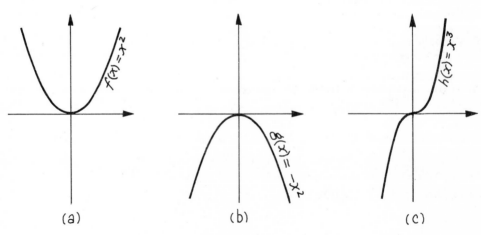

(a)   (b)   (c)

FIGURE 3.8.1

Exercises

1. Find an equation for the tangent to the graph of f at the point $(x_0, f(x_0))$ if

   (a)* $f(x) = x^3 - x$ and $x_0 = -2$.

   (b) $f(x) = x + \dfrac{1}{x}$ and $x_0 = 5$.

   (c)* $f(x) = \dfrac{1}{x-1}$ and $x_0 = \dfrac{1}{2}$.

   (d) $f(x) = \dfrac{x}{1+x^2}$ and $x_0 = 1$.

2. At what point (or points) is the tangent to the curve
   (a)* $y = -x^2 - 6$ parallel to the line $y = 4x - 1$?
   (b) $xy = 1$ parallel to the line $y = x$?
   (c)* $xy = 1$ perpendicular to the line $y = x$?
   (d) $x + y^2 = 1$ parallel to the line $x + 2y = 0$?
   (e)* $x + y^2 = 1$ perpendicular to the line $x + 2y = 0$?

3. Find an equation for the line (or lines) tangent to the curve $y = x^3$ which passes through the point $(0, 2)$.

4. Find the points of the graph if any at which the tangent is horizontal:

   (a)* $f(x) = \dfrac{x}{1-x}$.

   (c)* $f(x) = \left(\dfrac{x}{1-x}\right)^2$.

   (e)* $f(x) = \left(\dfrac{1-x}{x}\right)^2$.

   (b) $f(x) = \dfrac{x^2}{1-x}$.

   (d) $f(x) = x - \sqrt[3]{x}$.

   (f)* $f(x) = (x-1)^2(x+1)^2$.

5. Given that the slope to the graph of f at (a, b) is m, find the slope to the graph of f^{-1} at (b, a).

3.9 The mean-value theorem

The main object of this section is to state and prove a result which is known as the *mean-value theorem*. At first glance the theorem may appear innocuous. It is certainly easy to understand. Its remarkable feature is its immense usefulness.

The Mean-Value Theorem

If f is differentiable on (a, b) and continuous on $[a, b]$, then there is at least one number c in (a, b) at which

$$f'(c) = \frac{f(b) - f(a)}{b - a}.$$

To explain what this means geometrically we refer to Figure 3.9.1.
The number

$$\frac{f(b) - f(a)}{b - a}$$

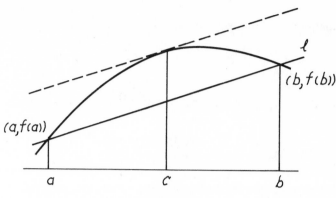

FIGURE 3.9.1

is the slope of the line l which passes through the points $(a, f(a))$ and $(b, f(b))$. To say that there is at least one number c at which

$$f'(c) = \frac{f(b) - f(a)}{b - a}$$

is to say that the graph of f has at least one point $(c, f(c))$ at which the tangent is parallel to l.

To prove the mean-value theorem we need first some other results.

Theorem 3.9.1

Let f be differentiable at x_0. If $f'(x_0) > 0$, then

$$f(x_0 - h) < f(x_0) < f(x_0 + h)$$

for all positive h sufficiently small. If $f'(x_0) < 0$, then

$$f(x_0 + h) < f(x_0) < f(x_0 - h)$$

for all positive h sufficiently small.

PROOF.   We take the case $f'(x_0) > 0$ and leave the other case to you. By definition of derivative

$$\lim_{k \to 0} \frac{f(x_0 + k) - f(x_0)}{k} = f'(x_0).$$

With $f'(x_0) > 0$ we can use $f'(x_0)$ itself as ϵ and conclude that there exists $\delta > 0$ such that

$$\text{if} \quad 0 < |k| < \delta, \quad \text{then} \quad \left| \frac{f(x_0 + k) - f(x_0)}{k} - f'(x_0) \right| < f'(x_0).$$

For such k we have

$$\frac{f(x_0 + k) - f(x_0)}{k} > 0.$$

If now $0 < h < \delta$, then

$$\frac{f(x_0 + h) - f(x_0)}{h} > 0 \quad \text{and} \quad \frac{f(x_0 - h) - f(x_0)}{-h} > 0.$$

The first inequality gives us

$$f(x_0) < f(x_0 + h)$$

and the second gives us

$$f(x_0 - h) < f(x_0). \quad \square$$

Next we prove a special case of the mean-value theorem, known as Rolle's theorem. In Rolle's theorem we make the additional assumption that $f(a)$ and $f(b)$ are both 0. (See Figure 3.9.2.) In this case the line joining $(a, f(a))$ to $(b, f(b))$ is horizontal. (It is the x-axis.) The conclusion is that there is a point $(c, f(c))$ at which the tangent is horizontal.

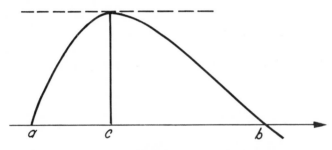

FIGURE 3.9.2

Rolle's Theorem

Let f be differentiable on (a, b) and continuous on $[a, b]$. If $f(a)$ and $f(b)$ are both 0, then there is at least one number c in (a, b) at which

$$f'(c) = 0.$$

PROOF. If f is constantly 0 on $[a, b]$, the result is obvious. If f is not constantly 0 on $[a, b]$, then either f takes on some positive values or some negative ones. We assume the former and leave the other case to you.

Since f is continuous on $[a, b]$, at some point c of $[a, b]$, f must take on a maximum value. (Theorem 2.6.2.) This maximum value, $f(c)$, must be positive. Since $f(a)$ and $f(b)$ are both 0, c cannot be a and it cannot be b. This means that c must be in the open interval (a, b) and therefore $f'(c)$ exists. Now $f'(c)$ cannot be greater than 0 and it cannot be less than 0 because each of these conditions would imply that f takes on values greater than $f(c)$. (This follows from Theorem 3.9.1.) We conclude therefore that $f'(c) = 0. \quad \square$

We are now ready to give a proof of the mean-value theorem. The idea of the proof is to create a function g which satisfies the conditions of Rolle's theorem and is so related to f that the conclusion $g'(c) = 0$ leads to the conclusion

$$f'(c) = \frac{f(b) - f(a)}{b - a}.$$

It is not hard to see that

$$g(x) = f(x) - \left[\frac{f(b) - f(a)}{b - a} (x - a) + f(a) \right]$$

is exactly such a function. Geometrically $g(x)$ is represented in Figure 3.9.3. The line that passes through $(a, f(a))$ and $(b, f(b))$ has equation

$$y = \frac{f(b) - f(a)}{b - a} (x - a) + f(a).$$

(This is not hard to verify. The slope is right and when $x = a$, $y = f(a)$.) The difference

$$g(x) = f(x) - \left[\frac{f(b) - f(a)}{b - a} (x - a) + f(a) \right]$$

is simply the vertical difference between the graph of f and the line in question.

If f is differentiable on (a, b) and continuous on $[a, b]$, then so is g. As you can check, $g(a)$ and $g(b)$ are both 0. Therefore by Rolle's theorem there is at least one point c in (a, b) at which $g'(c) = 0$. Since in general

$$g'(x) = f'(x) - \frac{f(b) - f(a)}{b - a},$$

in particular

$$g'(c) = f'(c) - \frac{f(b) - f(a)}{b - a}.$$

With $g'(c) = 0$, we have

$$f'(c) = \frac{f(b) - f(a)}{b - a}. \quad \square$$

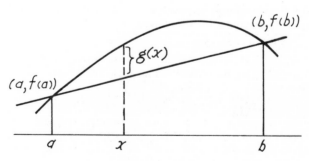

FIGURE 3.9.3

Exercises

Find $f'(x)$ if $f(x)$ is as follows.

1.* $(1 - x)^2(1 + x)^2$.

4. $\left(\dfrac{3x - 5}{1 - x^2}\right)^{-1}$.

7.* $\left(\dfrac{1}{1 - x^2} + \dfrac{1}{1 + x^2}\right)^{-1}$.

2. $(1 - x^2)^5$.

5.* $\left(\dfrac{3x - 5}{1 - x^2}\right)^2$.

8. $\dfrac{2\sqrt{x}}{x^2 + 1}$.

3.* $\dfrac{3x - 5}{1 - x^2}$.

6. $(5x^3 - 10)^2$.

9.* $x(x + 1)(x + 2)$.

Find the points (if any) at which the tangent to the curve is parallel to the line $y = x$.

10. $y = x^2$.

12. $y = \sqrt[3]{x}$.

14. $y = \sqrt{x} - x^2$.

11.* $y = \sqrt{x}$.

13.* $y = (x - 1)^3$.

15.* $y = (3x + 2)/(x + 1)$.

With f, a, and b as below find those numbers c which satisfy the condition of the mean-value theorem.

16. $f(x) = 3\sqrt{x} - 4x$, $\quad a = 1, b = 4$.

17.* $f(x) = x^3$, $\qquad\qquad a = 1, b = 3$.

18. $f(x) = x^{2/3}$, $\qquad\quad a = 1, b = 8$.

19. Graph the function

$$f(x) = |2x - 1| - 3.$$

Verify that $f(-1)$ and $f(2)$ are both 0 and yet f' does not take on the value 0. Explain how this does not contradict Rolle's theorem.

20. Given that $|f'(x)| \leq 1$ for all numbers x, show that

$$|f(x_1) - f(x_2)| \leq |x_1 - x_2| \qquad \text{for all numbers } x_1, x_2.$$

21. Let P be a nonconstant polynomial

$$P(x) = a_n x^n + \cdots + a_1 x + a_0.$$

Show that between any two consecutive roots of the equation $P'(x) = 0$ there is at most one root of the equation $P(x) = 0$.

3.10　Increasing and decreasing functions

It is often useful to know on what intervals a given function is "increasing" and on what intervals it is "decreasing." If the function in question is differentiable, we can answer such questions by looking at the sign of the derivative. As we shall see (and as one would expect from the interpretation of the derivative as the slope of the graph), a function is

(a) "increasing" on any interval in which its derivative is positive,

(b) "decreasing" on any interval in which its derivative is negative, and

(c) constant on any interval in which its derivative is identically 0.

Before attempting to prove these results, we will explain exactly what we mean by a function "increasing" or "decreasing" on an interval.

Definition 3.10.1

A function f is said to be
(i) *increasing* on the interval I iff for every two numbers x_1, x_2 in I

$$x_1 < x_2 \quad \text{implies} \quad f(x_1) < f(x_2).$$

(ii) *decreasing* on the interval I iff for every two numbers x_1, x_2 in I

$$x_1 < x_2 \quad \text{implies} \quad f(x_1) > f(x_2).$$

Preliminary Examples

1. The squaring function

$$f(x) = x^2 \qquad \text{(Figure 3.10.1)}$$

is decreasing on $(-\infty, 0]$ and increasing on $[0, \infty)$. □

2. The function

$$f(x) = \begin{cases} 1, & x < 0 \\ x, & x \geq 0 \end{cases} \qquad \text{(Figure 3.10.2)}$$

is constant on $(-\infty, 0)$ and increasing on $[0, \infty)$. □

3. The cubing function

$$f(x) = x^3 \qquad \text{(Figure 3.10.3)}$$

is everywhere increasing. □

4. In the case of the Dirichlet function

$$g(x) = \begin{cases} 1, & x \text{ rational} \\ 0, & x \text{ irrational} \end{cases} \qquad \text{(Figure 3.10.4)}$$

FIGURE 3.10.1   FIGURE 3.10.2

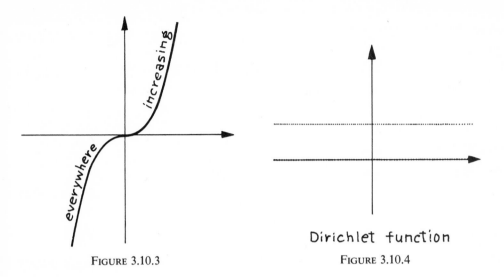

FIGURE 3.10.3   FIGURE 3.10.4

there is no interval on which the function increases and no interval on which the function decreases. On every interval it jumps back and forth between 0 and 1 an infinite number of times.   □

Now we start proving some theorems. As you will see, all of them are consequences of the mean-value theorem.

Theorem 3.10.2

Let I be an open interval.

  (i) If $f'(x) > 0$ for all x in I, then f is increasing on I.
  (ii) If $f'(x) < 0$ for all x in I, then f is decreasing on I.
  (iii) If $f'(x) = 0$ for all x in I, then f is constant on I.

PROOF. We take x_1 and x_2 in I with $x_1 < x_2$. Since f is differentiable on (x_1, x_2) and continuous on $[x_1, x_2]$, we see from the mean-value theorem that there is a number c in (x_1, x_2) such that

$$f'(c) = \frac{f(x_2) - f(x_1)}{x_2 - x_1}.$$

In (i), we have

$$\frac{f(x_2) - f(x_1)}{x_2 - x_1} > 0 \qquad \text{and thus} \qquad f(x_1) < f(x_2).$$

In (ii), we have

$$\frac{f(x_2) - f(x_1)}{x_2 - x_1} < 0 \qquad \text{and thus} \qquad f(x_1) > f(x_2).$$

In (iii), we have

$$\frac{f(x_2) - f(x_1)}{x_2 - x_1} = 0 \qquad \text{and thus} \qquad f(x_1) = f(x_2). \quad \square$$

The theorem we just proved is useful but it has some deficiencies. For example, in the case of the squaring function

$$f(x) = x^2$$

the derivative

$$f'(x) = 2x$$

is negative for x in $(-\infty, 0)$, 0 for $x = 0$, and positive for x in $(0, \infty)$. Theorem 3.10.2 assures us that

$$f \text{ decreases on } (-\infty, 0) \text{ and increases on } (0, \infty)$$

but actually stronger results are true:

$$f \text{ decreases on } (-\infty, 0] \text{ and increases on } [0, \infty).$$

To get these stronger results we need a theorem that works for closed intervals.

To extend Theorem 3.10.2 so that it works for a closed interval I, the only thing we need is continuity at the end point(s).

Theorem 3.10.3

Let f be continuous on a closed interval I.

  (i) If $f'(x) > 0$ for all x in the interior of I, then f is increasing on all of I.
 (ii) If $f'(x) < 0$ for all x in the interior of I, then f is decreasing on all of I.
(iii) If $f'(x) = 0$ for all x in the interior of I, then f is constant on all of I.

A proof of this result is not hard to construct. As you can verify, a word-for-word copy of our proof of Theorem 3.10.2 also works here. $\square$

It is time to give more examples.

Example.   The function

$$f(x) = \sqrt{1 - x^2}$$

has as a graph the upper semicircle of Figure 3.10.5. It is therefore obvious that f increases on $[-1, 0]$ and decreases on $[0, 1]$. We can get this information without reference to Figure 3.10.5.

That f increases on $[-1, 0]$ can be seen from the fact that the derivative

$$f'(x) = -\frac{x}{\sqrt{1 - x^2}}$$

is positive for x in $(-1, 0)$ and f itself is continuous on $[-1, 0]$. That f decreases on $[0, 1]$ can be seen from the fact that f' is negative for x in $(0, 1)$ and f is continuous on $[0, 1]$. $\square$

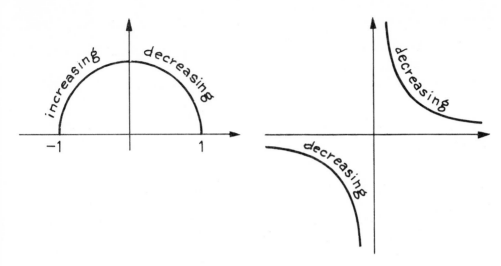

FIGURE 3.10.5   FIGURE 3.10.6

Example. The function

$$f(x) = \frac{1}{x}$$

has derivative

$$f'(x) = -\frac{1}{x^2}.$$

Since $f'(x) < 0$ for all $x \neq 0$ and f is not defined at 0, f decreases both on $(-\infty, 0)$ and on $(0, \infty)$. (Figure 3.10.6.) As x approaches 0, the graph becomes steeper; it flattens out as x tends away from 0. □

Example. If

$$g(x) = 4x^5 - 15x^4 - 20x^3 + 110x^2 - 120x + 40,$$

then g is everywhere differentiable and

$$\begin{aligned}
g'(x) &= 20x^4 - 60x^3 - 60x^2 + 220x - 120 \\
&= 20(x^4 - 3x^3 - 3x^2 + 11x - 6) \\
&= 20(x + 2)(x - 1)^2(x - 3).
\end{aligned}$$

The derivative g' takes on the value 0 at -2, at 1, and at 3. Moreover it is not hard to see that

$$g'(x) \text{ is } \begin{cases} \text{positive} & \text{for } x \text{ in } (-\infty, -2) \\ \text{negative} & \text{for } x \text{ in } (-2, 1) \\ \text{negative} & \text{for } x \text{ in } (1, 3) \\ \text{positive} & \text{for } x \text{ in } (3, \infty) \end{cases}.$$

Since g' is positive on $(-\infty, -2)$ we can conclude that g is increasing on $(-\infty, -2]$. Since g' is negative on $(-2, 1)$ and on $(1, 3)$, we can conclude that g decreases both on $[-2, 1]$ and on $[1, 3]$. This tells us that g actually decreases on $[-2, 3]$. (Explain.) Finally, since g' is positive on $(3, \infty)$, g must increase on $[3, \infty)$. $\square$

If two differentiable functions differ by a constant,

$$f(x) = g(x) + C,$$

then their derivatives are obviously equal:

$$f'(x) = g'(x).$$

The converse is also true. In fact we have the following theorem.

Theorem 3.10.4

I   If

$$f'(x) = g'(x) \quad \text{for all } x \text{ in an open interval } I,$$

   then

$$f \text{ and } g \text{ differ by a constant on } I.$$

II   If

$$f'(x) = g'(x) \quad \text{for all } x \text{ in the interior of a closed interval } I$$

   and

$$f \text{ and } g \text{ are continuous at the end points of } I,$$

   then

$$f \text{ and } g \text{ differ by a constant on } I.$$

PROOF.   Set $h = f - g$. For the first assertion apply (iii) of Theorem 3.10.2 to h'. For the second assertion apply (iii) of Theorem 3.10.3 to h'. We leave the details as an exercise. $\square$

For an illustration of this theorem see Figure 3.10.7. At points with the same first coordinate the slopes are equal and therefore the curves have the same steepness. The separation between the curves remains constant.

Problem.   Find a general expression for $f(x)$ given that

$$f'(x) = x^2 - x \quad \text{for all real } x \qquad \text{and} \qquad f(0) = 1.$$

SOLUTION.   Since

$$\frac{d}{dx}\left(\frac{x^3}{3} - \frac{x^2}{2}\right) = x^2 - x,$$

we know that $f(x)$ has the form

$$f(x) = \frac{x^3}{3} - \frac{x^2}{2} + C.$$

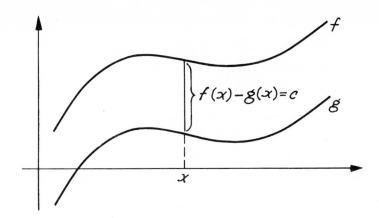

FIGURE 3.10.7

On the one hand

$$f(0) = C,$$

(Set $x = 0$)

and on the other

$$f(0) = 1.$$

(Given)

This forces $C = 1$ and

$$f(x) = \frac{x^3}{3} - \frac{x^2}{2} + 1. \quad \square$$

Problem. Find a general expression for $g(x)$ given that

$$g'(x) = \frac{3}{(x + 1)^2} \quad \text{for } x > -1 \quad \text{and} \quad g(1) = 2.$$

SOLUTION. It is not hard to see that

$$\frac{d}{dx}\left(\frac{1}{x + 1}\right) = \frac{d}{dx}(x + 1)^{-1} = -\frac{1}{(x + 1)^2}$$

and therefore

$$\frac{d}{dx}\left(-\frac{3}{x + 1}\right) = \frac{3}{(x + 1)^2}.$$

This means that

$$g(x) = -\frac{3}{x + 1} + C.$$

To require $g(1) = 2$ is to require

$$-\frac{3}{2} + C = 2.$$

This leads to

$$C = \frac{7}{2}.$$

The solution is therefore

$$g(x) = -\frac{3}{x+1} + \frac{7}{2}. \quad \square$$

Exercises

Find the intervals on which f is increasing and those on which it is decreasing, if $f(x)$ is as follows.

1.* $x^3 - 3x + 2$.

7.* $\dfrac{1}{|x - 2|}$.

13*. $\dfrac{x - 1}{x + 1}$.

2. $x^4 - 4x^2 + 6$.

8. $\dfrac{1}{1 + x^2}$.

14. $x^3(1 - x)$.

3.* $x + \dfrac{1}{x}$.

9.* $\dfrac{x^2 + 1}{x^2 - 1}$.

15.* $\left(\dfrac{1 - \sqrt{x}}{1 + \sqrt{x}}\right)^7$.

4. $x^2 + \dfrac{1}{x^2}$.

10. $\dfrac{x}{x^2 + 1}$.

16. $\sqrt{\dfrac{2 + x^2}{1 + x^2}}$.

5.* $x(x + 1)(x + 2)$.

11.* $|x^2 - 5|$.

17.* $\sqrt{\dfrac{1 + x^2}{2 + x^2}}$.

6. $(x^2 + 1)^4$.

12. $x^2(1 - x)^2$.

18. $|x - 1||x - 2|$.

Find a general expression for $f(x)$ given the following.

19.* $f'(x) = x^2 - 1$ for all real x and $f(0) = 1$.

20. $f'(x) = x^2 - 1$ for all real x and $f(1) = 1$.

21.* $f'(x) = 2x - 5$ for all real x and $f(2) = 4$.

22. $f'(x) = 5x^4 + 4x^3 + 3x^2 + 2x + 1$ for all real x and $f(0) = 2$.

23.* $f'(x) = \dfrac{4}{x^3}$ for $x \neq 0$ and $f(1) = 0$.

24. $f'(x) = x(x^2 + 1)^4$ for all real x and $f(0) = 1$.
     [HINT: Differentiate $(x^2 + 1)^5$.]

25.* $f'(x) = 3x^2(x^3 - 1)^4$ for all real x and $f(1) = 0$.

26. Given that

$$f'(x) > g'(x) \quad \text{for all real } x \quad \text{and} \quad f(0) = g(0)$$

compare $f(x)$ with $g(x)$

(a) on $(-\infty, 0)$.   (b) on $(0, \infty)$.

Justify your answers.

27. Prove Theorem 3.10.4.

3.11 Maxima and minima

Closely related to the material just discussed is the problem of determining the maximum and minimum values of functions. There is a practical aspect to this matter. In many problems of economics, engineering, and physics it is important to find out how large or how small a certain quantity may become. If the problem admits a mathematical formulation, it is often reducible to the problem of finding the extreme values of some function.

In this section we consider functions which are defined on an open interval or on the union of open intervals. We begin with a definition.

A function f is said to have a *local* (or *relative*) *maximum* at c iff

$$f(c) \geq f(x) \quad \text{for all } x \text{ sufficiently close to } c.$$

It is said to have a *local* (or *relative*) *minimum* at c iff

$$f(c) \leq f(x) \quad \text{for all } x \text{ sufficiently close to } c.$$

We illustrate these notions in Figure 3.11.1 and Figure 3.11.2. A careful look at the figures suggests that local maxima and minima occur only at points where the tangent is horizontal $[f'(c) = 0]$ or where there is no tangent line $[f'(c)$ does not exist]. This is indeed the case.

Theorem 3.11.1

If f has a local maximum or minimum at c then

$$\text{either} \quad f'(c) = 0 \quad \text{or} \quad f'(c) \quad \text{does not exist.}$$

PROOF. If $f'(c) > 0$ or $f'(c) < 0$, then, by Theorem 3.9.1, there must be numbers x_1 and x_2 which are arbitrarily close to c and yet satisfy

$$f(x_1) < f(c) < f(x_2).$$

This makes it impossible for a local maximum or minimum to occur at c. □

FIGURE 3.11.1

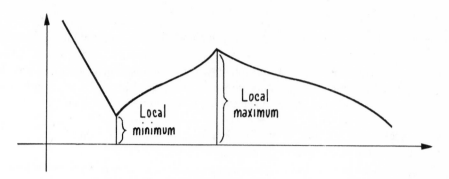

FIGURE 3.11.2

In view of this result, in searching for local maxima and local minima of a function f, the only points we need to test are those points c at which $f'(c) = 0$ or $f'(c)$ does not exist. Such points are called *critical points*.

We illustrate the technique for finding local maxima and local minima by some examples. In each example the first step will be to find the critical points. We begin with very simple cases.

Example.   In the case of

$$f(x) = 3 - x^2 \qquad \text{(Figure 3.11.3)}$$

the derivative

$$f'(x) = -2x$$

exists everywhere. Since $f'(x) = 0$ only at $x = 0$, 0 is the only critical point. The number $f(0) = 3$ is obviously a local maximum.   □

Example.   In the case of

$$f(x) = |x + 1| + 2 \qquad \text{(Figure 3.11.4)}$$

the derivative is

$$f'(x) = \begin{cases} 1, & x > -1 \\ -1, & x < -1 \end{cases}.$$

This derivative is never 0. It fails to exist only at -1. The number -1 is the only critical point. The value $f(-1) = 2$ is a local minimum.   □

Example.   In the case of

$$f(x) = \frac{1}{x - 1} \qquad \text{(Figure 3.11.5)}$$

the derivative

$$f'(x) = -\frac{1}{(x - 1)^2}$$

exists throughout the domain of f and is never 0. There are therefore no critical points and no local extreme values.   □

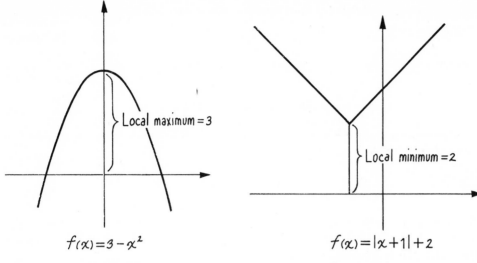

$$f(x) = 3 - x^2$$

FIGURE 3.11.3

$$f(x) = |x + 1| + 2$$

FIGURE 3.11.4

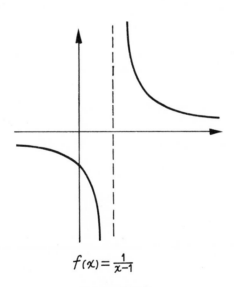

$$f(x) = \frac{1}{x-1}$$

FIGURE 3.11.5

CAUTION: The fact that c is a critical point of f does not guarantee that $f(c)$ is a local extreme value. This is illustrated in the next two examples.

Example.   In the case of the cubing function

$$f(x) = x^3 \qquad \text{(Figure 3.11.6)}$$

the derivative

$$f'(x) = 3x^2$$

is 0 at 0 but $f(0) = 0$ is not a local extreme value. The cubing function is everywhere increasing. ☐

Example. The function

$$f(x) = \begin{cases} 2x, & x < 1 \\ \frac{1}{2}x + \frac{3}{2}, & x \geq 1 \end{cases} \qquad \text{(Figure 3.11.7)}$$

is everywhere increasing. Although 1 is a critical point ($f'(1)$ does not exist), $f(1) = 2$ is not a local extreme value. ☐

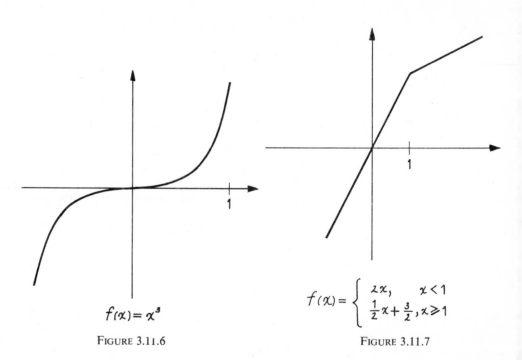

$f(x) = x^3$

FIGURE 3.11.6

$f(x) = \begin{cases} 2x, & x < 1 \\ \frac{1}{2}x + \frac{3}{2}, & x \geq 1 \end{cases}$

FIGURE 3.11.7

The following test is often useful in determining the behavior of a function at a critical point.

Test 1 (*The first–derivative test*). Suppose that c is a critical point for f and that f is continuous at c. If there exists an interval $(c - \delta, c + \delta)$ such that $f'(x) > 0$ for all x in $(c - \delta, c)$ and $f'(x) < 0$ for all x in $(c, c + \delta)$, then $f(c)$ is a local maximum. If both inequalities are reversed, then $f(c)$ is a local minimum.

PROOF. The proof is easy. In the first case f increases on $(c - \delta, c]$ and decreases on $[c, c + \delta)$. This makes $f(c)$ a local maximum (Figures 3.11.8 and 3.11.9). In the second case f decreases on $(c - \delta, c]$ and increases on $[c, c + \delta)$. This makes $f(c)$ a local minimum (Figures 3.11.10 and 3.11.11). ☐

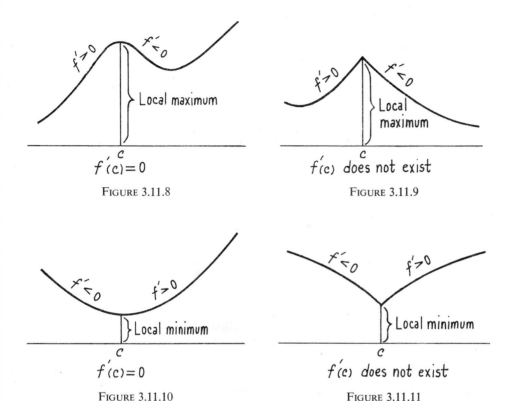

FIGURE 3.11.8

FIGURE 3.11.9

FIGURE 3.11.10

FIGURE 3.11.11

Example. In the case of

$$f(x) = |x^2 - 1| \qquad \text{(Figure 3.11.12)}$$

the derivative is given by

$$f'(x) = \begin{cases} 2x, & x < -1 \\ -2x, & -1 < x < 1. \\ 2x, & 1 < x \end{cases} \qquad \text{(Check this out)}$$

The critical points are 0, -1, and 1. At 0, $f'(x) = 0$. At -1 and 1, $f'(x)$ does not exist. To analyze the behavior of f at the critical points we use Test 1. Since

$$f'(x) \text{ is } \begin{cases} \text{negative,} & \text{for} & x < -1 \\ \text{positive,} & \text{for} & -1 < x < 0 \\ \text{negative,} & \text{for} & 0 < x < 1 \\ \text{positive,} & \text{for} & 1 < x \end{cases}$$

we see that $f(-1) = 0$ is a local minimum, $f(0) = 1$ is a local maximum, and $f(1) = 0$ is a local minimum. □

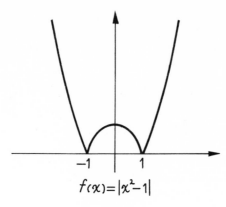

$$f(x) = |x^2 - 1|$$

FIGURE 3.11.12

Example.   Here we begin with

$$f(x) = (x - 2)(x - 1)^4.$$

Differentiating we obtain

$$f'(x) = (x - 2)4(x - 1)^3 + (x - 1)^4$$
$$= (x - 1)^3(4x - 8 + x - 1)$$
$$= (x - 1)^3(5x - 9).$$

The critical points are 1 and $\frac{9}{5}$. Since

$$f'(x) \text{ is } \begin{cases} \text{positive,} & \text{for } x < 1 \\ \text{negative,} & \text{for } 1 < x < \frac{9}{5} \\ \text{positive,} & \text{for } \frac{9}{5} < x \end{cases}$$

we see that $f(1) = 0$ is a local maximum and $f(\frac{9}{5}) = -4^4/5^5$ is a local minimum.   □

In certain cases it may be difficult to determine the sign of the first derivative both to the left of c and to the right of c. If f is twice differentiable at c, the following test may be easier to apply.

Test 2 (*The second-derivative test*).   Suppose that $f'(c) = 0$.

If $f''(c) > 0$,   then $f(c)$ is a local minimum value.

If $f''(c) < 0$,   then $f(c)$ is a local maximum value.

PROOF.   We handle the case $f''(c) > 0$. The other is left as an exercise. Since f'' is the derivative of f' we see from Theorem 3.9.1, that there exists $\delta > 0$ such that, if

$$c - \delta < x_1 < c < x_2 < c + \delta,$$

then

$$f'(x_1) < f'(c) < f'(x_2).$$

Since $f'(c) = 0$, we have

$$f'(x) < 0 \qquad \text{for } x \text{ in } (c - \delta, c)$$

and

$$f'(x) > 0 \qquad \text{for } x \text{ in } (c, c + \delta).$$

By Test 1 this shows that $f(c)$ is a local minimum.   □

Now we illustrate the second-derivative test:

Example.   For

$$f(x) = x^3 - x$$

we have

$$f'(x) = 3x^2 - 1.$$

The critical points are $-1/\sqrt{3}$ and $1/\sqrt{3}$. At both of these points the derivative is 0. As a second derivative we have

$$f''(x) = 6x.$$

Since $f''(-1/\sqrt{3}) < 0$ and $f''(1/\sqrt{3}) > 0$ we can conclude from the second-derivative test that $f(-1/\sqrt{3}) = 2/3\sqrt{3}$ is a local maximum and $f(1/\sqrt{3}) = -2/3\sqrt{3}$ is a local minimum.   □

Exercises

Find the critical points and the local extreme values.

1.* $x^3 + 3x - 2$.

2. $x^4 - 4x^2 + 6$.

3.* $x + \dfrac{1}{x}$.

4. $x^3(1 - x)$.

5.* $x(x + 1)(x + 2)$.

6. $(1 - x)^2(1 + x)^2$.

7.* $\dfrac{1}{|x - 2|}$.

8. $\dfrac{1 - x}{1 + x}$.

9.* $\dfrac{2 - 3x}{2 + x}$.

10. $\dfrac{2x}{x^2 + 1}$.

11.* $|x^2 - 16|$.

12. $x^2(1 - x)^2$.

13.* $\left(\dfrac{x - 2}{x + 2}\right)^3$.

14. $(1 + 2x)(x - 1)^3$.

15.* $(1 - x)(1 + x)^3$.

16. $\dfrac{x}{1 + |x|}$.

17.* $\dfrac{|x|}{1 + |x|}$.

18. $(|x| - 1)^2$.

19.* $|x - 1||x + 2|$.

20. $x|x|$.

21.* $-\dfrac{x^3}{x + 1}$.

22. $\dfrac{1}{x - 1} - \dfrac{1}{x - 2}$.

23.* $\dfrac{1}{x + 1} - \dfrac{1}{x + 2}$.

24. $|x - 3| - |2x + 1|$.

25. Prove the validity of the second-derivative test in the case that $f''(c) < 0$.

3.12 More on maxima and minima

End-Point Maxima and Minima

For functions defined on an open interval or on the union of open intervals the critical points are those at which the derivative is 0 or the derivative does not exist. For functions defined on a closed interval

$$[a, b], \quad [a, \infty), \quad \text{or} \quad (-\infty, b]$$

the *end points* of the domain (a and b in the case of $[a, b]$, a in the case of $[a, \infty)$, and b in the case of $(-\infty, b]$) are also called *critical points*.

End points can give rise to what are called *end-point maxima* and *end-point minima*. See Figures 3.12.1, 3.12.2, and 3.12.3.

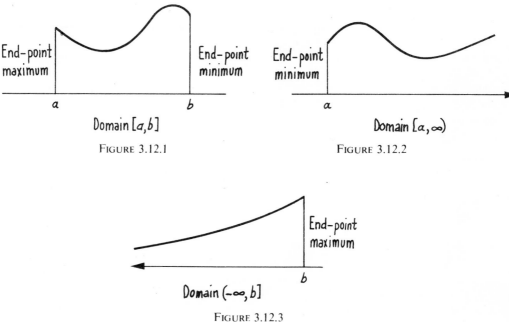

FIGURE 3.12.1

FIGURE 3.12.2

FIGURE 3.12.3

The figures render the general idea so obvious that formal definitions seem unnecessary. Nevertheless, here they are:

> If c is an end point of the domain of f, then f is said to have an *end-point maximum* at c iff
>
> $f(c) \geq f(x)$ for all x in the domain of f which are sufficiently close to c.
>
> It is said to have an *end-point minimum* at c iff
>
> $f(c) \leq f(x)$ for all x in the domain of f which are sufficiently close to c.

Absolute Maxima and Minima

Whether or not a function f has a local or end-point extreme at some point depends entirely on the behavior of f for x close to that point. Absolute-extreme values, which we define below, depend on the behavior of the function on its entire domain.

We begin with a number d in the domain of f. Here d can be an interior point or an end point.

$f(d)$ is called *the absolute-maximum value* of f (or simply *the maximum value* of f) iff

$$f(d) \geq f(x) \quad \text{for all } x \text{ in the domain of } f.$$

$f(d)$ is called *the absolute-minimum value* of f (or simply *the minimum value* of f) iff

$$f(d) \leq f(x) \quad \text{for all } x \text{ in the domain of } f.$$

Usually the most practical way of determining the absolute extremes of a function is to gather together the local extremes and the end-point extremes. The largest of these numbers (if there is a largest) is obviously the absolute maximum, and the smallest (if there is a smallest) is the absolute minimum.

It is worth repeating here that in the case of a function continuous on a bounded closed interval $[a, b]$ there is both an absolute maximum and an absolute minimum (Theorem 2.6.2).

Summary

We summarize the central ideas of this section and of the last one by outlining a step-by-step procedure for finding the extreme values (local, end-point, and absolute) of a function f.

1. Find the critical points. These are the points at which $f'(x) = 0$, the points at which $f'(x)$ does not exist, and the end points of the domain.

2. Test each interior critical point for local extremes
   (a) by inspection (some graphing may help),
   (b) by applying Test 1 (the first-derivative test),
   (c) or, if $f'(c) = 0$, by applying Test 2 (the second-derivative test).

3. Test each end point for end-point extremes.

4. Test for absolute extremes by examining the local extremes and the end-point extremes.

Problem.   Find the critical points and classify the extreme values of

$$f(x) = \frac{\sqrt{x} - 1}{\sqrt{x} + 1}.$$

SOLUTION.   The domain here is $[0, \infty)$. First we check the interior points $x \in (0, \infty)$.

On $(0, \infty)$ f is differentiable and

$$f'(x) = \frac{(\sqrt{x}+1)\dfrac{1}{2\sqrt{x}} - (\sqrt{x}-1)\dfrac{1}{2\sqrt{x}}}{(\sqrt{x}+1)^2}$$

$$= \frac{1}{\sqrt{x}(\sqrt{x}+1)^2}.$$

Since the derivative $f'(x)$ is never 0, there are no interior critical points.

The number 0 is a critical point because it is an end point. Since $f'(x) > 0$ for all x in $(0, \infty)$ and f is continuous on $[0, \infty)$, f must be increasing on $[0, \infty)$. This makes $f(0) = -1$ an end-point minimum. It is also the absolute minimum. For the graph see Figure 3.12.4.   □

Problem.   Find the critical points and classify the extreme values of

$$f(x) = x^2 - 2|x| + 2, \qquad x \in [-\tfrac{1}{2}, \tfrac{3}{2}].$$

SOLUTION.   First we check the interior points $x \in (-\tfrac{1}{2}, \tfrac{3}{2})$. On the open interval $(-\tfrac{1}{2}, \tfrac{3}{2})$ f is differentiable except at 0:

$$f'(x) = \begin{cases} 2x + 2, & -\tfrac{1}{2} < x < 0 \\ 2x - 2, & 0 < x < \tfrac{3}{2} \end{cases}. \qquad\qquad \text{(Check this out)}$$

This makes 0 a critical point. Since $f'(x) = 0$ at $x = 1$, 1 is also a critical point. The end points $-\tfrac{1}{2}$ and $\tfrac{3}{2}$ are also critical points.

A little to the left of 0, $f' > 0$ and a little to the right of 0, $f' < 0$. By Test 1, this means that $f(0) = 2$ is a local maximum.

A little to the left of 1, $f' < 0$ and a little to the right of 1, $f' > 0$. This makes $f(1) = 1$ a local minimum. (Again by Test 1.)

Now we check the end points. Since $f' > 0$ a little to the right of $-\tfrac{1}{2}$,

$$f(-\tfrac{1}{2}) = (-\tfrac{1}{2})^2 - 2|-\tfrac{1}{2}| + 2 = \tfrac{1}{4} - 1 + 2 = 1\tfrac{1}{4}$$

is an end-point minimum. (Explain.) Since $f' > 0$ a little to the left of $\tfrac{3}{2}$,

$$f(\tfrac{3}{2}) = (\tfrac{3}{2})^2 - 2|\tfrac{3}{2}| + 2 = \tfrac{9}{4} - 3 + 2 = 1\tfrac{1}{4}$$

is an end-point maximum. (Explain.)

In short, the critical points are $-\tfrac{1}{2}$, 0, 1, and $\tfrac{3}{2}$.

$f(-\tfrac{1}{2}) = 1\tfrac{1}{4}$ is an end-point minimum.
$f(0) \quad = 2$ is a local maximum; it is also the absolute maximum.
$f(1) \quad = 1$ is a local minimum; it is also the absolute minimum.
$f(\tfrac{3}{2}) \quad = 1\tfrac{1}{4}$ is an end-point maximum.

For the graph see Figure 3.12.5.   □

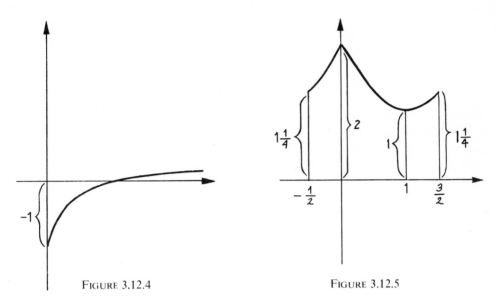

FIGURE 3.12.4   FIGURE 3.12.5

Problem. Find the critical points and classify the extreme values of

$$f(x) = \sqrt{1 - x^2} + \frac{x}{2}.$$

SOLUTION. The domain is the closed interval $[-1, 1]$. The end-points -1 and 1 are critical points. To check the interior points $x \in (-1, 1)$ we differentiate. This gives

$$f'(x) = -\frac{x}{\sqrt{1 - x^2}} + \frac{1}{2}.$$

Setting $f'(x) = 0$ gives

$$\frac{x}{\sqrt{1 - x^2}} = \frac{1}{2}.$$

Squaring both sides, we get

$$\frac{x^2}{1 - x^2} = \frac{1}{4}$$
$$4x^2 = 1 - x^2$$
$$5x^2 = 1$$

and thus

$$x = \pm \frac{1}{\sqrt{5}}.$$

Of these two numbers only $1/\sqrt{5}$ is a root of the equation $f'(x) = 0$. The other, $-1/\sqrt{5}$, is an extraneous root that we introduced when we did some squaring. In short there are three critical points to examine: -1, $1/\sqrt{5}$, and 1. Since $f' > 0$ a little to the right of -1, $f(-1) = -1/2$ is an end-point minimum. To test $f(1/\sqrt{5})$ we apply the second-derivative test:

$$f''(x) = -\left(\frac{\sqrt{1-x^2}\cdot 1 - x\left(-\dfrac{x}{\sqrt{1-x^2}}\right)}{1-x^2}\right)$$

$$= -(1-x^2)^{-3/2}.$$

It is not hard to see that $f''(1/\sqrt{5})$ is negative and therefore

$$f\left(\frac{1}{\sqrt{5}}\right) = \sqrt{1 - \frac{1}{5}} + \frac{1}{2\sqrt{5}} = 2\frac{1}{\sqrt{5}} + \frac{1}{2\sqrt{5}} = \frac{5}{2\sqrt{5}} = \frac{\sqrt{5}}{2}$$

is a local maximum value. Since $f' < 0$ a little to the left of 1, $f(1) = 1/2$ is an end-point minimum.

To summarize, the critical points are -1, $1/\sqrt{5}$, and 1.

$$f(-1) = -\frac{1}{2} \quad \text{is an end-point minimum; it is also the absolute minimum.}$$

$$f\left(\frac{1}{\sqrt{5}}\right) = \frac{\sqrt{5}}{2} \quad \text{is a local maximum; it is also the absolute maximum.}$$

$$f(1) = \frac{1}{2} \quad \text{is an end-point minimum.} \quad \square$$

Exercises

Find the critical points and classify the extreme values of the following functions.

1.* $f(x) = \sqrt{x+2}$.

2. $f(x) = (x-1)(x-2)$.

3.* $f(x) = x^2 - 4x + 1$, $x \in [0, 3]$.

4. $f(x) = 2x^2 + 5x - 1$, $x \in [-2, 0]$.

5.* $f(x) = x^2 + \dfrac{1}{x}$.

6. $f(x) = x + \dfrac{1}{x^2}$.

7.* $f(x) = x^2 + \dfrac{1}{x}$, $x \in \left[\dfrac{1}{10}, 2\right]$.

8. $f(x) = x + \dfrac{1}{x^2}$, $x \in (-1, 0)$.

9.* $f(x) = (x-1)(x-2)$, $x \in [0, 2]$.

10. $f(x) = (x-1)^2(x-2)^2$, $x \in [0, 4]$.

11.* $f(x) = \dfrac{1 - 3\sqrt{x}}{3 - \sqrt{x}}$.

12. $f(x) = \dfrac{x^2}{1+x^2}$, $x \in [-1, 2]$.

13.* $f(x) = (x - \sqrt{x})^2$.

14. $f(x) = x\sqrt{4-x^2}$.

15.* $f(x) = x\sqrt{3-x}$.

16. $f(x) = \sqrt{x} - \dfrac{1}{\sqrt{x}}$.

17.* $f(x) = 1 - \sqrt[3]{x-1}$.

18. $f(x) = (4x-1)^{1/3}(2x-1)^{2/3}$.

19.* $f(x) = \begin{cases} -2x, & x < 1 \\ x - 3, & 1 \le x \le 4. \\ 5 - x, & 4 < x \end{cases}$

20. $f(x) = \begin{cases} -x^2, & 0 \le x < 1 \\ -2x, & 1 < x < 2. \\ -\dfrac{x^2}{2}, & 2 \le x \le 3 \end{cases}$

3.13   Additional maximum-minimum problems

The techniques of the last two sections can be applied to a wide variety of maximum-minimum problems. Here are some examples.

Problem.   A window in the shape of a rectangle capped by a semicircle is to be surrounded by p inches of metal border. Find the radius of the semicircular part if the total area of the window is to be a maximum.

SOLUTION.   As in Figure 3.13.1 we let r be the radius of the semicircular part and let $h(r)$ be the height of the rectangular part. The total area of the window is then given by the function

$$A(r) = 2rh(r) + \frac{\pi r^2}{2} .$$

Since the total perimeter of the window is p, we have

$$p = 2r + 2h(r) + \pi r \quad \text{and thus} \quad h(r) = \frac{p - 2r - \pi r}{2} .$$

Substituting

$$h(r) = \frac{p - 2r - \pi r}{2}$$

into the area formula, we get

$$A(r) = 2r\left(\frac{p - 2r - \pi r}{2}\right) + \frac{\pi r^2}{2} = pr - 2r^2 - \frac{\pi r^2}{2} .$$

FIGURE 3.13.1

Our problem now is simply to find out what value of r maximizes the function A. Differentiating, we get

$$A'(r) = p - 4r - \pi r.$$

Setting $A'(r) = 0$ gives

$$p - 4r - \pi r = 0 \quad \text{and consequently} \quad r = \frac{p}{4 + \pi} \cdot$$

Since the second derivative is constantly negative

$$[A''(r) = -4 - \pi < 0],$$

we can conclude that $r = p/(4 + \pi)$ does give the desired maximum.   □

Problem.   Find the dimensions of the base of the rectangular box of greatest volume that can be constructed from 200 sq in. of cardboard if the base is to be three times as long as it is wide.

SOLUTION.   If the dimensions of the base are x and $3x$ and the height is $h(x)$ then the volume is given by

$$V(x) = 3x^2 h(x). \qquad \text{(Figure 3.13.2)}$$

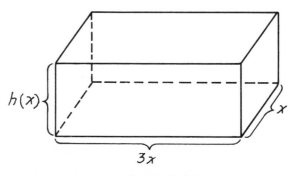

FIGURE 3.13.2

To obtain $h(x)$ in terms of x, we use the fact that the total surface area is 200 sq. in. This gives

$$200 = 6xh(x) + 6x^2 + 2xh(x)$$

and thus

$$h(x) = \frac{200 - 6x^2}{8x} = \frac{100 - 3x^2}{4x} \cdot$$

Substitution of this last expression for $h(x)$ into the volume formula gives

$$V(x) = 3x^2 \left(\frac{100 - 3x^2}{4x} \right) = \frac{3}{4}(100x - 3x^3).$$

Differentiation yields

$$V'(x) = \frac{3}{4}(100 - 9x^2) \quad \text{and} \quad V''(x) = -\frac{27}{2}x.$$

Setting

$$V'(x) = 0,$$

we get

$$100 - 9x^2 = 0 \quad \text{and thus} \quad x = \pm\frac{10}{3}.$$

Of these two answers the only one that fits the conditions of the problem is $x = \frac{10}{3}$. Since the second derivative

$$V''(x) = -\frac{27}{2}x$$

is negative at $x = \frac{10}{3}$, we can conclude that $x = \frac{10}{3}$ gives rise to a maximum. The rectangle must be $\frac{10}{3}$ in. wide and 10 in. long. □

Problem.   Find the point on the curve $y = x^{3/2}$ which is closest to the point $P(\frac{1}{2}, 0)$.

SOLUTION.   See Figure 3.13.3. Points on the curve $y = x^{3/2}$ are of the form $Q(x, x^{3/2})$, $x \geq 0$. The distance between P and such points Q is given by the expression

$$\sqrt{(x - \tfrac{1}{2})^2 + (x^{3/2})^2} = \sqrt{x^3 + x^2 - x + \tfrac{1}{4}}.$$

To solve the problem we need only find out what value of x minimizes the function

$$f(x) = \sqrt{x^3 + x^2 - x + \tfrac{1}{4}}, \qquad x \geq 0.$$

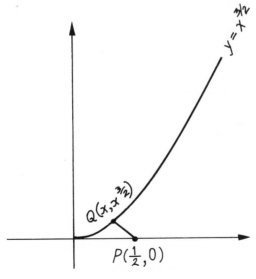

FIGURE 3.13.3

On $(0, \infty)$ the derivative

$$f'(x) = \frac{3x^2 + 2x - 1}{2\sqrt{x^3 + x^2 - x + \frac{1}{4}}} = \frac{(3x - 1)(x + 1)}{2\sqrt{x^3 + x^2 - x + \frac{1}{4}}}$$

is 0 only at $x = \frac{1}{3}$. This makes $\frac{1}{3}$ the only interior critical point. There is also an end point $x = 0$ to consider. Since

$$f(0) = \frac{1}{2} \quad \text{and} \quad f\left(\frac{1}{3}\right) = \sqrt{\left(\frac{1}{3}\right)^3 + \left(\frac{1}{3}\right)^2 - \frac{1}{3} + \frac{1}{4}} = \frac{\sqrt{21}}{18},$$

the smaller of these two numbers, $f(\frac{1}{3}) = \sqrt{21}/18$, is obviously the minimum value of f. Of all the points on the curve, the closest to $P(\frac{1}{2}, 0)$ is the point $Q(\frac{1}{3}, (\frac{1}{3})^{3/2})$. $\square$

Exercises

1.* Find the two positive numbers whose sum is 40 and whose product is a maximum.

2. Find the dimensions of the rectangle of perimeter p that has the largest area.

3.* A rectangular garden two hundred square feet in area is to be fenced off against rabbits. Find the dimensions that will require the least amount of fencing if one side of the garden is already protected by a barn.

4. Find the largest area that a rectangle can have if its base lies on the x-axis and its upper vertices lie on the curve

$$y = 4 - x^2.$$

5.* Find the point on the curve $y = \sqrt{x}$ that is closest to the point $P(2, 0)$.

6. Find the point on the parabola $y = x^2$ that is closest to the point $P(3, \frac{1}{2})$.

7.* Find the largest possible area for a rectangle inscribed in a circle of radius r.

8. Find the largest possible area for a rectangle inscribed in the ellipse

$$\frac{x^2}{a^2} + \frac{y^2}{b^2} = 1.$$

9.* Of all the isosceles triangles with a given perimeter, which has the largest area?

10. What are the dimensions of the base of the rectangular box of greatest volume that can be constructed from 100 square inches of cardboard if the base is to be twice as long as it is wide?

11.* Find the maximum area that a parallelogram can have and be inscribed in a triangle ABC in such a way that one vertex coincides with A while the others fall one on each side of the triangle.

12. Find the dimensions of the triangle of least area that can circumscribe a circle of radius r.

13.* From a rectangular piece of cardboard of dimensions $a \times b$ four congruent squares are to be cut out, one at each corner. The remaining crosslike piece is then to be folded into an open box. What size squares should be cut out if the volume of the resulting box is to be a maximum?

14. What is the maximum area possible for a triangle inscribed in a circle of radius r?

In the remaining exercises make use of the usual formulas.

15.* A string of length l is to be cut into two pieces, one piece to form an equilateral triangle and the other to form a circle. How should the string be cut so as to (a) maximize the sum of the two areas? (b) minimize the sum of the two areas?

16. Given a right circular cone of height h and base radius r, find the inscribed cylinder:
(a)* with the greatest volume.
(b) with the greatest curved surface.

17. Cylinders and right circular cones are inscribed in a sphere of radius R. Find:
(a)* the cylinder with the greatest volume, (b) the cylinder with the greatest curved surface, (c)* the cone with the greatest volume.

18.* What is the maximum volume of a right circular cone of slant height a?

3.14 Concavity and points of inflection

If you look at the graph of the cubing function (Figure 3.14.1), you will see that for x in $(-\infty, 0]$ the graph is "curving down" and for x in $[0, \infty)$ the graph is "curving up." In the language of calculus we say that the graph is *concave down* on $(-\infty, 0]$ and *concave up* on $[0, \infty)$.

Definition of Concavity

The graph of a differentiable function f is said to be *concave up* on the interval I iff f' is increasing on I; it is said to be *concave down* on I iff f' is decreasing on I.

If f'' exists, it serves well as a test for concavity. If $f''(x) > 0$ for all x in I, then f' is increasing there, so that the graph of f is concave up on I. If $f''(x) < 0$ for all x in I, then f' is decreasing there, so that the graph of f is concave down on I.

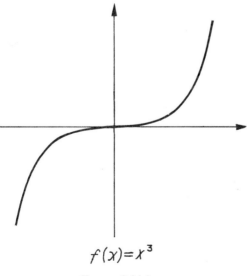

$$f(x) = x^3$$

FIGURE 3.14.1

Of special interest in curve sketching are the points which separate arcs of opposite concavity. These are called *points of inflection*.

Definition of Point of Inflection

The point $(c, f(c))$ is called a *point of inflection* iff there exists $\delta > 0$ such that the graph of f is concave in one sense on $(c - \delta, c]$ and concave in the opposite sense on $[c, c + \delta)$.

It is not hard to see that if $(c, f(c))$ is a point of inflection then the derivative f' either has a local maximum at c (Figure 3.14.2) or it has a local minimum at c (Figure 3.14.3). It follows therefore that

---

if $(c, f(c))$ is a point of inflection, then either $f''(c) = 0$ or $f''(c)$ does not exist.

(To show this, all you have to do is apply Theorem 3.11.1, not to f, but to f'.)

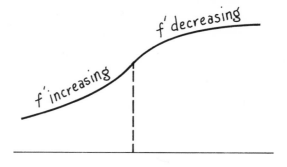

f' has a local maximum at c

FIGURE 3.14.2

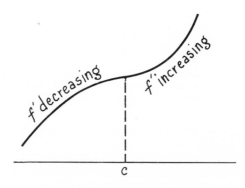

f' has a local minimum at c

FIGURE 3.14.3

Example. For

$$f(x) = x^3 + \frac{x^2}{2} - 2x + 1$$

we have

$$f'(x) = 3x^2 + x - 2 \quad \text{and} \quad f''(x) = 6x + 1.$$

Since

$$f''(x) \text{ is } \begin{cases} \text{negative,} & \text{for } x < -\frac{1}{6} \\ 0, & \text{for } x = -\frac{1}{6}, \\ \text{positive,} & \text{for } x > -\frac{1}{6} \end{cases}$$

the graph of f is concave down on $(-\infty, -\frac{1}{6}]$ and concave up on $[-\frac{1}{6}, \infty)$. The point $(-\frac{1}{6}, f(-\frac{1}{6}))$ is a point of inflection. □

Example. For

$$f(x) = 3x^{5/3} - x$$

we have

$$f'(x) = 5x^{2/3} - 1 \quad \text{and} \quad f''(x) = \tfrac{10}{3}x^{-1/3}.$$

The second derivative fails to exist at 0. Since

$$f''(x) \text{ is } \begin{cases} \text{negative,} & \text{for } x < 0 \\ \text{positive,} & \text{for } x > 0 \end{cases},$$

the point $(0, f(0)) = (0, 0)$ is a point of inflection. The graph is concave down on $(-\infty, 0]$ and concave up on $[0, \infty)$. □

Exercises

Describe the concavity of the graph and find the points of inflection (if any).

1.* $\dfrac{1}{x}$.

2. $x + \dfrac{1}{x}$.

3.* $x^3 - 3x + 2$.

4. $2x^2 - 5x + 2$.

5.* $\dfrac{1}{4}x^4 - \dfrac{1}{2}x^2$.

6. $x^3(1 - x)$.

7.* $\dfrac{x}{x^2 - 1}$.

8. $\dfrac{x + 2}{x - 2}$.

9.* $(1 - x)^2(1 + x)^2$.

10. $\dfrac{6x}{x^2 + 1}$.

11.* $\dfrac{1 - \sqrt{x}}{1 + \sqrt{x}}$.

12. $(x - 3)^{1/5}$.

13.* Find d given that $(d, f(d))$ is a point of inflection of

$$f(x) = (x - a)(x - b)(x - c).$$

14.   Find c given that the graph of

$$f(x) = cx^2 + \frac{1}{x^2}$$

has an inflection point at $(1, f(1))$.

15.* Find a and b given that the graph of

$$f(x) = ax^3 + bx^2$$

passes through $(-1, 1)$ and has an inflection point when $x = \frac{1}{3}$.

3.15   Some curve sketching

During the course of the last few sections you have seen how to determine the extreme values of a function and how to find where a function is increasing and where it is decreasing. Now you have seen how to determine the concavity of the graph and how to find the points of inflection. By putting all this information together you can get a good idea of what the graph of a given function looks like.

Example.   In the case of

$$f(x) = \tfrac{1}{4}(x^3 - \tfrac{3}{2}x^2 - 6x + 2),$$

$f(0) = \frac{1}{2}$ and therefore the graph of f intersects the y-axis at the point $(0, \frac{1}{2})$.† Differentiation gives

$$f'(x) = \tfrac{1}{4}(3x^2 - 3x - 6) = \tfrac{3}{4}(x + 1)(x - 2)$$

and

$$f''(x) = \tfrac{1}{4}(6x - 3) = \tfrac{3}{4}(2x - 1).$$

The first derivative is 0 at $x = -1$ and $x = 2$. These are the only critical points. Since $f''(-1) < 0$,

$$f(-1) = \tfrac{1}{4}[(-1)^3 - \tfrac{3}{2}(-1)^2 - 6(-1) + 2] = \tfrac{1}{4}[-1 - \tfrac{3}{2} + 6 + 2] = 1\tfrac{3}{8}$$

is a local maximum. Since $f''(2) > 0$,

$$f(2) = \tfrac{1}{4}[(2)^3 - \tfrac{3}{2}(2)^2 - 6(2) + 2] = -2$$

is a local minimum. Since

$$f''(x) \text{ is } \begin{cases} \text{negative,} & \text{for } x < \tfrac{1}{2} \\ \phantom{\text{negative,}} 0, & \text{for } x = \tfrac{1}{2}, \\ \text{positive,} & \text{for } x > \tfrac{1}{2} \end{cases}$$

---

† It would be nice to find out exactly where the graph intersects the x-axis, but this would require that we solve the equation

$$x^3 - \tfrac{3}{2}x^2 - 6x + 2 = 0.$$

the point $(\frac{1}{2}, f(\frac{1}{2})) = (\frac{1}{2}, -\frac{5}{16})$ is the only point of inflection. The graph is concave down on $(-\infty, \frac{1}{2}]$ and concave up on $[\frac{1}{2}, \infty)$.

If you now put together all this information and plot a few points, you will not find it hard to come up with a graph that looks like the one displayed in Figure 3.15.1. □

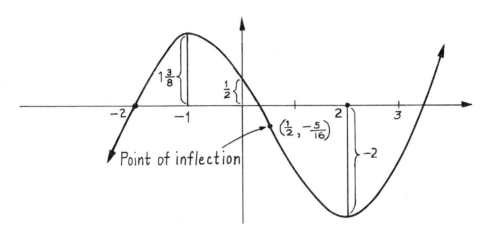

$$f(x) = \frac{1}{4}\left(x^3 - \frac{3}{2}x^2 - 6x + 2\right)$$

FIGURE 3.15.1

Example.   The function

$$g(x) = \frac{1}{1 + x^2}$$

remains positive throughout. Since $g(-x) = g(x)$, the function is even and its graph is symmetric with respect to the y-axis. When $x = 0, g(x) = 1$. This is clearly the maximum value of g. As x tends away from zero

$$1 + x^2 \quad \text{increases without bound}$$

and therefore

$$g(x) = \frac{1}{1 + x^2} \quad \text{decreases toward 0.}$$

So far we have not used calculus in this example but we need it now to determine the concavity of the graph. Differentiation gives

$$g'(x) = -\frac{2x}{(1 + x^2)^2} \quad \text{and} \quad g''(x) = \frac{2(3x^2 - 1)}{(1 + x^2)^3}.$$

Since

$$g''(x) \text{ is } \begin{cases} \text{positive,} & \text{for } x < -\dfrac{1}{\sqrt{3}} \\[2mm] 0, & \text{for } x = -\dfrac{1}{\sqrt{3}} \\[2mm] \text{negative,} & \text{for } -\dfrac{1}{\sqrt{3}} < x < \dfrac{1}{\sqrt{3}}, \\[2mm] 0, & \text{for } x = \dfrac{1}{\sqrt{3}} \\[2mm] \text{positive,} & \text{for } \dfrac{1}{\sqrt{3}} < x \end{cases}$$

the graph is concave down on $[-1/\sqrt{3}, 1/\sqrt{3}]$ and concave up on $(-\infty, -1/\sqrt{3}]$ and $[1/\sqrt{3}, \infty)$. The points $(-1/\sqrt{3}, 3/4)$ and $(1/\sqrt{3}, 3/4)$ are points of inflection.
It is now easy to see that the graph is as in Figure 3.15.2.   □

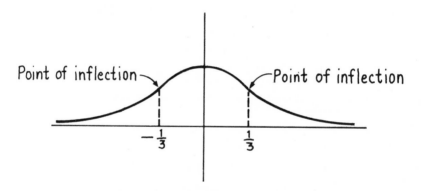

FIGURE 3.15.2

Example.   As our final example we take the function

$$f(x) = 3\,(x^{5/3} - x^{4/3}).$$

We can rewrite this as

$$f(x) = 3x^{4/3}(x^{1/3} - 1)$$

and therefore see that f takes on the value 0 at $x = 0$ and at $x = 1$. The graph thus crosses the x-axis at the origin and at the point $(1, 0)$.
The derivative

$$f'(x) = 3(\tfrac{5}{3}x^{2/3} - \tfrac{4}{3}x^{1/3}) = x^{1/3}(5x^{1/3} - 4)$$

exists everywhere and is 0 only at $x = 0$ and at $x = 4^3/5^3 = 64/125$. Therefore 0 and $64/125$ are the only critical points.

Since

$$f'(x) \text{ is } \begin{cases} \text{positive,} & \text{for } x < 0 \\ 0, & \text{for } x = 0 \\ \text{negative,} & \text{for } 0 < x < 64/125 \\ 0, & \text{for } x = 64/125 \\ \text{positive,} & \text{for } x > 64/125 \end{cases}$$

$f(0) = 0$ is a local maximum and $f(64/125) \overset{\text{approx}}{=} -1/4$

is a local minimum.

From $f'(x) = 5x^{2/3} - 4x^{1/3}$ we get the second derivative

$$f''(x) = \tfrac{10}{3}x^{-1/3} - \tfrac{4}{3}x^{-2/3} = \tfrac{2}{3}x^{-2/3}(5x^{1/3} - 2).$$

The second derivative $f''(x)$ does not exist for $x = 0$. It is 0 for $x = 2^3/5^3 = 8/125$. Since

$$f''(x) \text{ is } \begin{cases} \text{negative,} & \text{for } x < 0 \\ \text{nonexistent,} & \text{at } x = 0 \\ \text{negative,} & \text{for } 0 < x < 8/125, \\ 0, & \text{at } x = 8/125 \\ \text{positive,} & \text{for } x > 8/125 \end{cases}$$

the graph is concave down on all of $(-\infty, 8/125]$ (explain) and concave up on $[8/125, \infty)$. The point $(8/125, f(8/125)) \overset{\text{approx}}{=} (.06, -.04)$ is the only point of inflection. Note that this is very close to the origin.

Before trying to sketch the graph we gather a little more information. The easiest numbers to work with here are perfect cubes.

$$f'(1) = 1 \qquad [\text{the graph at } (1,0) \text{ has slope } 1]$$

$$f\left(\frac{5^3}{4^3}\right) = \frac{3 \cdot 5^4}{4^5} \qquad [\text{at } x \overset{\text{approx}}{=} 2, f(x) \overset{\text{approx}}{=} 1.8]$$

$$f'\left(\frac{5^3}{4^3}\right) = \frac{45}{4^2} \qquad [\text{at } (x,y) \overset{\text{approx}}{=} (2,1.8), \text{ slope} \overset{\text{approx}}{=} 3]$$

$$f\left(-\frac{2^3}{3^3}\right) = -\frac{5 \cdot 2^4}{3^4} \qquad [\text{at } x \overset{\text{approx}}{=} -.3, f(x) \overset{\text{approx}}{=} -.1]$$

$$f'\left(-\frac{2^3}{3^3}\right) = \frac{44}{3^2} \qquad [\text{at } (x,y) \overset{\text{approx}}{=} (-.3, -.1), \text{ slope} \overset{\text{approx}}{=} 5]$$

$$f\left(-\frac{4^3}{5^3}\right) = -\frac{3^3 \cdot 4^4}{5^5} \qquad [\text{at } x \overset{\text{approx}}{=} -.5, f(x) \overset{\text{approx}}{=} -2.2]$$

$$f'\left(-\frac{4^3}{5^3}\right) = \frac{32}{5} \qquad [\text{at } (x,y) \overset{\text{approx}}{=} (-.5, -2.2), \text{ slope } = 6.4].$$

If you use all this information, you will come up with a graph for f that looks much like the one displayed in Figure 3.15.3. $\square$

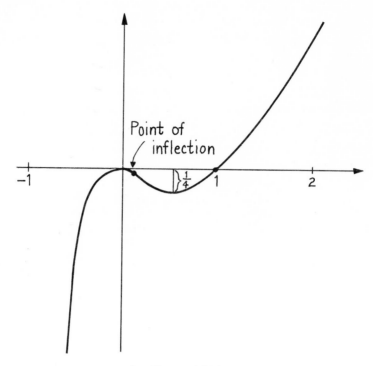

FIGURE 3.15.3

Exercises

For each of the following functions (i) find the critical points, (ii) find and classify the extreme values (local, end-point, absolute), (iii) indicate where the function is increasing and where it is decreasing, (iv) indicate the concavity of the graph, (v) specify the points of inflection, and then (vi) sketch the graph.

1.* $f(x) = (x - 2)^2$.

2. $f(x) = 1 - (x - 2)^2$.

3.* $f(x) = x^3 - 2x^2 + x + 1$.

4. $f(x) = \dfrac{2}{3}x^3 - \dfrac{1}{2}x^2 - 10x - 1$.

5.* $f(x) = \dfrac{x}{3x - 1}$.

6. $f(x) = \dfrac{2x}{4x - 3}$.

7.* $f(x) = \dfrac{x^2}{3x + 1}$.

8. $f(x) = \dfrac{2x^2}{-x + 1}$.

9.* $f(x) = \dfrac{x}{(3x + 1)^2}$.

10. $f(x) = \dfrac{2x}{(x + 1)^2}$.

11.* $f(x) = 3x^5 + 5x^3$.

12. $f(x) = 3x^4 + 4x^3$.

13.* $f(x) = 1 + (x - 2)^{4/3}$.

14. $f(x) = 1 + (x - 2)^{5/3}$.

15.* $f(x) = x^2(1 + x)^2$.

16. $f(x) = x^2(1 + x)^3$.

17.* $f(x) = x\sqrt{1 - x}$.

18. $f(x) = \sqrt{x - x^2}$.

19.* $f(x) = \dfrac{2x}{x^2 + 2}$.

20. $f(x) = \dfrac{2x^2}{x^2 + 2}$.

21.* $f(x) = 2 + (x + 1)^{6/5}$.

22. $f(x) = 2 + (x + 1)^{7/5}$.

3.16   Rates of change per unit time

You have already seen that the derivative of a function gives its rate of change. Suppose now that $f(t)$ represents some quantity at time t. The derivative $f'(t)$ then gives the *rate of change* of that quantity per unit time.

Example.   Suppose that a spherical balloon is expanding under the influence of solar radiation. If its radius is increasing at the rate of 2 in/min, how fast is the volume increasing when the radius is 5 in.?

SOLUTION.   We can express the volume at time t in terms of the radius at time t by the formula

$$V(t) = \tfrac{4}{3}\pi[r(t)]^3.$$

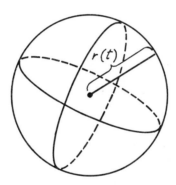

FIGURE 3.16.1

Differentiation gives

$$V'(t) = 4\pi[r(t)]^2 r'(t).$$

If at time t_0 the radius is 5 in., then

$$V'(t_0) = 4\pi(25)2 = 200\pi.$$

This means that the volume is increasing at the rate of 200π in³/min.   □

Example. A point is moving along the unit circle. Every time it has coordinates $(1/2, \sqrt{3}/2)$ its ordinate is decreasing at the rate of 3 units/sec. At what rate is the abscissa changing?

SOLUTION.   At each time t,

$$[x(t)]^2 + [y(t)]^2 = 1,$$

and thus

$$2x(t)x'(t) + 2y(t)y'(t) = 0.$$

Canceling the 2, we have

$$x(t)x'(t) + y(t)y'(t) = 0.$$

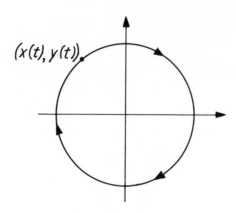

FIGURE 3.16.2

If we let t_0 be a time at which the moving point has coordinates $(\frac{1}{2}, \sqrt{3}/2)$, we then have

$$\frac{1}{2} x'(t_0) + \frac{\sqrt{3}}{2} (-3) = 0,$$

which implies that

$$x'(t_0) = 3 \sqrt{3}.$$

The abscissa is thus increasing at the rate of $3 \sqrt{3}$ units/sec.   □

Example.   A water trough with vertical cross section in the shape of an equilateral triangle (one vertex down) is being filled at the rate of 4 ft³/min. Given that the trough is 12 ft long, how fast is the water level rising when the water reaches a depth of $1\frac{1}{2}$ ft?

SOLUTION.   When the water is x feet deep, a vertical cross section of water has area $x^2/\sqrt{3}$. Since the trough is 12 ft long, the volume of the water is then $12x^2/\sqrt{3}$. If we denote by $x(t)$ the depth of the water at time t, then we obtain

$$V(t) = \frac{12}{\sqrt{3}} \, [x(t)]^2$$

and thus

$$V'(t) = \frac{24}{\sqrt{3}} x(t)x'(t).$$

FIGURE 3.16.3

If it is at time t_0 that the water is $1\frac{1}{2}$ ft deep, then we have

$$4 = \frac{24}{\sqrt{3}} (1\tfrac{1}{2})x'(t_0),$$

so that

$$x'(t_0) = \frac{1}{3\sqrt{3}}.$$

This tells us that the water is rising at the rate of $1/3\sqrt{3}$ ft/min. ☐

Velocity and Acceleration

Suppose now that an object is moving along a straight line and that for each time t during a certain time interval the object has position (coordinate) $x(t)$. If $x'(t)$ exists, then $x'(t)$ gives the rate of change of position at time t. This rate of change of position is called the *velocity* of the object at time t; in symbols,

$$v(t) = x'(t).$$

If the velocity function is itself differentiable, then its rate of change at time t is called the *acceleration* at time t; in symbols,

$$a(t) = v'(t) = x''(t).$$

In the Leibniz notation,

$$v = \frac{dx}{dt} \quad \text{and} \quad a = \frac{dv}{dt} = \frac{d^2x}{dt^2}.$$

A positive velocity indicates an increase in coordinate and thus a motion in the positive direction. A negative velocity indicates a decrease in coordinate and thus a motion in the negative direction. When the direction of motion is immaterial, we speak of *speed*. This is by definition the absolute value of the velocity:

$$\text{speed at time } t = |v(t)|.$$

A word about units is in order. If distance is measured in feet and time in seconds, then velocity and speed are given in feet per second (ft/sec) and acceleration is given in feet per second per second (ft/sec²).

We can illustrate these ideas by considering the motion of an object which falls freely under the influence of gravity. If we neglect air resistance, then the height of the object at time t is given by the equation

$$x(t) = \tfrac{1}{2}gt^2 + v_0 t + x_0.$$

Here v_0 represents the velocity at time $t = 0$ (called the *initial velocity*) and x_0 represents the height at time $t = 0$ (called the *initial position*). The constant g, called the gravitational constant, is the acceleration due to gravity. If we measure time in seconds and distances in feet, then g is approximately -32 ft/sec². (Why is it negative?) In making numerical calculations we shall take g as -32 ft/sec². Doing so we obtain

$$x(t) = -16t^2 + v_0 t + x_0.$$

Problem.   A stone is dropped from a height of 1600 ft. How long does it take to reach the ground and what is its speed at impact?

SOLUTION.   Here $x_0 = 1600$ and $v_0 = 0$. Consequently

$$x(t) = -16t^2 + 1600.$$

To find t at the moment of impact we set $x(t) = 0$. This gives

$$-16t^2 + 1600 = 0$$
$$t^2 = 100$$
$$t = \pm 10.$$

We can disregard the negative answer because the stone had not even been dropped before $t = 0$. We conclude that it takes 10 seconds for the stone to reach the ground.

The velocity at impact is the velocity when $t = 10$. Since

$$v(t) = x'(t) = -32t$$

we have

$$v(10) = -320.$$

The speed at impact is therefore 320 ft/sec.   □

Problem. A stone is projected from ground level vertically upward with an initial speed of 72 ft/sec.

(a) How many seconds later does it attain its maximum height?

(b) What is this maximum height?

(c) How fast is it traveling when it reaches a height of 32 ft?

(i) going up? (ii) going down?

SOLUTION. The basic equation is again

$$x(t) = -16t^2 + v_0 t + x_0.$$

Here $x_0 = 0$ (it starts at ground level) and $v_0 = 72$. (The initial velocity is 72 ft/sec.) The equation of motion is therefore

$$x(t) = -16t^2 + 72t.$$

Differentiation gives

$$v(t) = x'(t) = -32t + 72.$$

The maximum height is obviously reached when the velocity is 0. This occurs when $t = \frac{72}{32} = \frac{9}{4}$. To get the maximum height attained we need only evaluate $x(t)$ at $t = \frac{9}{4}$. Since

$$x(\tfrac{9}{4}) = 81,$$

we see that the maximum height attained is 81 ft.

To answer part (c) we must find those numbers t for which

$$x(t) = 32.$$

Since

$$x(t) = -16t^2 + 72t,$$

we are led to the quadratic equation

$$16t^2 - 72t + 32 = 0.$$

This quadratic has two solutions $t = \frac{1}{2}$ and $t = 4$. For (i) we have $v(\frac{1}{2}) = 56$; and for (ii), $v(4) = -56$. The speed in each case is 56 ft/sec. □

Exercises

1.* A point moves along the straight line $x + 2y = 2$. Find: (a) the rate of change of the y-coordinate, given that the x-coordinate increases 4 units/sec; (b) the rate of change of the x-coordinate, given that the y-coordinate decreases 2 units/sec.

2. The volume of a contracting cube is decreasing at the rate of 2 in³/min. Find (a) the rate of change of an edge, and (b) the rate of change of the total surface area when the volume of the cube is 64 in³.

3.* A point P is moving in the circular orbit $x^2 + y^2 = 25$. As it passes through the point $(3, 4)$, its y-coordinate is decreasing at the rate of 2 units/sec. How is the x-coordinate changing?

4. A ladder 13 ft long is leaning against a wall. If the base of the ladder is being pulled away from the wall at the rate of $\frac{1}{2}$ ft/sec, how fast is the top of the ladder being lowered when the base is 5 ft from the wall?

5.* Taking

$$x = -t\sqrt{t+1}, \qquad t \geq 0$$

as the equation of motion, find
(a) the velocity when $t = 1$,
(b) the acceleration when $t = 1$,
(c) the speed when $t = 1$,
(d) the rate of change of the speed when $t = 1$,
(e) the time t, if it exists, when the velocity is a maximum,
(f) the time t, if it exists, when the speed is a maximum.

6.* The height of a cylinder is being increased at the rate of 4 in./min. If the volume of the cylinder is to be kept constant, at what rate must the radius be diminished at each instant?

7. In the special theory of relativity the mass of a particle moving at velocity v is

$$m\left(1 - \frac{v^2}{c^2}\right)^{-1/2},$$

where m is the mass at rest and c is the speed of light. At what rate is the mass changing when the particle's velocity is $\frac{1}{2}c$ and the rate of change of the velocity is $0.01c$/sec?

8.* A conical paper cup of radius 2 in. and height 6 in. is leaking water at the rate of 1 in³/min. At what rate is the level of the water being lowered: (a) when the water is 3 in. deep, (b) when the cup is half full?

9. The shadow cast by a man standing 3 ft from a lamp post is 4 ft long. If the man is 6 ft tall and walks away from the lamp post at a speed of 400 ft/min, at what rate will his shadow be lengthening: (a) a quarter of a minute later, (b) when he is 20 ft from the lamp post?

10* A stone is thrown upward from ground level with an initial speed of 32 ft/sec. (a) How many seconds later will it hit the ground? (b) What will be the maximum height attained? (c) With what initial speed should it be thrown if it is to reach a maximum height of 36 ft?

11. To estimate the height of a bridge a man drops a stone into the water below. How high is the bridge (a) if the stone hits the water 3 seconds later? (b) if the man hears the splash 3 seconds later? (Use 1080 ft/sec as the speed of sound.)

12.* A falling stone is observed to be at a height of 100 ft. Two seconds later it is observed to be at a height of 16 ft. (a) From what height was it dropped? (b) If it was thrown down with an initial speed of 5 ft/sec, from what height was it thrown? (c) If it was thrown upward with an initial speed of 10 ft/sec, from what height was it thrown?

3.17 The little-o h idea; differentials

For small h, πh^2 is small compared to h, in the sense that

$$\lim_{h \to 0} \frac{\pi h^2}{h} = 0.$$

For small h, $h^{5/3}\sqrt{1 - h}$ is small compared to h, in the sense that

$$\lim_{h \to 0} \frac{h^{5/3}\sqrt{1 - h}}{h} = 0.$$

Expressions $g(h)$, such as πh^2 and $h^{5/3}\sqrt{1 - h}$ that tend to 0 with h when divided by h, are called *little-o h*. More briefly,

$$g(h) \text{ is } \textit{little-o h} \quad \text{iff} \quad \lim_{h \to 0} \frac{g(h)}{h} = 0.$$

To indicate that $g(h)$ is *little-o h* we write

$$g(h) = o(h).$$

For example, as you can check,

$$h^3 = o(h) \quad \text{and} \quad \frac{h^2}{h - 1} = o(h),$$

but

$$h^{1/3} \neq o(h) \quad \text{and} \quad \frac{h}{h - 1} \neq o(h).$$

We can use the *little-o h* notation in connection with differentiation. If f is differentiable at x, then

$$\lim_{h \to 0} \frac{f(x + h) - f(x)}{h} = f'(x)$$

and therefore

$$\lim_{h \to 0} \frac{[f(x + h) - f(x)] - f'(x)h}{h} = 0.$$

In short,

$$\boxed{[f(x + h) - f(x)] - f'(x)h = o(h).}$$

This last statement says that the difference

$$[f(x + h) - f(x)] - f'(x)h$$

is small compared to h. In other words, for small h

$$\boxed{f(x + h) - f(x) \cong f'(x)h} \quad \text{and} \quad \boxed{f(x + h) \cong f(x) + f'(x)h.} \quad \dagger$$

$\dagger \cong$ means *approximately equal*.

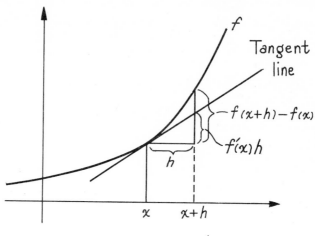

$$f(x+h) - f(x) \cong f'(x)h$$

FIGURE 3.17.1

We illustrate the approximation in Figure 3.17.1. The expression $f'(x)h$ is called a *differential*; more precisely, it is called the *differential of f at x with increment h*.

Differentials are used to calculate approximate values and to estimate errors. We begin with a square-root problem.

Problem. Use differentials to find an approximate value for $\sqrt{104}$.

SOLUTION. Here

$$f(x) = \sqrt{x} \quad \text{and} \quad f'(x) = \frac{1}{2\sqrt{x}}.$$

The approximation formula

$$f(x + h) \cong f(x) + f'(x)h$$

becomes

$$\sqrt{x + h} \cong \sqrt{x} + \frac{h}{2\sqrt{x}}.$$

Taking $x = 100$ (we know $\sqrt{100}$) and taking $h = 4$, we get

$$\sqrt{104} = \sqrt{100 + 4} \cong \sqrt{100} + \frac{4}{2\sqrt{100}} = 10 + \frac{1}{5} = 10.2.$$

As you can check, $(10.2)^2 = 104.04$, so that we are not far off.   □

When a quantity $f(x)$ is calculated to be $f(x + h)$ the *error*, $f(x + h) - f(x)$, can be approximated by the differential, $f'(x)h$:

$$\boxed{\text{error:} \quad f(x + h) - f(x) \cong f'(x)h.}$$

To obtain the *relative error* we divide the error by $f(x)$:

$$\text{relative error:} \qquad \frac{f(x+h)-f(x)}{f(x)} \cong \frac{f'(x)h}{f(x)}.$$

To get the *percentage error* we multiply by 100:

$$\text{percentage error:} \qquad 100\frac{f(x+h)-f(x)}{f(x)} \cong 100\frac{f'(x)h}{f(x)}.$$

Here is a problem that illustrates these ideas.

Problem.   A sphere of diameter 6 in. is incorrectly measured to have diameter 6.2 in. Estimate (a) the error in the volume, (b) the relative error in the volume, (c) the percentage error in the volume.

SOLUTION.   For a sphere of diameter x,

$$V(x) = \tfrac{1}{6}\pi x^3 \qquad \text{and} \qquad V'(x) = \tfrac{1}{2}\pi x^2.$$

With $x = 6$ in. and $h = .2$ in., we have

$$\text{error} = V(6+.2) - V(6) \cong V'(6)(.2) = (18\pi)(.2) = 3.6\pi \text{ cu in.}$$

$$\text{relative error} = \frac{V(6+.2)-V(6)}{V(6)} \cong \frac{V'(6)(.2)}{V(6)} = \frac{3.6\pi}{36\pi} = .1$$

$$\text{percentage error} = 100\left[\frac{V(6+.2)-V(6)}{V(6)}\right] \cong 100\left[\frac{V'(6)(.2)}{V(6)}\right] = 10\%. \quad \square$$

Exercises

Use differentials to find the approximate value.

1.* $\sqrt[3]{1010}$.   3.* $\dfrac{1}{\sqrt{22}}$.   5.* $\sqrt[5]{30}$.   7.* $(33)^{3/5}$.

2. $\sqrt{125}$.   4. $\dfrac{1}{\sqrt{24}}$.   6. $(26)^{2/3}$.   8. $(33)^{-1/5}$.

9.* Using differentials, find the approximate area of a ring of inner radius r and width h. What is the exact area?

10. Show that the relative error in the volume of a cube, due to an error in measuring the edge, is approximately three times the relative error in the edge.

11. Show that the relative error in the surface area of a sphere, due to an error in estimating the radius, is approximately twice the relative error in the radius.

12. Show that the relative error in the nth root of a number is approximately $1/n$ times the relative error in the number.

13.* Find the approximate volume of a thin cylindrical sheet with open ends if the inner radius is r, the height is h, and the thickness is t.

14.* A box is to be constructed in the form of a cube to hold 1000 cu ft. Use differentials to estimate how accurately the inner edge must be made so that the volume will be correct to within 3 cu ft.

15. Use differentials to estimate for what values of x
   (a)* $\sqrt{x+1} - \sqrt{x} < 0.01$.
   (b) $\sqrt[4]{x+1} - \sqrt[4]{x} < 0.002$.

16.* The time of one vibration of a pendulum is given by the formula

$$ t = \pi \sqrt{\frac{l}{g}}, $$

where t is measured in seconds, $g = 32.2$, and l is the length of the pendulum measured in feet. Taking $\pi = 3.14$, find
   (a) the length of a pendulum that vibrates once a second;
   (b) the approximate change in t if the pendulum is lengthened 0.01 ft;
   (c) the approximate time gained or lost per day by a pendulum clock with this error.

17. Show that the derivative $f'(x)$ is the *only* number that can satisfy the equation

$$ f(x + h) - f(x) = f'(x)h + o(h). $$

[HINT: Show that, if $f(x + h) - f(x) = Nh + o(h)$, then $N = f'(x)$.]

SUPPLEMENT

You have seen that $f'(x)h$ is called the differential of f at x with increment h. Often people write

$$ df(x, h) = f'(x)h \qquad \text{or more briefly} \qquad df = f'(x)h. $$

The difference $f(x + h) - f(x)$ is often referred to as the *increment of f from x to $x + h$*. In symbols,

$$ \Delta f(x, x + h) = f(x + h) - f(x) $$

or more simply

$$ \Delta f = f(x + h) - f(x). $$

With these abbreviated notations, the relation

$$ f(x + h) - f(x) \cong f'(x)h $$

can be written

$$ \Delta f(x, x + h) \cong df(x, h) \qquad \text{or even} \qquad \Delta f \cong df. $$

In some books you may find the formula

$$ df = f'(x)\, dx. $$

This comes simply from letting $h = dx$.

3.18 Implicit differentiation

When a function y is given implicitly by an equation in x and y, say

$$4x^2 + 2xy - xy^3 = 0 \quad \text{or} \quad x^3 - 3xy^2 + y^3 = 0,$$

the derivative dy/dx can be obtained (in terms of x and y) without first solving the equation for y.

Problem. Find dy/dx given that $4x^2 + 2xy - xy^3 = 0$.

SOLUTION.   The relation

$$4x^2 + 2xy - xy^3 = 0$$

gives

$$\frac{d}{dx}[4x^2 + 2xy - xy^3] = 0$$

$$8x + \left[2x\frac{dy}{dx} + 2y\right] - \left[x3y^2\frac{dy}{dx} + y^3\right] = 0$$

$$8x + 2y - y^3 + x(2 - 3y^2)\frac{dy}{dx} = 0$$

$$\frac{dy}{dx} = \frac{y^3 - 2y - 8x}{x(2 - 3y^2)} \cdot \quad \square$$

Problem. Find the slope of the curve

$$x^3 - 3xy^2 + y^3 = 0 \quad \text{at} \quad (2, -1).$$

SOLUTION.   Differentiation gives

$$3x^2 - 3x\left(2y\frac{dy}{dx}\right) - 3y^2 + 3y^2\frac{dy}{dx} = 0$$

$$3x^2 - 6xy\frac{dy}{dx} - 3y^2 + 3y^2\frac{dy}{dx} = 0.$$

At $x = 2$ and $y = -1$, the equation becomes

$$12 + 12\frac{dy}{dx} - 3 + 3\frac{dy}{dx} = 0$$

$$15\frac{dy}{dx} = -9$$

$$\frac{dy}{dx} = -\frac{3}{5} \cdot$$

The slope is $-\frac{3}{5}$. $\square$

The angle between two curves is the angle between their tangents at the point of intersection. If the slopes are m_1 and m_2, then the angle of intersection can be obtained from the formula

$$\tan \theta = \frac{m_1 - m_2}{1 + m_1 m_2}.$$

Problem. Find the angle of intersection of the circles

$$C_1: \quad (x - 1)^2 + y^2 = 10$$
$$C_2: \quad x^2 + (y - 2)^2 = 5.$$

SOLUTION. If you solve the equations simultaneously, you will find that $(2, 3)$ and $(-2, 1)$ are the points of intersection. Differentiating the first equation implicitly, we get

$$2(x - 1) + 2y \frac{dy}{dx} = 0$$

and therefore

$$m_1 = \frac{dy}{dx} = \frac{1 - x}{y}.$$

Differentiating the second equation, we get

$$2x + 2(y - 2) \frac{dy}{dx} = 0$$

and therefore

$$m_2 = \frac{dy}{dx} = \frac{x}{2 - y}.$$

At $(2, 3)$,

$$m_1 = \frac{1 - 2}{3} = -\frac{1}{3}, \qquad m_2 = \frac{2}{2 - 3} = -2,$$

so that

$$\tan \theta = \frac{m_1 - m_2}{1 + m_1 m_2} = \frac{-\frac{1}{3} + 2}{1 + \frac{2}{3}} = 1.$$

As a value of θ, we can take $\pi/4$ radians (or $45°$). At $(-2, 1)$,

$$m_1 = \frac{1 + 2}{1} = 3, \qquad m_2 = \frac{-2}{2 - 1} = -2$$

so that

$$\tan \theta = \frac{m_1 - m_2}{1 + m_1 m_2} = \frac{3 + 2}{1 - 6} = -1.$$

As a value of θ we could take $\theta = -\pi/4$ radians $(-45°)$. However, it is customary to take θ positive. So doing, we once again have $\theta = \pi/4$ radians $(45°)$. □

Exercises

Find dy/dx by implicit differentiation.

1.* $x^2 + y^2 = r^2$.

2. $x^3 + y^3 - 3axy = 0$.

3.* $b^2x^2 + a^2y^2 = a^2b^2$.

4. $\sqrt{x} + \sqrt{y} = \sqrt{a}$.

5.* $x^{2/3} + y^{2/3} = a^{2/3}$.

6. $y^2 = 4cx$.

7.* $x^4 + 4x^3y + y^4 = 1$.

8. $(2y)^{1/2} + (3y)^{1/3} = x$.

9.* $x + 2xy + y = 1$.

10. $x^2 + axy + y^2 = b^2$.

Find the slope at the indicated point.

11.* $2x + 3y = 5$; $(-2, 3)$.

12. $9x^2 + 4y^2 = 72$; $(2, 3)$.

13.* $x^2 + xy + 2y^2 = 28$; $(-2, -3)$.

14. $x^3 - axy + 3ay^2 = 3a^3$; (a, a).

15.* At what angles do the parabolas

$$y^2 = 2px + p^2 \quad \text{and} \quad y^2 = p^2 - 2px$$

intersect?

16. At what angle does the line $y = 2x$ cut the curve $x^2 - xy + 2y^2 = 28$?

17. Show that the hyperbola $x^2 - y^2 = 5$ and the ellipse $4x^2 + 9y^2 = 72$ intersect at right angles.

Find the second derivative d^2y/dx^2.

18.* $b^2x^2 + a^2y^2 = a^2b^2$.

19. $b^2x^2 - a^2y^2 = a^2b^2$.

20.* $ax^2 + 2xy + by^2 = 1$.

21. $y^2 + 2xy = 16$.

Evaluate dy/dx and d^2y/dx^2 at the given point.

22.* $x^2 - 4y^2 = 9$; $(5, 2)$.

23.* $x^2 + 4xy + y^2 + 3 = 0$; $(2, -1)$.

24. Find equations for the tangents to the ellipse $4x^2 + y^2 = 72$ that pass through the point $(4, 4)$.

3.19 Additional problems

1.* Determine the coefficients A, B, C so that the curve $y = Ax^2 + Bx + C$ will pass through the point $(1, 3)$ and be tangent to the line $x - y + 1 = 0$ at the point $(2, 3)$.

2. Determine the coefficients A, B, C, D so that the curve $y = Ax^3 + Bx^2 + Cx + D$ will be tangent to the line $y = 5x - 4$ at the point $(1, 1)$ and tangent to the line $y = 9x$ at the point $(-1, -9)$.

3.* Determine the coefficients A, B so that the function $y = Ax^{-1/2} + Bx^{1/2}$ has a minimum value of 6 at $x = 9$.

4. Find a relation between A, B, C given that the function $y = Ax^3 + 3Bx^2 + 3Cx$ has a critical point in common with its derivative.

Test the following functions for extreme values.

5.* $f(x) = \dfrac{x^2 + x + 4}{x^2 + 2x + 4}$.

7.* $f(x) = \dfrac{(x - 1)(2 - x)}{x^2}$.

6. $f(x) = \dfrac{1}{x} + \dfrac{1}{1 - x}$.

8. $f(x) = \dfrac{x^2}{x^2 + a^2}$.

9.* If three sides of a trapezoid are each 10 inches long, how long must the fourth side be if the area is a maximum?

10. A rectangular box with a square base and an open top is to be made. Find the volume of the largest box that can be made from 1200 sq ft of material.

11.* A point moves along the parabola $y^2 = 12x$ in such a way that its x-coordinate increases uniformly at the rate of 2 in. per second. At what point do the x-coordinate and the y-coordinate increase at the same rate?

12. A circular plate of metal expands by heat so that its radius increases at the rate of 0.02 in. per second. At what rate is the surface area increasing when the radius is 2 in.?

13.* A light is hung 12 ft directly above a straight horizontal walk on which a boy 5 ft tall is walking. How fast is the boy's shadow lengthening if he is walking away from the light at the rate of 168 ft per minute?

14. Find the dimensions of the rectangular solid of maximum volume that can be cut from a solid sphere of radius r.

15.* Find the base and altitude of the isosceles triangle of minimum area that circumscribes the ellipse $b^2x^2 + a^2y^2 = a^2b^2$ and whose base is parallel to the x-axis.

16. At what point of the first quadrant on the ellipse $b^2x^2 + a^2y^2 = a^2b^2$ does the tangent form with the coordinate axes a triangle of minimum area?

17.* The diameter and altitude of a right circular cylinder are found at a certain instant to be 10 in. and 20 in. respectively. If the diameter is increasing at the rate of 1 in. per minute, what change in the altitude will keep the volume constant?

18. A steel plant is capable of producing x tons per day of low-grade steel and y tons per day of high-grade steel, where

$$y = \frac{40 - 5x}{10 - x}.$$

If the market price of low-grade steel is half that of high-grade steel, show that about $5\frac{1}{2}$ tons of low-grade steel should be produced per day for maximum receipts.

19. The total cost of producing x articles per week is $ax^2 + bx + c$ dollars and the price at which each can be sold is $p = \beta - \alpha x^2$. Show that the output for maximum profit is

$$x = \frac{\sqrt{a^2 + 3\alpha(\beta - b)} - a}{3\alpha}.$$

(Take a, b, c, α, β as positive.)

20. Given that PQ is the longest or shortest line segment that can be drawn from $P(a, b)$ to the differentiable curve

$$y = f(x), \qquad -c < x < c$$

show that PQ is perpendicular to the tangent to the curve at Q.

21.* The equation of the path of a ball is

$$y = mx - \frac{(m^2 + 1)x^2}{800},$$

where the origin is taken at the point from which the ball is thrown and m is the slope of the curve at the origin. For what value of m will the ball strike (a) at the greatest distance along the same horizontal level? (b) at the greatest height on a vertical wall 300 ft away?

22. A horizontal trough 12 ft long has a vertical cross section in the shape of a trapezoid, the bottom being 3 ft wide and the sides inclined to the vertical at an angle whose sine is $\frac{4}{5}$. Water is being poured into it at the rate of 10 cu ft per minute. How fast is the water level rising when the water is 2 ft deep?

23. In Problem 22, at what rate is the water being drawn from the trough if the level is falling 0.1 ft per minute when the water is 3 ft deep?

24.* A point P moves along the parabola $y = x^2$ so that its x-coordinate increases at the constant rate of k units per second. The projection of P on the x-axis is M. At what rate is the area of triangle OMP changing when P is at the point where $x = a$?

25.* If $y = 4x - x^3$ and x is increasing steadily at the rate of $\frac{1}{3}$ unit per second, find how fast the slope of the graph is changing at the instant when $x = 2$.

26. The sum of the surface areas of a sphere and a cube being given, show that the sum of the volumes will be least when the diameter of the sphere is equal to the edge of the cube. When will the sum of the volumes be greatest?

27.* A miner wishes to dig a tunnel from a point A to a point B 200 ft below and 600 ft to the east of A. Below the level of A it is bed rock and above A is soft earth. If the cost of tunneling through earth is $5 per linear foot and through rock $13, find the minimum cost of a tunnel.

28.* The distance between two sources of heat A and B, with intensities a and b respectively, is l. The intensity of heat at a point P between A and B is given by the formula

$$I = \frac{a}{x^2} + \frac{b}{(l - x)^2},$$

where x is the distance between P and A. For what position P will the temperature be lowest?

4

INTEGRATION

4.1 Motivation

We were led to the notion of derivative by considering a tangent problem. By considering two new problems, we will be led to the notion of integral.

An Area Problem

In Figure 4.1.1 we display a region Ω which is bounded above by the graph of a continuous function f, bounded below by the x-axis, bounded to the left by $x = a$, and bounded to the right by $x = b$.

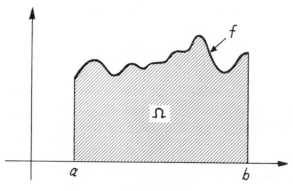

What number, if any, should be called the area of Ω? This is the question we wish to resolve.

To do this, we begin by splitting up the interval $[a, b]$ into a finite number of nonoverlapping intervals

$$[x_0, x_1], [x_1, x_2], \ldots, [x_{n-1}, x_n] \qquad \text{with } a = x_0 < x_1 < \cdots < x_n = b.$$

This breaks up Ω into n subregions:

$$\Omega_1, \Omega_2, \ldots, \Omega_n. \qquad\qquad \text{(Figure 4.1.2)}$$

We can estimate the total area of Ω by estimating the area of each subregion Ω_j and adding up the results.

Let us denote by M_j the maximum value of f on $[x_{j-1}, x_j]$ and by m_j the minimum value. Consider now the rectangles r_j and R_j of Figure 4.1.3.

Since

$$r_j \subseteq \Omega_j \subseteq R_j,$$

we must have

$$\text{area of } r_j \leq \text{area of } \Omega_j \leq \text{area of } R_j.$$

FIGURE 4.1.2

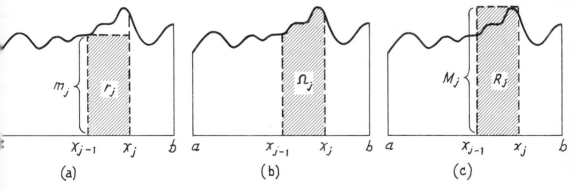

FIGURE 4.1.3

Taking the area of rectangles to be given by length times width, we obtain

$$m_j(x_j - x_{j-1}) \leq \text{area of } \Omega_j \leq M_j(x_j - x_{j-1}).$$

This is presumably true for $j = 1, j = 2, \ldots$ and so on. Adding up these results, we get on the one hand

(4.1.1) $m_1(x_1 - x_0) + \cdots + m_n(x_n - x_{n-1}) \leq \text{area of } \Omega$

and on the other hand

(4.1.2) $\text{area of } \Omega \leq M_1(x_1 - x_0) + \cdots + M_n(x_n - x_{n-1}).$

A sum of the form

$$m_1(x_1 - x_0) + \cdots + m_n(x_n - x_{n-1}) \qquad \text{(Figure 4.1.4)}$$

is called a *lower sum* for f. A sum of the form

$$M_1(x_1 - x_0) + \cdots + M_n(x_n - x_{n-1}) \qquad \text{(Figure 4.1.5)}$$

is called an *upper sum* for f.

Area of shaded region is
a lower sum for f

FIGURE 4.1.4

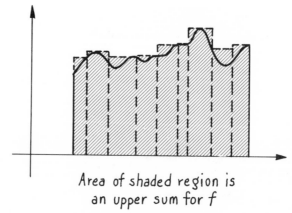

Area of shaded region is
an upper sum for f

FIGURE 4.1.5

Inequalities (4.1.1) and (4.1.2) together tell us that for a number to be a candidate for the title of area of Ω it must be greater than or equal to every lower sum for f and less than or equal to every upper sum for f. By an argument that we omit, it can be proven that there is one and only one such number. This number we call the area of Ω. □

Later we shall return to the subject of area. At this point we turn to a speed-distance problem. As you will see, this new problem can be solved by the same technique that we just applied to the area problem.

A Speed-Distance Problem

If an object moves at a constant speed for a given amount of time then the total distance traveled is given by the familiar formula

$$\text{distance} = (\text{speed}) \times (\text{time}).$$

Suppose now that during the course of the motion the speed does not remain constant but instead varies continuously. How can the total distance traveled be computed then?

To answer this question, we suppose that the motion begins at time a, ends at time b, and during the time interval $[a, b]$ the speed varies continuously.

As in the case of the area problem we begin by breaking up the interval $[a, b]$ into a finite number of nonoverlapping intervals

$$[t_0, t_1], [t_1, t_2], \ldots, [t_{n-1}, t_n].$$

On each subinterval $[t_{j-1}, t_j]$ the object attains a certain maximum speed M_j and a certain minimum speed m_j. (How do we know this?) If throughout the time interval $[t_{j-1}, t_j]$ the object were to move constantly at its minimum speed, m_j, then it would cover a distance of $m_j(t_j - t_{j-1})$ units. If instead it were to move constantly at its maximum speed, M_j, then it would cover a distance of $M_j(t_j - t_{j-1})$ units. As it is, the actual distance traveled, call it s_j, must lie somewhere in between; namely, we must have

$$m_j(t_j - t_{j-1}) \leq s_j \leq M_j(t_j - t_{j-1}).$$

The total distance traveled during the time interval $[a, b]$, call it s, must be the sum of the distances traveled during the subintervals $[t_{j-1}, t_j]$. In other words we must have

$$s = s_1 + s_2 + \cdots + s_n.$$

Since

$$m_1(t_1 - t_0) \leq s_1 \leq M_1(t_1 - t_0)$$
$$m_2(t_2 - t_1) \leq s_2 \leq M_2(t_2 - t_1)$$

$$\cdot$$
$$\cdot$$
$$\cdot$$

$$m_n(t_n - t_{n-1}) \leq s_n \leq M_n(t_n - t_{n-1}),$$

it follows by the addition of these inequalities that

$$m_1(t_1 - t_0) + \cdots + m_n(t_n - t_{n-1}) \leq s \leq M_1(t_1 - t_0) + \cdots + M_n(t_n - t_{n-1}).$$

A sum of the form

$$m_1(t_1 - t_0) + \cdots + m_n(t_n - t_{n-1})$$

is called a *lower sum* for the speed function. A sum of the form

$$M_1(t_1 - t_0) + \cdots + M_n(t_n - t_{n-1})$$

is called an *upper sum* for the speed function. The inequality we just obtained for s tells us that s must be greater than or equal to every lower sum for the speed function and less than or equal to every upper sum for the speed function. As in the case of the area problem, it turns out that there is one and only one such number and it is the total distance traveled. $\square$

4.2 Definition of the definite integral

The procedure applied to the two problems of the last section is called integration, and the numbers so obtained are called definite integrals. The object of this section is to establish these notions more precisely. At this stage we restrict ourselves to continuous functions.

> By a *partition* of $[a, b]$ we mean a finite subset of $[a, b]$ which contains the points a and b.

It is convenient to index the elements of a partition according to increasing size. Thus if we write

$$P = \{x_0, x_1, \ldots, x_n\} \text{ is a partition of } [a, b],$$

you can conclude that

$$a = x_0 < x_1 < \cdots < x_n = b.$$

Example. The sets

$$\{0, 1\}, \{0, \tfrac{1}{2}, 1\}, \{0, \tfrac{1}{4}, \tfrac{1}{2}, 1\}, \quad \text{and} \quad \{0, \tfrac{1}{4}, \tfrac{1}{3}, \tfrac{1}{2}, \tfrac{5}{8}, 1\}$$

are all partitions of the interval $[0, 1]$. $\square$

Suppose now that f is continuous on $[a, b]$. If $P = \{x_0, x_1, \ldots, x_n\}$ is a partition of $[a, b]$, then P breaks up $[a, b]$ into a finite number of nonoverlapping intervals

$$[x_0, x_1], [x_1, x_2], \ldots, [x_{n-1}, x_n].$$

On each such interval $[x_{j-1}, x_j]$ f takes on a maximum value, M_j, and a minimum value, m_j.

> The number
>
> $$U_f(P) = M_1(x_1 - x_0) + M_2(x_2 - x_1) + \cdots + M_n(x_n - x_{n-1})$$
>
> is called the *upper sum* generated for f by P and the number
>
> $$L_f(P) = m_1(x_1 - x_0) + m_2(x_2 - x_1) + \cdots + m_n(x_n - x_{n-1})$$
>
> is called the *lower sum* generated for f by P.

Example.   If $[a, b] = [0, 1]$, $P = \{0, \frac{1}{4}, \frac{1}{2}, 1\}$, and $f(x) = x^2$, then

$$U_f(P) = \tfrac{1}{16}(\tfrac{1}{4}) + \tfrac{1}{4}(\tfrac{1}{4}) + 1(\tfrac{1}{2}) = \tfrac{37}{64} \qquad \text{and} \qquad L_f(P) = 0(\tfrac{1}{4}) + \tfrac{1}{16}(\tfrac{1}{4}) + \tfrac{1}{4}(\tfrac{1}{2}) = \tfrac{9}{64}. \quad \square$$

Example.   If $[a, b] = [-1, 0]$, $P = \{-1, -\frac{1}{4}, 0\}$ and $f(x) = -(x + 1)$, then

$$U_f(P) = (0)(\tfrac{3}{4}) + (-\tfrac{3}{4})(\tfrac{1}{4}) = -\tfrac{3}{16} \qquad \text{and} \qquad L_f(P) = (-\tfrac{3}{4})(\tfrac{3}{4}) + (-1)(\tfrac{1}{4}) = -\tfrac{13}{16}. \quad \square$$

By an argument that we omit here (it appears in the Appendix at the end of the book) it can be proved that, with f continuous on $[a, b]$, there is one and only one number I which satisfies the inequality

$$L_f(P) \le I \le U_f(P) \qquad \text{for } all \text{ partitions } P \text{ of } [a, b].$$

Definition of the definite integral

This unique number I is called the *definite integral* (or more simply the *integral*) of f on $[a, b]$ and is denoted by

$$\int_a^b f(x)\, dx.$$

In the expression

$$\int_a^b f(x)\, dx$$

the letter x is a "dummy variable;" that is, it may be replaced by any other letter not already engaged. Thus, for example, there is no difference between

$$\int_a^b f(x)\, dx, \qquad \int_a^b f(t)\, dt, \qquad \text{and} \qquad \int_a^b f(z)\, dz.$$

All of these mean the definite integral of f on $[a, b]$. Section 4.1 gives two immediate applications of the definite integral:

I   If f is nonnegative on $[a, b]$, then the area below the graph of f is given by the formula

$$A = \int_a^b f(x)\, dx.$$

II   If $|v(t)|$ gives the speed of an object at time t, then

$$s = \int_a^b |v(t)|\, dt$$

gives the distance traveled from time a to time b.

We will come back to these ideas later. Right now we carry out some simple computations.

Example.   If $f(x) = \alpha$ for all x in $[a, b]$, then

$$\int_a^b f(x)\, dx = \alpha(b - a).$$

To see this, we take $P = \{x_0, x_1, \ldots, x_n\}$ as an arbitrary partition of $[a, b]$. Since on each subinterval $[x_{j-1}, x_j]$ f has the constant value α, we see that M_j and m_j are both α. Thus

$$U_f(P) = \alpha(x_1 - x_0) + \alpha(x_2 - x_1) + \cdots + \alpha(x_n - x_{n-1})$$
$$= \alpha[(x_1 - x_0) + (x_2 - x_1) + \cdots + (x_n - x_{n-1})] = \alpha(b - a),$$

and, similarly,

$$L_f(P) = \alpha(b - a).$$

Since

$$L_f(P) \leq \alpha(b - a) \leq U_f(P)$$

for all partitions P of $[a, b]$, we do find that

$$\int_a^b f(x)\, dx = \alpha(b - a). \quad \square$$

The result of this last example can be written more simply as

$$\int_a^b \alpha\, dx = \alpha(b - a).$$

If $\alpha > 0$ then the region below the graph is simply a rectangle of height α erected on the interval $[a, b]$. (Figure 4.2.1.) The integral gives the area of the rectangle.

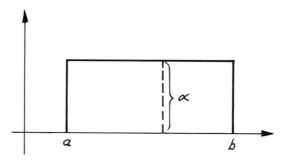

FIGURE 4.2.1

Example.

$$\int_a^b x\, dx = \frac{b^2 - a^2}{2}.$$

To see this, we take $P = \{x_0, x_1, \ldots, x_n\}$ as an arbitrary partition of $[a, b]$. On each subinterval $[x_{j-1}, x_j]$ the function

$$f(x) = x$$

has a maximum

$$M_j = x_j$$

and a minimum

$$m_j = x_{j-1}.$$

It follows that

$$U_f(P) = x_1(x_1 - x_0) + x_2(x_2 - x_1) + \cdots + x_n(x_n - x_{n-1})$$

and

$$L_f(P) = x_0(x_1 - x_0) + x_1(x_2 - x_1) + \cdots + x_{n-1}(x_n - x_{n-1}).$$

For each index j,

$$x_{j-1} \leq \frac{x_j + x_{j-1}}{2} \leq x_j,$$

and therefore

$$L_f(P) \leq \frac{x_1 + x_0}{2}(x_1 - x_0) + \frac{x_2 + x_1}{2}(x_2 - x_1) + \cdots + \frac{x_n + x_{n-1}}{2}(x_n - x_{n-1}) \leq U_f(P).$$

Since the middle expression can be rewritten as

$$\frac{x_1^2 - x_0^2}{2} + \frac{x_2^2 - x_1^2}{2} + \cdots + \frac{x_n^2 - x_{n-1}^2}{2} = \frac{x_n^2 - x_0^2}{2} = \frac{b^2 - a^2}{2},$$

we do have

$$L_f(P) \leq \frac{b^2 - a^2}{2} \leq U_f(P).$$

Since P was chosen arbitrarily, we can conclude that this inequality holds for all partitions P of $[a, b]$. It follows therefore that

$$\int_a^b x\, dx = \frac{b^2 - a^2}{2}. \quad \square$$

If the interval $[a, b]$ lies to the right of the origin then the region below the graph of

$$f(x) = x, \qquad x \text{ in } [a, b]$$

is the trapezoid of Figure 4.2.2.

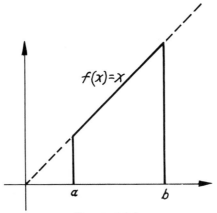

FIGURE 4.2.2

The integral

$$\int_a^b x \, dx$$

simply gives the area of that trapezoid.

Example

$$\int_0^1 x^2 \, dx = \frac{1}{3}.$$

To see this, we take $P = \{x_0, x_1, \ldots, x_n\}$ as a partition of $[0, 1]$. On each subinterval $[x_{j-1}, x_j]$ the function

$$f(x) = x^2$$

has a maximum

$$M_j = x_j^2$$

and a minimum

$$m_j = x_{j-1}^2.$$

It follows that

$$U_f(P) = x_1^2 (x_1 - x_0) + \cdots + x_n^2 (x_n - x_{n-1})$$

and

$$L_f(P) = x_0^2 (x_1 - x_0) + \cdots + x_{n-1}^2 (x_n - x_{n-1}).$$

For each index j,

$$x_{j-1}^2 \leq \frac{x_{j-1}^2 + x_{j-1}x_j + x_j^2}{3} \leq x_j^2.$$

If we now multiply this inequality by

$$x_j - x_{j-1},$$

then the middle term reduces to

$$\frac{x_j^3 - x_{j-1}^3}{3} \qquad \text{(Check this out)}$$

and consequently we get

$$x_{j-1}^2(x_j - x_{j-1}) \leq \frac{x_j^3 - x_{j-1}^3}{3} \leq x_j^2(x_j - x_{j-1}).$$

Adding up the terms on the left, we get $L_f(P)$. Adding up the middle terms, we get a collapsing sum which reduces to $\frac{1}{3}$:

$$\frac{x_1^3 - x_0^3}{3} + \frac{x_2^3 - x_1^3}{3} + \cdots + \frac{x_n^3 - x_{n-1}^3}{3} = \frac{x_n^3 - x_0^3}{3} = \frac{1^3 - 0^3}{3} = \frac{1}{3}.$$

Adding up the terms on the right, we get $U_f(P)$. It follows therefore that

$$L_f(P) \leq \tfrac{1}{3} \leq U_f(P).$$

Since P was chosen arbitrarily, we can conclude that this inequality holds for all P. It follows therefore that

$$\int_0^1 x^2 \, dx = \frac{1}{3}. \quad \square$$

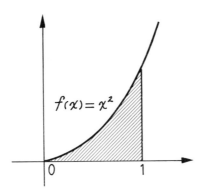

Area of shaded region $= \int_0^1 x^2 \, dx = \frac{1}{3}$

FIGURE 4.2.3

Exercises

Find $L_f(P)$ and $U_f(P)$ for each of the following:

1.* $f(x) = 2x$, $x \in [0, 1]$; $P = \{0, \tfrac{1}{4}, \tfrac{1}{2}, 1\}$.
2. $f(x) = 1 - x$, $x \in [0, 2]$; $P = \{0, \tfrac{1}{3}, \tfrac{3}{4}, 1, 2\}$.
3.* $f(x) = x^2$, $x \in [-1, 0]$; $P = \{-1, -\tfrac{1}{2}, -\tfrac{1}{4}, 0\}$.
4. $f(x) = 1 - x^2$, $x \in [0, 1]$; $P = \{0, \tfrac{1}{4}, \tfrac{1}{2}, 1\}$.
5.* $f(x) = 1 + x^3$, $x \in [0, 1]$; $P = \{0, \tfrac{1}{2}, 1\}$.

6. (a) Given that $P = \{x_0, x_1, \ldots, x_n\}$ is an arbitrary partition of $[a, b]$, find $L_f(P)$ and $U_f(P)$ if

$$f(x) = 1 + 2x.$$

   (b) Use your answers to part (a) to evaluate

$$\int_a^b (1 + 2x) \, dx.$$

7.* (a) Given that $P = \{x_0, x_1, \ldots, x_n\}$ is an arbitrary partition of $[a, b]$, find $L_f(P)$ and $U_f(P)$ if

$$f(x) = -3x.$$

(b) Use your answers to part (a) to evaluate

$$\int_a^b (-3x)\, dx.$$

8. (*Optional*) Evaluate

$$\int_0^1 x^3\, dx$$

by the methods of this section.

4.3   The function $F(x) = \int_a^x f(t)\, dt$

The evaluation of

$$\int_a^b f(x)\, dx$$

by its definition as the unique number I satisfying

$$L_f(P) \le I \le U_f(P) \qquad \text{for all partitions } P \text{ of } [a, b]$$

is at best a laborious process. Try for example to evaluate

$$\int_2^5 \left(x^3 + x^{5/2} - \frac{2x}{1 - x^2} \right) dx \qquad \text{or} \qquad \int_{-1/2}^{1/4} \frac{x}{1 - x^2}\, dx$$

in this manner. Fortunately there is another way that we can evaluate such integrals. This other way does not work for all functions but it works for many of the elementary functions. This other way of evaluating definite integrals is described in Section 4.4 in what is called the fundamental theorem of the integral calculus. Its success depends on a connection between differentiation and integration which is described in Theorem 4.3.2. Before we can prove Theorem 4.3.2 we need some other results.

Theorem

Let P and Q be partitions of the interval $[a, b]$. If $P \subseteq Q$ then

$$L_f(P) \le L_f(Q) \qquad \text{and} \qquad U_f(Q) \le U_f(P).$$

This result is obvious. By adding points to a partition we tend to make the subintervals $[x_{j-1}, x_j]$ smaller. This tends to make the minima, m_j, larger and the maxima, M_j, smaller. Thus the lower sums are made bigger and the upper sums are made smaller. This idea is illustrated in Figures 4.3.1 and 4.3.2.

The next theorem says that the integral is additive on intervals.

Theorem 4.3.1

$$\text{If } a < c < b, \quad \text{then} \quad \int_a^c f(t)\, dt + \int_c^b f(t)\, dt = \int_a^b f(t)\, dt.$$

For nonnegative functions this theorem is easily understood in terms of area. (See Figure 4.3.3.)

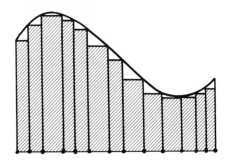

As points are added to a partition, the lower sums tend to get bigger.

FIGURE 4.3.1

 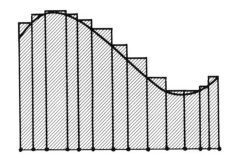

As points are added to a partition, the upper sums tend to get smaller.

FIGURE 4.3.2

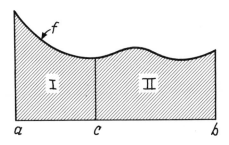

FIGURE 4.3.3

The area of part I is given by

$$\int_a^c f(t)\, dt.$$

The area of part II is given by

$$\int_c^b f(t)\, dt.$$

The area of the entire region is given by

$$\int_a^b f(t)\, dt.$$

The theorem says that

> the area of part I $+$ the area of part II $=$ the area of the entire region.

Theorem 4.3.1 can also be viewed in terms of speed and distance. With $f(t) \geq 0$, we can interpret $f(t)$ as the speed of an object at time t. With this interpretation,

$$\int_a^c f(t)\, dt = \text{distance traveled from time } a \text{ to time } c.$$

$$\int_c^b f(t)\, dt = \text{distance traveled from time } c \text{ to time } b.$$

$$\int_a^b f(t)\, dt = \text{distance traveled from time } a \text{ to time } b.$$

It is not surprising that the sum of the first two distances should equal the third.

The fact that the additivity theorem is so easy to understand does not relieve us of the necessity to prove it. Here is a proof.

PROOF OF THEOREM 4.3.1.   To prove the theorem we need only show that for each partition P of $[a, b]$

$$L_f(P) \leq \int_a^c f(t)\, dt + \int_c^b f(t)\, dt \leq U_f(P). \qquad \text{(Why?)}$$

We begin with

$$P = \{x_0, x_1, \ldots, x_n\}$$

as an arbitrary partition of $[a, b]$. Since the partition $Q = P \cup \{c\}$ contains P, we know from the first theorem that

(1) $$L_f(P) \leq L_f(Q) \qquad \text{and} \qquad U_f(Q) \leq U_f(P).$$

The sets

$$Q_1 = Q \cap [a, c] \qquad \text{and} \qquad Q_2 = Q \cap [c, b]$$

are partitions of $[a, c]$ and $[c, b]$ respectively and clearly satisfy

$$L_f(Q_1) + L_f(Q_2) = L_f(Q) \qquad \text{and} \qquad U_f(Q_1) + U_f(Q_2) = U_f(Q).$$

Since

$$L_f(Q_1) \leq \int_a^c f(t)\, dt \leq U_f(Q_1) \qquad \text{and} \qquad L_f(Q_2) \leq \int_c^b f(t)\, dt \leq U_f(Q_2),$$

we have

$$L_f(Q_1) + L_f(Q_2) \leq \int_a^c f(t)\, dt + \int_c^b f(t)\, dt \leq U_f(Q_1) + U_f(Q_2).$$

It follows that

$$L_f(Q) \leq \int_a^c f(t)\, dt + \int_c^b f(t)\, dt \leq U_f(Q)$$

and thus by (1) that

$$L_f(P) \leq \int_a^c f(t)\, dt + \int_c^b f(t)\, dt \leq U_f(P). \quad \square$$

Until now we have considered the definite integral only over an interval $[a, b]$; namely, in writing

$$\int_a^b f(t)\, dt$$

we have assumed that a was less than b. We can also integrate in the other direction; by definition

$$\boxed{\int_b^a f(t)\, dt = -\int_a^b f(t)\, dt.}$$

Moreover the integral from any point c to itself is defined to be zero:

$$\boxed{\int_c^c f(t)\, dt = 0.}$$

With these two extra conventions, it is not hard to show that, if f is continuous on an interval I, then the additivity condition

$$\int_a^c f(t)\, dt + \int_c^b f(t)\, dt = \int_a^b f(t)\, dt$$

holds for any choice of a, b, c from I, no matter what the order is.

We are now ready to establish the basic link that exists between differentiation and integration. To describe this link, we begin with a function f that is continuous on a closed interval $[a, b]$. For each x in $[a, b]$ the integral

$$\int_a^x f(t)\, dt$$

is a number and consequently we can define a function F on $[a, b]$ by setting

$$F(x) = \int_a^x f(t)\, dt.$$

Theorem 4.3.2

If f is continuous on $[a, b]$, the function F defined on $[a, b]$ by setting

$$F(x) = \int_a^x f(t)\, dt$$

is continuous on $[a, b]$, differentiable on (a, b), and satisfies

$$F'(x) = f(x) \qquad \text{for all } x \text{ in } (a, b).$$

PROOF.   We begin with x in the half-open interval $[a, b)$ and show that

$$\lim_{h \downarrow 0} \frac{F(x + h) - F(x)}{h} = f(x).$$

(For a pictorial outline of the proof in the case that f is nonnegative see Figure 4.3.4.)

If $x < x + h \le b$, then

$$F(x + h) - F(x) = \int_a^{x+h} f(t)\, dt - \int_a^x f(t)\, dt.$$

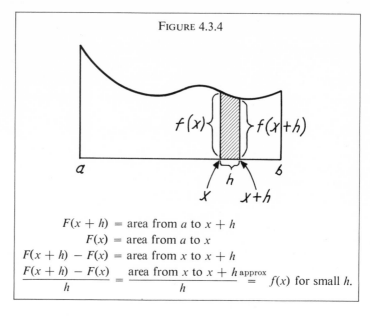

FIGURE 4.3.4

$$f(x) \qquad f(x+h)$$

$$a \qquad b$$

$$h$$

$$x \qquad x+h$$

$F(x + h) =$ area from a to $x + h$

$F(x) =$ area from a to x

$F(x + h) - F(x) =$ area from x to $x + h$

$\dfrac{F(x + h) - F(x)}{h} = \dfrac{\text{area from } x \text{ to } x + h}{h} \overset{\text{approx}}{=} f(x)$ for small h.

It follows that

$$F(x + h) - F(x) = \int_x^{x+h} f(t)\, dt. \qquad \text{(Justify this step)}$$

Now we set

$$M_h = \text{maximum value of } f \text{ on } [x, x + h]$$

and

$$m_h = \text{minimum value of } f \text{ on } [x, x + h].$$

Since

$$M_h[(x + h) - x] = M_h \cdot h$$

is an upper sum for f on $[x, x + h]$ and

$$m_h[(x + h) - x] = m_h \cdot h$$

is a lower sum for f on $[x, x + h]$, we know that

$$m_h \cdot h \le \int_x^{x+h} f(t)\, dt \le M_h \cdot h$$

and thus that

$$m_h \le \frac{F(x + h) - F(x)}{h} \le M_h.$$

Since f is continuous on $[x, x + h]$, it follows that

(1) $$\lim_{h \downarrow 0} m_h = f(x) = \lim_{h \downarrow 0} M_h$$

and thus that

(2) $$\lim_{h \downarrow 0} \frac{F(x + h) - F(x)}{h} = f(x).$$

In a similar manner, you can verify that if x is in the half-open interval $(a, b]$, then

(3) $$\lim_{h \uparrow 0} \frac{F(x + h) - F(x)}{h} = f(x).$$

If x is in the open interval (a, b), then both (2) and (3) hold, and therefore

$$F'(x) = \lim_{h \to 0} \frac{F(x + h) - F(x)}{h} = f(x).$$

This proves the differentiability condition. Applying (2) to $x = a$, we have

$$\lim_{h \downarrow 0} \frac{F(a + h) - F(a)}{h} = f(a).$$

This implies that

$$\lim_{h \downarrow 0} F(a + h) - F(a) = 0$$

and thus that

$$\lim_{h \downarrow 0} F(a + h) = F(a).$$

This shows that F is continuous from the right at a. That F is continuous from the left at b can be shown by applying (3) to $x = b$. $\square$

Exercises

1. Show that if f is continuous on the interval I then

$$\int_a^c f(t)\,dt + \int_c^b f(t)\,dt = \int_c^b f(t)\,dt$$

for every choice of a, b, c in I.
2. Show the validity of step (1) in the proof of Theorem 4.3.2.
3. Complete the proof of Theorem 4.3.2 by showing that

$$\lim_{h \uparrow 0} \frac{F(x + h) - F(x)}{h} = f(x).$$

4. Extend Theorem 4.3.2 by showing that if f is continuous in $[a, b]$ and c is any point in $[a, b]$, then

$$F(x) = \int_c^x f(t)\,dt$$

is continuous on $[a, b]$, differentiable on (a, b), and satisfies

$$F'(x) = f(x) \qquad \text{for all } x \text{ in } (a, b).$$

[HINT: $\int_c^x f(t)\,dt = \int_c^a f(t)\,dt + \int_a^x f(t)\,dt$.]

4.4   The fundamental theorem of integral calculus

Definition of Antiderivative

A function G is called an antiderivative for f on $[a, b]$ iff G is continuous on $[a, b]$ and $G'(x) = f(x)$ for all x in (a, b).

Theorem 4.3.2 says that, if f is continuous on $[a, b]$, then

$$F(x) = \int_a^x f(t)\, dt$$

is an antiderivative for f on $[a, b]$. This gives us a prescription for constructing antiderivatives. It tells us that we can construct an antiderivative for f by integrating f.

The so-called "fundamental theorem" goes the other way. It gives us a prescription, not for finding antiderivatives, but for evaluating integrals. It tells us that we can evaluate

$$\int_a^b f(t)\, dt$$

by finding an antiderivative for f.

Theorem 4.4.1   The Fundamental Theorem of Integral Calculus

Let f be continuous on $[a, b]$. If G is an antiderivative of f on $[a, b]$, then

$$\int_a^b f(t)\, dt = G(b) - G(a).$$

PROOF.   From Theorem 4.3.2 we know that the function

$$F(x) = \int_a^x f(t)\, dt$$

is an antiderivative for f on $[a, b]$. If G is also an antiderivative for f on $[a, b]$, then we have both F and G continuous on $[a, b]$ and satisfying $F'(x) = G'(x)$ for all x in (a, b). From Theorem 3.10.4 we can conclude that there exists a constant C such that

$$F(x) = G(x) + C \qquad \text{for all } x \text{ in } [a, b].$$

Since $F(a) = 0$, we must have

$$G(a) + C = 0,$$

and thus

$$C = -G(a).$$

This means that

$$F(x) = G(x) - G(a) \qquad \text{for all } x \text{ in } [a, b].$$

In particular,

$$F(b) = G(b) - G(a).$$

Since

$$F(b) = \int_a^b f(t)\, dt,$$

the theorem is proved.   □

Applying the fundamental theorem

Example. To evaluate

$$\int_a^b x \, dx,$$

we can use

$$G(x) = \frac{x^2}{2}$$

as an antiderivative. Doing so, we obtain

$$\int_a^b x \, dx = \frac{b^2}{2} - \frac{a^2}{2}. \quad \square$$

Example. More generally, to evaluate

$$\int_a^b x^n \, dx, \quad n \text{ a positive integer,}$$

we can use the antiderivative

$$G(x) = \frac{x^{n+1}}{n+1}.$$

This gives

$$\int_a^b x^n \, dx = \frac{b^{n+1}}{n+1} - \frac{a^{n+1}}{n+1}. \quad \square$$

The formula

$$\int_a^b f(x) \, dx = G(b) - G(a),$$

is so useful that we frequently write expressions of the form

$$G(b) - G(a).$$

This difference is often denoted by

$$\Big[G(x) \Big]_a^b.$$

Using this notation, we have

$$\int_a^b x^3 \, dx = \left[\frac{x^4}{4} \right]_a^b = \frac{b^4}{4} - \frac{a^4}{4}.$$

Example. For the integral

$$\int_0^1 (2x - 6x^4 + 5) \, dx$$

we choose

$$G(x) = x^2 - \frac{6}{5} x^5 + 5x$$

as an antiderivative and obtain

$$\int_0^1 (2x - 6x^4 + 5) \, dx = \left[x^2 - \frac{6}{5} x^5 + 5x \right]_0^1 = 4\frac{4}{5}. \quad \square$$

Example. To evaluate

$$\int_{-1}^{1} (x - 1)(x + 2)\,dx$$

we first carry out the indicated multiplication

$$(x - 1)(x + 2) = x^2 + x - 2.$$

It is clear that

$$G(x) = \frac{x^3}{3} + \frac{x^2}{2} - 2x$$

serves as an antiderivative. Thus

$$\int_{-1}^{1} (x - 1)(x + 2)\,dx = \left[\frac{x^3}{3} + \frac{x^2}{2} - 2x\right]_{-1}^{1} = -\frac{10}{3}. \qquad \square$$

Example. To evaluate

$$\int_{1}^{2} \frac{dt}{t^2}$$

we need a function with derivative

$$\frac{1}{t^2}.$$

Since

$$\frac{d}{dt}\left(\frac{1}{t}\right) = -\frac{1}{t^2},$$

it is obvious that

$$\frac{d}{dt}\left(-\frac{1}{t}\right) = \frac{1}{t^2}.$$

It follows that

$$\int_{1}^{2} \frac{dt}{t^2} = \left[-\frac{1}{t}\right]_{1}^{2} = \left(-\frac{1}{2}\right) - (-1) = \frac{1}{2}. \qquad \square$$

Example. To evaluate

$$\int_{4}^{9} \frac{dt}{\sqrt{t}}$$

we need a function with derivative

$$\frac{1}{\sqrt{t}}.$$

We know that

$$\frac{d}{dt}\left(\sqrt{t}\right) = \frac{1}{2\sqrt{t}}.$$

It follows that

$$\frac{d}{dt}(2\sqrt{t}) = \frac{1}{\sqrt{t}}$$

and that

$$\int_4^9 \frac{dt}{\sqrt{t}} = \left[2\sqrt{t}\right]_4^9 = 2\sqrt{9} - 2\sqrt{4} = 2. \quad \square$$

Example.   To evaluate

$$\int_1^2 \sqrt{x-1}\, dx$$

we need a function with derivative

$$\sqrt{x-1}.$$

It is not hard to see that

$$\frac{d}{dx}(x-1)^{3/2} = \frac{3}{2}(x-1)^{1/2} = \frac{3}{2}\sqrt{x-1}$$

and therefore

$$\frac{d}{dx}\left[\frac{2}{3}(x-1)^{3/2}\right] = \sqrt{x-1}.$$

This means that

$$\int_1^2 \sqrt{x-1}\, dx = \left[\frac{2}{3}(x-1)^{3/2}\right]_1^2 = \frac{2}{3}. \quad \square$$

Example.   To evaluate

$$\int_{-1}^1 x(x^2-1)^4\, dx$$

we need a function with derivative

$$x(x^2-1)^4.$$

Since

$$\frac{d}{dx}(x^2-1)^5 = 5(x^2-1)^4\frac{d}{dx}(x^2-1) = 5(x^2-1)^4 2x = 10x(x^2-1)^4,$$

we have

$$\frac{d}{dx}\left[\frac{1}{10}(x^2-1)^5\right] = x(x^2-1)^4.$$

It follows that

$$\int_{-1}^1 x(x^2-1)^4\, dx = \left[\frac{1}{10}(x^2-1)^5\right]_{-1}^1 = 0. \quad \square$$

Example. To evaluate

$$\int_0^1 20x^2(x^3 - 1)^{1/3}\, dx$$

we need a function with derivative

$$20x^2(x^3 - 1)^{1/3}.$$

It is not hard to see that

$$\frac{d}{dx}(x^3 - 1)^{4/3} = \frac{4}{3}(x^3 - 1)^{1/3}3x^2 = 4x^2(x^3 - 1)^{1/3}$$

and therefore

$$\frac{d}{dx}[5(x^3 - 1)^{4/3}] = 20x^2(x^3 - 1)^{1/3}.$$

This gives

$$\int_0^1 20x^2(x^3 - 1)^{1/3}\, dx = \left[5(x^3 - 1)^{4/3}\right]_0^1 = 5(0) - 5(-1)^{4/3} = -5. \quad \square$$

Exercises

Evaluate the following integrals by applying the fundamental theorem.

1.* $\int_0^1 (2x - 3)\, dx.$

2. $\int_0^1 (3x - 2)\, dx.$

3.* $\int_{-1}^0 5x^4\, dx.$

4. $\int_1^2 (2x - x^2)\, dx.$

5.* $\int_1^4 \sqrt{x}\, dx.$

6. $\int_0^4 \sqrt{x}\, dx.$

7.* $\int_1^5 2\sqrt{x - 1}\, dx.$

8. $\int_{-2}^0 (x + 1)(x - 1)\, dx.$

9.* $\int_1^2 \left(\frac{3}{x^3} + 5x\right) dx.$

10. $\int_{-2}^0 \frac{dx}{(x - 1)^2}.$

11.* $\int_0^1 (x^{3/2} - x^{1/2})\, dx.$

12. $\int_0^1 (x^{3/4} + 2x^{1/2})\, dx.$

13.* $\int_0^1 (x + 1)^{17}\, dx.$

14. $\int_{-1}^1 (x + 2)^2\, dx.$

15.* $\int_1^2 \frac{6 - t}{t^3}\, dt.$

16. $\int_1^2 \frac{2 + t}{t^3}\, dt.$

17.* $\int_0^3 \sqrt{2(t + 1)}\, dt.$

18. $\int_1^3 \left(x^2 + \frac{1}{x^2}\right) dx.$

19.* $\int_0^1 x^2(x - 1)\, dx.$

20. $\int_1^2 \frac{3x^2}{(x^3 + 1)^2}\, dx.$

21.* $\int_0^{1/2} 4x\,(1 - x^2)^{-3}\, dx.$

22. $\int_{-2}^1 \frac{dx}{\sqrt{2 - x}}.$

23.* $\int_0^1 x(x^2 - 1)^4\, dx.$

24. $\int_{-a}^a x(x^2 - a^2)^4\, dx.$

4.5   Problems

Problem.   Find the area of the region bounded above by the curve $y = -x^2 + 4$ and below by the x-axis.

SOLUTION.   The curve intersects the x-axis at $x = -2$ and $x = 2$. The region in question is depicted in Figure 4.5.1.

The area is given by the integral

$$\int_{-2}^{2} (-x^2 + 4)\, dx = \left[-\frac{x^3}{3} + 4x \right]_{-2}^{2} = \frac{32}{3} \cdot \quad \square$$

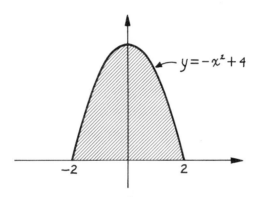

FIGURE 4.5.1

Problem.   Find the area of the crescent depicted in Figure 4.5.2.

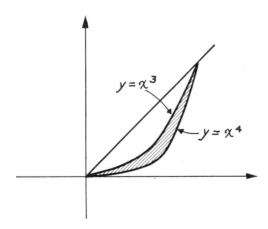

FIGURE 4.5.2

SOLUTION.   The two curves meet at $x = 0$ and at $x = 1$. We can obtain the area of the crescent by finding the area below

$$y = x^3,$$

and subtracting from it the area below

$$y = x^4.$$

This gives

$$A = \int_0^1 x^3\, dx - \int_0^1 x^4\, dx = \left[\frac{x^4}{4}\right]_0^1 - \left[\frac{x^5}{5}\right]_0^1 = \frac{1}{4} - \frac{1}{5} = \frac{1}{20} \cdot \quad \square$$

The fundamental theorem gives

$$f(b) - f(a) = \int_a^b f'(x)\, dx$$

and thus

$$f(b) = f(a) + \int_a^b f'(x)\, dx.$$

Problem.   Find $f(3)$ given that $f(0) = 1$ and $f'(x) = x\sqrt{x^2 + 1}$.

SOLUTION.   Here

$$f(3) = f(0) + \int_0^3 f'(x)\, dx.$$

so that

$$f(3) = 1 + \int_0^3 x\sqrt{x^2 + 1}\, dx.$$

To evaluate the integral we note that

$$\frac{d}{dx}(x^2 + 1)^{3/2} = \frac{3}{2}(x^2 + 1)^{1/2} 2x = 3x\sqrt{x^2 + 1}$$

and therefore

$$\frac{d}{dx}\left[\frac{1}{3}(x^2 + 1)^{3/2}\right] = x\sqrt{x^2 + 1}.$$

This gives

$$\int_0^3 x\sqrt{x^2 + 1}\, dx = \left[\frac{1}{3}(x^2 + 1)^{3/2}\right]_0^3 = \frac{1}{3}(10^{3/2} - 1).$$

It follows that

$$f(3) = 1 + \frac{1}{3}(10^{3/2} - 1) = \frac{2}{3}(5\sqrt{10} + 1). \quad \square$$

Problem. An object moves along a coordinate line with velocity

$$v(t) = (1 - t)(2 - t) \text{ units/sec.}$$

Its initial position (its position at time $t = 0$) is 2 units to the right of the origin.
  (a) Find the position of the object 4 seconds later.
  (b) Find the total distance traveled by the object during those first 4 seconds.

SOLUTION.   (a) Let $x(t)$ be the position (coordinate) of the object at time t. Then

$$x'(t) = v(t).$$

This means that the position function is an antiderivative for the velocity function. Consequently

$$x(4) - x(0) = \int_0^4 v(t) \, dt.$$

Since the initial position of the object is 2 units to the right of the origin, we have

$$x(0) = 2.$$

From

$$v(t) = (1 - t)(2 - t) = 2 - 3t + t^2,$$

we see that

$$\int_0^4 v(t) \, dt = \int_0^4 (2 - 3t + t^2) \, dt = \left[2t - \tfrac{3}{2}t^2 + \tfrac{1}{3}t^3 \right]_0^4 = 5\tfrac{1}{3}.$$

From

$$x(0) = 2 \quad \text{together with} \quad \int_0^4 v(t) \, dt = 5\tfrac{1}{3},$$

we have

$$x(4) = x(0) + \int_0^4 v(t) \, dt = 2 + 5\tfrac{1}{3} = 7\tfrac{1}{3}.$$

At the end of 4 seconds the object ends up $7\tfrac{1}{3}$ units to the right of the origin.
  (b) The total distance traveled by the object during the first 4 seconds is given by the integral

$$s = \int_0^4 |v(t)| \, dt.$$

In this instance

$$s = \int_0^4 |(1 - t)(2 - t)| \, dt.$$

The easiest way to evaluate this integral is to first remove the absolute-value signs. Since

$$|(1 - t)(2 - t)| = \begin{cases} 2 - 3t + t^2, & t \le 1 \\ -2 + 3t - t^2, & 1 \le t \le 2 , \\ 2 - 3t + t^2, & 2 \le t \end{cases}$$

we have

$$s = \int_0^4 |(1-t)(2-t)|\, dt$$

$$= \int_0^1 (2-3t+t^2)\, dt + \int_1^2 (-2+3t-t^2)\, dt + \int_2^4 (2-3t+t^2)\, dt$$

$$= \left[2t - \tfrac{3}{2}t^2 + \tfrac{1}{3}t^3\right]_0^1 + \left[-2t + \tfrac{3}{2}t^2 - \tfrac{1}{3}t^3\right]_1^2 + \left[2t - \tfrac{3}{2}t^2 + \tfrac{1}{3}t^3\right]_2^4.$$

$$= 5\tfrac{2}{3}.$$

The total distance is $5\tfrac{2}{3}$ units.   ☐

Exercises

1.* In the motion we just discussed an object started out 2 units to the right of the origin. After traveling a distance of $5\tfrac{2}{3}$ units it ended up only $7\tfrac{1}{3}$ units to the right of the origin. Explain how this is possible.

In exercises 2–8 find the area below the graph.

2. $f(x) = 2 + x^3$, $x \in [0, 1]$.

3.* $f(x) = \dfrac{1}{(x+1)^2}$, $x \in [0, 2]$.

4. $f(x) = \sqrt{x+1}$, $x \in [3, 8]$.

5.* $f(x) = \dfrac{1}{2\sqrt{x+1}}$, $x \in [0, 8]$.

6. $f(x) = x\sqrt{2x^2+1}$, $x \in [0, 2]$.

7.* $f(x) = \dfrac{x}{(2x^2+1)^2}$, $x \in [0, 2]$.

8. $f(x) = (2x^2+1)^2$, $x \in [0, 1]$.

9.* Sketch the region which is bounded above by $y = \sqrt{x}$ and below by $y = x^2$. Find the area of this region.

10. Sketch the region which is bounded above by $y = -x^2 + 5$ and below by $y = -x + 3$. Find the area of this region.

11.* Sketch the region which is bounded above by $y = -x^2 + 8$ and below by $y = x^2$. Find the area of this region.

12. Find the area of that portion of the first quadrant which is bounded above by $y = 2x$ and below by $y = x\sqrt{3x^2+1}$.

13.* Find $f(2)$ given that

$$f(0) = 0 \quad \text{and} \quad f'(x) = \frac{x}{\sqrt{4x^2+9}}.$$

14. Find $f(-2)$ given that

$$f(0) = 9 \quad \text{and} \quad f'(x) = \frac{x}{(4x^2+9)^2}.$$

15.* An object moves along a coordinate line with velocity

$$v(t) = t(1-t) \text{ units/sec.}$$

Its initial position (its position at time $t = 0$) is 2 units to the left of the origin.
(a) Find the position of the object 10 seconds later.
(b) Find the total distance traveled by the object during the first 10 seconds.

16. An object moves along a coordinate line with acceleration

$$a(t) = \frac{1}{\sqrt{t+1}} \text{ units/sec}^2.$$

(a) Find its velocity at time t_0 given that its initial velocity is 1 unit/sec.
(b) Find the position of the object at time t_0 given that its initial velocity is 1 unit/sec. and its initial position is the origin.

17.* A point moves along the plane in such a manner that its x-coordinate is changing at the rate of $t/(t^2 + 1)^2$ units/sec and its y-coordinate is changing at the rate of $\sqrt{t}$ units/sec. Find the position of the point one second after the motion starts if the initial position is the point $P(x_0, y_0)$.

18. An automobile with varying velocity $v(t)$ moves in a fixed direction for 5 minutes and covers a distance of 4 miles. What theorem would you invoke to argue that for at least one instant the speedometer must have read 48 mph?

4.6 Some properties of the integral

In this section we feature some of the important properties of the integral. The first seven of these are easily derived, either from the definition of the integral or from the fundamental theorem (4.4.1). The proofs are left to you. You can assume in each case that all the functions involved are continuous.

I Constants may be factored through the integral sign:

$$\boxed{\int_a^b \alpha f(x)\, dx = \alpha \int_a^b f(x)\, dx.}$$

Example

$$\int_0^{10} \frac{3(x-5)}{7}\, dx = \frac{3}{7} \int_0^{10} (x-5)\, dx = \frac{3}{7} \left[\frac{(x-5)^2}{2} \right]_0^{10} = 0. \quad \square$$

Example

$$\int_0^1 -(x^2+1)^4 x\, dx = -\frac{1}{2} \int_0^1 2x(x^2+1)^4\, dx$$

$$= -\frac{1}{2} \left[\frac{(x^2+1)^5}{5} \right]_0^1 = -\frac{1}{2} \left(\frac{32}{5} - \frac{1}{5} \right) = -\frac{31}{10}. \quad \square$$

II The integral of a sum is the sum of the integrals:

$$\boxed{\int_a^b [f(x) + g(x)]\, dx = \int_a^b f(x)\, dx + \int_a^b g(x)\, dx.}$$

Example

$$\int_1^2 \left[(x-1)^2 + \frac{1}{(x+2)^2} \right] dx = \int_1^2 (x-1)^2 \, dx + \int_1^2 \frac{dx}{(x+2)^2}$$

$$= \left[\frac{(x-1)^3}{3} \right]_1^2 + \left[-(x+2)^{-1} \right]_1^2 = \frac{1}{3} - \frac{1}{4} + \frac{1}{3} = \frac{5}{12}. \quad \square$$

Combining I and II, the next property becomes obvious.

III   The integral of a linear combination is the linear combination of the integrals:

$$\int_a^b [\alpha f(x) + \beta g(x)] \, dx = \alpha \int_a^b f(x) \, dx + \beta \int_a^b g(x) \, dx.$$

Example

$$\int_2^{5/2} \left[\frac{3}{(x-1)^2} - 4x \right] dx$$

$$= 3 \int_2^{5/2} \frac{dx}{(x-1)^2} - 2 \int_2^{5/2} 2x \, dx = 3 \left[-(x-1)^{-1} \right]_2^{5/2} - 2 \left[x^2 \right]_2^{5/2}$$

$$= 3 \left(-\frac{2}{3} + 1 \right) - 2 \left(\frac{25}{4} - 4 \right) = -\frac{7}{2}. \quad \square$$

IV   The integral of a nonnegative function is nonnegative:

$$\text{if } f(x) \geq 0 \text{ on } [a, b], \qquad \text{then } \int_a^b f(x) \, dx \geq 0.$$

The integral of a positive function is positive:

$$\text{if } f(x) > 0 \text{ on } [a, b], \qquad \text{then } \int_a^b f(x) \, dx > 0.$$

The next property is an immediate consequence of properties III and IV.

V   The integral is order preserving:

$$\text{if } f(x) \leq g(x) \text{ on } [a, b], \qquad \text{then } \int_a^b f(x) \, dx \leq \int_a^b g(x) \, dx$$

and

$$\text{if } f(x) < g(x) \text{ on } [a, b], \qquad \text{then } \int_a^b f(x) \, dx < \int_a^b g(x) \, dx.$$

VI   Just as the absolute value of a sum is less than or equal to the sum of the absolute values,

$$|x_1 + x_2 + \cdots + x_n| \leq |x_1| + |x_2| + \cdots + |x_n|,$$

the absolute value of an integral is less than or equal to the integral of the absolute value:

$$\left| \int_a^b f(x) \, dx \right| \leq \int_a^b |f(x)| \, dx.$$

[HINT FOR PROOF OF VI: Show that

$$\int_a^b f(x)\, dx \quad\text{and}\quad -\int_a^b f(x)\, dx$$

are both less than or equal to $\int_a^b |f(x)|\, dx$.]

The next property is one with which you are already familiar.

VII   If m is the minimum value of f on $[a, b]$ and M is the maximum then

$$\boxed{m(b - a) \le \int_a^b f(x)\, dx \le M(b - a).}$$

We come now to a generalization of Theorem 4.3.2. The importance of it will become apparent in chapter 5.

VIII   If g is differentiable (and f is continuous), the function

$$\boxed{H(x) = \int_a^{g(x)} f(t)\, dt \quad \text{has derivative} \quad H'(x) = f(g(x))g'(x).}$$

PROOF.   The key here is to recognize that H is the composition of differentiable functions; namely,

$$H(x) = F(g(x)), \quad \text{where} \quad F(x) = \int_a^x f(t)\, dt.$$

Since

$$H'(x) = F'(g(x))g'(x) \quad \text{and} \quad F'(x) = f(x),$$

we have

$$H'(x) = f(g(x))g'(x). \quad \square$$

Examples

If $H(x) = \int_0^{x^2+1} t^2\, dt,$ then $H'(x) = (x^2 + 1)^2 2x.$ $\square$

If $H(x) = \int_0^{x^3} \dfrac{dt}{t + 1},$ then $H'(x) = \dfrac{3x^2}{x^3 + 1} \cdot$ $\square$

If $H(x) = \int_0^{x^3} \dfrac{dt}{\sqrt{1 + t^2}},$ then $H'(x) = \dfrac{3x^2}{\sqrt{1 + x^6}} \cdot \square$

In the first example, we can also first carry out the integration and then differentiate:

$$H(x) = \int_0^{x^2+1} t^2\, dt = \left[\frac{t^3}{3}\right]_0^{x^2+1} = \frac{(x^2 + 1)^3}{3}, \qquad H'(x) = \frac{3(x^2 + 1)^2 2x}{3} = (x^2 + 1)^2 2x.$$

Exercises

Evaluate.

1.* $\displaystyle\int_{-1}^{-1/2} \frac{dx}{x^2}$.

2. $\displaystyle\int_{0}^{\sqrt{2}} (t^3 - t)\, dt$.

3.* $\displaystyle\int_{-3}^{3} 5|x + 2|\, dx$.

4. $\displaystyle\int_{1}^{2} \frac{x^4 - 4x}{x^3}\, dx$.

5.* $\displaystyle\int_{0}^{1} \frac{6\sqrt{x + 1}}{5}\, dx$.

6. $\displaystyle\int_{0}^{1} |3x - 1|\, dx$.

7.* $\displaystyle\int_{-1}^{1} (|2x| - 2x)\, dx$.

8. $\displaystyle\int_{x}^{x^2} (1 + t)^4\, dt$.

9.* $\displaystyle\int_{-2}^{0} |x^2 - 1|\, dx$.

10. $\displaystyle\int_{0}^{-1} 5x(1 + x^2)^4\, dx$.

11.* $\displaystyle\int_{0}^{-2} |x^2 - 1|\, dx$.

12. $\displaystyle\int_{0}^{1} [(x - 1)(x - 2)(x - 3)]\, dx$.

13.* $\displaystyle\int_{1}^{2} (6 - x)^{-3}\, dx$.

14. $\displaystyle\int_{-1}^{1} \frac{x}{(1 + x^2)^4}\, dx$.

15.* $\displaystyle\int_{0}^{x} xt\, dt$.

16. $\displaystyle\int_{t}^{0} (t + 1)x^2\, dx$.

For what number (or numbers) α do we have the following?

17.* $\displaystyle\int_{0}^{1} (t - \alpha t^2)\, dt = 0$.

18. $\displaystyle\int_{-1}^{1} (t + \alpha t^2)\, dt = 0$.

Find $H'(x)$.

19.* $\displaystyle H(x) = \int_{1}^{x^2} \frac{dt}{t}$.

20. $\displaystyle H(x) = \int_{1}^{1+x^2} \frac{dt}{\sqrt{2t + 5}}$.

21.* $\displaystyle H(x) = \int_{1}^{\sqrt{x}} \frac{dt}{t}$.

22. $\displaystyle H(x) = \int_{x}^{x^2} \frac{dt}{t}$.

23.* $\displaystyle H(x) = \int_{x}^{a} f(t)\, dt$.

24. $\displaystyle H(x) = \int_{x}^{x^2} f(t)\, dt$.

25.* $\displaystyle H(x) = \int_{0}^{x} f(x)\, dx$.

26. $\displaystyle H(x) = \int_{0}^{x} xf(t)\, dt$.

27. Derive properties I–VI.

28. (*Optional*) Prove that if f is continuous on $[a, b]$ and

$$\int_{a}^{b} |f(x)|\, dx = 0,$$

then

$$f(x) = 0 \qquad \text{for all } x \text{ in } [a, b].$$

4.7 The indefinite integral notation

If F is an antiderivative for f on $[a, b]$, then we have

$$\int_{a}^{b} f(x)\, dx = \Big[F(x)\Big]_{a}^{b}.$$

The result is obviously unchanged if we replace $F(x)$ by $F(x) + C$, where C is an arbitrary constant:

$$\int_{a}^{b} f(x)\, dx = \Big[F(x) + C\Big]_{a}^{b}.$$

If we have no particular interest in the interval $[a, b]$, but wish instead to emphasize that F is an antiderivative for f on *some* interval, then we can omit the a and the b and simply write

$$\int f(x)\, dx = F(x) + C.$$

Antiderivatives expressed in this manner are called *indefinite integrals*.

Examples

$$\int x^n \, dx = \frac{x^{n+1}}{n+1} + C \qquad \text{for } n \neq -1,$$

$$\int \sqrt{t}\, dt = \frac{2}{3} t^{3/2} + C,$$

$$\int \frac{-s}{\sqrt{1-s^2}}\, ds = \sqrt{1-s^2} + C. \quad \square$$

Exercises

Find the following indefinite integrals.

1.* $\displaystyle \int \frac{dx}{x^4}.$

2. $\displaystyle \int (x-1)^6 \, dx.$

3.* $\displaystyle \int \sqrt{1+x}\, dx.$

4. $\displaystyle \int t\sqrt{1+t^2}\, dt.$

5.* $\displaystyle \int \frac{dx}{\sqrt{1+x}}.$

6. $\displaystyle \int \frac{s}{\sqrt{1+s^2}}\, ds.$

7.* $\displaystyle \int \frac{x}{(1+x^2)^2}\, dx.$

8. $\displaystyle \int \frac{x}{(1-x^2)^2}\, dx.$

9.* $\displaystyle \int \left(\sqrt{x} - \frac{1}{\sqrt{x}} \right) dx.$

10. $\displaystyle \int x(\sqrt{x}-1)\, dx.$

11.* $\displaystyle \int \sqrt{x}(x-1)\, dx.$

12. $\displaystyle \int x^{-1/3}\, (x^{2/3}-1)^2 \, dx.$

13.* $\displaystyle \int \left(\frac{x^3-1}{x^2} \right) dx.$

14. $\displaystyle \int (\sqrt{x+a} - \sqrt{x+b})\, dx.$

15.* $\displaystyle \int (x-a)(x-b)\, dx.$

16. $\displaystyle \int (x^2-a)(x^2-b)\, dx.$

17.* $\displaystyle \int [f(x)g'(x) + f'(x)g(x)]\, dx.$

18. $\displaystyle \int \frac{g'(x)}{[g(x)]^2}\, dx.$

19.* $\displaystyle \int \frac{f(x)f'(x)}{\sqrt{1+[f(x)]^2}}\, dx.$

20. $\displaystyle \int \frac{g(x)f'(x) - g'(x)f(x)}{[g(x)]^2}\, dx.$

21. Compare

$$\frac{d}{dx}\left[\int f(x)dx \right] \quad \text{with} \quad \int \frac{d}{dx}\, [f(x)]\, dx.$$

5

THE LOGARITHM AND EXPONENTIAL FUNCTIONS

5.1   The logarithm function

If n is an integer different from -1, we can solve the equation

$$f'(x) = x^n$$

by setting

$$f(x) = \frac{x^{n+1}}{n+1} + C.$$

What if $n = -1$? How can we solve the equation

$$f'(x) = x^{-1} = \frac{1}{x}\, ?$$

In a sense you already know the answer. By Theorem 4.3.2, extended by Exercise 4 of Section 4, you know that the function

$$f(x) = \int_c^x \frac{dt}{t}$$

has the desired derivative — provided that $1/t$ is continuous on the interval joining c to x. Since $1/t$ is infinite at $t = 0$, we must exclude 0 from the interval of integration. One way to do this is to set $c = 1$ and restrict ourselves to $x > 0$. By doing so, we obtain the function

$$l(x) = \int_1^x \frac{dt}{t}, \qquad x > 0.$$

Why we choose $c = 1$ will become apparent later.

Obvious properties of the function l:

(1) $l'(x) = 1/x$ for all $x > 0$, and thus l is increasing on $(0, \infty)$.

(2) l is continuous on $(0, \infty)$ since it is there differentiable.

(3) $l(x) < 0$ if $0 < x < 1$; $l(1) = 0$; $l(x) > 0$ if $x > 1$.

(4) For $x > 1$ $l(x)$ gives the area below the graph of the function

$$g(t) = \frac{1}{t}, \qquad 1 \le t \le x. \qquad\qquad \text{(Figure 5.1.1)}$$

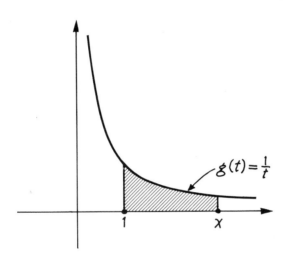

FIGURE 5.1.1

Not so obvious is the fact that l has a remarkable algebraic property.

Theorem 5.1.1

If a and b are positive, then

$$l(ab) = l(a) + l(b).$$

PROOF. Since

$$l(ab) = \int_1^{ab} \frac{dt}{t} = \int_1^a \frac{dt}{t} + \int_a^{ab} \frac{dt}{t} = l(a) + \int_a^{ab} \frac{dt}{t},$$

it is enough to show that

$$\int_a^{ab} \frac{dt}{t} = l(b).$$

To do this, we note that the function

$$H(x) = \int_a^{ax} \frac{dt}{t} \qquad \text{for } x > 0$$

satisfies

$$H'(x) = \frac{a}{ax} = \frac{1}{x} \qquad \text{for } x > 0. \quad \text{(Property VIII, Section 4.6)}$$

This means that

$$H'(x) = l'(x) \qquad \text{for } x > 0.$$

Since

$$H(1) = \int_a^a \frac{dt}{t} = 0 = l(1),$$

we can conclude from Theorem 3.10.4 that

$$H(x) = l(x) \qquad \text{for all } x > 0.$$

In particular, we have $H(b) = l(b)$ and thus

$$\int_a^{ab} \frac{dt}{t} = l(b). \quad \square$$

By now the function l should begin to look like a logarithm. The next theorem should reinforce this idea.

Theorem 5.1.2

For each positive number a and each rational number p/q

$$l(a^{p/q}) = \frac{p}{q} l(a).$$

PROOF.   We show first that for all nonnegative integers n

$$l(a^n) = nl(a).$$

If n is 0 or 1, the result is trivial. Let us suppose that the result holds for $n = k$. Now

$$l(a^{k+1}) = l(a^k \cdot a) = l(a^k) + l(a),$$

the second equality holding by Theorem 5.1.1. By our inductive assumption

$$l(a^k) = kl(a).$$

Thus

$$l(a^{k+1}) = kl(a) + l(a) = (k + 1)l(a),$$

which means that the result holds for $n = k + 1$. This shows that

$$l(a^n) = nl(a) \qquad \text{for all nonnegative integers } n.$$

Since

$$0 = l(1) = l(a \cdot a^{-1}) = l(a) + l(a^{-1}),$$

we see that

$$l(a^{-1}) = -l(a).$$

If n is a positive integer, we have

$$l(a^{-n}) = -l(a^n) = -nl(a),$$

so that the formula holds for all negative integers.

Let q be a positive integer. Now

$$l(a) = l([a^{1/q}]^q) = ql(a^{1/q}).$$

Dividing by q, we obtain

$$l(a^{1/q}) = \frac{1}{q} l(a).$$

Let us now take p/q as an arbitrary rational number. We can assume that q is positive and absorb the sign in p. Since p is an integer, it follows that

$$l(a^{p/q}) = l([a^{1/q}]^p) = pl(a^{1/q}).$$

Since

$$l(a^{1/q}) = \frac{1}{q} l(a),$$

we can finally conclude that

$$l(a^{p/q}) = \frac{p}{q} l(a). \quad \square$$

The domain of l is $(0, \infty)$. What is the range of l?

Theorem 5.1.3

The range of l is $(-\infty, \infty)$.

PROOF. Since l is continuous on $(0, \infty)$, we know from the intermediate-value theorem that it "skips" no values. Thus, its range is an interval. To show that the interval is $(-\infty, \infty)$, we need only show that it is unbounded above and unbounded below. We can do this by taking M as an arbitrary positive number and showing that l takes on values greater than M and values less than $-M$.

Since

$$l(2) = \int_1^2 \frac{dt}{t}$$

is positive (explain), we know that some positive multiple of $l(2)$ must be greater than M; namely, we know that there exists a positive integer n such that

$$nl(2) > M.$$

Multiplying this equation by -1 we have

$$-nl(2) < -M.$$

Since

$$nl(2) = l(2^n) \quad \text{and} \quad -nl(2) = l(2^{-n})$$

we have

$$l(2^n) > M \quad \text{and} \quad l(2^{-n}) < -M.$$

This proves the unboundedness. □

Since the range of l is $(-\infty, \infty)$ and l is increasing, we know that l takes on every value and it does so only once. In particular, there is one and only one number at which the function l takes on the value 1. *This unique number is denoted by the letter e* (after Leonard Euler, 1707–1783).† With

$$l(e) = 1$$

we have (by Theorem 5.1.2)

$$l(e^{p/q}) = \frac{p}{q} \quad \text{for each rational number } \frac{p}{q}.$$

We come now to the irrational powers of e. Rational powers of e already have an established meaning: by $e^{p/q}$ we mean the qth root of e raised to the pth power. But what is meant by $e^{\sqrt{2}}$ or e^{π}?

Definition

If y is irrational, then e^y is that unique number which satisfies

$$l(e^y) = y.$$

The advantage of this definition will become apparent in the next section. Right now we content ourselves by observing that, as a consequence of this definition, we have

$$l(e^x) = x \quad \text{for all real numbers } x.$$

Because of this relation we call l the *natural logarithm* or the *logarithm* to the base e and write

$$l(x) = \log x = \log_e x.‡$$

---

† The problem of evaluating e is taken up in Section 5.3. There we show that e lies between 2.71 and 2.73.
‡ What is so natural about this logarithm, in contrast to the others, is made clear in Section 5.3. Another common notation for $\log x$ is $\ln x$.

Summary

(1) For $x > 0$ the number

$$\log (x) = \int_1^x \frac{dt}{t}$$

is called the natural logarithm of x.

(2) For $x > 0$ and $y > 0$

$$\log xy = \log x + \log y$$

and

$$\log \frac{x}{y} = \log x - \log y. \qquad \text{(Check this out)}$$

(3) For $x > 0$ and p/q rational

$$\log (x^{p/q}) = \frac{p}{q} \log x.$$

(4) The number e is defined as the number which has natural logarithm 1:

$$\log e = 1.$$

(5) For y irrational, e^y is defined as the number with natural logarithm y:

$$\log (e^y) = y.$$

(6) For all real x,

$$\log (e^x) = x.$$

The Graph of The Logarithm Function

We know that the logarithm is defined on $(0, \infty)$ and has range $(-\infty, \infty)$. We know that

$$\frac{d}{dx} (\log x) = \frac{1}{x}.$$

The derivative is therefore positive for all x in $(0, \infty)$. It is very large for small x and very small for large x. In other words, for x close to 0, the curve is very steep and for large x the curve is very flat. At $x = 1$ the function is 0 and its derivative $1/x$ is 1. The second derivative

$$\frac{d^2}{dx^2} (\log x) = -\frac{1}{x^2}$$

is negative for all x in the domain. This tells us that the graph, pictured in Figure 5.1.2, is concave down throughout.

We now verify the formula

$$\int \frac{dx}{x} = \log |x| + C.$$

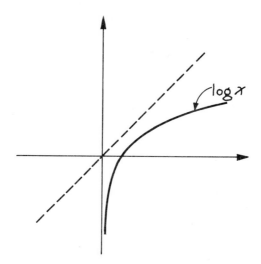

FIGURE 5.1.2

VERIFICATION.   For $x > 0$,

$$\frac{d}{dx}\,(\log |x|) = \frac{d}{dx}\,(\log x) = \frac{1}{x}\,.$$

For $x < 0$,

$$\frac{d}{dx}\,(\log |x|) = \frac{d}{dx}\,[\log\,(-x)] = \frac{1}{-x}\frac{d}{dx}\,(-x) = \left(\frac{1}{-x}\right)(-1) = \frac{1}{x}\,. \quad \Box$$

By applying the chain rule to

$$\log |f(x)|$$

we get

$$\frac{d}{dx}\,(\log |f(x)|) = \frac{1}{f(x)} \cdot f'(x) = \frac{f'(x)}{f(x)}\,,$$

provided of course that $f(x) \neq 0$. The corresponding integration formula is

$$\boxed{\int \frac{f'(x)}{f(x)}\,dx = \log |f(x)| + C.}$$

Problem.   Find the domain of f and find $f'(x)$, given that

$$f(x) = (\log x^2)^3.$$

SOLUTION.   Since the logarithm function is defined only for positive numbers, we must have $x^2 > 0$. The domain of f is thus $(-\infty, 0) \cup (0, \infty)$.

$$f'(x) = 3(\log x^2)^2 \frac{d}{dx}\,(\log x^2) = 3(\log x^2)^2 \frac{1}{x^2}\,2x = \frac{6(\log x^2)^2}{x}\,. \quad \Box$$

Problem.   Find the domain of f and find $f'(x)$, if

$$f(x) = \log\left(-x\sqrt{1+x}\right).$$

SOLUTION.   For x to be in the domain of f, it must be such that

$$-x\sqrt{1+x} > 0.$$

Thus x must satisfy the inequalities

$$x < 0 \quad \text{and} \quad x > -1.$$

The domain is thus the interval $(-1, 0)$. Before differentiating f, we make use of the special properties of the logarithm

$$f(x) = \log\left(-x\sqrt{1+x}\right) = \log\left(-x\right) + \frac{1}{2}\log\left(1+x\right).$$

From this, we have

$$f'(x) = \frac{-1}{-x} + \frac{1}{2}\left(\frac{1}{1+x}\right) = \frac{1}{x} + \frac{1}{2(1+x)} \cdot \quad \square$$

Problem.   Evaluate

$$\int_{\sqrt{3}}^{3} \frac{8x}{x^2 - 1}\, dx \quad \text{and} \quad \int_{-3}^{-\sqrt{3}} \frac{8x}{x^2 - 1}\, dx.$$

SOLUTION

$$\int_{\sqrt{3}}^{3} \frac{8x}{x^2 - 1}\, dx = 4\int_{\sqrt{3}}^{3} \frac{2x}{x^2 - 1}\, dx = 4\left[\log\left|x^2 - 1\right|\right]_{\sqrt{3}}^{3}$$

$$= 4(\log 8 - \log 2) = 4\log 4.$$

$$\int_{-3}^{-\sqrt{3}} \frac{8x}{x^2 - 1}\, dx = 4\int_{-3}^{-\sqrt{3}} \frac{2x}{x^2 - 1}\, dx = 4\left[\log\left|x^2 - 1\right|\right]_{-3}^{-\sqrt{3}}$$

$$= 4(\log 2 - \log 8) = -4\log 4.$$

This last answer can also be written

$$4\log\frac{1}{4} \cdot \quad \square$$

Problem.   Solve the following equation for x.

$$\int_{0}^{x} \frac{t}{t^2 + 1}\, dt = 1.$$

SOLUTION

$$\int_0^x \frac{t}{t^2+1}\,dt = \frac{1}{2}\int_0^x \frac{2t}{t^2+1}\,dt = \frac{1}{2}\left[\log(t^2+1)\right]_0^x$$

$$= \tfrac{1}{2}[\log(x^2+1) - \log 1] = \tfrac{1}{2}\log(x^2+1).$$

The initial equation is therefore equivalent to

$$\tfrac{1}{2}\log(x^2+1) = 1.$$

This equation can be solved in a straightforward manner

$$\log(x^2+1) = 2$$

$$x^2+1 = e^2$$

$$x^2 = e^2 - 1$$

$$x = \pm\sqrt{e^2-1}. \quad \square$$

Here are some natural logarithms rounded off to the nearest tenth.

	n	$\log n$
	2	.7
	3	1.1
	4	1.4
Table	5	1.6
5.1.4	6	1.8
	7	1.9
	8	2.1
	9	2.2
	10	2.3

Problem.   Use Table 5.1.4 to estimate the following logarithms:

(a) $\log .2$.   (c) $\log 2.4$.

(b) $\log .25$.   (d) $\log 90$.

SOLUTION

(a) $\log .2 = \log \tfrac{1}{5} = -\log 5 \overset{\text{approx}}{=} -1.6$.

(b) $\log .25 = \log(.5)^2 = 2\log\tfrac{1}{2} = -2\log 2 \overset{\text{approx}}{=} -1.4$.

(c) $\log 2.4 = \log[(3)(.8)] = \log 3 + \log 8 - \log 10 \overset{\text{approx}}{=} .9$.

(d) $\log 90 = \log[(9)(10)] = \log 9 + \log 10 \overset{\text{approx}}{=} 4.5$. $\quad \square$

Problem. Let

$$f(x) = \log\left(\frac{x^4}{x-1}\right).$$

(a) Specify the domain of f. (b) On what intervals is f increasing? Decreasing? (c) Find the extreme values of f. (d) Determine the concavity of the graph and find the points of inflection. (e) Sketch the graph.

SOLUTION.   Since the logarithm function is defined only for positive numbers the domain of f consists of all numbers greater than 1.

Making use of the special properties of the logarithm we get

$$f(x) = \log x^4 - \log (x - 1) = 4 \log x - \log (x - 1).$$

This gives

$$f'(x) = \frac{4}{x} - \frac{1}{x-1} = \frac{4(x-1)-x}{x(x-1)} = \frac{3x-4}{x(x-1)},$$

and, as you can verify,

$$f''(x) = \frac{x(x-1)3 - (3x-4)(2x-1)}{x^2(x-1)^2} = -\frac{(3x-2)(x-2)}{x^2(x-1)^2}.$$

Since the domain of f is $(1, \infty)$ we need concern ourselves only with $x > 1$. It is easy to see that

$$f'(x) \text{ is } \begin{cases} \text{negative,} & \text{if } 1 < x < \frac{4}{3} \\ \qquad 0, & \text{if } x = \frac{4}{3} \\ \text{positive,} & \text{if } x > \frac{4}{3}. \end{cases}$$

This means that f decreases on $(1, \frac{4}{3}]$ and increases on $[\frac{4}{3}, \infty)$. The value

$$f(\tfrac{4}{3}) = 4 \log 4 - 3 \log 3 \overset{\text{approx}}{=} 2.3$$

is a local and absolute minimum. There are no other extreme values.
    Since

$$f''(x) \text{ is} \begin{cases} \text{positive,} & \text{if } 1 < x < 2 \\ \qquad 0, & \text{if } x = 2 \\ \text{negative,} & \text{if } x > 2 \end{cases}$$

the graph is concave up on $(1, 2]$ and concave down on $[2, \infty)$. The point

$$(2, f(2)) = (2, 4 \log 2) \overset{\text{approx}}{=} (2, 2.8)$$

is the only point of inflection.

Before sketching the graph we note that the derivative

$$f'(x) = \frac{4}{x} - \frac{1}{x-1}$$

is very large negative for x close to 1 and very close to 0 for x large. This means that the graph is very steep for x close to 1 and very flat for x large. The graph appears in Figure 5.1.3. □

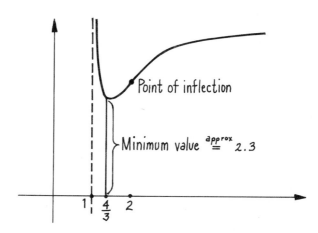

FIGURE 5.1.3

Logarithmic Differentiation

The logarithm function is sometimes useful in the computation of derivatives. If $f(x)$ is the product of several positive factors, say

$$f(x) = (x^2 + 1)^3(x^4 + 2)^2 x^6, \qquad x > 0,$$

the derivative $f'(x)$ can usually be obtained more readily by first applying the logarithm function and then using the formula

$$\frac{d}{dx}[\log f(x)] = \frac{f'(x)}{f(x)}.$$

This process, called logarithmic differentiation, is illustrated in the next problem.

Problem. Find $f'(1)$, given that

$$f(x) = (x^2 + 1)^3(x^4 + 2)^2 x^6.$$

SOLUTION. First we apply the logarithm function:

$$\log f(x) = 3 \log (x^2 + 1) + 2 \log (x^4 + 2) + 6 \log x.$$

Differentiation gives

$$\frac{f'(x)}{f(x)} = 3\frac{2x}{x^2 + 1} + 2\frac{4x^3}{x^4 + 2} + \frac{6}{x}$$

and thus

$$\frac{f'(1)}{f(1)} = \frac{6}{2} + \frac{8}{3} + 6.$$

Since $f(1) = 72$,

$$f'(1) = (3 + \frac{8}{3} + 6)72 = 840. \quad \square$$

Exercises

1. Prove that if x and y are positive then

$$\log\left(\frac{x}{y}\right) = \log x - \log y.$$

2. Find the domain of f and compute $f'(x)$, if $f(x)$ is given by:

(a)* $\log 4x$.

(b) $\log |x|$.

(c)* $\log (x + 1)$.

(d)* $\log (x^3)$.

(e) $\log \sqrt{1 + x^2}$.

(f)* $\dfrac{1}{\log x}$.

(g)* $(\log x)^3$.

(h) $\log\left(\dfrac{x-1}{x+1}\right)$.

(i)* $\log (\log x)$.

3. Evaluate.

(a)* $\displaystyle\int_1^e \frac{dx}{x}$.

(b) $\displaystyle\int_1^{e^2} \frac{dx}{x}$.

(c)* $\displaystyle\int_e^{e^2} \frac{dx}{x}$.

(d)* $\displaystyle\int_1^2 \frac{3x^2 - 1}{x^3 - x + 1} dx$.

(e) $\displaystyle\int_1^e \frac{\log x}{x} dx$.

(f)* $\displaystyle\int_e^{e^2} \frac{1}{x(\log x)^2} dx$.

(g)* $\displaystyle\int_1^{\sqrt{e}} \frac{\log (x^2)}{x} dx$.

(h) $\displaystyle\int_0^1 \frac{\log (x + 1)}{x + 1} dx$.

(i)* $\displaystyle\int_0^c \frac{\log (x + c)}{x + c} dx$.

4. Evaluate.

(a)* $\displaystyle\int_{-e}^{-1} \frac{dx}{x}$.

(b) $\displaystyle\int_1^e -\frac{dx}{x}$.

(c)* $\displaystyle\int_3^4 \frac{dx}{1 - x}$.

(d)* $\displaystyle\int_4^3 \frac{x}{x^2 - 1} dx$.

(e) $\displaystyle\int_{-4}^{-3} \frac{x}{x^2 - 1} dx$.

(f)* $\displaystyle\int_0^1 \left(\frac{1}{x + 1} - \frac{1}{x + 2}\right) dx$.

5. Find.

(a)* $\displaystyle\int \frac{x}{3 - x^2} dx$.

(b) $\displaystyle\int \frac{x}{(3 - x^2)^2} dx$.

(c)* $\displaystyle\int \frac{\sqrt{x}}{1 + x\sqrt{x}} dx$.

(d)* $\displaystyle\int \left(\frac{1}{x - a} - \frac{1}{x - b}\right) dx$.

(e) $\displaystyle\int x\left(\frac{1}{x^2 - a^2} - \frac{1}{x^2 - b^2}\right) dx$.

(f)* $\displaystyle\int \frac{2x - 1}{x(x - 1)} dx$.

6. Use Table 5.1.4 to estimate the following logarithms.

(a)* $\log 20$.

(b) $\log 16$.

(c)* $\log 3^4$.

(d)* $\log .1$.

(e) $\log 1.6$.

(f)* $\log 2.5$.

7. Use logarithmic differentiation to compute $f'(2)$ given the following:

(a)* $f(x) = (x^2 + 1)^2(x - 1)^5x^3$.

(b) $f(x) = \dfrac{x^4(x - 1)}{x + 2}$.

(c)* $f(x) = \dfrac{x^2(1 + x)^2}{2 + x}$.

(d) $f(x) = \dfrac{(1 + x)(2 + x)x}{4 + x}$.

8. Solve for x.

(a)* $\log x = 0$.

(b) $\log x = 2$.

(c)* $\log x = -1$.

(d) $\log x = a$.

(e)* $(2 - \log x) \log x = 0$.

(f) $\log x < x$.

(g)* $\log x > x$.

(h) $\frac{1}{2} \log x = \log (2x - 1)$.

(i)* $\displaystyle\int_0^x \frac{dt}{t + 1} = 1$.

(j) $\displaystyle\int_1^x \frac{dt}{t + 1} = 1$.

(k)* $\displaystyle\int_1^a \frac{dt}{t} = \int_{-a}^{-x} \frac{dt}{t}$.

(l) $\displaystyle\lim_{h \to 0} \frac{\log (x + h) - \log x}{h} = 3$.

9. Find the area of that portion of the first quadrant which lies between

(a)* $x + 4y - 5 = 0$ and $xy = 1$.

(b) $x + y - 3 = 0$ and $xy = 2$.

10. A particle moves along a line with acceleration

$$a(t) = -\frac{1}{(t + 1)^2} \text{ ft/sec}^2.$$

Find the distance traveled by the particle during the time interval $[0, 4]$, given that the initial velocity $v(0)$ is:

(a)* 1 ft/sec.

(b) 2 ft/sec.

11. Find formulas for the nth derivatives:

(a) $\dfrac{d^n}{dx^n}(\log x)$.

(b) $\dfrac{d^n}{dx^n}[\log (1 - x)]$.

12. For each of the functions below, (i) find the domain, (ii) find the intervals where it is increasing and the intervals where it is decreasing, (iii) find the extreme values, (iv) determine the concavity of the graph and find the points of inflection, and finally, (v) sketch the graph.

(a)* $f(x) = \log 2x$.

(b) $f(x) = \log \left(\dfrac{1}{x}\right)$.

(c)* $f(x) = \log |x|$.

(d)* $f(x) = x - \log x$.

(e) $f(x) = \log \left(\dfrac{x^3}{x - 1}\right)$.

(f)* $f(x) = \log \left(\dfrac{x}{1 + x^2}\right)$.

5.2 The exponential function

Definition

The function

$$f(x) = e^x \qquad \text{for all real } x$$

is called the *exponential function*.

Some properties of e^x

(1) Since we have the relation

$$\log (e^x) = x \qquad \text{for all real } x,$$

the exponential function is the *inverse* of the logarithm function. Thus its graph, depicted in Figure 5.2.1, can be obtained by reflecting the graph of the logarithm function in the line $y = x$.

(2) Since the graph of the logarithm function remains to the right of the y-axis, the graph of the exponential function remains above the x-axis; namely,

$$e^x > 0 \qquad \text{for all real } x.$$

(3) Since the graph of the logarithm function crosses the x-axis at $(1, 0)$, the graph of the exponential function crosses the y-axis at $(0, 1)$:

$$\log 1 = 0 \quad \text{gives} \quad e^0 = 1.$$

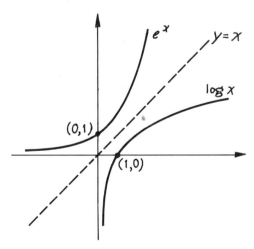

FIGURE 5.2.1

(4) Since the logarithm function is increasing, we have

$$e^{h_1} < e^{h_2} \quad \text{iff} \quad \log(e^{h_1}) < \log(e^{h_2})$$

and thus

$$e^{h_1} < e^{h_2} \quad \text{iff} \quad h_1 < h_2.$$

This means that

$$e^x \quad \text{is increasing.}$$

(More generally, the inverse of any increasing function is increasing, and the inverse of a decreasing function is decreasing.)

(5) For all $x > 0$,

$$\boxed{e^{\log x} = x,}$$

as can be verified by taking the log of both sides:

$$\log(e^{\log x}) = \log x \log e = \log x. \quad \square$$

We come now to the two most interesting properties of the exponential function.

(6) For all real x and y

$$e^{x+y} = e^x \cdot e^y.$$

PROOF

$$\log(e^x \cdot e^y) = \log e^x + \log e^y = x + y.$$

Since we also have

$$\log(e^{x+y}) = x + y$$

and the logarithm function is one-to-one, we must have

$$e^{x+y} = e^x \cdot e^y. \quad \square$$

(7) The exponential function is its own derivative:

$$\boxed{\frac{d}{dx}(e^x) = e^x \quad \text{for all real } x.}$$

PROOF. Since the logarithm function is differentiable and its derivative is never 0, its inverse, e^x, is itself differentiable. (Section 3.7.) An easy way to show that

$$\frac{d}{dx}(e^x) = e^x$$

is to differentiate the identity

$$\log e^x = x.$$

On the left-hand side the chain rule gives

$$\frac{d}{dx}(\log e^x) = \frac{1}{e^x}\frac{d}{dx}(e^x).$$

On the right-hand side the derivative is 1. Equating the derivatives we get

$$\frac{1}{e^x}\frac{d}{dx}(e^x) = 1$$

and thus

$$\frac{d}{dx}(e^x) = e^x. \quad \square$$

You will frequently run across expressions of the form $e^{f(x)}$. If f is differentiable, the chain rule gives

$$\boxed{\frac{d}{dx}e^{f(x)} = e^{f(x)}f'(x).}$$

For example,

$$\frac{d}{dx}(e^{kx}) = ke^{kx}, \qquad \frac{d}{dx}(e^{-x^2}) = -2xe^{-x^2},$$

$$\frac{d}{dx}(e^{\sqrt{x}}) = \frac{1}{2\sqrt{x}}e^{\sqrt{x}}, \qquad \frac{d}{dx}(e^{1/x}) = -\frac{1}{x^2}e^{1/x}. \quad \square$$

Problem. Let

$$f(x) = xe^{-x} \qquad \text{for all real } x.$$

(a) On what intervals is f increasing? Decreasing? (b) Find the extreme values of f. (c) Determine the concavity of the graph and find the points of inflection. (d) Sketch the graph.

SOLUTION. We have

$$f(x) = xe^{-x}$$
$$f'(x) = x(-1)e^{-x} + e^{-x} = (1 - x)e^{-x}$$
$$f''(x) = (1 - x)(-1)e^{-x} - e^{-x} = (x - 2)e^{-x}.$$

Since

$$f'(x) \text{ is } \begin{cases} \text{positive,} & \text{for } x < 1 \\ 0, & \text{at } x = 1, \\ \text{negative,} & \text{for } x > 1 \end{cases}$$

f increases on $(-\infty, 1]$ and decreases on $[1, \infty)$.

The number

$$f(1) = \frac{1}{e} \overset{\text{approx}}{=} \frac{1}{2.72}$$

is a local and absolute maximum. There are no other extreme values.   Since

$$f''(x) \text{ is} \begin{cases} \text{negative,} & \text{for } x < 2 \\ 0, & \text{at } x = 2, \\ \text{positive,} & \text{for } x > 2 \end{cases}$$

the graph is concave down on $(-\infty, 2]$ and concave up on $[2, \infty)$. The point

$$(2, f(2)) = (2, 2e^{-2}) \overset{\text{approx}}{=} \left(2, \frac{2}{(2.72)^2}\right)$$

is the only point of inflection. A sketch of the graph is given in Figure 5.2.2.   □

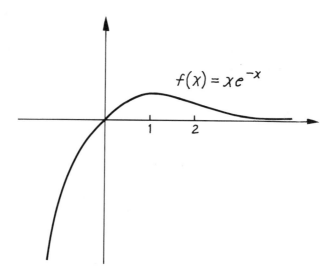

FIGURE 5.2.2

Problem. Let

$$f(x) = xe^{x^2} \qquad \text{for all } x \text{ in } (-1, 1).$$

(a) On what intervals is f increasing? Decreasing? (b) Find the extreme values of f. (c) Determine the concavity of the graph and find the points of inflection. (d) Sketch the graph.

SOLUTION.   We have

$$f(x) = xe^{x^2}$$
$$f'(x) = x \cdot 2x \cdot e^{x^2} + e^{x^2} = (1 + 2x^2)e^{x^2}$$
$$f''(x) = (1 + 2x^2)(2x)e^{x^2} + 4xe^{x^2} = 2x(2x^2 + 3)e^{x^2}.$$

Since $f'(x) > 0$ for all x in $(-1, 1)$, f increases on $(-1, 1)$ and there are no extreme values. Since

$$f''(x) \text{ is } \begin{cases} \text{negative}, & \text{for } x \text{ in } (-1, 0) \\ 0, & \text{for } x = 0 \\ \text{positive}, & \text{for } x \text{ in } (0, 1) \end{cases},$$

the graph is concave down on $(-1, 0]$ and concave up on $[0, 1)$. The point

$$(0, f(0)) = (0, 0)$$

is the only point of inflection. Since

$$f(x) = -f(-x),$$

f is an odd function and thus its graph, given in Figure 5.2.3, is symmetric with respect to the origin.   □

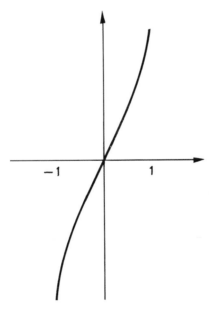

FIGURE 5.2.3

Problem.   Compute

$$\int_0^{\log 2} e^{-x}\, dx.$$

SOLUTION

$$\int_0^{\log 2} e^{-x}\, dx = -\int_0^{\log 2} - e^{-x}\, dx = -\left[e^{-x}\right]_0^{\log 2} = e^0 - e^{-\log 2}$$

$$= 1 - e^{\log (1/2)} = 1 - \frac{1}{2} = \frac{1}{2}.\quad □$$

Problem. Find the area of the region between the curves

$$y = xe^{x^2}, \quad x \in [0, 1], \qquad \text{and} \qquad y = -xe^{-x^2}, \quad x \in [0, 1].$$

SOLUTION.

$$\text{area} = \int_0^1 xe^{x^2}\, dx - \int_0^1 -xe^{-x^2}\, dx = \frac{1}{2} \int_0^1 2xe^{x^2}\, dx - \frac{1}{2} \int_0^1 -2xe^{-x^2}\, dx.$$

Since

$$\int_0^1 2xe^{x^2}\, dx = \Big[e^{x^2}\Big]_0^1 = e - 1 \qquad \text{and} \qquad \int_0^1 -2xe^{-x^2}\, dx = \Big[e^{-x^2}\Big]_0^1 = \frac{1}{e} - 1,$$

we have

$$\text{area} = \frac{1}{2}\left(e - \frac{1}{e}\right). \quad \square$$

Problem. Given that $e^{f(x)} = xe^{-x}$ for all $x > 0$, find the rate of change of f at 1.

SOLUTION. The desired number is simply $f'(1)$. Taking the log of both sides, we obtain

$$f(x) = \log (xe^{-x}) = \log x + \log e^{-x} = \log x - x.$$

Thus

$$f'(x) = \frac{1}{x} - 1 \qquad \text{and} \qquad f'(1) = 0. \quad \square$$

Here are some values of the exponential function rounded off to the nearest tenth.

	t	e^t	t	e^t
	.1	1.1	1.1	3.0
	.2	1.2	1.2	3.3
	.3	1.3	1.3	3.7
	.4	1.5	1.4	4.1
Table	.5	1.6	1.5	4.5
5.2.1	.6	1.8	1.6	5.0
	.7	2.0	1.7	5.5
	.8	2.2	1.8	6.0
	.9	2.5	1.9	6.7
	1.0	2.7	2.0	7.4

Problem. Use Table 5.2.1 to estimate the following powers of e.

(a) $e^{-.2}$. (b) $e^{2.4}$. (c) $e^{3.1}$. (d) e^4.

SOLUTION.   The idea of course is to make use of the relation

$$e^{x+y} = e^x \cdot e^y.$$

(a) $e^{-.2} = \dfrac{1}{e^{.2}} \overset{\text{approx}}{=} \dfrac{1}{1.2} \overset{\text{approx}}{=} .8.$

(b) $e^{2.4} = e^{2+.4} = (e^2)(e^{.4}) \overset{\text{approx}}{=} (7.4)(1.5) = 11.1.$

(c) $e^{3.1} = e^{1.7+1.4} = (e^{1.7})(e^{1.4}) \overset{\text{approx}}{=} (5.5)(4.1) = 22.55.$

(d) $e^4 = e^{2+2} = (e^2)(e^2) \overset{\text{approx}}{=} (7.4)(7.4) = 54.76.$ □

A function of the form Ce^{kx} has the special property that its rate of change at x is proportional to its value at x:

$$\frac{d}{dx}(Ce^{kx}) = k(Ce^{kx}).$$

The next two problems feature this idea.

Problem.   A positive function, everywhere defined, has the property that at each point of its graph the slope is twice the y-coordinate. Given that the graph passes through the point $(0, \sqrt{2})$, find the function.

SOLUTION.   For each x we have $f'(x) = 2f(x)$, and thus

$$\frac{f'(x)}{f(x)} = 2.$$

This means that

$$\frac{d}{dx}[\log f(x)] = 2,$$

and thus

$$\log f(x) = 2x + c.$$

Applying the exponential function to both sides, we find that

$$f(x) = e^{2x+c} = e^{2x} \cdot e^c.$$

Setting $C = e^c$, we can rewrite f in the form

$$f(x) = Ce^{2x}.$$

To require that the graph pass through the point $(0, \sqrt{2})$ is to require that

$$f(0) = \sqrt{2}.$$

Since

$$f(0) = Ce^{2.0} = Ce^0 = C,$$

we must have

$$C = \sqrt{2}.$$

The function in question is thus

$$f(x) = \sqrt{2}e^{2x}. \quad \square$$

Problem. The rate of decay of radioactive material is proportional to the amount of such material present.

(a) Find the amount of material present t years later given that the initial amount is A_0 pounds and it takes 5 years for a third of the material to decay.

(b) How long does it take for half of the material to decay?

SOLUTION.   Let $A(t)$ be the amount of radioactive material present at time t. Since the rate of decay is proportional to the amount present, we see that

$$A'(t) = kA(t),$$

where k is some constant. Since it takes 5 yrs for a third of the substance to decay we know that

$$A(5) = \frac{2}{3}A_0.$$

The equation

$$A'(t) = kA(t)$$

yields in turn

$$\frac{A'(t)}{A(t)} = k$$

$$\log A(t) = kt + c$$

$$A(t) = e^{kt+c} = e^{kt}\cdot e^{c}.$$

Rewriting e^c as C, we get

$$A(t) = Ce^{kt}.$$

Since

$$A_0 = A(0) = Ce^0 = C,$$

the constant C is simply the amount initially present; in other words, we have

$$A(t) = A_0 e^{kt}.$$

We can evaluate k by using the condition

$$A(5) = \frac{2}{3}A_0.$$

This condition gives

$$\frac{2}{3}A_0 = A_0 e^{5k}$$

$$\frac{2}{3} = e^{5k}$$

$$\log \frac{2}{3} = 5k$$

$$k = \frac{1}{5}\log\frac{2}{3}.$$

Now that we know k we can write
$$A(t) = A_0 e^{(1/5)[\log (2/3)]t}.$$

This answers part (a).

To answer part (b) we must find the value of t for which
$$\frac{1}{2} A_0 = A_0 e^{(1/5)[\log (2/3)]t}.$$

To find t, we first divide by A_0 and get
$$\frac{1}{2} = e^{(1/5)[\log (2/3)]t}.$$

Taking the log of both sides, we get
$$\log \frac{1}{2} = \frac{1}{5} \left(\log \frac{2}{3} \right) t.$$

This gives
$$5 \log \frac{1}{2} = \left(\log \frac{2}{3} \right) t$$
$$-5 \log 2 = (\log 2 - \log 3)t$$
$$t = \frac{5 \log 2}{\log 3 - \log 2} \cong 8\frac{3}{4}.$$

It takes about eight years and nine months for half of the material to decay.   □

Exercises

1. Find $f'(x)$, given that $f(x)$ is defined as follows.

(a)* e^{-2x}.

(b) $3e^{x^2}$.

(c)* $\dfrac{e^x + e^{-x}}{2}$.

(d)* $\dfrac{e^x - e^{-x}}{2}$.

(e) $e^x \log x$.

(f)* $(x + \log x)^2$.

(g)* $xe^{x-1} + (x - 1)e^x$.

(h) $\dfrac{e^{1/x}}{x}$.

(i)* $e^{(x-1)/(x+2)}$.

(j)* $\log \dfrac{x - 1}{x + 2}$.

(k) $\log (-xe^x)$.

(l)* $e^{x \log x}$.

(m)* $\dfrac{e^{2x} - 1}{e^{2x} + 1}$.

(n) $\log (x^2 e^x)$.

(o)* $\displaystyle\int_x^0 \log (t + 1) \, dt$.

(p)* $\displaystyle\int_0^x e^{t^2} \, dt$.

(q) $e^{1/x} - e^{-1/x}$.

(r)* $e^{-1/(1-x)}$.

2. Find.

(a)* $\displaystyle\int e^{2x} \, dx$.

(b) $\displaystyle\int e^{-2x} \, dx$.

(c)* $\displaystyle\int e^{kx} \, dx$.

(d)* $\displaystyle\int xe^{x^2} \, dx$.

(e) $\displaystyle\int xe^{-x^2} \, dx$.

(f)* $\displaystyle\int \frac{e^{1/x}}{x^2} \, dx$.

(g)* $\displaystyle\int \frac{e^{2\sqrt{x}}}{\sqrt{x}} \, dx$.

(h) $\displaystyle\int f'(x)e^{f(x)} \, dx$.

(i)* $\displaystyle\int (e^{-x} - 1)^2 \, dx$.

3. Evaluate.

(a)* $\displaystyle\int_0^1 e^x\,dx.$

(b) $\displaystyle\int_0^1 e^{-x}\,dx.$

(c)* $\displaystyle\int_0^1 \frac{e^x - e^{-x}}{2}\,dx.$

(d)* $\displaystyle\int_0^{\log \pi} e^{-6x}\,dx.$

(e) $\displaystyle\int_0^1 xe^{-x^2}\,dx.$

(f)* $\displaystyle\int_0^1 \frac{e^x + e^{-x}}{2}\,dx.$

(g)* $\displaystyle\int_0^e \frac{3}{x+2}\,dx.$

(h) $\displaystyle\int_0^1 \left(\frac{1}{x+1} - \frac{1}{x+2}\right)dx.$

(i)* $\displaystyle\int_{\log 2}^4 \frac{e^{\sqrt{x}}}{\sqrt{x}}\,dx.$

(j)* $\displaystyle\int_0^1 (3e^x - 2e^{x-1})\,dx.$

(k) $\displaystyle\int_0^1 \frac{x^2}{x^3+1}\,dx.$

(l)* $\displaystyle\int_1^{\log 2} \frac{e^{-\sqrt{x}}}{\sqrt{x}}\,dx.$

4. Use Table 5.2.1 to estimate the following powers of e.

(a)* $e^{-.4}.$ (b) $e^{2.6}.$ (c)* $e^{2.8}.$ (d) $e^{-2.1}.$

5. Sketch the region between the graphs of f and g and compute its area if

(a)* $f(x) = e^x,\ x \in [0, 1]$ and $g(x) = e^{-x},\ x \in [0, 1]$.
(b) $f(x) = e^x,\ x \in [1, 4]$ and $g(x) = 1/x,\ x \in [1, 4]$.
(c)* $f(x) = e^{-x},\ x \in [-2, -1]$ and $g(x) = 1/x,\ x \in [-2, -1]$.

6. The tangent to the graph of f at the point P passes through the origin. Find the coordinates of P if

(a)* $f(x) = e^x.$ (b) $f(x) = e^{-x}.$

7. Find a function y such that

(a)* $y'(x) = 2y(x)$ for all real x and $y(0) = 1$.
(b) $y'(x) = -2y(x)$ for all real x and $y(0) = 1$.
(c)* $y'(x) = y(x)$ and $y(0) = \pi$.
(d) $y'(x) = -y(x)$ and $y(0) = \pi$.
(e)* $y'(x) = \pi y(x)$ and $y(0) = 0$.

8. A positive function everywhere defined has the property that at each point of its graph the slope is three times the y-coordinate. Find the function given that the graph passes through the point

(a)* $(0, 2)$.   (b) $(1, 1)$.   (c)* $(2, e)$.

9. For each of the functions below, (i) find the domain, (ii) find the intervals where it is increasing, (iii) find the extreme values, (iv) determine the concavity and find the

points of inflection, and finally, (v) sketch the graph.

(a)* $f(x) = e^{x^2}$.

(b) $f(x) = e^{-x^2}$.

(c)* $f(x) = \dfrac{e^x + e^{-x}}{2}$.

(d) $f(x) = \dfrac{e^x - e^{-x}}{2}$.

(e)* $f(x) = xe^x$.

(f) $f(x) = (1 - x)e^x$.

(g)* $f(x) = e^{(1/x)^2}$.

(h) $f(x) = x^2 e^{-x}$.

10. A particle moves along a coordinate line so that its position at time t is given by

$$x(t) = Ae^{ct} + Be^{-ct}.$$

Show that the acceleration of the particle is proportional to its position.

11. The rate of decay of a radioactive substance is proportional to the amount of the substance present.

(a) How long will it take for half of the substance to decay

    (i)* if it takes 4 years for a quarter of the substance to decay?

    (ii) if it takes 3 years for a quarter of the substance to decay?

(b) A year ago there were 4 lbs of the substance. Now there are 3 lbs.

    (i)* How many pounds were there 2 years ago?

    (ii) How many pounds were there 10 years ago?

    (iii)* How many pounds will be left 10 years from now?

12. Prove that for all $x > 0$ and all positive integers n

$$e^x > 1 + x + \frac{x^2}{2!} + \frac{x^3}{3!} + \cdots + \frac{x^n}{n!},$$

where $n!$, read "n factorial," is shorthand for

$$n(n - 1)(n - 2) \cdots 2 \cdot 1.$$

$\left[\text{HINT:} \qquad e^x = 1 + \int_0^x e^t \, dt > 1 + \int_0^x dt = 1 + x \right.$

and therefore

$$e^x = 1 + \int_0^x e^t \, dt > 1 + \int_0^x (1 + t) \, dt = 1 + x + \frac{x^2}{2}.$$

$\left. \text{Proceed by induction.} \right]$

13. Prove that if n is a positive integer, then

$$e^x > x^n \qquad \text{for all } x \text{ sufficiently large.}$$

$\Big[\text{HINT: By Exercise 12,}$

$$e^x > \frac{x^{n+1}}{(n + 1)!} \qquad \text{for all } x > 0. \Big]$$

5.3   The functions x^r, p^x, and $\log_p x$; estimating e.

The elementary notion of exponent applies only to rational numbers. Expressions such as

$$10^{1/3}, \qquad 2^{-4/5}$$

make sense, but so far we have attached no meaning to expressions such as

$$10^{\sqrt{2}}, \qquad 2^{-\pi}.$$

The extension of our sense of exponent to allow for irrational exponents is conveniently done by making use of the logarithm and exponential functions. The heart of the matter is to observe that for $x > 0$ and p/q rational

$$\boxed{x^{p/q} = e^{(p/q)\,\log x}.}$$

(To verify this, take the log of both sides.) The right-hand side of this equation already makes sense for irrational numbers z; namely,

$$e^{z\,\log x}$$

already makes sense. To define x^z, we can simply set

$$x^z = e^{z\,\log x}.$$

This is exactly what we do.

> **Definition**
>
> If z is irrational and x is positive, we define the number x^z by setting
>
> $$x^z = e^{z\,\log x}.$$

Having made this definition, we now have

$$x^r = e^{r\,\log x} \qquad \text{for all real numbers } r.$$

For example,

$$10^{\sqrt{2}} = e^{\sqrt{2}\,\log 10} \qquad \text{and} \qquad 2^{-\pi} = e^{-\pi\,\log 2}. \quad \square$$

With this extended sense of exponent the usual laws of exponents

$$\boxed{x^{r+s} = x^r x^s, \qquad x^{r-s} = \frac{x^r}{x^s}, \qquad (x^r)^s = x^{rs}}$$

still hold:

$$x^{r+s} = e^{(r+s)\,\log x} = e^{r\,\log x} \cdot e^{s\,\log x} = x^r x^s$$

$$x^{r-s} = e^{(r-s)\,\log x} = e^{r\,\log x} \cdot e^{-s\,\log x} = \frac{e^{r\,\log x}}{e^{s\,\log x}} = \frac{x^r}{x^s}.$$

$$(x^r)^s = e^{s\,\log x^r} = e^{rs\,\log x} = x^{rs}. \quad \square$$

The differentiation of arbitrary powers is extremely easy

$$\frac{d}{dx}(x^r) = rx^{r-1}.$$

PROOF

$$\frac{d}{dx}(x^r) = \frac{d}{dx}(e^{r \log x}) = e^{r \log x} \frac{d}{dx}(r \log x) = x^r \frac{r}{x} = rx^{r-1}. \quad \square$$

To compute

$$\frac{d}{dx}[f(x)]^r$$

we need only apply the chain rule. Doing so gives

$$\frac{d}{dx}[f(x)]^r = r[f(x)]^{r-1}\frac{d}{dx}[f(x)].$$

Some Simple Examples

1. $\dfrac{d}{dx}(x^{\sqrt{2}}) = \sqrt{2}x^{\sqrt{2}-1}$.

2. $\dfrac{d}{dx}(x^2 + 5)^{\sqrt{2}} = (\sqrt{2})(x^2 + 5)^{\sqrt{2}-1}(2x) = 2(\sqrt{2})x(x^2 + 5)^{\sqrt{2}-1}$.

3. $\displaystyle\int (3x + 1)^{\sqrt{2}}\, dx = \frac{1}{3}\int 3(3x + 1)^{\sqrt{2}}\, dx = \frac{(3x + 1)^{\sqrt{2}+1}}{3(\sqrt{2} + 1)} + C$.

4. $\displaystyle\int \frac{x^2}{(x^3 + 1)^{\sqrt{2}}}\, dx = \frac{1}{3}\int \frac{3x^2}{(x^3 + 1)^{\sqrt{2}}}\, dx = \frac{(x^3 + 1)^{1-\sqrt{2}}}{3(1 - \sqrt{2})} + C. \quad \square$

To form the function

$$f(x) = x^r$$

we take a positive variable x and raise it to a constant power r. To form the function

$$g(x) = p^x$$

we take a positive constant p and raise it to a variable power x.

The high status enjoyed by Euler's number e comes from the fact that

$$\frac{d}{dx}(e^x) = e^x.$$

In general, for $p > 0$,

$$\frac{d}{dx}(p^x) = p^x \log p.$$

PROOF

$$\frac{d}{dx}(p^x) = \frac{d}{dx}(e^{x \log p}) = e^{x \log p} \log p = p^x \log p. \quad \square$$

The chain rule gives

$$\frac{d}{dx}[p^{f(x)}] = p^{f(x)} \log p \frac{d}{dx}[f(x)].$$

Example 1

$$\frac{d}{dx}(e^{3x^2}) = 6xe^{3x^2}, \qquad \frac{d}{dx}(5^{3x^2}) = 5^{3x^2}(\log 5)(6x) = 5^{3x^2} 6x \log 5. \quad \square$$

Example 2

$$\int 2^x \, dx = \frac{1}{\log 2} \int 2^x \log 2 \, dx = \frac{2^x}{\log 2} + C. \quad \square$$

Example 3

$$\int_0^3 3^x \, dx = \frac{1}{\log 3} \int_0^3 3^x \log 3 \, dx = \frac{1}{\log 3} \left[3^x \right]_0^3 = \frac{26}{\log 3}. \quad \square$$

If p is positive, then

$$\log p^t = t \log p.$$

If in addition p is different from 1, then $\log p \neq 0$, and therefore

$$\frac{\log p^t}{\log p} = t.$$

This means that the function

$$f(x) = \frac{\log x}{\log p}$$

satisfies the relation

$$f(p^t) = t.$$

In view of this we call

$$\frac{\log x}{\log p}$$

the log *of x to the base p* and write

(5.3.1)
$$\log_p x = \frac{\log x}{\log p}.$$

As examples, we have

$$\log_2 32 = \frac{\log 32}{\log 2} = \frac{\log 2^5}{\log 2} = \frac{5 \log 2}{\log 2} = 5$$

and

$$\log_{100}(\tfrac{1}{10}) = \frac{\log(\tfrac{1}{10})}{\log 100} = \frac{\log 10^{-1}}{\log 10^2} = \frac{-\log 10}{2 \log 10} = -\frac{1}{2}. \quad \square$$

We can obtain the same results more quickly by using the fact that

$$\boxed{\log_p p^t = t.}$$

Thus

$$\log_2 32 = \log_2 2^5 = 5 \quad \text{and} \quad \log_{100} (\tfrac{1}{10}) = \log_{100}(100^{-1/2}) = -\tfrac{1}{2}. \quad \square$$

If we differentiate the function

$$\log_p x = \frac{\log x}{\log p}$$

we obtain the formula

$$\boxed{\frac{d}{dx} (\log_p x) = \frac{1}{x \log p}.}$$

When p is e the factor $\log p$ in the denominator becomes 1, and the formula is simply

$$\frac{d}{dx} (\log_e x) = \frac{1}{x}.$$

We view the logarithm to the base e

$$\log = \log_e$$

as the "natural logarithm" because it is the logarithm with the simplest derivative.

Estimating the Number e

We have defined the number e as the number which satisfies

$$1 = \int_1^e \frac{dt}{t}.$$

It is time to discuss how to obtain a numerical estimate for e.

Since e is irrational (Exercise 27, Section 10.8), we cannot hope to express e as a terminating decimal (nor as a repeating decimal). What we can do is describe a simple technique by which one can compute the value of e to within any desired degree of accuracy.

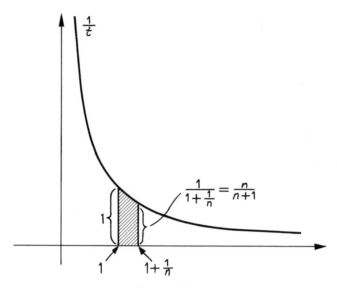

FIGURE 5.3.1

Theorem 5.3.2

For each positive integer n,

$$\left(1+\frac{1}{n}\right)^{n} \le e \le \left(1+\frac{1}{n}\right)^{n+1}.$$

PROOF

$$\log\left(1+\frac{1}{n}\right) = \int_{1}^{1+1/n} \frac{dt}{t} \le \int_{1}^{1+1/n} 1 \, dt = \frac{1}{n}.$$

since $\frac{1}{t} \le 1$ for all t in $\left[1, 1+\frac{1}{n}\right]$

From

$$\log\left(1+\frac{1}{n}\right) \le \frac{1}{n}$$

we get

$$\left(1+\frac{1}{n}\right) \le e^{1/n}$$

and thus

$$\left(1+\frac{1}{n}\right)^{n} \le e.$$

Now

$$\log\left(1 + \frac{1}{n}\right) = \int_1^{1+1/n} \frac{dt}{t} \geq \int_1^{1+1/n} \frac{dt}{1 + 1/n} = \frac{1}{1 + 1/n} \cdot \frac{1}{n} = \frac{1}{n+1}.$$

since $\frac{1}{t} \geq \frac{1}{1+1/n}$ for all t in $\left[1, 1 + \frac{1}{n}\right]$

From

$$\log\left(1 + \frac{1}{n}\right) \geq \frac{1}{n+1}$$

we get

$$\left(1 + \frac{1}{n}\right) \geq e^{1/(n+1)}$$

and thus

$$\left(1 + \frac{1}{n}\right)^{n+1} \geq e. \quad \square$$

It is easy to see how to estimate e by using Theorem 5.3.2. Since

$$(1 + \tfrac{1}{1})^1 = 2 \quad \text{and} \quad (1 + \tfrac{1}{1})^2 = 4,$$

we have

$$2 \leq e \leq 4.$$

Since

$$(1 + \tfrac{1}{2})^2 = \tfrac{9}{4} = 2.25 \quad \text{and} \quad (1 + \tfrac{1}{2})^3 = \tfrac{27}{8} = 3.375,$$

we have

$$2.25 \leq e \leq 3.375.$$

With a little more patience you can verify that

$$2.59 \leq (1 + \tfrac{1}{10})^{10} \quad \text{and} \quad (1 + \tfrac{1}{10})^{11} \leq 2.85$$

and thus arrive at

$$2.59 \leq e \leq 2.85.$$

Lengthier calculations show that

$$2.70 \leq (1 + \tfrac{1}{100})^{100} \quad \text{and} \quad (1 + \tfrac{1}{100})^{101} \leq 2.74$$

and thus

$$2.70 \leq e \leq 2.74.$$

Still lengthier calculations show that

$$2.71 \leq (1 + \tfrac{1}{200})^{200} \quad \text{and} \quad (1 + \tfrac{1}{200})^{201} \leq 2.73,$$

and thus

$$2.71 \leq e \leq 2.73.$$

A look at an eight-place table reveals the estimate

$$2.71828182.$$

For our purposes the estimate 2.72 is sufficient.
  The inequality

$$\left(1 + \frac{1}{n}\right)^n \le e \le \left(1 + \frac{1}{n}\right)^{n+1}$$

is rather elegant but, as you saw, it does not provide a very efficient way of estimating e.
(We have to go to $n = 200$ to show that $2.71 \le e \le 2.73$). We shall have a much more
efficient way of estimating e when we have infinite series at our disposal.

Exercises

1. Find.

    (a)* $\log_2 (64)$.   (e) $\log_{64} (\frac{1}{2})$.   (h) $\log_5 (1)$.

    (b) $\log_2 (\frac{1}{64})$.   (f)* $\log_{10} (0.01)$.   (i)* $\log_5 (.2)$.

    (c)* $\log_{1/2} (64)$.

    (d)* $\log_{64} (2)$.   (g)* $\log_{e^2} \left(\dfrac{1}{e}\right)$.

2. Find.

    (a)* $\displaystyle\int 3^x \, dx$.   (f)* $\displaystyle\int (2^x + 2^{-x}) \, dx$.

    (b) $\displaystyle\int x^3 \, dx$.   (g)* $\displaystyle\int \frac{dx}{x \log 5}$.

    (c)* $\displaystyle\int 2^{-x} \, dx$.

    (d)* $\displaystyle\int x10^{x^2} \, dx$.   (h) $\displaystyle\int \frac{\log_5 x}{x} \, dx$.

    (e) $\displaystyle\int x10^{-x^2} \, dx$.   (i)* $\displaystyle\int (2^x - 2^{-x}) \, dx$.

3. Find $f'(e)$.

    (a)* $f(x) = \log_3 x$.   (d) $f(x) = \log_3 (\log_2 x)$.

    (b) $f(x) = \dfrac{\log_3 x}{x}$.   (e)* $f(x) = e^{\log_3 x}$.

    (c)* $f(x) = \log (\log x)$.   (f) $f(x) = \log_2 \left(\dfrac{1}{x}\right)$.

4. Find.

    (a)* $\dfrac{d}{dx} (x^x)$.   (d)* $\dfrac{d}{dx} \left(\dfrac{1}{x}\right)^x$.

    (b) $\dfrac{d}{dx} (x + 1)^x$.   (e) $\dfrac{d}{dx} (\log x)^{x^2+2}$.

    (c)* $\dfrac{d}{dx} (x^2 + 2)^{\log x}$.   (f)* $\dfrac{d}{dx} (\log x)^{\log x}$.

5. Sketch figures in which you compare the following pairs of graphs.

(a) $f(x) = e^x$ and $g(x) = 2^x$.
(b) $f(x) = e^x$ and $g(x) = 3^x$.
(c) $f(x) = e^x$ and $g(x) = e^{-x}$.
(d) $f(x) = 2^x$ and $g(x) = 2^{-x}$.
(e) $f(x) = 3^x$ and $g(x) = 3^{-x}$.
(f) $f(x) = \log x$ and $g(x) = \log_2 x$.
(g) $f(x) = 2^x$ and $g(x) = \log_2 x$.
(h) $f(x) = 10^x$ and $g(x) = \log_{10} x$.
(i) $f(x) = \log_2 x$ and $g(x) = \log_{10} x$.

6. Show that if a, b, c are positive then

$$\log_a c = \log_a b \, \log_b c$$

provided that a and b are both different from 1.

7. Show that

(i) $\log_a xy = \log_a x + \log_a y$,

(ii) $\log_a \dfrac{x}{y} = \log_a x - \log_a y$,

(iii) $\log_a x^y = y \log_a x$.

8. Find those numbers x, if any, for which

(a)* $10^x = e^x$.

(b) $\log_5 x = 0.04$.

(c)* $\log_x 2 = \log_3 x$.

(d) $\log_2 x = \displaystyle\int_2^x \dfrac{dt}{t}$.

(e)* $\log_x 10 = \log_4 100$.

(f) $\log_x 10 = \log_2 \left(\dfrac{1}{10}\right)$.

9. (i)* Estimate $\log a$ given that

$$e^{t_1} < a < e^{t_2}.$$

(ii)* Estimate e^b given that

$$\log x_1 < b < \log x_2.$$

10. For each of the functions below (i) specify the domain, (ii) find the intervals where the function is increasing and those where it is decreasing, (iii) find the extreme values.

(a)* $f(x) = 10^{x^2-1}$.

(b) $f(x) = 10^{1-x^2}$.

(c)* $f(x) = 10^{1/(1-x^2)}$.

(d) $f(x) = 10^{1/(x^2-1)}$.

(e)* $f(x) = 10^{\sqrt{1-x^2}}$.

(f) $f(x) = 10^{1/\sqrt{1-x^2}}$.

(g)* $f(x) = \log_{10}\left(\dfrac{1}{x}\right)$.

(h) $f(x) = \log_{10} \sqrt{1-x^2}$.

11. Evaluate.

(a)* $\int_0^1 (x + 1)^{-1/4}\, dx.$

(b) $\int_{-1}^1 \dfrac{x}{(x^2 + 1)^{1/3}}\, dx.$

(c)* $\int_2^3 2(x - 1)^{4/7}\, dx.$

(d)* $\int_0^1 \dfrac{x^2}{x^3 + 1}\, dx.$

(e) $\int_0^1 x\sqrt{1 - x^2}\, dx.$

(f)* $\int_0^t \dfrac{x}{\sqrt{1 - x^2}}\, dx.$

(g)* $\int_1^2 (2^{\pi x} + x^{2\pi})\, dx.$

(h) $\int_1^4 \sqrt{\dfrac{1 + \sqrt{x}}{x}}\, dx.$

(i)* $\int_1^4 \dfrac{dx}{x \log 2}.$

12. Show that

$$e^x(1 - x) \le 1 \qquad \text{for all real } x.$$

[HINT: Analyze the function

$$f(x) = e^x(1 - x).]$$

13.* The number of bacteria present in a given culture increases at a rate proportional to the number present. When first observed the culture contained n_0 bacteria; an hour later, n_1. Find the number present t hours after the observations began.

14. Prove that

$$\lim_{h \to 0} (1 + h)^{1/h} = e.$$

$\left[\vphantom{\rule{0pt}{8cm}}\right.$ HINT: From

$$\frac{d}{dx}(\log x) = \frac{1}{x},$$

it follows that

$$\lim_{h \to 0} \frac{\log (1 + h) - \log 1}{h} = 1,$$

and thus that

$$\lim_{h \to 0} \frac{1}{h}[\log (1 + h)] = 1. \left.\vphantom{\rule{0pt}{8cm}}\right]$$

5.4 Integration by parts

We begin with the differentiation formula

$$f(x)g'(x) + f'(x)g(x) = (f \cdot g)'(x).$$

Integrating both sides, we get

$$\int f(x)g'(x)\, dx + \int f'(x)g(x)\, dx = \int (f \cdot g)'(x)\, dx.$$

Since

$$\int (f \cdot g)'(x)\, dx = f(x)g(x) + C, \qquad \text{(Explain)}$$

we have

$$\int f(x)g'(x)\, dx + \int f'(x)g(x)\, dx = f(x)g(x) + C$$

and therefore

(5.4.1)

$$\int f(x)g'(x)\, dx = f(x)g(x) - \int f'(x)g(x)\, dx + C.$$

The application of (5.4.1) is called *integration by parts*.

The value of integration by parts is that it enables us to find

$$\int f(x)g'(x)\, dx$$

by finding instead

$$\int f'(x)g(x)\, dx.$$

Of course, all this is of practical use only if the second integral is easier to find than the first.

We illustrate the technique of integration by parts in some problems.

Problem. Find

$$\int xe^x\, dx.$$

SOLUTION.   If we set

$$f(x) = x \qquad \text{and} \qquad g'(x) = e^x,$$

then we can write

$$f'(x) = 1 \qquad \text{and} \qquad g(x) = e^x.$$

The formula

$$\int f(x)g'(x)\, dx = f(x)g(x) - \int f'(x)g(x)\, dx + C$$

then gives

$$\int xe^x\, dx = xe^x - \int 1 \cdot e^x\, dx + C$$
$$= xe^x - e^x + C.$$

This result can easily be checked by differentiation. $\square$

Problem. Find

$$\int \log x\, dx.$$

SOLUTION.   We have

$$\log x = (\log x)\cdot(1).$$

If we set

$$f(x) = \log x \quad\text{and}\quad g'(x) = 1,$$

then we can write

$$f'(x) = \frac{1}{x} \quad\text{and}\quad g(x) = x.$$

The formula

$$\int f(x)g'(x)\,dx = f(x)g(x) - \int f'(x)g(x)\,dx + C$$

then gives

$$\int \log x\,dx = x\log x - \int \frac{1}{x}\cdot x\,dx + C$$

$$= x\log x - \int 1\,dx + C$$

$$= x\log x - x + C. \quad\square$$

Problem.   Find

$$\int \log(x + a)\,dx.$$

SOLUTION.   If we set

$$f(x) = \log(x + a) \quad\text{and}\quad g'(x) = 1,$$

then we can write

$$f'(x) = \frac{1}{x + a} \quad\text{and}\quad g(x) = x.$$

The formula

$$\int f(x)g'(x)\,dx = f(x)g(x) = \int f'(x)g(x)\,dx + C$$

gives in this case

$$\int \log(x + a)\,dx = x\log(x + a) - \int \frac{x}{x + a}\,dx + C.$$

Since

$$\int \frac{x}{x + a}\,dx = \int \frac{x + a}{x + a}\,dx - \int \frac{a}{x + a}\,dx$$

$$= \int 1\,dx - a\int \frac{dx}{x + a}$$

$$= x - a\log(x + a),$$

we have

$$\int \log(x+a)\, dx = x \log(x+a) - x + a \log(x+a) + C$$
$$= (x+a) \log(x+a) - x + C.$$

The same result can be obtained with more dispatch by a wiser choice of $g(x)$. For $g(x)$ we are at liberty to choose any function that satisfies

$$g'(x) = 1.$$

If we choose

$$g(x) = x + a,$$

then integration by parts gives

$$\int \log(x+a)\, dx = (x+a) \log(x+a) - \int \frac{x+a}{x+a}\, dx + C$$
$$= (x+a) \log(x+a) - \int 1 \cdot dx + C$$
$$= (x+a) \log(x+a) - x + C. \quad \Box$$

Problem. Find

$$\int \frac{x^3}{(1+x^2)^3}\, dx.$$

SOLUTION.   Here we are confronted with the problem of how to break up

$$\frac{x^3}{(1+x^2)^3}$$

into parts. Since

$$\frac{d}{dx}\left[\frac{1}{(1+x^2)^2}\right] = \frac{-4x}{(1+x^2)^3},$$

it seems reasonable to try the decomposition

$$f(x) = -\frac{x^2}{4}, \qquad g'(x) = \frac{-4x}{(1+x^2)^3}.$$

With

$$f'(x) = -\frac{x}{2} \quad \text{and} \quad g(x) = \frac{1}{(1+x^2)^2},$$

integration by parts gives

$$\int \frac{x^3}{(1+x^2)^3}\, dx = -\frac{x^2}{4(1+x^2)^2} - \int \frac{-x}{2(1+x^2)^2}\, dx + C$$
$$= -\frac{x^2}{4(1+x^2)^2} - \frac{1}{4(1+x^2)} + C. \quad \Box$$

The final problem shows that it is sometimes useful to integrate by parts more than once.

Problem. Evaluate

$$\int_0^1 x^2 e^x \, dx.$$

SOLUTION.   First we find the indefinite integral

$$\int x^2 e^x \, dx$$

and then the definite integral

$$\int_0^1 x^2 e^x \, dx.$$

If we set

$$f(x) = x^2 \quad \text{and} \quad g'(x) = e^x,$$

then we can write

$$f'(x) = 2x \quad \text{and} \quad g(x) = e^x.$$

Integration by parts gives

(1) $$\int x^2 e^x \, dx = x^2 e^x - \int 2x e^x \, dx + C.$$

The integral on the right can now itself be evaluated by parts. Setting

$$f(x) = 2x \quad \text{and} \quad g'(x) = e^x,$$

we can write

$$f'(x) = 2 \quad \text{and} \quad g(x) = e^x.$$

This gives

$$\int 2x e^x \, dx = 2x e^x - \int 2 e^x \, dx + C_1$$
$$= 2x e^x - 2 e^x + C_1.$$

Substituting this result in (1), we get

$$\int x^2 e^x \, dx = x^2 e^x - 2x e^x + 2 e^x - C_1 + C.$$

We can absorb the arbitrary constant C_1 into the arbitrary constant C and therefore write

$$\int x^2 e^x \, dx = x^2 e^x - 2x e^x + 2 e^x + C.$$

For

$$\int_0^1 x^2 e^x \, dx$$

we have

$$\left[x^2 e^x - 2x e^x + 2 e^x + C \right]_0^1 = (e - 2e + 2e + C) - (2 + C)$$
$$= e - 2. \quad \square$$

Exercises

Find the following.

1.* $\int xe^{-x}\, dx.$

2. $\int x \log x\, dx.$

3.* $\int x \log (x + 1)\, dx.$

4.* $\int x^2 e^{-x}\, dx.$

5. $\int x^2 \log x\, dx.$

6.* $\int \log (-x)\, dx.$

7.* $\int \sqrt{x} \log x\, dx.$

8. $\int x^2 e^{-x^3}\, dx.$

9.* $\int x^3 e^{-x^2}\, dx.$

10.* $\int x^2 (e^x - 1)\, dx.$

11. $\int \dfrac{x}{\sqrt{1 - x^2}}.$

12.* $\int \dfrac{x^2}{\sqrt{1 - x}}\, dx.$

13.* $\int x\sqrt{x + 1}\, dx.$

14. $\int x \log x^2\, dx.$

15.* $\int (\log x)^2\, dx.$

16.* $\int x 2^x\, dx.$

17. $\int \dfrac{dx}{x(\log x)^3}.$

18.* $\int (x \log x)^2\, dx.$

19. Verify the reduction formula

$$\int x^n e^x\, dx = x^n e^x - n \int x^{n-1} e^x\, dx$$

and use it to find

$$\int x^3 e^x\, dx.$$

20. Sketch the region under the graph and compute its area.
    (a)* $f(x) = \log x, \quad x \in [1, e].$
    (b) $f(x) = \log |x|, \quad x \in [-e, -1].$
    (c)* $f(x) = x2^x, \quad x \in [0, 2].$
    (d) $f(x) = (1 - x)2^x, \quad x \in [0, 1].$

5.5 (Optional) The Equation $y'(x) + P(x)y(x) = Q(x)$

Differential equations (equations involving functions and their derivatives) arise so frequently in scientific problems that their study constitutes an important branch of mathematics.

The exponential function, being fixed under differentiation, that is, being endowed with the property

$$\frac{d}{dx} e^x = e^x,$$

plays an interesting role in the theory of differential equations.

In the case of linear differential equations, equations of the form

$$y^n(x) + P_1(x)y^{n-1}(x) + \cdots + P_{n-1}(x)y'(x) + P_n(x)y(x) = Q(x),$$

the exponential function plays a dominant role. We illustrate this by considering the first-order case:

$$y'(x) + P(x)y(x) = Q(x).$$

We begin with a special instance.

Problem 1.   Let a be a real number. Find all functions y satisfying the equation

$$y'(x) + ay(x) = 0 \quad \text{for all real } x.$$

SOLUTION.   Since $e^{ax} \neq 0$, we see that equivalent to

$$y'(x) + ay(x) = 0$$

is the equation

$$e^{ax}y'(x) + ae^{ax}y(x) = 0.$$

This last equation can be rewritten as

$$\frac{d}{dx}[e^{ax}y(x)] = 0.$$

This means that

$$e^{ax}y(x) = C \quad \text{and} \quad y(x) = Ce^{-ax}. \quad \square$$

Problem 2.   Of all the solutions to Problem 1, which satisfy the initial condition $y(x_0) = y_0$?

SOLUTION.   We have

$$y(x) = Ce^{-ax} \quad \text{for all real } x.$$

To require $y(x_0) = y_0$ is to require

$$y_0 = Ce^{-ax_0}$$

and thus

$$C = y_0e^{ax_0}.$$

This tells us that

$$y(x) = y_0e^{a(x_0-x)}$$

is the only solution of Problem 1 satisfying the condition

$$y(x_0) = y_0. \quad \square$$

Example 1. The only solution to the initial-value problem

$$y'(x) + 3y(x) = 0, \qquad y(1) = \pi,$$

is the function

$$y(x) = \pi e^{3(1-x)}. \quad \square$$

A little more general is the following problem.

Problem 3. Let a and b be real numbers, $a \neq 0$. Find all functions y satisfying

$$y'(x) + ay(x) = b.$$

SOLUTION. Again we multiply by e^{ax} and obtain this time

$$e^{ax}y'(x) + ae^{ax}y(x) = be^{ax}.$$

This means that

$$\frac{d}{dx}[e^{ax}y(x)] = be^{ax}$$

and thus

$$e^{ax}y(x) = \frac{b}{a}e^{ax} + C.$$

Multiplying through by e^{-ax}, we see that

$$y(x) = \frac{b}{a} + Ce^{-ax}. \quad \square$$

Problem 4. Of all the solutions of Problem 3, which satisfy the initial condition $y(x_0) = y_0$?

SOLUTION. We have

$$y(x) = \frac{b}{a} + Ce^{-ax}.$$

To require $y(x_0) = y_0$ is to require

$$y_0 = \frac{b}{a} + Ce^{-ax_0}$$

and thus

$$C = \left(y_0 - \frac{b}{a}\right)e^{ax_0}.$$

This tells us that

$$y(x) = \frac{b}{a} + \left(y_0 - \frac{b}{a}\right)e^{a(x_0-x)}$$

is the only solution of Problem 3 satisfying

$$y(x_0) = y_0. \quad \square$$

Example 2.   The only solution to the initial-value problem

$$y'(x) - \tfrac{1}{3}y(x) = 1, \qquad y(\tfrac{1}{2}) = -2,$$

is the function

$$y(x) = -3 + e^{(x-1/2)/3}. \quad \square$$

Problem 5.   Let P and Q be functions continuous on the interval (a, b). Find all functions y satisfying the equation

$$y'(x) + P(x)y(x) = Q(x) \qquad \text{for all } x \in (a, b).$$

SOLUTION.   The idea here is to suitably generalize the technique which worked well for Problems 1 and 3. We begin by defining the function

$$H(x) = \int_{x_0}^{x} P(t)\, dt,$$

where x_0 is an arbitrary number in (a, b). If we multiply the equation by $e^{H(x)}$, we obtain

$$e^{H(x)}y'(x) + P(x)e^{H(x)}y(x) = Q(x)e^{H(x)}.$$

Since

$$H'(x) = P(x),$$

we can rewrite the above equation as

$$\frac{d}{dx}[e^{H(x)}y(x)] = Q(x)e^{H(x)}.$$

This leads to

$$e^{H(x)}y(x) = C + \int_{x_0}^{x} Q(s)e^{H(s)}\, ds,$$

and thus to

$$y(x) = e^{-H(x)}\left[C + \int_{x_0}^{x} Q(s)e^{H(s)}\, ds\right]. \quad \square$$

Problem 6.   Of all the solutions to Problem 5, which satisfy the initial condition $y(x_0) = y_0$?

SOLUTION.   We have

$$y(x) = e^{-H(x)}\left[C + \int_{x_0}^{x} Q(s)e^{H(s)}\, ds\right], \qquad \text{with } H(x) = \int_{x_0}^{x} P(t)\, dt.$$

Since

$$e^{-H(x_0)} = e^0 = 1 \qquad \text{and} \qquad \int_{x_0}^{x_0} Q(s)e^{H(s)}\, ds = 0,$$

to require that $y(x_0) = y_0$ is simply to require that

$$C = y_0.$$

Thus

$$y(x) = e^{-H(x)} \left[y_0 + \int_{x_0}^{x} Q(s)e^{H(s)} \, ds \right]$$

is the only solution of Problem 5 which satisfies the condition

$$y(x_0) = y_0. \quad \square$$

Example 3. Let us solve the initial-value problem

$$y'(x) + 2y(x) = x^2, \qquad y(0) = 1.$$

SOLUTION. Here we have $P(x) = 2$ and $Q(x) = x^2$. Thus

$$H(x) = \int_0^x 2 \, dt = 2x \qquad \text{and} \qquad y(x) = e^{-2x}\left(1 + \int_0^x s^2 e^{2s} \, ds\right).$$

Evaluating the integral by twice integrating by parts, we find that

$$\int_0^x s^2 e^{2s} \, ds = e^{2x}(\tfrac{1}{2}x^2 - \tfrac{1}{2}x + \tfrac{1}{4}) - \tfrac{1}{4},$$

so that

$$y(x) = \tfrac{3}{4}e^{-2x} + \tfrac{1}{2}x^2 - \tfrac{1}{2}x + \tfrac{1}{4}. \quad \square$$

Exercises

Solve the following initial-value problems.

1.* $y'(x) + y(x) = 0$, $y(2) = -1$.
2. $y'(x) + y(x) = 0$, $y(0) = 0$.
3.* $y'(x) - y(x) = 1$, $y(\tfrac{1}{3}) = 2$.
4. $4y'(x) + 5y(x) - 2 = 0$, $y(\pi) = 1$.
5. $2y'(x) + y(x) = -3$, $y(-2) = -1$.
6.* $y'(x) + y(x) = x$, $y(0) = 1$.
7.* $y'(x) - y(x) = e^x$, $y(0) = 2$.
8. $y'(x) - y(x) = e^{2x}$, $y(1) = 1$.

9.* $y'(x) + \dfrac{1}{x}y(x) = 2x$, $y(3) = \dfrac{1}{2}$.

10. $y'(x) + \dfrac{2}{x}y(x) = e^{-x}$, $y(1) = -1$.

11.* $y'(x) + y(x) = \dfrac{1}{1 + e^x}$, $y(0) = e$.

12. $y'(x) + y(x) = \dfrac{1}{1 + 2e^x}$, $y(0) = e$.

13.* A 200-gal tank initially full of water develops a leak at the bottom. Given that 20% of the water leaks out in the first 5 min, find the amount of water left in the tank t minutes after the leak develops
   (i) if the water drains off at a rate that is proportional to the amount of water present;
   (ii) if the water drains off at a rate that is proportional to the product of the time elapsed and the amount of water present.

14. An object falling in air is subject not only to gravitational force but also to air resistance. Find $v(t)$, the velocity of the object at time t, given that

$$v'(t) + Kv(t) = 32, \qquad K > 0$$

and

$$v(0) = 0.$$

Show that $v(t)$ cannot exceed $32/K$. ($32/K$ is called the *terminal velocity*.)

15.* At a certain moment a 100-gal mixing tank is full of brine containing 0.25 lbs of salt per gallon. Find the amount of salt present t minutes later if the brine is being continuously drawn off at the rate of 3 gal per minute and replaced by brine containing 0.2 lbs of salt per gallon.

5.6   Additional problems

1.* Find the minimum value of

$$y = ae^{kx} + be^{-kx}, \qquad a > 0, \quad b > 0.$$

2.   Show that if

$$y = \tfrac{1}{2}a(e^{x/a} + e^{-x/a})$$

then

$$y'' = \frac{y}{a^2}.$$

3.* Find the points of inflection of the graph of

$$y = e^{-x^2}.$$

4.   A rectangle has one side on the x-axis and the two upper vertices on the graph of

$$y = e^{-x^2}.$$

At what points should the upper vertices be so as to maximize the area of the rectangle?

5.* A telegraph cable consists of a core of copper wires with a covering made of non-conducting material. If x denotes the ratio of the radius of the core to the thickness of the covering, it is known that the speed of signaling is proportional to $x^2 \log (1/x)$. For what value of x is the speed a maximum?

6.   A rectangle has two sides along the coordinate axes and one vertex at a point P which moves along the curve $y = e^x$ in such a way that y increases at the rate of $\tfrac{1}{2}$ unit per minute. How fast is the area of the rectangle increasing when $y = 3$?

7.* Find

$$\lim_{h \to 0} \frac{1}{h} (e^h - 1).$$

8.   Show that

$$y = Ae^{\alpha x} + Be^{-\alpha x}$$

satisfies the differential equation

$$y'' - \alpha^2 y = 0.$$

9.   Find a function y which satisfies the differential equation of Problem 8 and the initial conditions below.
   (a)* $y(0) = 0$, $y'(0) = \alpha$.   (c)* $y(0) = 1$, $y'(0) = \alpha$.
   (b) $y(0) = \alpha$, $y'(0) = 0$.   (d) $y(0) = \alpha^2$, $y(1) = \alpha$.

10.   A particle moves along a coordinate line so that at time t it has coordinate $x(t)$, velocity $v(t)$, and acceleration $a(t)$. Find
   (a)* $x(1)$ given that $x(0) = 0$, $v(0) = 2$ and $a(t) = 4x(t)$.
   (b) $x(2)$ given that $x(0) = 1$, $v(0) = 0$ and $a(t) = 9x(t)$.

6

THE TRIGONOMETRIC AND HYPERBOLIC FUNCTIONS

6.1 Differentiating the trigonometric functions

An outline of what you are expected to remember about trigonometry appears in Chapter 1.

Just as the calculus of logarithms is simplified by the use of the base e, the calculus of the trigonometric functions is simplified by the use of radian measurement. Throughout our discussion we will use radian measurement and only radian measurement.

We begin our discussion with the sine function, the graph of which appears in Figure 6.1.1.

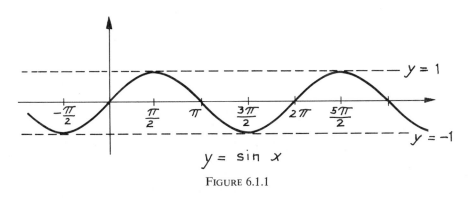

$$y = \sin x$$

FIGURE 6.1.1

To differentiate the sine function we must form the difference quotient

$$\frac{\sin (x + h) - \sin x}{h}$$

and take its limit as h tends to 0. Since

$$\sin (x + h) = \sin x \cos h + \cos x \sin h,$$

we obtain for $h \neq 0$

$$\frac{\sin (x + h) - \sin x}{h} = \cos x \frac{\sin h}{h} - \sin x \frac{1 - \cos h}{h}.$$

We are thus led to consider the behavior of

$$\frac{\sin h}{h} \quad \text{and} \quad \frac{1 - \cos h}{h}$$

as h tends to 0. In the exercises you are asked to show that

$$|\sin h| \leq |h|$$

and then that

$$\lim_{h \to 0} \sin h = 0 \quad \text{and} \quad \lim_{h \to 0} \cos h = 1.$$

Assuming these results, we can now prove that

$$\lim_{h \to 0} \frac{\sin h}{h} = 1 \quad \text{and} \quad \lim_{h \to 0} \frac{1 - \cos h}{h} = 0.$$

PROOF. First we prove that

$$\lim_{h \to 0} \frac{\sin h}{h} = 1.$$

For small $h > 0$, we refer to Figure 6.1.2.

$$\text{Area of triangle } OAP = \frac{1}{2} \sin h$$

$$\text{Area of sector } = \frac{h}{2}$$

$$\text{Area of triangle } OAQ = \frac{1}{2} \tan h = \frac{1}{2} \frac{\sin h}{\cos h}.$$

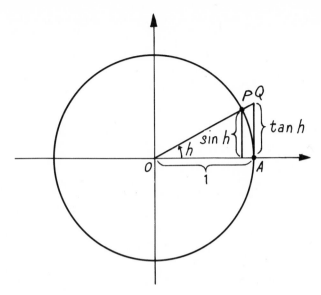

FIGURE 6.1.2

Since

$$\text{triangle } OAP \subseteq \text{sector} \subseteq \text{triangle } OAQ$$

(and these are all proper containments), we must have

$$\frac{1}{2} \sin h < \frac{h}{2} < \frac{1 \sin h}{2 \cos h}$$

$$\sin h < h < \frac{\sin h}{\cos h}$$

$$\frac{\cos h}{\sin h} < \frac{1}{h} < \frac{1}{\sin h}$$

$$\cos h < \frac{\sin h}{h} < 1.$$

This last inequality was derived for $h > 0$ but since

$$\cos(-h) = \cos h \qquad \text{and} \qquad \frac{\sin(-h)}{-h} = \frac{-\sin h}{-h} = \frac{\sin h}{h},$$

the inequality also holds for $h < 0$.

With

$$\cos h < \frac{\sin h}{h} < 1$$

together with

$$\lim_{h \to 0} \cos h = 1,$$

we can conclude from the pinching theorem that

$$\lim_{h \to 0} \frac{\sin h}{h} = 1.$$

The proof that

$$\lim_{h \to 0} \frac{1 - \cos h}{h} = 0$$

is easier:

$$\left| \frac{1 - \cos h}{h} \right| \underset{\text{since } |\sin h| < |h|}{\leq} \left| \frac{1 - \cos h}{\sin h} \right| \underset{\text{since } 1 - \cos^2 h = \sin^2 h}{=} \left| \frac{\sin h}{1 + \cos h} \right| \to \frac{0}{2} = 0.$$

The details are not hard to fill in.   □

From

$$\frac{\sin (x + h) - \sin x}{h} = \cos x \frac{\sin h}{h} - \sin x \frac{1 - \cos h}{h}$$

together with

$$\lim_{h \to 0} \frac{\sin h}{h} = 1 \quad \text{and} \quad \lim_{h \to 0} \frac{1 - \cos h}{h} = 0,$$

it follows that

$$\boxed{\frac{d}{dx} (\sin x) = \cos x.}$$

The other differentiation formulas are now easy to obtain. Since

$$\cos x = \sin \left(\frac{\pi}{2} - x \right),$$

the chain rule gives

$$\frac{d}{dx} (\cos x) = \frac{d}{dx} \left[\sin \left(\frac{\pi}{2} - x \right) \right] = -\cos \left(\frac{\pi}{2} - x \right) = -\sin x.$$

In short

$$\boxed{\frac{d}{dx} (\cos x) = -\sin x.}$$

Since

$$\tan x = \frac{\sin x}{\cos x},$$

we have

$$\frac{d}{dx}(\tan x) = \frac{\cos x \frac{d}{dx}(\sin x) - \sin x \frac{d}{dx}(\cos x)}{\cos^2 x}$$

$$= \frac{\cos^2 x + \sin^2 x}{\cos^2 x}$$

$$= \frac{1}{\cos^2 x}$$

$$= \sec^2 x$$

and thus the formula

$$\boxed{\frac{d}{dx}(\tan x) = \sec^2 x.}$$

The derivatives of the other trigonometric functions are as follows:

$$\boxed{\frac{d}{dx}(\cot x) = -\operatorname{cosec}^2 x}$$

$$\frac{d}{dx}(\sec x) = \sec x \tan x \qquad \frac{d}{dx}(\operatorname{cosec} x) = -\operatorname{cosec} x \cot x.$$

The verification of these formulas is left as an exercise. □
   For future reference we give on the next page the graphs of the cosine and tangent functions. The graphs of the other trigonometric functions are not so important to us.

Problem. Find

$$\frac{d}{dx}[(\cos ax)(\sin ax)].$$

SOLUTION

$$\frac{d}{dx}[(\cos ax)(\sin ax)] = \cos ax \frac{d}{dx}(\sin ax) + \sin ax \frac{d}{dx}(\cos ax)$$

$$= (\cos ax)(a \cos ax) + (\sin ax)(-a \sin ax)$$

$$= a[\cos^2 (ax) - \sin^2 (ax)]$$

$$= a \cos (2ax). \quad □$$

Problem. Find

$$\frac{d}{dx}(\tan \sqrt{1 - x^2}).$$

SOLUTION

$$\frac{d}{dx}(\tan\sqrt{1-x^2}) = \sec^2\sqrt{1-x^2} \cdot \frac{d}{dx}\sqrt{1-x^2}$$

$$= \sec^2\sqrt{1-x^2}\,\frac{-x}{\sqrt{1-x^2}}$$

$$= -\,\frac{x\sec^2\sqrt{1-x^2}}{\sqrt{1-x^2}} \cdot \quad\square$$

$$y = \cos x$$

FIGURE 6.1.3

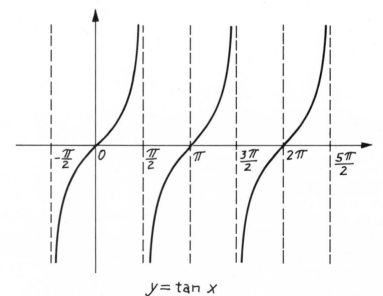

$$y = \tan x$$

FIGURE 6.1.4

Problem. Find

$$\frac{d}{dx} (\log |\cos x|).$$

SOLUTION

$$\frac{d}{dx} (\log |\cos x|) = \frac{1}{\cos x} \frac{d}{dx} (\cos x)$$

$$= \frac{1}{\cos x} (-\sin x)$$

$$= -\tan x. \quad \square$$

Problem. Find

$$\frac{d}{dx} (\sqrt{x} \sec \sqrt{x}).$$

SOLUTION

$$\frac{d}{dx} (\sqrt{x} \sec \sqrt{x}) = \sqrt{x} \frac{d}{dx} (\sec \sqrt{x}) + (\sec \sqrt{x}) \frac{d}{dx} (\sqrt{x})$$

$$= \sqrt{x} \left(\sec \sqrt{x} \right) \left(\tan \sqrt{x} \right) \left(\frac{1}{2\sqrt{x}} \right) + \left(\sec \sqrt{x} \right) \left(\frac{1}{2\sqrt{x}} \right)$$

$$= \frac{\sec \sqrt{x}}{2\sqrt{x}} [(\sqrt{x} \tan \sqrt{x}) + 1]. \quad \square$$

Problem. Find

$$\frac{d}{dx} (x^{\sin x}).$$

SOLUTION

$$\frac{d}{dx} (x^{\sin x}) = \frac{d}{dx} (e^{\sin x \log x})$$

$$= e^{\sin x \log x} \frac{d}{dx} [\sin x \log x]$$

$$= x^{\sin x} \left[\sin x \frac{d}{dx} (\log x) + \log x \frac{d}{dx} (\sin x) \right]$$

$$= x^{\sin x} \left[(\sin x) \frac{1}{x} + (\log x)(\cos x) \right]. \quad \square$$

Problem.   Let

$$f(x) = \sin^2 x, \qquad x \in (0, \pi).$$

(a) On what intervals is f increasing? Decreasing? (b) Find the extreme values of f. (c) Determine the concavity of the graph and find the points of inflection. (d) Sketch the graph.

SOLUTION.   Here

$$f(x) = \sin^2 x$$

$$f'(x) = 2 \sin x \frac{d}{dx} (\sin x) = 2 \sin x \cos x = \sin 2x$$

$$f''(x) = 2 \cos 2x.$$

Since

$$f'(x) \text{ is } \begin{cases} \text{positive,} & \text{for } 0 < x < \pi/2 \\ \quad 0, & \text{at } x = \pi/2 \\ \text{negative,} & \text{for } \pi/2 < x < \pi \end{cases},$$

f increases on $(0, \pi/2]$ and decreases on $[\pi/2, \pi)$. The number

$$f\left(\frac{\pi}{2}\right) = 1$$

is a local and absolute maximum. There are no other extreme values. Since

$$f''(x) \text{ is } \begin{cases} \text{positive,} & \text{for } 0 < x < \pi/4 \\ \quad 0, & \text{at } x = \pi/4 \\ \text{negative,} & \text{for } \pi/4 < x < 3\pi/4 \\ \quad 0, & \text{at } x = 3\pi/4 \\ \text{positive,} & \text{for } 3\pi/4 < x < \pi \end{cases},$$

the graph is concave up on $(0, \pi/4]$, concave down on $[\pi/4, 3\pi/4]$, and concave up again on $[3\pi/4, \pi)$. The points of inflection are

$$\left(\frac{\pi}{4}, f\left(\frac{\pi}{4}\right)\right) = \left(\frac{\pi}{4}, \frac{1}{2}\right) \quad \text{and} \quad \left(\frac{3\pi}{4}, f\left(\frac{3\pi}{4}\right)\right) = \left(\frac{3\pi}{4}, \frac{1}{2}\right).$$

The graph is pictured in Figure 6.1.5. $\square$

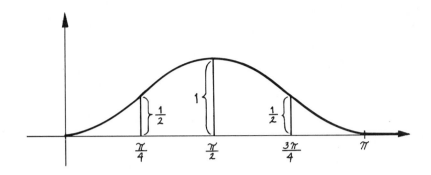

$$y = \sin^2 x, \ x \in (0, \pi)$$

FIGURE 6.1.5

Exercises

Differentiate.

1.* $y = \sin 3x$.

2. $y = \sin x \cos x$.

3.* $y = x \tan x$.

4.* $y = \sin x + \cos x$.

5. $y = \tan x^2$.

6.* $y = \sin \sqrt{x}$.

7.* $y = \cos \pi x \sin \pi x$.

8. $y = \sec x \tan x$.

9.* $y = x^2 \sin \pi x$.

10.* $y = \frac{1}{2} \sin^2 x$.

11. $y = \log |\sin x|$.

12.* $y = \tan^3 \frac{x}{2}$.

13.* $y = e^x \sin x$.

14. $y = e^x \cos x$.

15.* $y = \sqrt{\cos x^2}$.

16.* $y = (\cos \pi x)^x$.

17. $y = \sec ax$.

18.* $y = e^{-kx} \sin kx$.

19.* $y = 10^x \tan \pi x$.

20. $y = x^{2\pi} \cos 2\pi x$.

21.* $y = e^x \sin \frac{\pi x}{2}$.

22.* $y = \log \sqrt{\tan x}$.

23. $y = \frac{x - \sin x}{\tan x}$.

24.* $y = \tan^4 x$.

25.* $y = e^{\sin x}$.

26. $y = e^{\sin x} \cos x$.

27.* $y = \sec^2 x \tan^2 x$.

28.* $y = \sin nx \sin^n x$.

29. $y = \frac{\sin x}{x}$.

30.* $y = \log \sqrt{\cos 2x}$.

31. Find a formula for the nth derivative of

   (a) $y = \sin x$, (b) $y = \cos x$.

For each of the functions below, (i) find the intervals where it is increasing and the intervals where it is decreasing, (ii) find the extreme values, (iii) determine the concavity of the graph and find the points of inflection, and finally, (iv) sketch the graph.

32.* $f(x) = x + \sin x, \ 0 \le x \le 2\pi$.

33. $f(x) = x - \sin x, \ 0 \le x \le 2\pi$.

34.* $f(x) = x \tan x, \ -\pi/2 < x < \pi/2$.

35. $f(x) = e^x \cos x, \ 0 \le x \le 2\pi$.

36.* $f(x) = e^x(\cos x + \sin x), \ 0 \le x \le 2\pi$.

37. $f(x) = \cos^2 x$, $0 \le x \le \pi$.

38.   Prove that for all real x and y

(a) $|\cos x - \cos y| \le |x - y|$,   (b) $|\sin x - \sin y| \le |x - y|$.

[HINT: Apply the mean-value theorem.]

Find the limits which exist.

39.* $\displaystyle\lim_{x \to 0} \frac{\sin 3x}{x}$.

41.* $\displaystyle\lim_{x \to 0} \frac{2x}{\sin 3x}$.

43. $\displaystyle\lim_{x \to 0} \frac{\sin x^2}{x^2}$.

40. $\displaystyle\lim_{x \to 0} \frac{\sin x}{3x}$.

42.* $\displaystyle\lim_{x \to 0} \frac{\sin x^2}{x}$.

44.* $\displaystyle\lim_{x \to 0} \frac{\sin x}{x^2}$.

45.   Show that

$$|\sin h| \le |h|.$$ (Begin with Figure 6.1.2)

46.   Show that

$$\lim_{h \to 0} \sin h = 0.$$ (Use Exercise 45)

47.   Show that

$$\lim_{h \to 0} \cos h = 1.$$ $\left(\sin^2 \dfrac{t}{2} = \dfrac{1 - \cos t}{2}\right)$

6.2 Integrating the trigonometric functions

In the last section you saw that each trigonometric function is differentiable on its domain and that

$$\frac{d}{dx}(\sin x) = \cos x \qquad\qquad \frac{d}{dx}(\cos x) = -\sin x$$

$$\frac{d}{dx}(\tan x) = \sec^2 x \qquad\qquad \frac{d}{dx}(\cot x) = -\operatorname{cosec}^2 x$$

$$\frac{d}{dx}(\sec x) = \sec x \tan x \qquad\qquad \frac{d}{dx}(\operatorname{cosec} x) = -\operatorname{cosec} x \cot x.$$

Here we integrate the trigonometric functions. As we shall show in a moment, the following formulas are valid:

(i) $\displaystyle\int \sin x \, dx = -\cos x + C$

(ii) $\displaystyle\int \cos x \, dx = \sin x + C$

(iii) $\displaystyle\int \tan x \, dx = \log|\sec x| + C$

(iv) $\displaystyle\int \cot x \, dx = \log|\sin x| + C$

(v) $\displaystyle\int \sec x \, dx = \log|\sec x + \tan x| + C$

(vi) $\displaystyle\int \operatorname{cosec} x \, dx = \log|\operatorname{cosec} x - \cot x| + C$

VERIFICATION

(i) $\int \sin x \, dx = -\int -\sin x \, dx = -\int \frac{d}{dx} (\cos x) \, dx = -\cos x + C.$

(ii) $\int \cos x \, dx = \int \frac{d}{dx} (\sin x) \, dx = \sin x + C.$

(iii) $\int \tan x \, dx = \int \frac{\sin x}{\cos x} \, dx$

$$= -\int \frac{1}{\cos x} \frac{d}{dx} (\cos x) \, dx$$

$$= -\int \frac{d}{dx} \log|\cos x| \, dx$$

$$= \log \frac{1}{|\cos x|} + C$$

$$= \log |\sec x| + C.$$

(iv) $\int \cot x \, dx = \int \frac{\cos x}{\sin x} \, dx$

$$= \int \frac{1}{\sin x} \frac{d}{dx} (\sin x) \, dx$$

$$= \int \frac{d}{dx} \log|\sin x| \, dx$$

$$= \log|\sin x| + C.$$

(v) $\int \sec x \, dx = \int \sec x \frac{\sec x + \tan x}{\sec x + \tan x} \, dx$

$$= \int \frac{\sec x \tan x + \sec^2 x}{\sec x + \tan x} \, dx$$

$$= \int \frac{1}{\sec x + \tan x} \frac{d}{dx} (\sec x + \tan x) \, dx$$

$$= \int \frac{d}{dx} \log|\sec x + \tan x| dx$$

$$= \log|\sec x + \tan x| + C.$$

(vi) $\int \operatorname{cosec} x \, dx = \int \operatorname{cosec} x \frac{\operatorname{cosec} x - \cot x}{\operatorname{cosec} x - \cot x} \, dx$

$$= \int \frac{-\operatorname{cosec} x \cot x + \operatorname{cosec}^2 x}{\operatorname{cosec} x - \cot x} \, dx$$

$$= \int \frac{1}{\operatorname{cosec} x - \cot x} \frac{d}{dx} (\operatorname{cosec} x - \cot x) \, dx$$

$$= \int \frac{d}{dx} \log|\operatorname{cosec} x - \cot x| \, dx$$

$$= \log|\operatorname{cosec} x - \cot x| + C. \quad \square$$

Problem. Find

$$\int \sin x \cos x \, dx.$$

SOLUTION

$$\int \sin x \cos x \, dx = \int \sin x \frac{d}{dx} (\sin x) \, dx$$

$$= \int \frac{d}{dx} \left(\frac{\sin^2 x}{2} \right) dx$$

$$= \frac{\sin^2 x}{2} + C. \quad \square$$

Problem. Find

$$\int \sec^3 x \tan x \, dx.$$

SOLUTION

$$\int \sec^3 x \tan x \, dx = \int \sec^2 x \cdot \sec x \tan x \, dx$$

$$= \int \sec^2 x \frac{d}{dx} (\sec x) \, dx$$

$$= \int \frac{d}{dx} \left(\frac{\sec^3 x}{3} \right) dx$$

$$= \frac{\sec^3 x}{3} + C. \quad \square$$

Problem. Find

$$\int x \cos \pi x^2 \, dx.$$

SOLUTION

$$\int x \cos \pi x^2 \, dx = \frac{1}{2\pi} \int 2\pi x \cos \pi x^2 \, dx$$

$$= \frac{1}{2\pi} \int \cos \pi x^2 \frac{d}{dx} (\pi x^2) \, dx$$

$$= \frac{1}{2\pi} \int \frac{d}{dx} (\sin \pi x^2) \, dx$$

$$= \frac{1}{2\pi} \sin \pi x^2 + C. \quad \square$$

Problem. Find

$$\int \frac{\sec^2 x}{1 - \tan x} \, dx.$$

SOLUTION

$$\int \frac{\sec^2 x}{1 - \tan x} \, dx = -\int \frac{-\sec^2 x}{1 - \tan x} \, dx$$

$$= -\int \frac{1}{1 - \tan x} \frac{d}{dx} (1 - \tan x) \, dx$$

$$= -\int \frac{d}{dx} \log|1 - \tan x| \, dx$$

$$= -\log|1 - \tan x| + C$$

$$= \log \left| \frac{1}{1 - \tan x} \right| + C. \quad \square$$

Problem. Find

$$\int x \sin x \, dx$$

SOLUTION. What causes difficulty here is the factor x. We can eliminate the x by integrating by parts. If we set

$$f(x) = x \quad \text{and} \quad g'(x) = \sin x,$$

then we can write

$$f'(x) = 1 \quad \text{and} \quad g(x) = -\cos x.$$

The formula

$$\int f(x)g'(x) \, dx = f(x)g(x) - \int f'(x)g(x) \, dx + C$$

gives here

$$\int x \sin x \, dx = -x \cos x + \int \cos x \, dx + C$$

$$= -x \cos x + \sin x + C. \quad \square$$

Problem. Find

$$\int e^x \cos x \, dx.$$

SOLUTION. We integrate by parts twice. By setting

$$f(x) = e^x, \quad g'(x) = \cos x,$$
$$f'(x) = e^x, \quad g(x) = \sin x,$$

we have

(1) $$\int e^x \cos x \, dx = e^x \sin x - \int e^x \sin x \, dx + C.$$

To determine the integral on the right, we set

$$f(x) = e^x, \quad g'(x) = \sin x,$$
$$f'(x) = e^x, \quad g(x) = -\cos x.$$

This gives

(2) $$\int e^x \sin x \, dx = -e^x \cos x + \int e^x \cos x \, dx + C_1.$$

Substituting (2) into (1), absorbing the constant C_1 into C, we get

$$\int e^x \cos x \, dx = e^x \sin x + e^x \cos x - \int e^x \cos x \, dx + C.$$

$$2\int e^x \cos x \, dx = e^x \sin x + e^x \cos x + C$$

$$\int e^x \cos x \, dx = \frac{e^x}{2}(\sin x + \cos x) + C. \quad \square$$

Exercises

Find the following indefinite integrals.

1.* $\displaystyle\int \cos(3x - 1) \, dx.$

2. $\displaystyle\int \cos\left(\frac{\pi}{2}x\right) dx.$

3.* $\displaystyle\int 3 \sin^2 x \cos x \, dx.$

4.* $\displaystyle\int \sec 2x \tan 2x \, dx.$

5. $\displaystyle\int \cos^4 x \sin x \, dx.$

6.* $\displaystyle\int \sqrt{1 + \cos x} \, \sin x \, dx.$

7.* $\displaystyle\int e^{-\sin x} \cos x \, dx.$

8. $\displaystyle\int x \tan x^2 \, dx.$

9.* $\displaystyle\int \frac{\sin \sqrt{x}}{\sqrt{x}} \, dx.$

10.* $\displaystyle\int \frac{\cos x}{\sqrt{1 - \sin x}} \, dx.$

11. $\displaystyle\int \frac{\sin x}{\sqrt{1 + \cos x}} \, dx.$

12.* $\displaystyle\int \frac{\sin x}{1 + \cos x} \, dx.$

13.* $\displaystyle\int \cos^2(\pi x) \sin(\pi x) \, dx.$

14. $\displaystyle\int \frac{\cos x}{1 + 2\sin x} \, dx.$

15.* $\displaystyle\int \cot(\pi x) \, dx.$

16.* $\displaystyle\int \sec^2(\pi - x) \, dx.$

17. $\displaystyle\int \sec^2 x \tan x \, dx.$

18.* $\displaystyle\int \frac{\cos 2x}{2 - \sin 2x} \, dx.$

19.* $\displaystyle\int \frac{dx}{\cos^2 x} \, dx.$

20. $\displaystyle\int (1 + \tan^2 x) \sec^2 x \, dx.$

21.* $\displaystyle\int \sqrt{1 + \tan x} \, \sec^2 x \, dx.$

22.* $\displaystyle\int \cos^2\left(\frac{x}{2}\right) dx.$ $\quad\left[\text{HINT: } \cos^2\left(\frac{x}{2}\right) = \frac{1 + \cos x}{2}.\right]$

23.* $\displaystyle\int \cos^2 x \, dx.$

24. $\displaystyle\int \sin^2 x \, dx.$

25.* $\displaystyle\int \cos^2(\pi x) \, dx.$

Find the following by integrating by parts.

26.* $\displaystyle\int x \cos x \, dx.$

27. $\displaystyle\int x \cos(x + \pi) \, dx.$

28.* $\displaystyle\int e^x \sin x \, dx.$

29. $\displaystyle\int \sec^3 x \, dx.$

6.3　The inverse trigonometric functions

The Arc Sine of x

We begin with a number x in the interval $[-1, 1]$. Although there are infinitely many numbers at which the sine function takes on the value x, only one of these numbers lies in the interval $[-\pi/2, \pi/2]$.

> The *arc sine* of x is the unique number in $[-\pi/2, \pi/2]$ whose sine is x.

In symbols,

> $y = \text{arc sin } x$　iff　y is in $[-\pi/2, \pi/2]$ and $\sin y = x$.

The function

$$y = \text{arc sin } x$$

is called the *inverse sine function*. It is, of course, *not* the inverse of the sine function but rather the inverse of

$$y = \sin x, \quad \text{with } x \text{ restricted to } [-\pi/2, \pi/2].$$

The graphs of these two functions are given in Figures 6.3.1 and 6.3.2.

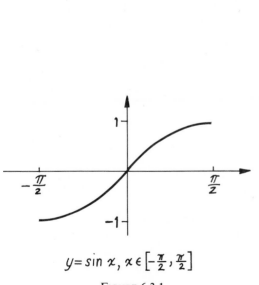

$y = \sin x, \; x \in \left[-\frac{\pi}{2}, \frac{\pi}{2}\right]$

FIGURE 6.3.1

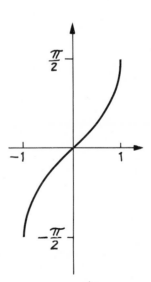

$y = \text{arc sin } x$

FIGURE 6.3.2

Since

$$\frac{d}{dx}(\sin x) = \cos x \neq 0$$

for x in the open interval $(-\pi/2, \pi/2)$, the arc sine function is differentiable on the open interval $(-1, 1)$. We can find its derivative

$$\frac{d}{dx}(\text{arc sin } x)$$

by differentiating the identity

$$\sin(\text{arc sin } x) = x.$$

So doing, we get

$$\frac{d}{dx}[\sin(\text{arc sin } x)] = 1$$

$$\cos(\text{arc sin } x)\frac{d}{dx}(\text{arc sin } x) = 1$$

$$\sqrt{1 - \sin^2(\text{arc sin } x)}\frac{d}{dx}(\text{arc sin } x) = 1$$

$$\sqrt{1 - x^2}\frac{d}{dx}(\text{arc sin } x) = 1$$

and therefore

$$\boxed{\frac{d}{dx}(\text{arc sin } x) = \frac{1}{\sqrt{1 - x^2}} \cdot}$$

To find

$$\int \text{arc sin } x \, dx$$

we integrate by parts. Setting

$$f(x) = \text{arc sin } x \quad \text{and} \quad g'(x) = 1,$$

we can write

$$f'(x) = \frac{1}{\sqrt{1 - x^2}} \quad \text{and} \quad g(x) = x.$$

This gives

$$\int \text{arc sin } x \, dx = x \text{ arc sin } x - \int \frac{x}{\sqrt{1 - x^2}} \, dx + C,$$

so that

$$\boxed{\int \text{arc sin } x \, dx = x \text{ arc sin } x + \sqrt{1 - x^2} + C.}$$

The Arc Tangent of x.

This time we begin with an arbitrary real number x. Although there are infinitely many numbers at which the tangent function takes on the value x, only one of these numbers lies in the interval $(-\pi/2, \pi/2)$.

> The *arc tangent* of x is the unique number in $(-\pi/2, \pi/2)$ whose tangent is x.

In symbols,

> $y = \text{arc tan } x$ iff y is in $(-\pi/2, \pi/2)$ and $\tan y = x$.

The function

$$y = \text{arc tan } x$$

is called the *inverse tangent function*. It is, of course, *not* the inverse of the tangent function but rather the inverse of

$$y = \tan x, \qquad \text{with } x \text{ restricted to } (-\pi/2, \pi/2).$$

The graphs of these two functions are given in Figures 6.3.3 and 6.3.4.

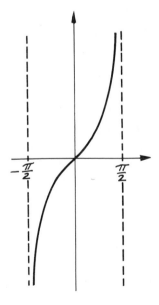

$$y = \tan x, \, x \in \left(-\frac{\pi}{2}, \frac{\pi}{2}\right)$$

FIGURE 6.3.3

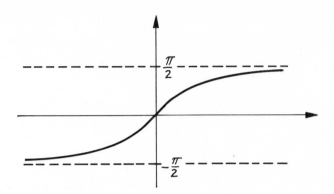

$$y = arc\ tan\ x$$

FIGURE 6.3.4

Since

$$\frac{d}{dx} (\tan x) = \sec^2 x \neq 0$$

for x in $(-\pi/2, \pi/2)$, the inverse tangent function is everywhere differentiable. We can find its derivative by differentiating the identity

$$\tan(arc\ tan\ x) = x.$$

Doing so, we get

$$\frac{d}{dx} [\tan (arc\ tan\ x)] = 1$$

$$\sec^2 (arc\ tan\ x) \frac{d}{dx} (arc\ tan\ x) = 1$$

$$[1 + \tan^2 (arc\ tan\ x)] \frac{d}{dx} (arc\ tan\ x) = 1$$

$$(1 + x^2) \frac{d}{dx} (arc\ tan\ x) = 1$$

and therefore

$$\boxed{\frac{d}{dx} (arc\ tan\ x) = \frac{1}{1 + x^2}.}$$

To find

$$\int arc\ tan\ x\ dx$$

we integrate by parts. Setting

$$f(x) = \text{arc tan } x \quad \text{and} \quad g'(x) = 1,$$

we can write

$$f'(x) = \frac{1}{1 + x^2} \quad \text{and} \quad g(x) = x.$$

This gives

$$\int \text{arc tan } x \, dx = x \text{ arc tan } x - \int \frac{x}{1 + x^2} \, dx + C$$

so that

$$\int \text{arc tan } x \, dx = x \text{ arc tan } x - \tfrac{1}{2} \log (1 + x^2) + C.$$

A Right-Triangle Interpretation

We can give a simple geometric interpretation to arc sin x and to arc tan x for which we refer to Figures 6.3.5 and 6.3.6.

There are four other trigonometric inverses. Instead of defining them in full we shall merely illustrate them in terms of right triangles.

FIGURE 6.3.5

FIGURE 6.3.6

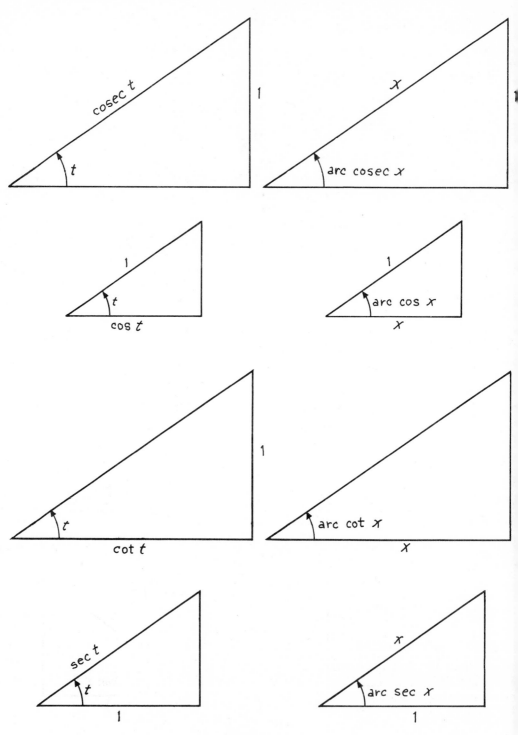

FIGURE 6.3.7

Exercises

Evaluate.

1.* arc sin 1.

2. arc tan 1.

3.* arc tan 0.

4.* arc cos 0.

5. arc tan (-1).

6.* arc sin $(1/\sqrt{2})$.

7.* arc cos $(1/\sqrt{2})$.

8. arc sin $\frac{1}{2}$.

9.* arc cos $\frac{1}{2}$.

10.* arc sin $(-\frac{1}{2})$.

11. arc sin (sin $5\pi/4$).

12.* arc tan [sin (-3π)].

Differentiate.

13.* $y =$ arc tan $(x + 1)$.

14. $y =$ arc tan $\sqrt{x}$.

15.* $y =$ arc sin x^2.

16. $f(x) = e^x$ arc sin x.

17.* $f(x) = x$ arc sin $2x$.

18. $f(x) = e^{\text{arc tan } x}$.

19.* $u = ($arc sin $x)^2$.

20. $v =$ arc tan (e^x).

21.* $y = \dfrac{\text{arc tan } x}{x}$.

22. $y =$ arc tan $\dfrac{2}{x}$.

23.* $f(x) = \sqrt{\text{arc tan } 2x}$.

24. $f(x) = \log ($arc tan $x)$.

25.* $y =$ arc tan $(\log x)$.

26. $y =$ arc tan $(\sin x)$.

27.* $\theta =$ arc sin $\sqrt{1 - r^2}$.

28. $\theta =$ arc sin $\left(\dfrac{r}{r + 1}\right)$.

29.* $\theta =$ arc tan $\left(\dfrac{c + r}{1 - cr}\right)$.

30. $\theta =$ arc tan $\left(\dfrac{1}{1 + r^2}\right)$.

31.* $f(x) = \sqrt{c^2 - x^2} + c$ arc sin $\dfrac{x}{c}$.

32. $f(x) = \dfrac{1}{3}$ arc sin $(3x - 4x^2)$.

33.* $y = \dfrac{x}{\sqrt{c^2 - x^2}} -$ arc sin $\dfrac{x}{c}$.

34. $y = x\sqrt{c^2 - x^2} + c^2$ arc sin $\dfrac{x}{c}$.

35. Show that

$$\int \frac{dx}{\sqrt{a^2 - x^2}} = \text{arc sin } \left(\frac{x}{a}\right) + C. \qquad (a > 0)$$

36. Show that

$$\int \frac{dx}{a^2 + x^2} = \frac{1}{a} \text{ arc tan } \left(\frac{x}{a}\right) + C. \qquad (a > 0)$$

37. Show that

$$\int \frac{dx}{a^2 + (x + b)^2} = \frac{1}{a} \text{ arc tan } \left(\frac{x + b}{a}\right) + C. \qquad (a > 0)$$

Evaluate.

38.* $\displaystyle\int_0^1 \frac{dx}{1 + x^2}$.

39. $\displaystyle\int_{-1}^1 \frac{dx}{1 + x^2}$.

40.* $\displaystyle\int_0^{1/\sqrt{2}} \frac{dx}{\sqrt{1 - x^2}}$.

41.* $\displaystyle\int_0^1 \frac{dx}{\sqrt{4-x^2}}$.

43.* $\displaystyle\int_0^5 \frac{dx}{25+x^2}$.

45. $\displaystyle\int_{-2}^0 \frac{dx}{25+(x+2)^2}$.

42.* $\displaystyle\int_1^3 \frac{dx}{\sqrt{4-x^2}}$.

44.* $\displaystyle\int_{-5}^5 \frac{dx}{25+x^2}$.

46. $\displaystyle\int_0^1 \frac{dx}{x^2+x+1}$.

47.   (i) Use the relation

$$\sec(\operatorname{arc sec} x) = x \quad \text{and} \quad \text{Figure 6.3.8}$$

to show that

$$\frac{d}{dx}(\operatorname{arc sec} x) = \frac{1}{x\sqrt{x^2-1}}, \qquad \text{for } x > 1.$$

Use a similar technique to figure out

(ii)* $\displaystyle\frac{d}{dx}(\operatorname{arc cos} x)$,   for $0 < x < 1$,

(iii)* $\displaystyle\frac{d}{dx}(\operatorname{arc cot} x)$,   for $x > 0$,

(iv)* $\displaystyle\frac{d}{dx}(\operatorname{arc cosec} x)$,   for $x > 1$.

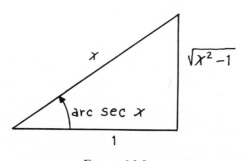

FIGURE 6.3.8

6.4 Additional problems

Find the area below the graph.

1.* $y = \dfrac{x}{x^2+1}$, $x \in [0, 1]$.

2. $y = \dfrac{1}{x^2+1}$, $x \in [0, 1]$.

3.* $y = \dfrac{1}{\sqrt{1-x^2}}$, $x \in \left[0, \dfrac{1}{2}\right]$.

4. $y = \dfrac{x}{\sqrt{1-x^2}}$, $x \in \left[0, \dfrac{1}{2}\right]$.

5.* $y = \operatorname{arc sin} x$, $x \in \left[0, \dfrac{\sqrt{3}}{2}\right]$.

6. $y = \operatorname{arc tan} x$, $x \in [0, 1]$.

7.* Find the maximum value of

$$y = a \sin x + b \cos x. \quad (a > 0, b > 0)$$

8. Find the maximum value of the slope of the curve in problem 7.

9. A particle moves along a coordinate line so that at time t it has coordinate $x(t)$, velocity $v(t)$, and acceleration $a(t)$. Find

(a)* $x(1)$ given that $x(0) = 0$ and $v(t) = 1/(t^2 + 1)$.

(b) $a(1)$ given that $v(t) = 1/(t^2 + 1)$.

(c)* $v(0)$ given that $v(1) = 1$ and $a(t) = (\text{arc tan } t)/(t^2 + 1)$.

(d) $x(1)$ given that $x(0) = 0$, $v(0) = 1$, and $a(t) = 1/(t^2 + 1)$.

(e)* $a(0)$ given that $x(t) = \text{arc tan } (1 + t)$.

10. A balloon, which leaves the ground 500 ft from an observer, rises vertically at the rate of 140 ft per minute. At what rate is the inclination of the observer's line of sight increasing when the balloon is 500 ft above the ground?

11.* The base of an isosceles triangle is 6 ft. If the altitude is 4 ft and increasing at the rate of 2 in. per minute, at what rate is the vertex angle changing?

12.* As a boy winds up the cord, his kite is moving horizontally at a height of 60 ft with a speed of 10 ft per minute. How fast is the inclination of the cord changing when its length is 100 ft?

13.* A revolving search light which is $\frac{1}{2}$ mi from shore makes 1 revolution per minute. How fast is the light traveling along the straight beach when at a distance of 1 mi from the nearest point of the shore?

14.* A tapestry 7 ft in height is hung on a wall so that its lower edge is 9 ft above an observer's eye. At what distance from the wall should he stand in order to obtain the most favorable view? [HINT: The vertical angle subtended by the tapestry in the eye of the observer must be a maximum.]

15.* Find the dimensions of the cylinder of maximum volume which can be inscribed in a sphere of radius 6 in. (Use the central angle θ subtended by the radius of the base.)

16. Solve Problem 15 if the curved surface of the cylinder is to be a maximum.

17.* A body of weight W is dragged along a horizontal plane by means of a force P whose line of action makes an angle θ with the plane. The magnitude of the force is given by the equation

$$P = \frac{mW}{m \sin \theta + \cos \theta},$$

where m denotes the coefficient of friction. For what value of θ is the pull a minimum?

18.* If a projectile is fired from O so as to strike an inclined plane which makes a constant angle α with the horizontal at O, the range is given by the formula

$$R = \frac{2v^2 \cos \theta \sin (\theta - \alpha)}{g \cos^2 \alpha},$$

where v and g are constants and θ is the angle of elevation. Calculate the value of θ which gives the maximum range.

19. Set

$$F(x) = \begin{cases} \sin (1/x), & x \neq 0 \\ 0, & x = 0 \end{cases},$$

$$G(x) = \begin{cases} x \sin 1/(x), & x \neq 0 \\ 0, & x = 0 \end{cases},$$

$$H(x) = \begin{cases} x^2 \sin (1/x), & x \neq 0 \\ 0, & x = 0 \end{cases}.$$

(a) Sketch the graph of F.
(b) Sketch the graph of G.
(c) Sketch the graph of H.
(d) Which of these functions are continuous at 0?
(e) Which of these functions are differentiable at 0?

6.5   The hyperbolic sine and cosine

The *hyperbolic sine* and *cosine* are the functions

$$\sinh x = \frac{e^x - e^{-x}}{2} \quad \text{and} \quad \cosh x = \frac{e^x + e^{-x}}{2}.$$

The reason for these names will become apparent as we go on.

Since

$$\frac{d}{dx} (\sinh x) = \frac{d}{dx} \left(\frac{e^x - e^{-x}}{2} \right) = \frac{e^x + e^{-x}}{2}$$

and

$$\frac{d}{dx} (\cosh x) = \frac{d}{dx} \left(\frac{e^x + e^{-x}}{2} \right) = \frac{e^x - e^{-x}}{2},$$

we have

$$\frac{d}{dx} (\sinh x) = \cosh x \quad \text{and} \quad \frac{d}{dx} (\cosh x) = \sinh x.$$

In short, each of these functions is the derivative of the other.

The Graphs

We begin with the hyperbolic sine. Since

$$\sinh (-x) = \frac{e^{-x} - e^x}{2} = -\frac{e^x - e^{-x}}{2} = -\sinh x,$$

the hyperbolic sine is an odd function and therefore its graph is symmetric with respect to the origin. Since

$$\frac{d}{dx}(\sinh x) = \cosh x = \frac{e^x + e^{-x}}{2} > 0 \qquad \text{for all real } x$$

the hyperbolic sine increases everywhere. From

$$\frac{d^2}{dx^2}(\sinh x) = \frac{d}{dx}(\cosh x) = \sinh x = \frac{e^x - e^{-x}}{2}$$

we see that

$$\frac{d^2}{dx^2}(\sinh x) \text{ is } \begin{cases} \text{negative,} & \text{for } x < 0 \\ 0, & \text{at } x = 0 \\ \text{positive,} & \text{for } x > 0 \end{cases}.$$

The graph is therefore concave down on $(-\infty, 0]$ and concave up on $[0, \infty)$. The point

$$(0, \sinh 0) = (0, 0)$$

is a point of inflection. The slope of the tangent at the origin is $\cosh 0 = 1$. A sketch of the graph appears in Figure 6.5.1. □

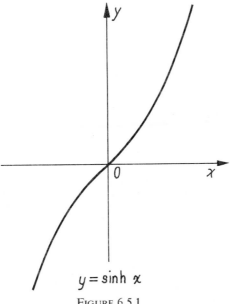

$$y = \sinh x$$

FIGURE 6.5.1

We turn now to the hyperbolic cosine. Since

$$\cosh(-x) = \frac{e^{-x} + e^{x}}{2} = \frac{e^{x} + e^{-x}}{2} = \cosh x,$$

the hyperbolic cosine is an even function. Its graph is therefore symmetric with respect to the y-axis. Since

$$\frac{d}{dx}(\cosh x) = \sinh x,$$

we see that

$$\frac{d}{dx}(\cosh x) \text{ is } \begin{cases} \text{negative,} & \text{for } x < 0 \\ 0, & \text{at } x = 0 \\ \text{positive,} & \text{for } x > 0 \end{cases}.$$

The function therefore decreases on $(-\infty, 0]$ and increases on $[0, \infty)$. The number

$$\cosh 0 = \frac{e^{0} + e^{-0}}{2} = \frac{1 + 1}{2} = 1$$

is a minimum. There are no other extreme values. Since

$$\frac{d^{2}}{dx^{2}}(\cosh x) = \frac{d}{dx}(\sinh x) = \cosh x > 0 \qquad \text{for all real } x,$$

the graph is everywhere concave up. For a picture of the graph see Figure 6.5.2. □

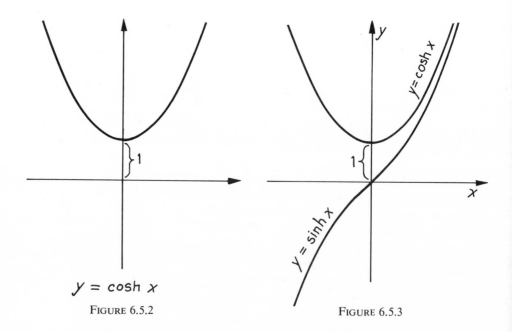

$y = \cosh x$

FIGURE 6.5.2

FIGURE 6.5.3

Figure 6.5.3 shows a comparison between the two graphs. The graph of $y = \cosh x$ remains above the graph of $y = \sinh x$,

$$\left[\cosh x - \sinh x = \frac{e^x + e^{-x}}{2} - \frac{e^x - e^{-x}}{2} = e^{-x} > 0 \right]$$

but the difference tends to 0 as x tends to $+\infty$.

Identities

These functions satisfy identities which are similar to those satisfied by the "circular" sine and cosine.

$$\cosh^2 t - \sinh^2 t = 1$$
$$\sinh (t + s) = \sinh t \cosh s + \cosh t \sinh s$$
$$\cosh (t + s) = \cosh t \cosh s + \sinh t \sinh s$$
$$\sinh 2t = 2 \sinh t \cosh t$$
$$\cosh 2t = \cosh^2 t + \sinh^2 t.$$

The verification of these identities is left to you as an exercise.

Relation to the Hyperbola $x^2 - y^2 = 1$

That

$$\cosh^2 t - \sinh^2 t = 1$$

means that points of the form

$$P(\cosh t, \sinh t)$$

all lie on the hyperbola

$$x^2 - y^2 = 1.$$

This in itself might justify calling these functions hyperbolic but, as you will see in a moment, there is actually a much deeper reason.

Let us return briefly to the unit circle $x^2 + y^2 = 1$ and the ordinary sine and cosine. If t lies between 0 and 2π, then $t/2$ gives the area of the sector shaded in Figure 6.5.4. We have an entirely analogous situation in the case of the hyperbola

$$x^2 - y^2 = 1$$

and the hyperbolic sine and cosine.

If $t > 0$, then $t/2$ gives the area of the hyperbolic sector shaded in Figure 6.5.5.

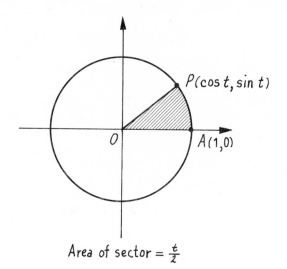

Area of sector $= \frac{t}{2}$

FIGURE 6.5.4

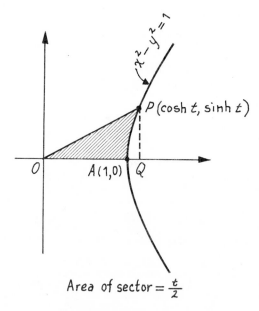

Area of sector $= \frac{t}{2}$

FIGURE 6.5.5

PROOF. Let's call the area of the shaded sector $A(t)$. It is not hard to see that

$$A(t) = \frac{1}{2} \cosh t \sinh t - \int_{1}^{\cosh t} \sqrt{x^2 - 1} \, dx.$$

The first term

$$\frac{1}{2} \cosh t \sinh t$$

gives the area of the triangle OPQ and the integral

$$\int_1^{\cosh t} \sqrt{x^2 - 1}\, dx$$

gives the area of the unshaded portion of the triangle. We wish to show that

$$A(t) = \frac{t}{2} \qquad \text{for all } t \geq 0.$$

Differentiation of $A(t)$ gives

$$A'(t) = \frac{1}{2}\left[\cosh t\, \frac{d}{dt} \sinh t + \sinh t\, \frac{d}{dt} \cosh t \right] - \frac{d}{dt} \int_1^{\cosh t} \sqrt{x^2 - 1}\, dx$$

and therefore

(1) $$A'(t) = \frac{1}{2}[\cosh^2 t + \sinh^2 t] - \frac{d}{dt} \int_1^{\cosh t} \sqrt{x^2 - 1}\, dx.$$

In Section 4.6 we showed that, in general,

$$\frac{d}{dt}\left[\int_a^{g(t)} f(x)\, dx \right] = f(g(t))g'(t).$$

In this case, then

$$\frac{d}{dt}\left(\int_1^{\cosh t} \sqrt{x^2 - 1}\, dx \right) = \sqrt{\cosh^2 t - 1}\, \frac{d}{dt}(\cosh t)$$

$$= \sinh t \cdot \sinh t$$

$$= \sinh^2 t.$$

Substitution of this last expression into equation (1) gives

$$A'(t) = \frac{1}{2}[\cosh^2 t + \sinh^2 t] - \sinh^2 t$$

$$= \frac{1}{2}[\cosh^2 t - \sinh^2 t]$$

$$= \frac{1}{2}.$$

It is not hard to see that $A(0) = 0$:

$$A(0) = \frac{1}{2} \cosh 0 \sinh 0 - \int_1^{\cosh 0} \sqrt{x^2 - 1}\, dx = 0.$$

The two conditions

$$A'(t) = \frac{1}{2} \quad \text{and} \quad A(0) = 0$$

together imply that

$$A(t) = \frac{t}{2}. \quad \Box$$

Exercises

Differentiate.

1.* $y = \sinh x^2$.

2. $y = \cosh (x + a)$.

3.* $y = \sqrt{\cosh ax}$.

4. $y = (\sinh ax)(\cosh ax)$.

5.* $y = \dfrac{\sinh x}{\cosh x - 1}$.

6. $y = \dfrac{\sinh x}{x}$.

7.* $y = a \sinh bx - b \cosh ax$.

8. $y = e^x (\cosh x + \sinh x)$.

9.* $y = \log |\sinh ax|$.

10. $y = \log |1 - \cosh ax|$.

Verify the following identities.

11. $\cosh^2 t - \sinh^2 t = 1$.

12. $\sinh (t + s) = \sinh t \cosh s + \cosh t \sinh s$.

13. $\cosh (t + s) = \cosh t \cosh s + \sinh t \sinh s$.

14. $\sinh 2t = 2 \sinh t \cosh t$.

15. $\cosh 2t = \cosh^2 t + \sinh^2 t$.

Find the extreme values.

16.* $y = 5 \cosh x + 4 \sinh x$.

17. $y = -5 \cosh x + 4 \sinh x$.

18.* $y = 4 \cosh x + 5 \sinh x$.

19. Show that for each positive integer n
$$(\cosh x + \sinh x)^n = \cosh nx + \sinh nx.$$

20. Verify that
$$y = A \cosh cx + B \sinh cx$$
satisfies the differential equation
$$y'' - c^2 y = 0.$$

21.* Find the solution of the differential equation
$$y'' - 9y = 0$$
which satisfies
$$y(0) = 2 \quad \text{and} \quad y'(0) = 1.$$

22. Find the solution of the differential equation
$$4y'' - y = 0$$
which satisfies
$$y(0) = 1 \quad \text{and} \quad y'(0) = 2.$$

6.6 Other hyperbolic functions

The *hyperbolic tangent* is defined by setting

$$\tanh x = \frac{\sinh x}{\cosh x} = \frac{e^x - e^{-x}}{e^x + e^{-x}}.$$

There is also a *hyperbolic cotangent*

$$\coth x = \frac{\cosh x}{\sinh x},$$

a *hyperbolic secant*

$$\operatorname{sech} x = \frac{1}{\cosh x},$$

and a *hyperbolic cosecant*

$$\operatorname{cosech} x = \frac{1}{\sinh x}.$$

The derivatives are as follows:

$$\frac{d}{dx}(\tanh x) = \operatorname{sech}^2 x$$

$$\frac{d}{dx}(\coth x) = -\operatorname{cosech}^2 x$$

$$\frac{d}{dx}(\operatorname{sech} x) = -\operatorname{sech} x \tanh x$$

$$\frac{d}{dx}(\operatorname{cosech} x) = -\operatorname{cosech} x \coth x.$$

These formulas are easy to verify. For instance,

$$\frac{d}{dx}(\tanh x) = \frac{d}{dx}\left(\frac{\sinh x}{\cosh x}\right)$$

$$= \frac{\cosh x \dfrac{d}{dx}(\sinh x) - \sinh x \dfrac{d}{dx}(\cosh x)}{\cosh^2 x}$$

$$= \frac{\cosh^2 x - \sinh^2 x}{\cosh^2 x}$$

$$= \frac{1}{\cosh^2 x}$$

$$= \operatorname{sech}^2 x.$$

We leave it to you to verify the other formulas. □

Let's analyze the hyperbolic tangent a little further. Since

$$\tanh(-x) = \frac{\sinh(-x)}{\cosh(-x)} = \frac{-\sinh x}{\cosh x} = -\tanh x,$$

the hyperbolic tangent is an odd function. Its graph is therefore symmetric with respect to the origin. Since

$$\frac{d}{dx}(\tanh x) = \operatorname{sech}^2 x > 0 \qquad \text{for all real } x,$$

the function is everywhere increasing. From

$$\tanh x = \frac{e^x - e^{-x}}{e^x + e^{-x}} = 1 - \frac{2}{e^{2x} + 1}$$

it is easy to see that $\tanh x$ always remains between -1 and 1. Moreover, it tends to 1 as x tends to $+\infty$ and it tends to -1 as x tends to $-\infty$. To check on the concavity of the graph, we take the second derivative:

$$\frac{d^2}{dx^2}(\tanh x) = \frac{d}{dx}(\operatorname{sech}^2 x) = 2\operatorname{sech} x \frac{d}{dx}(\operatorname{sech} x)$$

$$= 2\operatorname{sech} x\,(-\operatorname{sech} x \tanh x)$$

$$= -2\operatorname{sech}^2 x \tanh x.$$

It is not hard to see that

$$\tanh x \text{ is } \begin{cases} \text{negative,} & \text{for } x < 0 \\ 0, & \text{at } x = 0 \ , \\ \text{positive,} & \text{for } x > 0 \end{cases}$$

and therefore

$$\frac{d^2}{dx^2}(\tanh x) \text{ is } \begin{cases} \text{positive,} & \text{for } x < 0 \\ 0, & \text{at } x = 0 \ . \\ \text{negative,} & \text{for } x > 0 \end{cases}$$

The graph is therefore concave up on $(-\infty, 0]$ and concave down on $[0, \infty)$. The point

$$(0, \tanh 0) = (0, 0)$$

is a point of inflection. The tangent at the origin has slope

$$\operatorname{sech}^2 0 = \frac{1}{\cosh^2 0} = 1.$$

For a picture of the graph see Figure 6.6.1.

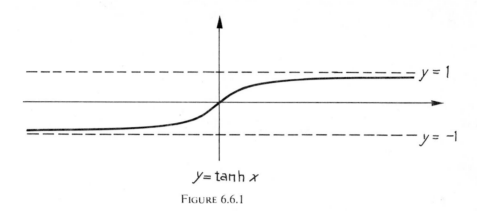

$$y = \tanh x$$

FIGURE 6.6.1

The Hyperbolic Inverses

The hyperbolic inverses that are important to us are the *inverse hyperbolic sine*, the *inverse hyperbolic cosine*, and the *inverse hyperbolic tangent*. These functions

$$y = \sinh^{-1} x, \qquad y = \cosh^{-1} x, \qquad y = \tanh^{-1} x$$

are respectively the inverses of

$$y = \sinh x, \qquad y = \cosh x \ (x \geq 0), \qquad y = \tanh x.$$

Theorem 6.6.1

(i) $$\sinh^{-1} x = \log (x + \sqrt{x^2 + 1}).$$

(ii) $$\cosh^{-1} x = \log (x + \sqrt{x^2 - 1}).$$

(iii) $$\tanh^{-1} x = \frac{1}{2} \log \left(\frac{1 + x}{1 - x} \right).$$

PROOF. To show (i), we solve the equation

$$x = \sinh y \qquad \text{for } y.$$

From $x = \sinh y$ we obtain in sequence

$$x = \frac{e^y - e^{-y}}{2}$$

$$2x = e^y - e^{-y}$$

$$e^{2y} - 2xe^y - 1 = 0.$$

This is a quadratic equation in e^y. From the general quadratic formula we get

$$e^y = \frac{2x \pm \sqrt{4x^2 + 4}}{2} = x \pm \sqrt{x^2 + 1}.$$

Since $e^y > 0$, the minus sign on the right is impossible. Consequently we have

$$e^y = x + \sqrt{x^2 + 1}$$

and, taking logs,

$$y = \log (x + \sqrt{x^2 + 1}).$$

To show (ii), we take the equation

$$x = \cosh y, \qquad y \geq 0$$

and solve it for y. From

$$x = \cosh y, \qquad y \geq 0$$

we obtain in sequence

$$x = \frac{e^y + e^{-y}}{2}$$

$$2x = e^y + e^{-y}$$

$$e^{2y} - 2xe^y + 1 = 0.$$

Again we have a quadratic in e^y. The general quadratic formula here gives

$$e^y = \frac{2x \pm \sqrt{4x^2 - 4}}{2} = x \pm \sqrt{x^2 - 1}.$$

Since y cannot be negative,

$$e^y = x \pm \sqrt{x^2 - 1}$$

cannot be less than 1. This renders the negative sign impossible (check this out) and leaves as the only possibility

$$e^y = x + \sqrt{x^2 - 1}.$$

Taking logs, we get

$$y = \log (x + \sqrt{x^2 - 1}).$$

The proof of (iii) is left as an exercise. □

Exercises

Differentiate.

1.* $y = \tanh^2 x$.

2. $y = \tanh^2 3x$.

3.* $y = \log (\tanh x)$.

4. $y = \tanh (\log x)$.

5.* $y = \sinh (\text{arc tan } e^{2x})$.

6. $y = \text{sech } (3x^2 + 1)$.

7.* $y = \coth (\sqrt{x^2 + 1})$.

8. $y = \log (\text{sech } x)$.

9.* $y = \dfrac{\text{sech } x}{1 + \cosh x}$.

10. $y = \dfrac{\cosh x}{1 + \text{sech } x}$.

11. Show that

$$\frac{d}{dx}(\coth x) = -\operatorname{cosech}^2 x.$$

12. Show that

$$\frac{d}{dx}(\operatorname{sech} x) = -\operatorname{sech} x \tanh x.$$

13. Show that

$$\frac{d}{dx}(\operatorname{cosech} x) = -\operatorname{cosech} x \coth x.$$

14. Show that

$$\tanh (t + s) = \frac{\tanh t + \tanh s}{1 + \tanh t \tanh s}.$$

15.* Given that

$$\tanh x_0 = \tfrac{4}{5}$$

find

(i) $\operatorname{sech} x_0$ [HINT: $1 - \tanh^2 x = \operatorname{sech}^2 x$]

and then find

(ii) $\cosh x_0$.   (iii) $\sinh x_0$.

(iv) $\coth x_0$.   (v) $\operatorname{cosech} x_0$.

16. Given that

$$\tanh t_0 = -\tfrac{5}{12}$$

evaluate the remaining hyperbolic functions at t_0.

17. Show that

$$x - \sqrt{x^2 - 1} \le 1 \text{ if } x^2 \ge 1.$$

18. Show that

$$\tanh^{-1} x = \frac{1}{2} \log \left(\frac{1 + x}{1 - x} \right).$$

19. Show that

$$\boxed{\frac{d}{dx}(\sinh^{-1} x) = \frac{1}{\sqrt{x^2 + 1}}.}$$

20. Show that

$$\boxed{\frac{d}{dx}(\cosh^{-1} x) = \frac{1}{\sqrt{x^2 - 1}}.}$$

21. Show that

$$\boxed{\frac{d}{dx}(\tanh^{-1} x) = \frac{1}{1 - x^2}.}$$

22.   Given that

$$\tan \phi = \sinh x$$

show that

(i) $$\frac{d\phi}{dx} = \operatorname{sech} x,$$

(ii) $$x = \log (\sec \phi + \tan \phi),$$

and

(iii) $$\frac{dx}{d\phi} = \sec \phi.$$

6.7 (Optional) The differential equation $y'' + ay' + by = 0$

This entire section is a collection of exercises based on the differential equation

(E) $$y'' + ay' + by = 0.$$

Here a and b are arbitrary real numbers. By a solution of (E) we mean a function y which satisfies

$$y''(x) + ay'(x) + by(x) = 0$$

for all real x.

Exercise 1. Given that $a^2 > 4b$, find distinct real numbers r_1 and r_2 such that the functions

$$y_1(x) = e^{r_1 x} \qquad \text{and} \qquad y_2(x) = e^{r_2 x}$$

satisfy (E). [HINT: Try a solution of the form $y(x) = e^{rx}$.]

Exercise 2. Given that $a^2 = 4b$, find a real number r_1 such that the functions

$$y_1(x) = e^{r_1 x} \qquad \text{and} \qquad y_2(x) = xe^{r_1 x}$$

satisfy (E).

Exercise 3. Given that $a^2 < 4b$, find a real number β such that the functions

$$y_1(x) = e^{-ax/2} \cos \beta x \qquad \text{and} \qquad y_2(x) = e^{-ax/2} \sin \beta x$$

satisfy (E).

Exercise 4. Show that, if y_1 and y_2 satisfy (E), then the linear combination $c_1 y_1 + c_2 y_2$ satisfies (E).

From Exercise 4, together with the previous exercises, it follows that

$a^2 > 4b$ yields solutions of the form $y(x) = c_1 e^{r_1 x} + c_2 e^{r_2 x}$,

$a^2 = 4b$ yields solutions of the form $y(x) = (c_1 + c_2 x)e^{r_1 x}$,

$a^2 < 4b$ yields solutions of the form $y(x) = (c_1 \cos \beta x + c_2 \sin \beta x)e^{-ax/2}$,

where

$$r_1 = \frac{-a + \sqrt{a^2 - 4b}}{2}, \qquad r_2 = \frac{-a - \sqrt{a^2 - 4b}}{2}, \qquad \beta = \frac{\sqrt{4b - a^2}}{2}.$$

Exercise 5.   Find a solution for the equation

$$y'' + 5y' + 4y = 0$$

satisfying the initial condition (a) $y(0) = 0$, $y'(0) = 1$; (b) $y(0) = -1$, $y'(0) = 1$.

Exercise 6.   Find a solution for the equation

$$y'' + 2y' + y = 0$$

satisfying the initial condition (a) $y(0) = 1$, $y'(0) = 0$; (b) $y(0) = -1$, $y'(0) = -1$.

Exercise 7.   Find a solution for the equation

$$y'' + 4y' + 5y = 0$$

satisfying the initial condition (a) $y(0) = \frac{1}{2}$, $y'(0) = 1$; (b) $y(0) = -1$, $y'(0) = -3$.

SOME ANALYTIC GEOMETRY

7.1 The distance between a point and a line; translations

First we compute the distance between a line and the origin.

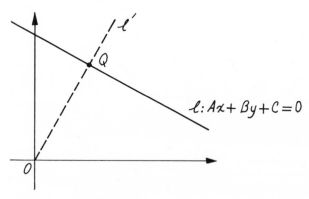

FIGURE 7.1.1

Theorem 7.1.1

The distance between the line l: $Ax + By + C = 0$ and the origin is given by the formula

$$d(0, l) = \frac{|C|}{\sqrt{A^2 + B^2}} .$$

PROOF.   If the line passes through the origin, then $C = 0$ and the formula holds. Suppose now that the line l does not pass through the origin and thus that $C \neq 0$. To find the desired distance, we will get the equation of the line l' which passes through the origin and is perpendicular to l. From this equation we will obtain the point Q at which l and l' intersect. The distance we want is the distance between O and Q. Since l has equation

$$Ax + By + C = 0,$$

l' has equation

$$Bx - Ay = 0. \qquad \text{(Check this out)}$$

By solving the two equations simultaneously, you will find that

$$Q = \left(-\frac{AC}{A^2 + B^2}, -\frac{BC}{A^2 + B^2} \right).$$

The distance between O and Q is therefore

$$\sqrt{A^2 C^2/(A^2 + B^2)^2 + B^2 C^2/(A^2 + B^2)^2}.$$

This expression can be simplified to

$$\frac{|C|}{\sqrt{A^2 + B^2}}. \qquad \square$$

To find the distance between the line l: $Ax + By + C = 0$ and an arbitrary point $P(x_0, y_0)$, we could proceed as we did in Theorem 7.1.1. The computations, however, would be cumbersome. They become much easier if we "translate" the coordinate system.

Translations

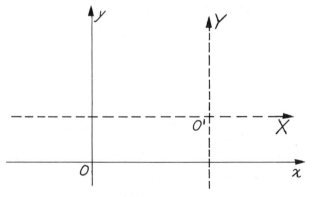

FIGURE 7.1.2

You already know how to impose a Cartesian coordinate system on the plane. Suppose that we have two such systems: the first possessing an origin O, an x-axis, and a y-axis; the second possessing an origin O', an X-axis and a Y-axis. If both systems are endowed with the same scale and if the corresponding axes are parallel and have the same orientation, then we say that the two coordinate systems differ by a *translation*. (See Figure 7.1.2.) Equivalently, we say that one system is obtained from the other by a *translation*.

Suppose now that we have in the plane two coordinate systems Oxy and $O'XY$ differing by a translation. A point P then possesses two pairs of coordinates (x, y) and (X, Y). If the xy-coordinates of O' are (x_0, y_0), then clearly we have $x - x_0 = X$ and $y - y_0 = Y$, and therefore

$$x = X + x_0 \qquad \text{and} \qquad y = Y + y_0.$$

These formulas are useful in simplifying geometric arguments. We put them to use in the proof of the theorem below.

Theorem 7.1.2

The distance between the line $l: Ax + By + C = 0$ and the point $P(x_0, y_0)$ is given by the formula

$$d(P, l) = \frac{|Ax_0 + By_0 + C|}{\sqrt{A^2 + B^2}}.$$

PROOF.   We introduce a new coordinate system $O'XY$ differing from Oxy by a translation. We choose O' to be the point $P(x_0, y_0)$. From our previous discussion, it follows that

$$x = X + x_0 \qquad \text{and} \qquad y = Y + y_0.$$

Our equation for l becomes, in the XY-system,

$$A(X + x_0) + B(Y + y_0) + C = 0,$$

from which we get

$$AX + BY + K = 0 \qquad \text{with } K = Ax_0 + By_0 + C.$$

The distance we want can now be expressed as the distance between the line l with equation $AX + BY + K = 0$ and the origin O'. By Theorem 7.1.1 this distance is

$$\frac{|K|}{\sqrt{A^2 + B^2}}.$$

Since $K = Ax_0 + By_0 + C$, we have

$$d(P, l) = \frac{|Ax_0 + By_0 + C|}{\sqrt{A^2 + B^2}}. \qquad \square$$

Exercises

1. Find the distance between
    (a)* $P(-2, 1)$ and l: $3x - 2y = 0$.
    (b) $P(1, 2)$ and l: $3y - 2x = 1$.
    (c)* $P(3, 5)$ and l: $y = 2x$.
2. Which of the points $(0, 1)$, $(1, 0)$, and $(-1, 1)$ is the closest to l: $8x + 7y - 6 = 0$? Which is the farthest from l?
3. Compute the area of the triangle
    (a)* with vertices $(1, -2)$, $(-1, 3)$, and $(2, 4)$.
    (b)   with vertices $(-1, 1)$, $(3, \sqrt{2})$, and $(\sqrt{2}, -1)$.
4.* A ray l is rotating clockwise about the point $Q(-b^2, 0)$ at the rate of one revolution per minute. How fast is the distance between l and the origin changing at the moment that l has slope $\frac{3}{4}$?
5. A ray l is rotating counterclockwise about the point $Q(-b^2, 0)$ at the rate of $\frac{1}{2}$ revolution per minute. What is the slope of l at the moment that l is receding most quickly from the point $P(b^2, -1)$?

7.2 The conic sections

If a "double right circular cone" is cut by a plane, the resulting intersection is called a *conic section* or, more briefly, a *conic*. In Figures 7.2.1, 7.2.2, and 7.2.3 we depict three important cases.

By choosing a plane parallel to the cross sections of the cone, we can obtain a circle. Quite obviously, the other possibilities are: a point, a line, or a pair of lines.

The study of conic sections from this point of view goes back to Apollonious of Perga, a Greek of the third century B.C. He wrote eight books on the subject.

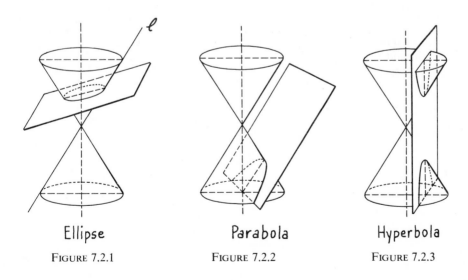

Ellipse   Parabola   Hyperbola

FIGURE 7.2.1   FIGURE 7.2.2   FIGURE 7.2.3

For our purposes, it is useful to dispense with cones and three-dimensional geometry and, instead, define ellipse, parabola, and hyperbola entirely in terms of plane geometry.

7.3   The parabola

We begin with a line l and a point F not on l. See Figure 7.3.1.

> The set of points P equidistant from F and l is called a *parabola*.   (Figure 7.3.2)

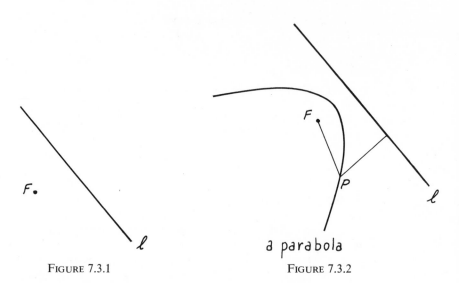

FIGURE 7.3.1   FIGURE 7.3.2

The line l is called the *directrix* of the parabola and F is called the *focus*. (You will see why later on.) The line through F which is perpendicular to l is called the *axis* of the parabola. The point at which the axis intersects the parabola is called the *vertex*. (See Figure 7.3.3.) The equation of a parabola is particularly simple if we place the vertex at the origin and the focus along one of the coordinate axes.

Suppose for a moment that the focus F is on the y-axis. Then F has coordinates of the form $(0, c)$, and, with the vertex at the origin, the directrix must have equation $y = -c$. (See Figure 7.3.4.)

Any point $P(x, y)$ which lies on this parabola has the property that

$$d(P, F) = d(P, l).$$

Since

$$d(P, F) = \sqrt{x^2 + (y - c)^2} \quad \text{and} \quad d(P, l) = |y + c|,$$

we must have

$$\sqrt{x^2 + (y - c)^2} = |y + c|.$$

FIGURE 7.3.3

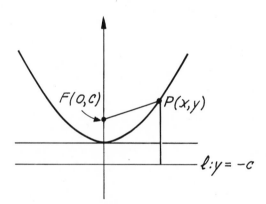

FIGURE 7.3.4

Squaring both sides gives

$$x^2 + (y - c)^2 = |y + c|^2 = (y + c)^2$$
$$x^2 + y^2 - 2cy + c^2 = y^2 + 2cy + c^2.$$

This last equation simplifies to

$$x^2 = 4cy. \quad \square$$

You have just seen that the equation

$$\boxed{x^2 = 4cy}$$

represents a parabola with vertex at the origin and focus at $(0, c)$. By interchanging the

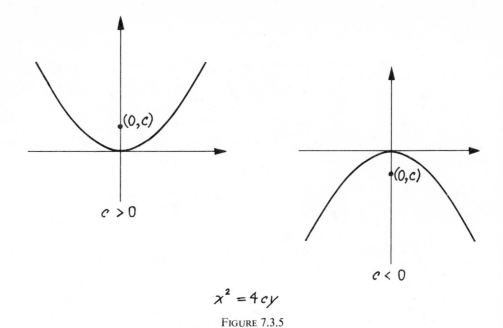

$$x^2 = 4cy$$

FIGURE 7.3.5

roles of x and y it is obvious that the equation

$$y^2 = 4cx$$

represents a parabola with vertex at the origin and focus at $(c, 0)$.

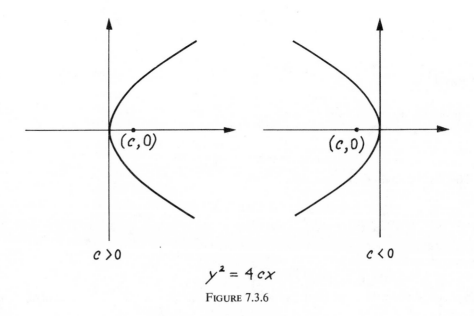

$$y^2 = 4cx$$

FIGURE 7.3.6

If the parabolas

$$x^2 = 4cy \quad \text{and} \quad y^2 = 4cx$$

are translated so that their vertices fall on the point (x_0, y_0) the new parabolas will have equations

$$(x - x_0)^2 = 4c(y - y_0) \quad \text{and} \quad (y - y_0)^2 = 4c(x - x_0).$$

Example. To identify the curve

$$(y - 1)^2 = 8(x + 3),$$

we first rewrite the equation as

$$(y - 1)^2 = 4 \cdot 2(x - (-3)).$$

The equation

$$y^2 = 4 \cdot 2x$$

represents the parabola which has vertex at the origin and focus 2 units to the right of the origin. The equation

$$(y - 1)^2 = 4 \cdot 2(x - (-3))$$

represents the parabola which has vertex at the point $(-3, 1)$ and focus at $(-1, 1)$. $\square$

Example. To identify the curve

$$y + 2 = x^2 + 2x,$$

we first complete the square on the right by adding 1 to both sides. This gives

$$y + 3 = (x + 1)^2,$$

which we can rewrite as

$$(x - (-1))^2 = 4 \cdot \tfrac{1}{4}(y - (-3)).$$

The equation

$$x^2 = 4 \cdot \tfrac{1}{4}y$$

represents the parabola which has vertex at the origin and focus $\tfrac{1}{4}$ of a unit above it. The equation

$$(x - (-1))^2 = 4 \cdot \tfrac{1}{4}(y - (-3))$$

represents the parabola which has vertex at $(-1, -3)$ and focus at $(-1, -11/4)$. $\square$

Parabolic Reflectors

Parabolic curves play a prominent role in the design of searchlights and telescopes. To show how this comes about, we take a parabola and choose the coordinate system so that the equation of the parabola takes the form

$$x^2 = 4cy.$$

We can express y in terms of x by writing

$$y = \frac{x^2}{4c}.$$

Since

$$\frac{dy}{dx} = \frac{2x}{4c} = \frac{x}{2c},$$

the tangent at the point $P(x_0, y_0)$ has slope

$$m = \frac{x_0}{2c}$$

and the tangent line has equation

$$(y - y_0) = \frac{x_0}{2c}(x - x_0).$$

For the rest we refer to Figure 7.3.7. To find the coordinates of the point marked T in the figure, we set $x = 0$ and solve for y. So doing, we find that T has coordinates

$$\left(0, y_0 - \frac{x_0^2}{2c}\right).$$

Since

$$x_0^2 = 4cy_0 \quad \text{(The point } (x_0, y_0) \text{ is on the parabola)}$$

we can rewrite the coordinates of T as

$$(0, -y_0).$$

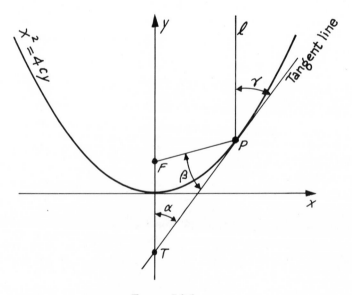

FIGURE 7.3.7

Since the focus F has coordinates $(0, c)$,

$$d(F, T) = c + y_0.$$

Now

$$
\begin{aligned}
d(F, P) &= \sqrt{x_0^2 + (y_0 - c)^2} \\
&= \sqrt{4cy_0 + (y_0 - c)^2} \qquad \text{(Since } x_0^2 = 4cy_0\text{)} \\
&= \sqrt{4cy_0 + y_0^2 - 2cy_0 + c^2} \\
&= \sqrt{y_0^2 + 2cy_0 + c^2} \\
&= \sqrt{(y_0 + c)^2} \\
&= c + y_0.
\end{aligned}
$$

We have shown that

$$d(F, T) = d(F, P).$$

It follows that the triangle TFP is isosceles, and the base angles marked α and β in the figure are equal. With l parallel to the y-axis,

$$\alpha = \gamma$$

and thus

$$\gamma = \beta.$$

From physics we know that when light is reflected, the angle of incidence equals the angle of reflection. We can take either γ or β as the angle of incidence; the other will then be the angle of reflection. The fact that $\gamma = \beta$ has important optical consequences. It means that *light from a source at the focus is reflected in a beam parallel to the axis.* It also means that *a beam of light parallel to the axis is reflected by the parabola through the focus.* The parabolic mirror of a searchlight uses the first principle, that of a reflecting telescope the second.

Parabolic mirrors

Principle of the reflecting telescope: parallel rays converge at the focus.

Principle of the searchlight: a light source at the focus sends out a beam of parallel rays.

FIGURE 7.3.8

Parabolic trajectories

In the early part of the seventeenth century Galileo Galilei observed the motion of stones hurled from the tower of Pisa and noted that their trajectory was parabolic (in the shape of a parabola). By very simple calculus, together with some simplifying physical assumptions, we obtain results which agree with Galileo's observations.

To fix ideas, we consider a projectile fired horizontally from an elevated position. We neglect air resistance and the curvature of the earth and assume that the only force acting upon the projectile (after its release) is the force of gravity. We coordinatize the plane in which the motion takes place, denoting by $(x(t), y(t))$ the position of the projectile at time t. We measure t in seconds, starting our clock with $t = 0$. We measure distance in feet and set

$$x(0) = 0, \qquad y(0) = 0.$$

(See Figure 7.3.9.) If the initial velocity is v_0 and we take -32 ft/sec^2 as the acceleration induced by gravity, then we find that

$$x'(t) = v_0 \qquad \text{and} \qquad y''(t) = -32.$$

From $x'(t) = v_0$, we find that

$$x(t) = v_0 t + c.$$

Since $x(0) = 0$, we have

$$x(t) = v_0 t.$$

From $y''(t) = -32$, we find that

$$y'(t) = -32t + D.$$

Since the initial velocity is horizontal, we have $y'(0) = 0$, and thus

$$y'(t) = -32t.$$

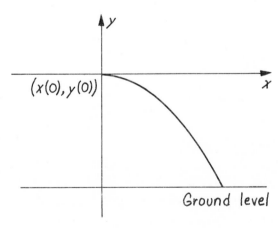

FIGURE 7.3.9

This means that

$$y(t) = -16t^2 + E.$$

Recalling that $y(0) = 0$, we have

$$y(t) = -16t^2.$$

Since $x(t) = v_0 t$, we can write

$$y(t) = -\frac{16}{v_0^2} [x(t)]^2.$$

The trajectory is the parabola with equation

$$y = -\frac{16}{v_0^2} x^2. \quad \square$$

The computations are hardly more difficult in the case of a projectile fired at an angle rather than horizontally. In such a case we can view the projectile as being endowed with the initial velocity

$$v_{0x} \quad \text{along the horizontal}$$

and

$$v_{0y} \quad \text{along the vertical.}$$

Our first equation remains unchanged:

$$x(t) = v_{0x}t.$$

The extra condition $y'(0) = v_{0y}$ in addition to

$$y''(t) = -32 \quad \text{and} \quad y(0) = 0$$

yields

$$y(t) = -16t^2 + v_{0y}t.$$

Using the equation $x(t) = v_{0x}t$, we see that

$$y(t) = -\frac{16}{v_{0x}^2} [x(t)]^2 + \frac{v_{0y}}{v_{0x}} x(t).$$

The trajectory in this case is given by

$$y = -\frac{16}{v_{0x}^2} x^2 + \frac{v_{0y}}{v_{0x}} x$$

and is thus again parabolic. $\quad \square$

Exercises

1. For each of the parabolas described below, find an equation and sketch the curve.
   (a)   vertex $(0, 0)$ and focus $(2, 0)$.
   (b)* vertex $(0, 0)$ and focus $(-2, 0)$.

(c)   vertex $(0, 0)$ and focus $(0, 2)$.

(d)*   vertex $(1, 2)$ and focus $(3, 2)$.

(e)   vertex $(1, 2)$ and focus $(1, 3)$.

(f)*   focus $(1, 1)$ and directrix $y = -1$.

(g)   focus $(1, 1)$ and directrix $x = 2$.

(h)*   focus $(2, -2)$ and directrix $x = 5$.

2.   Find the focus, the vertex, the axis, and the directrix of the parabolas below; sketch the curves.

   (a)* $y^2 = 2x$.   (e)* $(x + 2)^2 = 8y - 12$.

   (b) $x^2 = -5y$.   (f) $y - 3 = 2(x - 1)^2$.

   (c)* $y^2 = 2(x - 1)$.   (g)* $y = x^2 + x + 1$.

   (d) $2y = 4x^2 - 1$.   (h) $x = y^2 + y + 1$.

3.   Find an equation for the parabola with

   (a)* focus $(1, 2)$ and directrix $x + y + 1 = 0$.

   (b)   vertex $(2, 0)$ and directrix $2x - y = 0$.

   (c)* vertex $(2, 0)$ and focus $(0, 2)$.

4.   Show that every parabola has an equation of the form

$$(\alpha x + \beta y)^2 = \gamma x + \delta y + \epsilon \qquad \text{with } \alpha^2 + \beta^2 \neq 0.$$

   [HINT: As directrix take l: $Ax + By + C = 0$; as focus take $F(a, b)$.]

5.   Show that not every equation of the form

$$(\alpha x + \beta y)^2 = \gamma x + \delta y + \epsilon \qquad \text{with } \alpha^2 + \beta^2 \neq 0$$

   represents a parabola.

6.   Discuss the graph of

$$(x - y)^2 = b \qquad \text{for different values of } b.$$

7.   An object moves in a coordinate plane with constant horizontal velocity v_{0x} and constant vertical velocity v_{0y}. Find an equation for its trajectory if at time 0 it passes through (a) the origin, (b) $P(a, b)$.

8.* An object moves away from the origin along the ray

$$l: y = (\tan \theta)x, \qquad 0 < \theta < \pi/2,$$

   with constant velocity v_0. Find its horizontal velocity v_{0x} and its vertical velocity v_{0y}.

In Problems 9 through 15 we measure distances in feet and time in seconds. We neglect air resistance and the curvature of the earth. Taking O as the origin and the x-axis as ground level, we consider a projectile fired from the point O with initial velocity v_0 along the ray

$$l: y = (\tan \theta)x, \qquad 0 < \theta < \pi/2.$$

9.* Find the initial horizontal velocity v_{0x} and the initial vertical velocity v_{0y}.

10.* Find an equation for the trajectory.

11. What is the maximum height attained by the projectile?

12.* Find the range of the projectile.

13. How many seconds after firing does the impact take place?

14.* How should θ be chosen so as to maximize the range?

15. How should θ be chosen so that the range becomes r?

16. Show that every parabola with axis parallel to the y-axis is the graph of a function
of the form
$$g(x) = Ax^2 + Bx + C.$$

17. Show that there is one and only one parabola of the form
$$y = Ax^2 + Bx + C$$
which passes through three given noncollinear points.

18. Show that the function
$$g(x) = Ax^2 + Bx + C$$
satisfies the condition
$$\int_a^b g(x)\, dx = \frac{b-a}{6}\left[g(a) + 4g\left(\frac{a+b}{2}\right) + g(b)\right]$$
for every interval $[a, b]$.

7.4 The ellipse

We begin with two points F_1 and F_2. Using the line segment $\overline{F_1 F_2}$ as a base we construct
an isosceles triangle as in Figure 7.4.1.

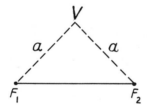

FIGURE 7.4.1

The vertex V has the property that
$$d(V, F_1) + d(V, F_2) = 2a.$$

The set of all points P such that
$$d(P, F_1) + d(P, F_2) = 2a$$
is called an *ellipse*. F_1 and F_2 are called the *foci*.

To derive the most convenient equation for the ellipse, we place the foci along the x-axis at equal distances from the origin. (See Figure 7.4.2.) For some $c > 0$ we have

$$F_1 \text{ at } (-c, 0) \qquad \text{and} \qquad F_2 \text{ at } (c, 0).$$

For a point $P(x, y)$ to lie on the ellipse, we must have

$$d(P, F_1) + d(P, F_2) = 2a.$$

In terms of coordinates, we must have

$$\sqrt{(x + c)^2 + y^2} + \sqrt{(x - c)^2 + y^2} = 2a.$$

By transferring the second term to the right-hand side and squaring both sides, we obtain

$$(x + c)^2 + y^2 = 4a^2 + (x - c)^2 + y^2 - 4a\sqrt{(x - c)^2 + y^2}.$$

This reduces to

$$4a\sqrt{(x - c)^2 + y^2} = 4(a^2 - cx).$$

Cancelling the factor 4 and squaring again, we obtain

$$a^2(x^2 - 2cx + c^2 + y^2) = a^4 - 2a^2cx + c^2x^2.$$

This in turn reduces to

$$(a^2 - c^2)x^2 + a^2y^2 = a^2(a^2 - c^2),$$

and thus to

$$\boxed{\frac{x^2}{a^2} + \frac{y^2}{a^2 - c^2} = 1.}$$

It is customary to set

$$b = \sqrt{a^2 - c^2}$$

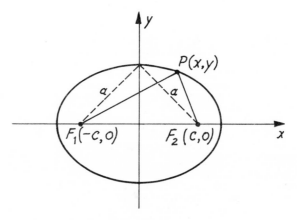

FIGURE 7.4.2

and then write the equation as

$$\frac{x^2}{a^2} + \frac{y^2}{b^2} = 1.$$

The relations between a, b, and c are illustrated in Figure 7.4.3.

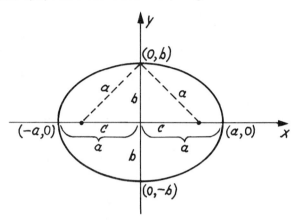

FIGURE 7.4.3

The line segment which joins $(-a, 0)$ to $(a, 0)$ is called the *major axis* and the line segment which joins $(0, -b)$ to $(0, b)$ is called the *minor axis*. The number 2a gives the length of the major axis and the number 2b gives the length of the minor axis.

If the foci are placed on the y-axis,

$$F_1 \text{ at } (0, -c) \qquad \text{and} \qquad F_2 \text{ at } (0, c),$$

the equation of the ellipse takes the form

$$\frac{x^2}{a^2 - c^2} + \frac{y^2}{a^2} = 1,$$

which we can rewrite as

$$\frac{x^2}{b^2} + \frac{y^2}{a^2} = 1.$$

The major axis is then vertical and the minor axis is horizontal.

Example.   The equation

$$16x^2 + 25y^2 = 400$$

can be rewritten as

$$\frac{x^2}{5^2} + \frac{y^2}{4^2} = 1$$

and thus as

$$\frac{x^2}{5^2} + \frac{y^2}{5^2 - 3^2} = 1.$$

This is the equation of an ellipse with foci at $(-3, 0)$ and $(3, 0)$. The major axis has length 10 and minor axis has length 8.   □

Example.   The ellipse

$$\frac{x^2}{4^2} + \frac{y^2}{5^2} = 1$$

has the same shape and size as the one of the previous example, but this time the foci are on the y-axis. The coordinates of the foci are $(0, -3)$ and $(0, 3)$.   □

Example.   The equation

$$\frac{(x - 1)^2}{13^2} + \frac{(y + 4)^2}{12^2} = 1$$

can be rewritten as

$$\frac{(x - 1)^2}{13^2} + \frac{(y + 4)^2}{13^2 - 5^2} = 1.$$

This represents the ellipse

$$\frac{x^2}{13^2} + \frac{y^2}{13^2 - 5^2} = 1$$

translated 1 unit to the right and 4 units down. [The center instead of being at the origin is at the point $(1, -4)$.] The length of the major axis is 26 and the length of the minor axis is 24. The foci are at $(-4, -4)$ and $(6, -4)$.   □

Example.   To identify the curve

$$4x^2 - 8x + y^2 + 4y - 8 = 0$$

we write

$$4(x^2 - 2x + \quad) + (y^2 + 4y + \quad) = 8.$$

By completing the squares within the parentheses we get

$$4(x^2 - 2x + 1) + (y^2 + 4y + 4) = 16$$
$$4(x - 1)^2 + (y + 2)^2 = 16$$
$$\frac{(x - 1)^2}{4} + \frac{(y + 2)^2}{16} = 1$$
$$\frac{(x - 1)^2}{2^2} + \frac{(y + 2)^2}{4^2} = 1.$$

This is the equation of an ellipse centered at $(1, -2)$. The major axis is vertical. The length of the major axis is 8 and the length of the minor axis is 4. As you can check, the foci are at $(1, -2 - 2\sqrt{3})$ and $(1, -2 + 2\sqrt{3})$.   □

To sketch the ellipse

$$\frac{x^2}{a^2} + \frac{y^2}{a^2 - c^2} = 1,$$

you can loop a string of length $2(a + c)$ over tacks placed at the foci. A pencil placed in the loop so as to keep the string taut will describe the given ellipse.

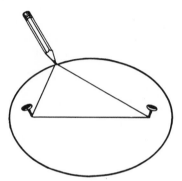

FIGURE 7.4.4

The Reflecting Property of the Ellipse

Like the parabola, the ellipse has an interesting reflecting property. To derive it, we consider the ellipse

$$\frac{x^2}{a^2} + \frac{y^2}{b^2} = 1.$$

Differentiation with respect to x gives

$$\frac{2x}{a^2} + \frac{2y}{b^2}\frac{dy}{dx} = 0$$

and thus

$$\frac{dy}{dx} = -\frac{b^2 x}{a^2 y}.$$

The slope at the point (x_0, y_0) is therefore

$$-\frac{b^2 x_0}{a^2 y_0}$$

and the tangent line has equation

$$y - y_0 = -\frac{b^2 x_0}{a^2 y_0}(x - x_0).$$

We can rewrite this last equation as

$$b^2 x_0 x + a^2 y_0 y - a^2 b^2 = 0.$$

We can now show the following:

> At each point P of the ellipse, the focal radii $\overline{F_1 P}$ and $\overline{F_2 P}$ make equal angles with the tangent.

PROOF. If P lies on the x-axis, the focal radii are coincident and there is nothing to show. To visualize the argument for P not on the x-axis, see Figure 7.4.5. To show that $\overline{F_1 P}$ and $\overline{F_2 P}$ make equal angles with the tangent we need only show that the triangles $PT_1 F_1$ and $PT_2 F_2$ are similar. We can do this by showing that

$$\frac{d(T_1, F_1)}{d(F_1, P)} = \frac{d(T_2, F_2)}{d(F_2, P)}$$

or equivalently by showing that

$$\frac{|-b^2 x_0 c - a^2 b^2|}{\sqrt{(x_0 + c)^2 + y_0^2}} = \frac{|b^2 x_0 c - a^2 b^2|}{\sqrt{(x_0 - c)^2 + y_0^2}}.$$

The validity of this last equation can be seen by cancelling the factor b^2 and then squaring. This gives

$$\frac{(x_0 c + a^2)^2}{(x_0 + c)^2 + y_0^2} = \frac{(x_0 c - a^2)^2}{(x_0 - c)^2 + y_0^2},$$

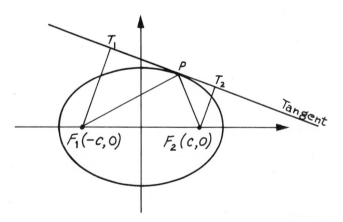

FIGURE 7.4.5

which can be simplified to

$$(a^2 - c^2)x_0^2 + a^2y_0^2 = a^2(a^2 - c^2)$$

and thus to

$$\frac{x_0^2}{a^2} + \frac{y_0^2}{b^2} = 1.$$

This last equation holds since the point $P(x_0, y_0)$ is on the ellipse.   □

The result we just proved has the following physical consequence:

An elliptical mirror takes light or sound originating at one focus and converges it at the other focus.

Exercises

For each of the following ellipses (i) find the foci, (ii) find the length of the major axis, (iii) find the length of the minor axis, and then (iv) sketch the figure.

1.* $\dfrac{x^2}{9} + \dfrac{y^2}{4} = 1.$

2. $\dfrac{x^2}{4} + \dfrac{y^2}{9} = 1.$

3.* $3x^2 + 2y^2 = 12.$

4. $(x - 1)^2 + 4y^2 = 64.$

5.* $3x^2 + 4y^2 - 12 = 0.$

6. $4x^2 + y^2 - 6y + 5 = 0.$

7.* $4(x - 1)^2 + y^2 = 64.$

8. $16(x - 2)^2 + 25(y - 3)^2 = 400.$

Find an equation for the ellipse which satisfies the given conditions.

9.* Foci at $(-1, 0)$, $(1, 0)$; major axis 6.

10. Foci at $(0, -1)$, $(0, 1)$; major axis 6.

11.* Foci at $(3, 1)$, $(9, 1)$; major axis 10.

12. Foci at $(1, 3)$, $(1, 9)$; minor axis 8.

13.* Focus at $(1, 1)$; center at $(1, 3)$; major axis 10.

14. Center at $(2, 1)$; one vertex at $(2, 6)$; another vertex at $(1, 1)$.

The *eccentricity* of an ellipse is the ratio

$$\frac{d(F_1, F_2)}{\text{length of major axis}}.$$

For the ellipse in standard position

$$\frac{x^2}{a^2} + \frac{y^2}{a^2 - c^2} = 1$$

the eccentricity is the number

$$e = \frac{c}{a}.$$

15.* What happens to the ellipse if a remains constant but e tends to 0?

16. What happens to the ellipse if a remains constant but e tends to 1?

17.* Find an equation for the ellipse in standard position which has major axis 10 and eccentricity $\frac{1}{2}$.

18. Find an equation for the ellipse in standard position which has minor axis $2\sqrt{3}$ and eccentricity $\frac{1}{2}$.

19. Like the parabola the ellipse can be defined in terms of one focus F and a directrix line l. Show that the ellipse

$$\frac{x^2}{a^2} + \frac{y^2}{a^2 - c^2} = 1$$

is the set of points $P(x, y)$ such that

$$d(P, F) = e\, d(P, l),$$

where

$$F \text{ is } (c, 0), \qquad e = \frac{c}{a}, \qquad \text{and} \qquad l : x = \frac{a^2}{c}.$$

7.5   The hyperbola

We begin with two points F_1 and F_2 and a number $2a < d(F_1, F_2)$.

> The set of all points P such that
> $$|d(P, F_1) - d(P, F_2)| = 2a$$
> is called a *hyperbola*. The points F_1 and F_2 are called the *foci* of the hyperbola.

The Equation of a Hyperbola

As in the case of the ellipse, to derive an equation for the hyperbola we take a system of coordinates in which F_1 is $(-c, 0)$ and F_2 is $(c, 0)$, with $c > 0$ (Figure 7.5.1). Since $d(F_1, F_2) = 2c$, we must have $a < c$. The condition

$$|d(P, F_1) - d(P, F_2)| = 2a$$

is equivalent to

$$d(P, F_1) - d(P, F_2) = \pm 2a,$$

the plus sign holding if $d(P, F_1) > d(P, F_2)$, the minus sign holding if $d(P, F_1) < d(P, F_2)$. In terms of coordinates, we get

$$\sqrt{(x + c)^2 + y^2} - \sqrt{(x - c)^2 + y^2} = \pm 2a.$$

Transferring the second term to the right and squaring both sides, we obtain

$$(x + c)^2 + y^2 = 4a^2 \pm 4a\sqrt{(x - c)^2 + y^2} + (x - c)^2 + y^2.$$

This equation reduces to

$$xc - a^2 = \pm a\sqrt{(x - c)^2 + y^2}.$$

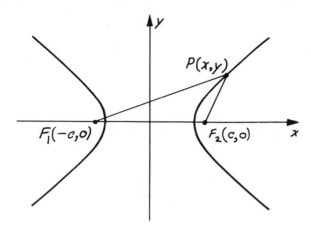

FIGURE 7.5.1

Squaring once more, we obtain

$$x^2c^2 - 2a^2xc + a^4 = a^2(x^2 - 2xc + c^2 + y^2),$$

which reduces to

$$(c^2 - a^2)x^2 - a^2y^2 = a^2(c^2 - a^2),$$

and thus to

$$\frac{x^2}{a^2} - \frac{y^2}{c^2 - a^2} = 1.$$

In this setting it is customary to set

$$b^2 = c^2 - a^2$$

and write

$$\boxed{\frac{x^2}{a^2} - \frac{y^2}{b^2} = 1.}$$

Excluded Region and Asymptotes

If

$$\frac{x^2}{a^2} - \frac{y^2}{b^2} = 1,$$

then $x^2/a^2 \geq 1$, so that

$$|x| \geq a.$$

It follows that no points of the hyperbola lie between the vertical lines $x = -a$ and $x = a$. The points (x, y) of the hyperbola that have $x \geq a$ are said to constitute the *right-hand branch* of the hyperbola, and the others the *left-hand branch*.

Returning to the equation

$$\frac{x^2}{a^2} - \frac{y^2}{b^2} = 1,$$

it is obvious that

$$\frac{y^2}{b^2} < \frac{x^2}{a^2}$$

and therefore

$$|y| < \frac{b}{a} |x|.$$

For $x < 0$, this implies that

$$|y| < -\frac{b}{a} x$$

and thus

(1) $$\frac{b}{a} x < y < -\frac{b}{a} x.$$

For $x > 0$, we have

$$|y| < \frac{b}{a} x,$$

and thus

(2) $$-\frac{b}{a} x < y < \frac{b}{a} x.$$

From (1) and (2) together we see that all points of the hyperbola lie between the lines

$$\boxed{y = -\frac{b}{a} x \quad \text{and} \quad y = \frac{b}{a} x.}$$

These lines are called the *asymptotes* of the hyperbola.

The role of asymptotes in the theory of the hyperbola is best seen by considering the distance between a point of the hyperbola and one of the asymptotes. For convenience we choose $P(x_0, y_0)$ with positive coordinates and compute its distance from the asymptote $l: y = (b/a)x$. Rewriting the equation of the asymptote as

$$l: bx - ay = 0,$$

we see that

$$d(P, l) = \frac{|bx_0 - ay_0|}{\sqrt{a^2 + b^2}}.$$

From Equation (2)

$$bx_0 - ay_0 > 0$$

and thus

(3) $$d(P, l) = \frac{bx_0 - ay_0}{\sqrt{a^2 + b^2}} .$$

If $P(x_0, y_0)$ lies on the hyperbola, we have

$$\frac{x_0^2}{a^2} - \frac{y_0^2}{b^2} = 1,$$

from which we get

$$b^2 x_0^2 - a^2 y_0^2 = a^2 b^2,$$

and thus

$$bx_0 - ay_0 = \frac{a^2 b^2}{bx_0 + ay_0} .$$

Substituting this into Equation (3), we get

$$d(P, l) = \frac{a^2 b^2}{\sqrt{a^2 + b^2}} \left(\frac{1}{bx_0 + ay_0} \right),$$

and since $y_0 > 0$,

$$d(P, l) < \frac{a^2 b^2}{\sqrt{a^2 + b^2}} \left(\frac{1}{bx_0} \right) .$$

Since a and b are fixed, we can make $d(P, l)$ as small as we wish simply by choosing x_0 sufficiently large. By symmetry, a similar situation prevails in the other quadrants. In summary, we can state that *as a point P proceeds away from the origin along a branch of the hyperbola, it gets closer to one of the asymptotes and the distance between P and the asymptote tends to zero.* (See Figure 7.5.2.)

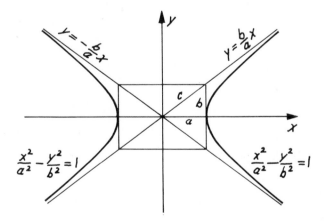

FIGURE 7.5.2

The Tangent to a Hyperbola

Proceeding as in the case of the ellipse, one can show that, if (x_0, y_0), $y_0 \neq 0$, is a point of the hyperbola

$$\frac{x^2}{a^2} - \frac{y^2}{b^2} = 1,$$

then the slope at (x_0, y_0) is given by the number

$$m = \frac{b^2 x_0}{a^2 y_0} \qquad \text{(Exercise 19)}$$

and the tangent line has equation

$$b^2 x_0 x - a^2 y_0 y - a^2 b^2 = 0. \qquad \text{(Exercise 20)}$$

Using this information, one can show that

> the tangent to the hyperbola at the point P bisects the angle between the focal radii $\overline{F_1 P}$ and $\overline{F_2 P}$.   (Exercise 21)

An Application to Range Finding

There is a simple application of the hyperbola to range-finding. If observers, located at two listening posts at a known distance apart, time the firing of a gun, the time difference multiplied by the velocity of sound gives the value of $2a$ and hence determines a hyperbola on which the gun must be located. A third listening post gives two more hyperbolas. The gun is found where the hyperbolas intersect.

Exercises

For each of the following hyperbolas (i) find the foci, (ii) find the asymptotes, and then (iii) sketch the figure.

1.* $x^2 - y^2 = 1$.

2. $y^2 - x^2 = 1$.

3.* $\dfrac{x^2}{9} - \dfrac{y^2}{16} = 1$.

4. $\dfrac{x^2}{16} - \dfrac{y^2}{9} = 1$.

5.* $\dfrac{y^2}{16} - \dfrac{x^2}{9} = 1$.

6. $\dfrac{y^2}{9} - \dfrac{x^2}{16} = 1$.

7.* $\dfrac{(x - 1)^2}{9} - \dfrac{(y - 3)^2}{16} = 1$.

8. $\dfrac{(x - 1)^2}{16} - \dfrac{(y - 3)^2}{9} = 1$.

9.* $-3x^2 + y^2 - 6x = 0$.

10. $4x^2 - 8x - y^2 + 6y - 1 = 0$.

Find an equation for the hyperbola that satisfies the given conditions.

11.* Foci at $(-5, 0)$, $(5, 0)$; $a = 3$.

12. Foci at $(-13, 0)$, $(13, 0)$; $a = 5$.

13.* Foci at $(0, -13)$, $(0, 13)$; $a = 5$.

14. Foci at $(0, -13)$, $(0, 13)$; $a = 12$.

15.* Foci at $(-5, 1)$, $(5, 1)$; $a = 3$.

16. Foci at $(-3, 1)$, $(7, 1)$; $a = 3$.

17.* Foci at $(-1, -1)$, $(1, 1)$; $a = 1$.

18.* Find the foci and the asymptotes of the hyperbola with equation $xy = 1$.
     [HINT: Define new XY-coordinates by $x = X + Y$ and $y = X - Y$.]

19. Show that if $y_0 \neq 0$ the slope of the hyperbola

$$\frac{x^2}{a^2} - \frac{y^2}{b^2} = 1$$

at the point (x_0, y_0) is given by

$$m = \frac{b^2 x_0}{a^2 y_0}.$$

20. Show that the tangent line at (x_0, y_0) has equation

$$b^2 x_0 x - a^2 y_0 y - a^2 b^2 = 0.$$

21. Show that the tangent to the hyperbola at the point P bisects the angle between
     the focal radii $\overline{F_1 P}$ and $\overline{F_2 P}$.

22. Like the parabola and the ellipse the hyperbola can be defined in terms of one focus
     F and a directrix line l. Show that the hyperbola

$$\frac{x^2}{a^2} - \frac{y^2}{a^2 - c^2} = 1$$

is the set of all points $P(x, y)$ such that

$$d(P, F) = e\, d(P, l),$$

where

$$F \text{ is } (c, 0), \qquad e = \frac{c}{a}, \qquad \text{and} \qquad l : x = \frac{a^2}{c}.$$

7.6 Polar coordinates

Since you have probably seen polar coordinates before, a short review will suffice. As usual we will measure angles only in radians.

In Figure 7.6.1 we have sketched a ray which begins at the origin and is at angle θ from the positive x-axis. The opposite ray is at an angle $\theta + \pi$.

In Figure 7.6.2 we have marked off some points along the same rays and have labelled the points with polar coordinates.

In general the point $[r, \theta]$ is at a distance $|r|$ from the origin

$$\begin{cases} \text{along the ray } \theta, & \text{if } r > 0. \\ \text{along the ray } \theta + \pi, & \text{if } r < 0. \end{cases}$$

FIGURE 7.6.1

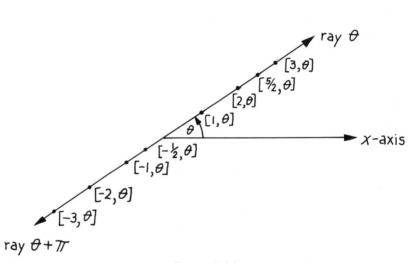

FIGURE 7.6.2

Polar coordinates are not unique. Many pairs $[r, \theta]$ can represent the same point.

1. If $r = 0$, it does not matter how we choose θ. The resulting point is still the origin:

$$\boxed{O = [0, \theta] \qquad \text{for all } \theta.}$$

2. Geometrically there is no distinction between angles that differ by an integral multiple of 2π. Consequently,

$$\boxed{[r, \theta] = [r, \theta + 2n\pi] \qquad \text{for all integers } n.} \qquad \text{(Figure 7.6.3)}$$

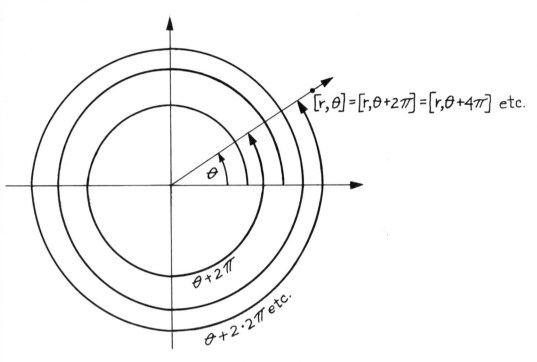

FIGURE 7.6.3

3. Finally, we observe that

$$[r, \theta] = [-r, \theta + \pi].$$ (Figure 7.6.4)

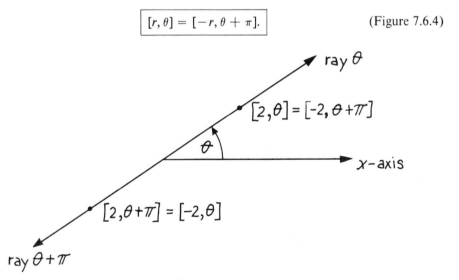

FIGURE 7.6.4

Symmetry with respect to each of the coordinate axes and with respect to the origin is illustrated in Figure 7.6.5, 7.6.6, and 7.6.7.

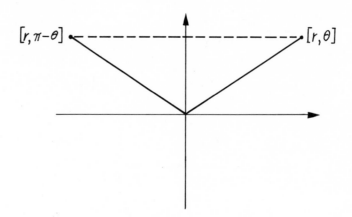

Symmetry about the y—axis

FIGURE 7.6.5

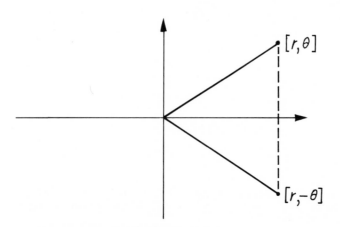

Symmetry about the x—axis

FIGURE 7.6.6

In applications it is often useful to change from one coordinate system to another. Keep in mind that in changing between polar coordinates $[r, \theta]$ and rectangular coordinates (x, y) the following relations hold:

$$x = r \cos \theta, \qquad y = r \sin \theta.$$

Problem.   Find the rectangular coordinates of the point

$$\left[-2, \frac{\pi}{3} \right].$$

SOLUTION. The relations

$$x = r \cos \theta, \qquad y = r \sin \theta$$

give here

$$x = -2 \cos \frac{\pi}{3} = -2 \left(\frac{1}{2} \right) = -1$$

and

$$y = -2 \sin \frac{\pi}{3} = -2 \left(\frac{\sqrt{3}}{2} \right) = -\sqrt{3}. \quad \square$$

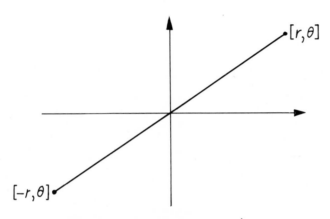

Symmetry about the origin

FIGURE 7.6.7

Problem. Find all possible polar coordinates for the point with rectangular coordinates $(-2, 2\sqrt{3})$.

SOLUTION. Here

$$-2 = r \cos \theta, \qquad 2\sqrt{3} = r \sin \theta$$

so that

$$r^2 = r^2 \cos^2 \theta + r^2 \sin^2 \theta = (-2)^2 + (2\sqrt{3})^2 = 4 + 12 = 16.$$

If we take $r = 4$, then we have

$$-2 = 4 \cos \theta, \qquad 2\sqrt{3} = 4 \sin \theta$$

and thus

$$-\frac{1}{2} = \cos \theta, \qquad \frac{\sqrt{3}}{2} = \sin \theta.$$

This means that we can take

$$\theta = \frac{2\pi}{3}$$ (Figure 7.6.8)

or more generally

$$\theta = \frac{2\pi}{3} + 2n\pi.$$

If we take $r = -4$, then we can take

$$\theta = \frac{2\pi}{3} + \pi = \frac{5\pi}{3}$$

or more generally

$$\theta = \frac{5\pi}{3} + 2n\pi. \quad \Box$$

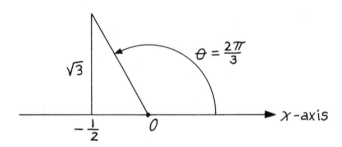

FIGURE 7.6.8

Here we examine some subsets of the plane as represented by polar coordinates:
(1) The circle of radius a

$$x^2 + y^2 = a^2$$

becomes in polar coordinates

$$r = a.$$

The interior of the circle is given by

$$0 \le r < a$$

and the exterior by

$$r > a. \quad \Box$$

(2) The line through the origin with inclination α is given by the equation

$$\theta = \alpha, r \ge 0.$$

(3) The vertical line $x = a$ becomes in polar coordinates

$$r \cos \theta = a \quad \text{or} \quad r = a \sec \theta. \quad \Box$$

(4) The horizontal line $y = b$ becomes

$$r \sin \theta = b \quad \text{or} \quad r = b \csc \theta. \quad \square$$

(5) The line $Ax + By + C = 0$ becomes

$$r(A \cos \theta + B \sin \theta) + C = 0. \quad \square$$

(6) The circle $(x - x_0)^2 + (y - y_0)^2 = a^2$ becomes

$$r^2 - 2r(x_0 \cos \theta + y_0 \sin \theta) = a^2 - x_0^2 - y_0^2.$$

If the circle passes through the origin, this reduces to

$$r = 2(x_0 \cos \theta + y_0 \sin \theta). \quad \square$$

(7) The equilateral hyperbola $x^2 - y^2 = a^2$ becomes

$$r^2 \cos^2 \theta - r^2 \sin^2 \theta = a^2$$

and therefore

$$r^2 \cos 2\theta = a^2. \quad \square$$

We show now that the equation

$$r = \frac{ed}{1 - e \cos \theta}$$

represents

an ellipse	if	$0 < e < 1$
a parabola	if	$e = 1$
a hyperbola	if	$e > 1.$

PROOF. From the equation

$$r = \frac{ed}{1 - e \cos \theta}$$

we obtain in sequence

$$r - er \cos \theta = ed$$

$$r = ed + ex$$

$$r^2 = e^2 d^2 + 2e^2 dx + e^2 x^2$$

$$x^2 + y^2 = e^2 d^2 + 2e^2 dx + e^2 x^2$$

$$(1 - e^2)x^2 - 2e^2 dx + y^2 = e^2 d^2.$$

If $e = 1$, the equation reduces to

$$y^2 = 2\,dx + d^2,$$

which you can recognize as a parabola.

If $0 < e < 1$, the equation can be written in the form

$$\frac{(x - x_0)^2}{a^2} + \frac{y^2}{b^2} = 1,$$ (Check this out)

which you can recognize as being an ellipse.

If $e > 1$, the equation can be written in the form

$$\frac{(x - x_0)^2}{a^2} - \frac{y^2}{b^2} = 1,$$ (Check this out)

which is the equation of a hyperbola.   □

Problem.   Sketch the graph of the lemniscate

$$r^2 = \cos 2\theta.$$

SOLUTION.   First we look for symmetry.   Since

$$\cos (2(-\theta)) = \cos (-2\theta) = \cos 2\theta,$$

the equation of the lemniscate is unchanged when we replace θ by $-\theta$. This means that the lemniscate is symmetric about the x-axis (Figure 7.6.6).
    Since

$$\cos (2(\pi - \theta)) = \cos (2\pi - 2\theta) = \cos (-2\theta) = \cos 2\theta$$

the equation of the lemniscate is unchanged when we replace θ by $\pi - \theta$. This means that the lemniscate is symmetric about the y-axis (Figure 7.6.5).
    With symmetry about both coordinate axes we can devote our attention to that portion of the curve which lies in the first quadrant. The rest we can handle later by symmetry.
    In the first quadrant we can take

$$0 \le \theta \le \pi/2.$$

The equation

$$r^2 = \cos 2\theta$$

tells us that $\cos 2\theta$ cannot be negative. Therefore we must exclude those values of θ which lie between $\pi/4$ and $\pi/2$:

$$\text{if } \frac{\pi}{4} < \theta < \frac{\pi}{2} \quad \text{then} \quad \frac{\pi}{2} < 2\theta < \pi \quad \text{and} \quad \cos 2\theta < 0.$$

To determine the look of the curve for θ in the interval $[0, \pi/4]$, we plot a few points:

$$\text{at } \theta = 0, \quad r^2 = \cos 2\theta = 1, \quad r = 1$$

$$\text{at } \theta = \frac{\pi}{8}, \quad r^2 = \cos 2 \cdot \frac{\pi}{8} = \cos \frac{\pi}{4} = \frac{1}{\sqrt{2}}, \quad r = 2^{-1/4}$$

$$\text{at } \theta = \frac{\pi}{6}, \quad r^2 = \cos 2 \cdot \frac{\pi}{6} = \cos \frac{\pi}{3} = \frac{1}{2}, \quad r = \frac{1}{\sqrt{2}}$$

$$\text{at } \theta = \frac{\pi}{4}, \quad r^2 = \cos 2 \cdot \frac{\pi}{4} = \cos \frac{\pi}{2} = 0, \quad r = 0.$$

Putting this information together it is not hard to see that in the first quadrant, the lemniscate looks as in Figure 7.6.9. From the symmetries discovered, the entire graph must look as in Figure 7.6.10. □

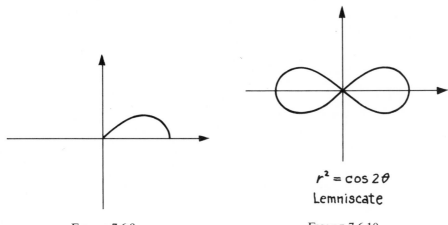

$$r^2 = \cos 2\theta$$
Lemniscate

FIGURE 7.6.9   FIGURE 7.6.10

The fact that a single point has many pairs of polar coordinates can cause complications. In particular it means that a point $[r_1, \theta_1]$ can lie on a curve

$$r = f(\theta)$$

although its coordinates r_1 and θ_1 do not satisfy the equation. For example, the coordinates of $[2, \pi]$ do not satisfy the equation

$$r^2 = 4 \cos \theta.$$

$$(r^2 = 2^2 = 4 \qquad \text{but} \qquad 4 \cos \theta = 4 \cos \pi = -4.)$$

Nevertheless the point $[2, \pi]$ does lie on the curve

$$r^2 = 4 \cos \theta.$$

It does lie on the curve because

$$[2, \pi] = [-2, 0] \qquad\qquad \text{(Check this out)}$$

and the coordinates of $[-2, 0]$ do satisfy the equation:

$$r^2 = (-2)^2 = 4, \qquad 4 \cos \theta = 4 \cos 0 = 4. \quad \square$$

The difficulties are compounded when we deal with two or more curves. Here is a simple example.

Problem. Find the points where the curves

$$r = a(1 - \cos \theta) \qquad \text{and} \qquad r = a(1 + \cos \theta)$$

intersect.

SOLUTION.   We begin by solving the two equations simultaneously. First we rewrite the equations as

$$\frac{r}{a} = 1 - \cos\theta, \qquad \frac{r}{a} = 1 + \cos\theta.$$

Adding the equations, we get

$$2\frac{r}{a} = 2$$

and therefore

$$r = a.$$

This means that

$$\cos\theta = 0 \qquad \text{and} \qquad \theta = \frac{\pi}{2} + n\pi.$$

As you can check, the points

$$\left[a, \frac{\pi}{2} + n\pi\right]$$

all lie on both curves. Not all of these points are distinct however:

$$\text{for } n \text{ even,} \quad \left[a, \frac{\pi}{2} + n\pi\right] = \left[a, \frac{\pi}{2}\right]$$

$$\text{for } n \text{ odd,} \quad \left[a, \frac{\pi}{2} + n\pi\right] = \left[a, \frac{3\pi}{2}\right].$$

In short, by solving the two equations simultaneously we have arrived at two common points:

$$[a, \pi/2] = (0, a) \qquad \text{and} \qquad [a, 3\pi/2] = (0, -a).$$

There is however a third point at which the curves intersect and that is the origin O. (Figure 7.6.12.)

The origin clearly lies on both curves:

$$\text{for } r = a(1 - \cos\theta) \quad \text{take } \theta = 0, 2\pi, \text{ etc.}$$

$$\text{for } r = a(1 + \cos\theta) \quad \text{take } \theta = \pi, 3\pi, \text{ etc.}$$

The reason that the origin does not appear when we solve the two equations simultaneously is that the curves do not pass through the origin "simultaneously"; that is, they do not pass through the origin for the same values of θ.†   □

---

† Think of each of the equations

$$r = a(1 - \cos\theta) \qquad \text{and} \qquad r = a(1 + \cos\theta)$$

as giving the position of an object at time θ. At the points we found by solving the two equations simultaneously, the objects will collide. (They both arrive there at the same time.) At the origin the situation is different. Both objects will pass through the origin, but no collision takes place because the objects pass through the origin at different times.

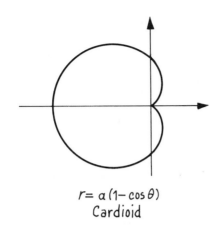

$$r = a(1 - \cos\theta)$$
Cardioid

FIGURE 7.6.11

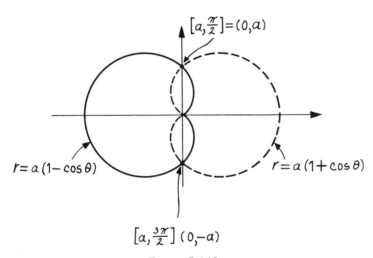

FIGURE 7.6.12

Exercises

Plot the following points.

1. $[1, \pi/3]$.   3. $[-1, \pi/3]$.   5. $[4, 5\pi/4]$.   7. $-1/2, \pi]$.
2. $[1, \pi/2]$.   4. $[-1, -\pi/3]$.   6. $[-2, 0]$.   8. $[1/3, 2\pi/3]$.

The following points are given in rectangular coordinates. Find all possible polar coordinates for each point.

9.* $(0, 1)$.   13.* $(2, -2)$.
10. $(1, 0)$.   14. $(3, -3\sqrt{3})$.
11.* $(-3, 0)$.   15.* $(4\sqrt{3}, 4)$.
12. $(4, 4)$.   16. $(\sqrt{3}, -1)$.

Determine whether the given point lies on the given curve.

17.* $r^2 \cos \theta = 1$; $[1, \pi]$.

18. $r^2 = \cos 2\theta$; $[1, \pi/4]$.

19.* $r = \sin \theta/3$; $[1/2, \pi/2]$.

20. $r^2 = \sin 3\theta$; $[1, -5\pi/6]$.

21.* Show that the point $[2, \pi]$ lies both on

$$r^2 = 4 \cos \theta \quad \text{and} \quad r = 3 + \cos \theta.$$

Find the points at which the curves intersect. Express your answers in rectangular coordinates.

22.* $r = 2 \sin \theta$, $r = 2 \cos \theta$.

23. $r = \dfrac{1}{1 - \cos \theta}$, $r \sin \theta = b$.

24.* $r^2 = \sin \theta$, $r = 2 - \sin \theta$.

Test the following curves for symmetry.

25.* $r = 2 + \cos \theta$.   28. $r(\sin \theta + \cos \theta) = 1$.

26. $r^2 = \cos 2\theta$.   29.* $r^2 \sin 2\theta = 1$.

27.* $r^2 = \sin \theta$.   30. $r = \cos 2\theta$.

Sketch the graph of the following polar equations.

31.* $r = 1$.

32. $\theta = -\pi/4$.   42. $r = \dfrac{1}{1 - 2 \cos \theta}$.

33.* $\theta = 3\pi$.

34. $\theta^2 = 9\pi^2$.   43.* $r = \dfrac{1}{2 - \cos \theta}$.

35.* $r \sin \theta = 1$.

36. $r \cos \theta = -2$.   44. $r = \dfrac{2}{1 + \cos \theta}$.

37.* $r = \sin \theta$.   45. $r^2 = \sin \theta$.

38. $r = \sin(\theta + \pi)$.   46. $r = e^\theta, \theta \geq 0$ (logarithmic spiral).

39.* $r^2 \sin 2\theta = 2$.   47. $r = e^{2\theta}, \theta \geq 0$.

40. $r^2 \cos 2\theta = 4$.   48. $r = \theta$. (spiral of Archimedes)

41.* $r = \dfrac{1}{1 - \cos \theta}$.   49. $r = 2\theta$.

50. Sketch the graph of

$$(x^2 + y^2)^2 = x^2 - y^2.$$

[HINT: Change into polar coordinates.]

7.7 Curves given parametrically

We begin with a pair of functions x and y differentiable on some interval I. At the end points we require only continuity.

For each t in I we can interpret $(x(t), y(t))$ as the point with x-coordinate $x(t)$ and y-coordinate $y(t)$. As t then ranges over I, the point $(x(t), y(t))$ traces out a curve in the plane. The curve so traced out is said to be given *parametrically* by the functions x and y.

Problem.   An object moves so that at time t it has coordinates

$$x(t) = t + 1, \qquad y(t) = 2t - 5.$$

Find the path generated by the motion.

SOLUTION.   Here we can express $y(t)$ in terms of $x(t)$:

$$y(t) = 2(x(t) - 1) - 5 = 2x(t) - 7.$$

The path generated is the line

$$y = 2x - 7. \quad \square$$

Problem.   Find the curve generated by

$$x(t) = a \cos t, \qquad y(t) = a \sin t.$$

SOLUTION.   Here

$$[x(t)]^2 + [y(t)]^2 = a^2 \cos^2 t + a^2 \sin^2 t = a^2$$

so that the curve is the circle

$$x^2 + y^2 = a^2. \quad \square$$

Problem.   Find the curve generated by

$$x(t) = a \cos t, \qquad y(t) = b \sin t.$$

SOLUTION.   Here

$$\frac{[x(t)]^2}{a^2} + \frac{[y(t)]^2}{b^2} = \cos^2 t + \sin^2 t = 1$$

so that the curve is the ellipse

$$\frac{x^2}{a^2} + \frac{y^2}{b^2} = 1. \quad \square$$

Problem.   Find the curve generated by

$$x(t) = a \cosh t, \qquad y(t) = b \sinh t. \qquad\qquad (a > 0, b > 0)$$

SOLUTION.   Here

$$\frac{[x(t)]^2}{a^2} - \frac{[y(t)]^2}{b^2} = \cosh^2 t - \sinh^2 t = 1.$$

Since $x(t)$ remains positive, the curve is the right-hand branch of the hyperbola

$$\frac{x^2}{a^2} - \frac{y^2}{b^2} = 1. \quad \square$$

A single curve can be parametrized in many different ways. As an example take the ellipse

$$\frac{x^2}{a^2} + \frac{y^2}{b^2} = 1$$

and think of t as time measured in seconds. A particle whose position is given by the equations

$$x(t) = a \cos t, \qquad y(t) = b \sin t, \quad t \in [0, 2\pi]$$

traverses the ellipse in a counterclockwise manner. It begins at the point

$$(x(0), y(0)) = (a, 0)$$

and makes a full circuit in 2π seconds. If the equations of motion are

$$x(t) = a \cos 2\pi t, \qquad y(t) = -b \sin 2\pi t, \quad t \in [0, 1]$$

the particle still travels the same ellipse, but in a different manner. Once again it starts at

$$(x(0), y(0)) = (a, 0)$$

but this time it moves clockwise and makes the full circuit in only one second. If the equations of motion are

$$x(t) = a \sin 4\pi t, \qquad y(t) = b \cos 4\pi t, \quad t \in [0, \infty)$$

the motion begins at

$$(x(0), y(0)) = (0, b)$$

and goes on in perpetuity. The motion is clockwise, a complete circuit taking place every half second. $\quad \square$

Problem.   Two particles start at the same instant, the first along the linear path

$$x_1(t) = \frac{16}{3} - \frac{8}{3} t, \qquad y_1(t) = 4t - 5, \quad t \geq 0$$

and the second along the elliptical path

$$x_2(t) = 2 \sin \frac{\pi}{2} t, \qquad y_2(t) = -3 \cos \frac{\pi}{2} t, \quad t \geq 0.$$

(i) At what points, if any, do the paths cross?
(ii) At what points, if any, do the particles collide?

SOLUTION.   To see where the paths intersect we first express them both as equations in x and y. The linear path can be written as

$$3x + 2y - 6 = 0, \qquad x \le \frac{16}{3}$$

and the elliptical path as

$$\frac{x^2}{4} + \frac{y^2}{9} = 1.$$

Solving the two equations simultaneously we get

$$x = 2, y = 0 \qquad \text{and} \qquad x = 0, y = 3.$$

This means that the paths intersect at the points

$$(2, 0) \qquad \text{and} \qquad (0, 3).$$

This answers part (i). Now for part (ii). The first particle passes through $(2, 0)$ only when

$$x_1(t) = \frac{16}{3} - \frac{8}{3} t = 2 \qquad \text{and} \qquad y_1(t) = 4t - 5 = 0.$$

As you can check, this happens only when $t = 5/4$. When $t = 5/4$ the second particle is elsewhere. Hence no collision takes place at $(2, 0)$. There is however a collision at $(0, 3)$ because both particles get there at exactly the same time, $t = 2$:

$$x_1(2) = 0 = x_2(2), \qquad y_1(2) = 3 = y_2(2). \quad \square$$

Tangents

The problem of finding tangent lines to a parametrized curve

$$C : x(t), y(t), \qquad t \in I$$

is complicated by the fact that such a curve can intersect itself. This means that at a given point a curve can have

   (i) one tangent
   (ii) two or more tangents, or
   (iii) no tangent at all.

We illustrate these possibilities in Figure 7.7.1.
   To make sure that at least one tangent line exists at each point we make the additional assumptions that

$$x' \text{ and } y' \text{ are continuous} \quad \text{and} \quad [x'(t)]^2 + [y'(t)]^2 \ne 0.$$

We now choose a point (x_0, y_0) of the curve C and a time t_0 at which

$$x(t_0) = x_0 \qquad \text{and} \qquad y(t_0) = y_0.$$

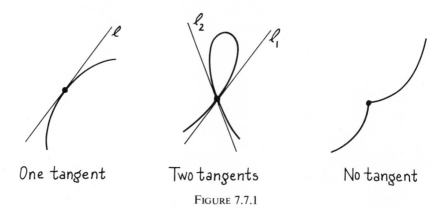

One tangent   Two tangents   No tangent

FIGURE 7.7.1

What we want is the slope of the curve as it passes through the point (x_0, y_0) at time t_0.†
To find this slope we assume that $x'(t_0) \neq 0$.   With $x'(t_0) \neq 0$, we can be sure that for h sufficiently small

$$x(t_0 + h) - x(t_0) \neq 0. \qquad \text{(Explain why)}$$

We can therefore form the quotient

$$\frac{y(t_0 + h) - y(t_0)}{x(t_0 + h) - x(t_0)}.$$

This quotient is the slope of the secant line pictured in Figure 7.7.2. The limit of this quotient as h tends to zero is the slope we want. Since

$$\frac{y(t_0 + h) - y(t_0)}{x(t_0 + h) - x(t_0)} = \frac{(1/h)[y(t_0 + h) - y(t_0)]}{(1/h)[x(t_0 + h) - x(t_0)]} \rightarrow \frac{y'(t_0)}{x'(t_0)},$$

we have

$$m = \frac{y'(t_0)}{x'(t_0)}.$$

As an equation for the tangent line, we can write

$$y - y(t_0) = \frac{y'(t_0)}{x'(t_0)} [x - x(t_0)]$$

which simplifies to

$$y'(t_0)[x - x(t_0)] - x'(t_0)[y - y(t_0)] = 0$$

and thus to

(7.7.1) $\boxed{y'(t_0)[x - x_0] - x'(t_0)[y - y_0] = 0.}$

---

† It could pass through the point (x_0, y_0) at other times also.

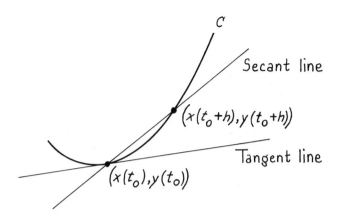

FIGURE 7.7.2

We derived this equation under the assumption that $x'(t_0) \neq 0$. If $x'(t_0) = 0$, (7.7.1) still makes sense. It is simply

$$y'(t_0)[x - x_0] = 0,$$

which, since $y'(t_0) \neq 0$,† can be simplified to

$$\boxed{x = x_0.}$$

In this instance the line is vertical and we say that the curve has a *vertical tangent*.

Problem. Find the tangent(s) to the curve

$$x(t) = t^3, \quad y(t) = 1 - t$$

at the point $(8, -1)$.

SOLUTION. Since the curve passes through the point only when $t = 2$, there is only one tangent line at $(8, -1)$. With

$$x(t) = t^3, \qquad y(t) = 1 - t$$

we have

$$x'(t) = 3t^2, \qquad y'(t) = -1$$

and therefore

$$x'(2) = 12, \qquad y'(2) = -1.$$

The tangent line has equation

$$(-1)[x - 8] - (12)[y - (-1)] = 0.$$

---

† We are assuming that $[x'(t)]^2 + [y'(t)]^2$ is never 0. Since $x'(t_0) = 0$, $y'(t_0) \neq 0$.

This reduces to

$$x + 12y + 4 = 0. \quad \square$$

Problem.   Find the points of the curve

$$x(t) = 3 - 4 \sin t, \qquad y(t) = 4 + 3 \cos t$$

at which there is

   (i) a horizontal tangent,   (ii) a vertical tangent.

SOLUTION.   Since

$$x'(t) = -4 \cos t \quad \text{and} \quad y'(t) = -3 \sin t$$

the derivatives are never 0 simultaneously. To find the points at which there is a horizontal tangent, we set

$$y'(t) = 0.$$

This gives

$$t = n\pi.$$

Horizontal tangents occur therefore at points of the form

$$(x(n\pi), y(n\pi)).$$

Since

$$x(n\pi) = 3 - 4 \sin n\pi = 3$$

and

$$y(n\pi) = 4 + 3 \cos n\pi = \begin{cases} 7, & n \text{ even} \\ 1, & n \text{ odd} \end{cases},$$

there is a horizontal tangent only at

$$(3, 7) \quad \text{and} \quad (3, 1).$$

To find the vertical tangents, we set $x'(t) = 0$. This gives

$$t = \frac{\pi}{2} + n\pi.$$

Vertical tangents occur therefore at points of the form

$$\left(x\left(\frac{\pi}{2} + n\pi\right), y\left(\frac{\pi}{2} + n\pi\right) \right).$$

Since

$$x\left(\frac{\pi}{2} + n\pi\right) = 3 - 4 \sin\left(\frac{\pi}{2} + n\pi\right) = \begin{cases} -1, & n \text{ even} \\ 7, & n \text{ odd} \end{cases}$$

and

$$y\left(\frac{\pi}{2} + n\pi\right) = 4 + 3\cos\left(\frac{\pi}{2} + n\pi\right) = 4,$$

there is a vertical tangent at

$$(-1, 4) \quad\text{and}\quad (7, 4). \quad\square$$

Problem. Find the tangent(s) to the curve

$$x(t) = t^2 - 2t + 1, \qquad y(t) = t^4 - 4t^2 + 4$$

at the point $(1, 4)$.

SOLUTION. The curve passes through the point $(1, 4)$ when $t = 0$ and when $t = 2$. (Check this out.) Differentiation gives

$$x'(t) = 2t - 2, \qquad y'(t) = 4t^3 - 8t.$$

At $t = 0$,

$$x'(t) \neq 0 \quad\text{and}\quad y'(t) = 0,$$

so that the tangent line is horizontal.

At $t = 2$,

$$x'(t) = 2 \quad\text{and}\quad y'(t) = 16,$$

and therefore the tangent line is given by

$$y - 4 = 8(x - 1). \quad\square$$

To apply these ideas to a curve given by a polar equation, we first apply the transformation formulas

$$x = r\cos\theta, \qquad y = r\sin\theta.$$

The polar curve

$$r = f(\theta)$$

then becomes

$$x(\theta) = f(\theta)\cos\theta, \qquad y(\theta) = f(\theta)\sin\theta.$$

Problem. Find the points of the cardioid

$$r = 1 - \cos\theta \qquad\qquad\text{(Figure 7.6.11)}$$

at which there is a vertical tangent.

SOLUTION. Since the cosine function has period 2π, we need only concern ourselves with θ in $[0, 2\pi)$. Parametrically we have

$$x(\theta) = (1 - \cos\theta)\cos\theta, \qquad y(\theta) = (1 - \cos\theta)\sin\theta$$

Differentiating and simplifying, we obtain

$$x'(\theta) = \sin \theta (2 \cos \theta - 1), \qquad y'(\theta) = (1 - \cos \theta)(1 + 2 \cos \theta).$$

The only numbers in the interval $[0, 2\pi)$ at which x' is zero and y' is not are $\pi/3$, π, and $5\pi/3$. Thus we have a vertical tangent at each of the following points:

$$[1/2, \pi/3], \quad [2, \pi], \quad [1/2, 5\pi/3].$$

In rectangular coordinates, these points are:

$$(1/4, \sqrt{3}/4), \quad (-2, 0), \quad (1/4, -\sqrt{3}/4). \quad \square$$

Exercises

Find a parametric representation for the following curves.

1.* $x = y$.

2. $y = -x$.

3.* $2x + 5y - 1 = 0$.

4.* $x = -2$.

5. $x^2 + y^2 = 4$.

6.* $\dfrac{x^2}{25} + \dfrac{y^2}{4} = 1$.

7.* $\dfrac{x^2}{25} - \dfrac{y^2}{4} = 1$.

8. $x^2 + 4ay = 0$.

9.* $y^2 + x - 1 = 0$.

10.* $x^2 - y - 1 = 0$.

11. $r = \theta$.

12.* $r = e^\theta$.

Find an equation in x and y for the tangent line at the point indicated.

13.* $x(t) = t,\ y(t) = t^3 - 1;\ t = 1$.

14. $x(t) = t^2,\ y(t) = t + 5;\ t = 0$.

15.* $x(t) = 2t,\ y(t) = \cos \pi t;\ t = 0$.

16. $x(t) = 2t - 1,\ y(t) = t^4;\ t = 1$.

17.* $x(t) = t^2,\ y(t) = (2 - t)^2;\ t = 1/2$.

18. $x(t) = 1/t,\ y(t) = 1/(t + 1);\ t = 1$.

19.* $x(t) = \cos t,\ y(t) = 1 + \sin t;\ t = \pi/4$.

20. $x(t) = 1 + \sin t,\ y(t) = \cos t;\ t = -\pi/2$.

21.* $r = \dfrac{4}{5 - \cos \theta},\ \theta = \dfrac{\pi}{2}$.

22. $r = \dfrac{5}{4 - \cos \theta},\ \theta = \dfrac{\pi}{6}$.

23.* $r = \dfrac{1}{1 - \cos \theta},\ \theta = \pi$.

24. $r = \dfrac{\sin \theta - \cos \theta}{\sin \theta + \cos \theta},\ \theta = 0$.

25.* $x(t) = \log (t - 2),\ y(t) = t/3;\ t = 3$.

26. $x(t) = e^t,\ y(t) = 3e^{-t};\ t = 0$.

Find the points (x, y) at which the curve has (i) a horizontal tangent, (ii) a vertical tangent. Then sketch the curve.

27.* $x(t) = 3t - t^3,\ y(t) = t + 1$.

28. $x(t) = t^2 - 2t, \quad y(t) = t^3 - 12t.$

29.* $x(t) = \sin 2t, \quad y(t) = \sin t.$

30. $x(t) = \cos^4 t, \quad y(t) = \sin^4 t.$

31.* Two particles start at the same instant, the first along the elliptical path

$$x_1(t) = 2 - 3 \cos \pi t, \qquad y_1(t) = 3 + 7 \sin \pi t, \quad t \geq 0$$

and the second along the parabolic path

$$x_2(t) = 3t + 2, \qquad y_2(t) = -\frac{7}{15}(3t + 1)^2 + \frac{157}{15}, \quad t \geq 0.$$

(i) At what points, if any, do these paths intersect?

(ii) At what points, if any, will the particles collide?

7.8   Rotations; eliminating the *xy*-term

We begin with a rectangular coordinate system Oxy. If we rotate this system α radians about the origin we obtain a new coordinate system OXY. See Figure 7.8.1.

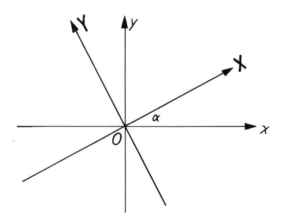

FIGURE 7.8.1

A point P will now have two pairs of rectangular coordinates:

$$(x, y) \text{ with respect to the } Oxy \text{ system}$$

and

$$(X, Y) \text{ with respect to the } OXY \text{ system.}$$

Here we investigate the relation between (x, y) and (X, Y). With P as in Figure 7.8.2,

$$x = r \cos (\alpha + \beta), \qquad y = r \sin (\alpha + \beta)$$

and

$$X = r \cos \beta, \qquad Y = r \sin \beta.$$

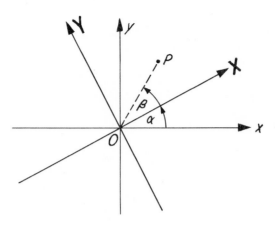

FIGURE 7.8.2

Since

$$\cos(\alpha + \beta) = \cos\alpha\cos\beta - \sin\alpha\sin\beta ,$$
$$\sin(\alpha + \beta) = \sin\alpha\cos\beta + \cos\alpha\sin\beta$$

we have

$$x = r\cos(\alpha + \beta) = \cos\alpha[r\cos\beta] - \sin\alpha[r\sin\beta]$$
$$y = r\sin(\alpha + \beta) = \sin\alpha[r\cos\beta] + \cos\alpha[r\sin\beta]$$

and therefore

$$\boxed{x = (\cos\alpha)X - (\sin\alpha)Y \quad\text{and}\quad y = (\sin\alpha)X + (\cos\alpha)Y.}$$

These formulas give the algebraic consequences of a rotation of α radians.

Eliminating the xy-term

Rotations of the coordinate system enable us to simplify equations of the second degree by eliminating the xy-term; that is, if in the Oxy system, S has an equation of the form

(1) $$ax^2 + bxy + cy^2 + dx + ey + f = 0, \quad\text{with } b \neq 0,$$

then there exists a coordinate system OXY, differing from Oxy by a rotation, such that in the OXY system S has an equation of the form

$$AX^2 + CY^2 + DX + EY + F = 0.$$

To see this, we substitute

$$x = (\cos\alpha)X - (\sin\alpha)Y, \quad y = (\sin\alpha)X + (\cos\alpha)Y$$

in Equation (1). Doing so, we obtain a second-degree equation in X and Y in which the coefficient of XY is

$$-2a\cos\alpha\sin\alpha + b(\cos^2\alpha - \sin^2\alpha) + 2c\cos\alpha\sin\alpha.$$

This coefficient can be simplied to

$$(c - a) \sin 2\alpha + b \cos 2\alpha.$$

It is zero provided that

$$(a - c) \sin 2\alpha = b \cos 2\alpha.$$

The case $a = c$, yields

$$\cos 2\alpha = 0,$$

$$2\alpha = \frac{\pi}{2} + n\pi, \qquad (n \quad \text{an arbitrary integer})$$

$$\alpha = \frac{\pi}{4} + \frac{n}{2} \pi.$$

The case $a = c$ can therefore be satisfied by setting

$$\alpha = \frac{\pi}{4}. \qquad\qquad \text{(Choose } n = 0)$$

The case $a \neq c$, yields

$$\tan 2\alpha = \frac{b}{a - c},$$

$$2\alpha = \arctan\left(\frac{b}{a - c}\right) + n\pi,$$

$$\alpha = \frac{1}{2} \arctan\left(\frac{b}{a - c}\right) + \frac{n}{2} \pi.$$

The case $a \neq c$ can therefore be satisfied by setting

$$\alpha = \frac{1}{2} \arctan\left(\frac{b}{a - c}\right). \quad \text{(Choose } n = 0) \quad \square$$

Example.   In the case of

$$xy - 2 = 0,$$

we have $a = c$ and thus can choose $\alpha = \pi/4$. Setting

$$x = \left(\cos\frac{\pi}{4}\right) X - \left(\sin\frac{\pi}{4}\right) Y = \frac{1}{\sqrt{2}} (X - Y)$$

$$y = \left(\sin\frac{\pi}{4}\right) X + \left(\cos\frac{\pi}{4}\right) Y = \frac{1}{\sqrt{2}} (X + Y),$$

we find that $xy - 2 = 0$ becomes

$$\frac{1}{2}(X^2 - Y^2) - 2 = 0,$$

which simplifies to

$$\frac{X^2}{4} - \frac{Y^2}{4} = 1.$$

This, we recognize, is the equation of a hyperbola in standard position with respect to the OXY system. The graph is shown in Figure 7.8.3. □

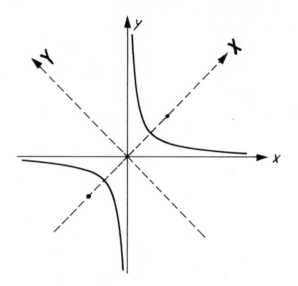

FIGURE 7.8.3

Example.   In the case of

$$11x^2 + 4\sqrt{3}xy + 7y^2 - 1 = 0,$$

we have $a = 11$, $b = 4\sqrt{3}$, and $c = 7$. Thus we can choose

$$\alpha = \frac{1}{2} \text{ arc tan } \frac{b}{a - c} = \frac{1}{2} \text{ arc tan } \sqrt{3} = \frac{\pi}{6}.$$

Setting

$$x = \left(\cos\frac{\pi}{6}\right) X - \left(\sin\frac{\pi}{6}\right) Y = \frac{1}{2}(\sqrt{3}X - Y)$$

$$y = \left(\sin\frac{\pi}{6}\right) X + \left(\cos\frac{\pi}{6}\right) Y = \frac{1}{2}(X + \sqrt{3}Y),$$

we find after simplification that our initial equation becomes

$$13X^2 + 5Y^2 - 1 = 0,$$

or

$$\frac{X^2}{(1/\sqrt{13})^2} + \frac{Y^2}{(1/\sqrt{5})^2} = 1.$$

This we recognize to be the equation of an ellipse. Its graph is pictured in Figure 7.8.4. □

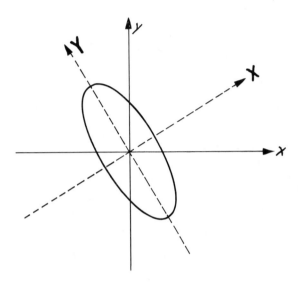

FIGURE 7.8.4

Exercises

For each of the equations below, (a) find a rotation α, $\alpha \in (-\pi/4, \pi/4]$, that eliminates the xy-term; (b) rewrite the equation in terms of the new coordinate system; (c) sketch the graph displaying both coordinate systems.

1.* $xy = 1$.
2. $xy - y + x = 1$.
3.* $11x^2 + 10\sqrt{3}xy + y^2 - 4 = 0$. '
4. $52x^2 - 72xy + 73y^2 - 100 = 0$.
5.* $x^2 - 2xy + y^2 + x + y = 0$.
6. $3x^2 + 2\sqrt{3}xy + y^2 - 2x + 2\sqrt{3}y = 0$.
7.* $x^2 + 2\sqrt{3}xy + 3y^2 + 2\sqrt{3}x - 2y = 0$.
8. $2x^2 + 4\sqrt{3}xy + 6y^2 + (8 - \sqrt{3})x + (8\sqrt{3} + 1)y + 8 = 0$.

For each of the equations below, find a rotation α, $\alpha \in (-\pi/4, \pi/4]$, that eliminates the xy-term. Then find $\cos \alpha$ and $\sin \alpha$.

9.* $x^2 + xy + Kx + Ly + M = 0$.
10. $5x^2 + 24xy + 12y^2 + Kx + Ly + M = 0$.

SUPPLEMENT TO SECTION 7.8

(Optional) The second-degree equation

It is possible to draw general conclusions about the graph of a second-degree equation

$$ax^2 + bxy + cy^2 + dx + ey + f = 0 \qquad a, b, c \quad \text{not all} \quad 0,$$

just from its *discriminant*

$$\Delta = b^2 - 4ac.$$

There are three cases.

Case 1. If $\Delta < 0$, the graph is an ellipse, a circle, a point, or empty.

Case 2. If $\Delta > 0$, the graph is a hyperbola or a pair of intersecting lines.

Case 3. If $\Delta = 0$, the graph is a parabola, a line, a pair of lines, or empty.

Below we outline how these assertions may be verified. A useful first step is to rotate the coordinate system so that the equation takes the form

$$(1) \qquad\qquad AX^2 + CY^2 + DX + EY + F = 0.$$

An elementary but time-consuming computation shows that the discriminant is unchanged by a rotation, so that in this instance we have

$$\Delta = b^2 - 4ac = -4AC.$$

Moreover, A and C cannot both be zero. If $\Delta < 0$, then $AC > 0$ and we can rewrite (1) as

$$\frac{X^2}{C} + \frac{D}{AC} X + \frac{Y^2}{A} + \frac{EY}{AC} + \frac{F}{AC} = 0.$$

By completing the squares, we obtain an equation of the form

$$\frac{(X - \alpha)^2}{(\sqrt{|C|})^2} + \frac{(Y - \beta)^2}{(\sqrt{|A|})^2} = K.$$

If $K > 0$, we have an ellipse or a circle. If $K = 0$, we have the point (α, β). If $K < 0$, the set is empty.

If $\Delta > 0$, then $AC < 0$. Proceeding as before, we obtain an equation of the form

$$\frac{(X - \alpha)^2}{(\sqrt{|C|})^2} - \frac{(Y - \beta)^2}{(\sqrt{|A|})^2} = K.$$

If $K \neq 0$, we have a hyperbola. If $K = 0$, the equation becomes

$$\left(\frac{X - \alpha}{\sqrt{|C|}} - \frac{Y - \beta}{\sqrt{|A|}} \right)\left(\frac{X - \alpha}{\sqrt{|C|}} + \frac{Y - \beta}{\sqrt{|A|}} \right) = 0,$$

so that we have a pair of lines intersecting at the point (α, β).

If $\Delta = 0$, then $AC = 0$, so that either $A = 0$ or $C = 0$. Since A and C are not both zero, there is no loss in generality in assuming that $A \neq 0$ and $C = 0$. In this case Equation (1) reduces to

$$AX^2 + DX + EY + F = 0.$$

Dividing by A, we obtain an equation of the form

$$X^2 + HX + IY + J = 0.$$

Completing the square gives us

$$(X - \alpha)^2 = \beta Y + K.$$

If $\beta \neq 0$, we have a parabola. If $\beta = 0$ and $K = 0$, we have a line. If $\beta = 0$ and $K > 0$, we have a pair of parallel lines. If $\beta = 0$ and $K < 0$, the set is empty. $\square$

THE TECHNIQUE OF INTEGRATION

8.1 A short table of integrals; review

For review and ready reference we begin with a short table of integrals. A more extended table appears at the end of the book.

1. $\int \alpha \, dx = \alpha x + C$

2. $\int x^n \, dx = \dfrac{x^{n+1}}{n+1} + C, \qquad n \neq -1$

3. $\int \dfrac{dx}{x} = \log |x| + C$

4. $\int e^x \, dx = e^x + C$

5. $\int p^x \, dx = \dfrac{p^x}{\log p} + C$

6. $\int \log x \, dx = x \log x - x + C$

7. $\int \cos x \, dx = \sin x + C$

8. $\int \sin x \, dx = -\cos x + C$

9. $\int \sec^2 x \, dx = \tan x + C$

10. $\int \operatorname{cosec}^2 x \, dx = -\cot x + C$

11. $\int \sec x \tan x \, dx = \sec x + C$

12. $\int \operatorname{cosec} x \cot x \, dx = -\operatorname{cosec} x + C$

13. $\int \tan x \, dx = \log |\sec x| + C$

14. $\int \cot x \, dx = \log |\sin x| + C$

15. $\int \sec x \, dx = \log |\sec x + \tan x| + C$

16. $\int \operatorname{cosec} x \, dx = \log |\operatorname{cosec} x - \cot x| + C$

17. $\int \dfrac{dx}{\sqrt{a^2 - x^2}} = \arcsin\left(\dfrac{x}{a}\right) + C$ [Throughout take $a > 0$]

18. $\int \dfrac{dx}{a^2 + x^2} = \dfrac{1}{a} \arctan \dfrac{x}{a} + C$

19. $\int \arcsin x \, dx = x \arcsin x + \sqrt{1 - x^2} + C$

20. $\int \arctan x \, dx = x \arctan x - \tfrac{1}{2} \log (1 + x^2) + C$

21. $\int \cosh x \, dx = \sinh x + C$

22. $\int \sinh x \, dx = \cosh x + C$

23. $\int \operatorname{sech}^2 x \, dx = \tanh x + C$

24. $\int \operatorname{cosech}^2 x \, dx = -\coth x + C$

25. $\int \operatorname{sech} x \tanh x \, dx = -\operatorname{sech} x + C$

26. $\int \operatorname{cosech} x \coth x \, dx = -\operatorname{cosech} x + C$

27. $\int \dfrac{dx}{x^2 - a^2} = \dfrac{1}{2a} \log \left|\dfrac{x - a}{x + a}\right| + C$

Of all these only Formula 27 is new. To derive it is a simple matter. The key is to observe that

$$\frac{1}{x^2 - a^2} = \frac{1}{2a} \left(\frac{1}{x - a} - \frac{1}{x + a} \right).$$

From this it follows that

$$\int \frac{dx}{x^2 - a^2} = \frac{1}{2a} \left(\int \frac{dx}{x - a} - \int \frac{dx}{x + a} \right)$$

$$= \frac{1}{2a} \left(\log |x - a| - \log |x + a| + C_1 \right)$$

$$= \frac{1}{2a} \log \frac{|x - a|}{|x + a|} + C \qquad \left(\text{Setting } C = \frac{C_1}{2a} \right)$$

$$= \frac{1}{2a} \log \left|\frac{x - a}{x + a}\right| + C. \quad \square$$

In the spirit of review we work out a few simple integrals.

Problem.   Compute

$$\int x \tan x^2 \, dx.$$

SOLUTION: We begin by noting that

$$\int \tan x \, dx = \log |\sec x| + C. \qquad\qquad \text{(Formula 13)}$$

Consequently

$$\int x \tan x^2 \, dx = \frac{1}{2} \int \tan x^2 \cdot \frac{d}{dx}(x^2) \, dx$$

$$= \frac{1}{2} \log |\sec x^2| + C. \quad \square$$

Problem.   Compute

$$\int_0^1 \frac{e^x}{e^x + 2} \, dx.$$

SOLUTION.

$$\int_0^1 \frac{e^x}{e^x + 2} \, dx = \int_0^1 \frac{1}{e^x + 2} \frac{d}{dx}(e^x + 2) \, dx$$

$$= \int_0^1 \frac{d}{dx} [\log(e^x + 2)] \, dx$$

$$= \Big[\log(e^x + 2)\Big]_0^1$$

$$= \log(e + 2) - \log 3$$

$$= \log\left(\frac{e + 2}{3}\right). \quad \square$$

The formula for integration by parts can be written

$$\boxed{\int f(x) \frac{d}{dx}[g(x)] \, dx = f(x)g(x) - \int g(x) \frac{d}{dx}[f(x)] \, dx.}$$

For further practice in the technique of integration by parts we refer to the next two problems.

Problem.   Compute

$$\int x \arctan x \, dx.$$

SOLUTION.   For each choice of c

$$x = \frac{d}{dx}\left(\frac{x^2}{2} + c\right).$$

Therefore

$$\int x \arctan x \, dx = \int \arctan x \cdot \frac{d}{dx}\left(\frac{x^2}{2} + c\right) dx$$

$$= \left(\frac{x^2}{2} + c\right)\arctan x - \int \left(\frac{x^2}{2} + c\right)\frac{d}{dx}[\arctan x] \, dx$$

$$= \left(\frac{x^2}{2} + c\right)\arctan x - \int \left(\frac{x^2}{2} + c\right)\frac{1}{x^2 + 1} \, dx.$$

To simplify the calculations we choose $c = 1/2$. This gives

$$\int x \arctan x \, dx = \frac{x^2 + 1}{2}\arctan x - \int \frac{1}{2} \, dx$$

$$= \frac{x^2 + 1}{2}\arctan x - \frac{x}{2} + C. \quad \square$$

Problem.   Compute

$$\int \log(x^2 + a^2) \, dx.$$

SOLUTION

$$\int \log(x^2 + a^2) \, dx = \int \log(x^2 + a^2)\frac{d}{dx}(x + c) \, dx$$

$$= (x + c)\log(x^2 + a^2) - \int (x + c)\frac{d}{dx}[\log(x^2 + a^2)] \, dx$$

$$= (x + c)\log(x^2 + a^2) - \int (x + c)\frac{2x}{x^2 + a^2} \, dx.$$

Choosing $c = 0$, we have

$$\int \log(x^2 + a^2) \, dx = x\log(x^2 + a^2) - \int \frac{2x^2}{x^2 + a^2} \, dx.$$

With

$$\int \frac{2x^2}{x^2 + a^2} \, dx = \int \frac{2(x^2 + a^2)}{x^2 + a^2} \, dx - \int \frac{2a^2}{x^2 + a^2} \, dx$$

$$= \int 2 \, dx - 2a^2 \int \frac{dx}{x^2 + a^2}$$

$$= 2x - 2a \arctan\frac{x}{a} + C_1,$$

we have

$$\int \log (x^2 + a^2) \, dx = x \log (x^2 + a^2) - 2x + 2a \arctan \left(\frac{x}{a}\right) + C. \quad \square$$

Exercises

Work out the following integrals.

1.* $\int e^{2-x} \, dx.$

2. $\int \frac{x}{\sqrt{1 - x^2}} \, dx.$

3.* $\int \cos \frac{2}{3} x \, dx.$

4.* $\int_0^c \frac{dx}{x^2 + c^2}.$

5. $\int_{-\pi/4}^{\pi/4} \frac{\sin x}{\cos^2 x} \, dx.$

6.* $\int_1^2 \frac{e^{1/x}}{x^2} \, dx.$

7.* $\int x \log (x + 1) \, dx.$

8. $\int \log 2x \, dx.$

9.* $\int \frac{dx}{5^x}.$

10.* $\int_{\pi/6}^{\pi/3} \cosec x \, dx.$

11. $\int_0^1 \sin \pi x \, dx.$

12.* $\int_{-\pi/4}^{\pi/4} \frac{dx}{\cos^2 x}.$

13.* $\int \sec^2(1 - x) \, dx.$

14. $\int \frac{e^{\sqrt{x}}}{\sqrt{x}} \, dx.$

15.* $\int x \, 5^x \, dx.$

16.* $\int_0^1 \frac{x^3}{1 + x^4} \, dx.$

17. $\int_0^t \sec \pi x \tan \pi x \, dx.$

18.* $\int_{\pi/6}^{\pi/3} \cot x \, dx.$

19.* $\int e^{-x} \sin 2x \, dx.$

20. $\int \frac{x^3}{\sqrt{1 - x^4}} \, dx.$

21.* $\int \frac{x}{\sqrt{1 - x^4}} \, dx.$

22.* $\int x \arcsin 2x \, dx.$

23. $\int \frac{x}{(x + \alpha)^2 + a^2} \, dx.$

24.* $\int \frac{1 + \cos 2x}{\sin^2 2x} \, dx.$

25.* $\int \frac{dx}{(x + \alpha)^2 + a^2}.$

26. $\int \cosh^2 x \, dx.$

27.* $\int \sinh^2 x \, dx.$

28.* $\int x \sinh x \, dx.$

29. $\int x \cosh x \, dx.$

30.* $\int \cos x \sinh x \, dx.$

31.* $\int \tanh^3 x \, dx.$

32. $\int \sinh^3 x \, dx.$

33.* $\int e^{ax} \cosh ax \, dx.$

8.2 Partial fractions

We begin by recalling that a rational function is by definition the quotient of two polynomials. Thus the expressions

$$\frac{1}{x^2 - 4}, \quad \frac{2x^2 + 3}{x(x - 1)^2}, \quad \frac{-2x}{(x + 1)(x^2 + 1)}, \quad \frac{1}{x(x^2 + x + 1)},$$

$$\frac{3x^4 + x^3 + 20x^2 + 3x + 31}{(x + 1)(x^2 + 4)^2}, \quad \frac{x^5}{x^2 - 1}$$

all define rational functions, but

$$\frac{1}{\sqrt{x}}, \quad \log x, \quad \frac{|x - 2|}{x}$$

do not.

To obtain the integral of a rational function, it is usually necessary to first decompose it into the sum of more readily integrable functions. It is shown in algebra that every rational function can be decomposed into a polynomial (which may be identically zero), plus fractions of the form

$$\frac{A}{(x-\alpha)^k} \quad \text{and} \quad \frac{Bx+C}{(x^2+\beta x+\gamma)^k}$$

with the quadratic irreducible (not factorable). These fractions are called *partial fractions*.

To show how partial-fraction decompositions are carried out in practice, we proceed by examples, at the end of which we make some general remarks.

Example 1. (*The denominator splits into distinct linear factors.*) Given

$$\frac{1}{x^2-4} = \frac{1}{(x-2)(x+2)},$$

we write

$$\frac{1}{x^2-4} = \frac{A}{x-2} + \frac{B}{x+2}$$

and note that this holds iff

$$1 = A(x+2) + B(x-2)$$

for all $x \neq \pm 2$. By the continuity of polynomials, this equation must also hold at -2 and at 2.† Setting $x = -2$, we find that

$$1 = -4B \quad \text{and} \quad B = -\tfrac{1}{4}.$$

Setting $x = 2$, we find that

$$1 = 4A \quad \text{and} \quad A = \tfrac{1}{4}.$$

Thus we have the decomposition

$$\frac{1}{x^2-4} = \frac{\tfrac{1}{4}}{x-2} + \frac{-\tfrac{1}{4}}{x+2}.$$

To check this, you need only add the fractions on the right.   □

---

† By assumption, the polynomial

$$P(x) = A(x+2) + B(x-2) - 1$$

satisfies the condition

$$P(x) = 0 \quad \text{for all } x \neq \pm 2.$$

Being a polynomial, P must be continuous everywhere. This means that we must have

$$P(-2) = 0 \quad \text{and} \quad P(2) = 0.$$

REMARK.   In general, each distinct linear factor $x - c$ in the denominator gives rise to a term of the form

$$\frac{A}{x - c}$$

in the decomposition.

Example 2.   (*The denominator has a repeated linear factor.*) Given

$$\frac{2x^2 + 3}{x(x - 1)^2},$$

we write

$$\frac{2x^2 + 3}{x(x - 1)^2} = \frac{A}{x} + \frac{B}{x - 1} + \frac{C}{(x - 1)^2}.$$

This leads to

$$2x^2 + 3 = A(x - 1)^2 + Bx(x - 1) + Cx.$$

Setting $x = 1$, we find that $C = 5$. Setting $x = 0$, we find that $A = 3$. Thus we have

$$2x^2 + 3 = 3(x - 1)^2 + Bx(x - 1) + 5x.$$

To evaluate B, we can use any number other than 1 and 0. Using -1, we have

$$5 = 12 + 2B - 5 \qquad \text{and} \qquad B = -1.$$

This leads to the decomposition

$$\frac{2x^2 + 3}{x(x - 1)^2} = \frac{3}{x} - \frac{1}{x - 1} + \frac{5}{(x - 1)^2}.$$

This decomposition, too, can be verified by adding the fractions on the right.   □

REMARK.   In general, each factor of the form $(x - c)^k$ in the denominator gives rise to an expression of the form

$$\frac{A_1}{x - c} + \frac{A_2}{(x - c)^2} + \cdots + \frac{A_k}{(x - c)^k}$$

in the decomposition.

Example 3.   (*The denominator has an irreducible quadratic factor.*) Given

$$\frac{-2x}{(x + 1)(x^2 + 1)},$$

we write

$$\frac{-2x}{(x + 1)(x^2 + 1)} = \frac{A}{x + 1} + \frac{Bx + C}{x^2 + 1}$$

and obtain

$$-2x = A(x^2 + 1) + (Bx + C)(x + 1).$$

Setting $x = -1$, we find that

$$2 = 2A \quad \text{and} \quad A = 1.$$

Thus

$$-2x = x^2 + 1 + (Bx + C)(x + 1).$$

Setting $x = 0$, we find that

$$0 = 1 + C \quad \text{and} \quad C = -1.$$

Thus

$$-2x = x^2 + 1 + (Bx - 1)(x + 1).$$

Setting $x = 1$, we find that

$$-2 = 1 + 1 + (B - 1)2,$$

and thus

$$B = -1.$$

This gives us the decomposition

$$\frac{-2x}{(x + 1)(x^2 + 1)} = \frac{1}{x + 1} - \frac{x + 1}{x^2 + 1},$$

which again can be verified by combining the fractions on the right.   □

Example 4.   (*The denominator has an irreducible quadratic factor.*) Consider

$$\frac{1}{x(x^2 + x + 1)}.$$

Here we write

$$\frac{1}{x(x^2 + x + 1)} = \frac{A}{x} + \frac{Bx + C}{x^2 + x + 1}$$

and obtain

$$1 = A(x^2 + x + 1) + (Bx + C)x.$$

To evaluate the constants, it is easier here to expand the polynomial on the right-hand side and equate coefficients. Doing this, we find that

$$1 = (A + B)x^2 + (A + C)x + A$$

and thus

$$0 = A + B, \quad 0 = A + C, \quad 1 = A.$$

We conclude that $A = 1$, $B = -1$, and $C = -1$, and obtain the decomposition

$$\frac{1}{x(x^2 + x + 1)} = \frac{1}{x} - \frac{x + 1}{x^2 + x + 1}.$$

REMARK.   In general, each irreducible quadratic factor $(x^2 + \beta x + \gamma)$ in the denominator gives rise to a term of the form

$$\frac{Ax + B}{x^2 + \beta x + \gamma}$$

in the decomposition.

Example 5.   (*The denominator has a repeated irreducible quadratic factor.*) For

$$\frac{3x^4 + x^3 + 20x^2 + 3x + 31}{(x + 1)(x^2 + 4)^2}$$

we write

$$\frac{3x^4 + x^3 + 20x^2 + 3x + 31}{(x + 1)(x^2 + 4)^2} = \frac{A}{x + 1} + \frac{Bx + C}{x^2 + 4} + \frac{Dx + E}{(x^2 + 4)^2}$$

and obtain

$$3x^4 + x^3 + 20x^2 + 3x + 31$$
$$= A(x^2 + 4)^2 + (Bx + C)(x + 1)(x^2 + 4) + (Dx + E)(x + 1).$$

The right-hand side we simplify to

$$(A + B)x^4 + (B + C)x^3 + (8A + 4B + C + D)x^2$$
$$+ (4B + 4C + D + E)x + (16A + 4C + E).$$

Equating coefficients, we are led to

$$A + B = 3, \quad B + C = 1, \quad 8A + 4B + C + D = 20,$$
$$4B + 4C + D + E = 3, \quad 16A + 4C + E = 31.$$

With a little patience we find that

$$A = 2, \quad B = 1, \quad C = 0, \quad D = 0, \quad \text{and} \quad E = -1.$$

This gives the decomposition

$$\frac{3x^4 + x^3 + 20x^2 + 3x + 31}{(x + 1)(x^2 + 4)^2} = \frac{2}{x + 1} + \frac{x}{x^2 + 4} - \frac{1}{(x^2 + 4)^2}. \quad \square$$

REMARK.   In general each multiple irreducible quadratic factor $(x^2 + \beta x + \gamma)^k$ in the denominator gives rise to an expression of the form

$$\frac{A_1 x + B_1}{x^2 + \beta x + \gamma} + \frac{A_2 x + B_2}{(x^2 + \beta x + \gamma)^2} + \cdots + \frac{A_k x + B_k}{(x^2 + \beta x + \gamma)^k}$$

in the decomposition.

In all the examples we examined so far, the degree of the denominator exceeded that of the numerator. If this does not happen, then a polynomial appears in the decomposition. Below we give an example.

Example 6.   (*The degree of the denominator does not exceed that of the numerator.*) Given

$$\frac{x^5 + 2}{x^2 - 1},$$

we first carry out the suggested division:

$$
\begin{array}{r}
x^3 + x \\
x^2 - 1 \overline{)\,x^5 + 2} \\
\underline{x^5 - x^3 } \\
x^3 \\
\underline{x^3 - x } \\
x + 2.
\end{array}
$$

Thus we have

$$\frac{x^5 + 2}{x^2 - 1} = x^3 + x + \frac{x + 2}{x^2 - 1}.$$

Setting

$$\frac{x + 2}{x^2 - 1} = \frac{A}{x + 1} + \frac{B}{x - 1},$$

we find that

$$x + 2 = A(x - 1) + B(x + 1),$$

so that $A = -\frac{1}{2}$ and $B = \frac{3}{2}$. Thus we have the decomposition

$$\frac{x^5 + 2}{x^2 - 1} = x^3 + x - \frac{1}{2(x + 1)} + \frac{3}{2(x - 1)}. \quad \square$$

Once a rational function has been decomposed into partial fractions, its integral becomes relatively easy to compute.

Example 1 gives

$$\int \frac{dx}{x^2 - 4} = \frac{1}{4} \int \left(\frac{1}{x - 2} - \frac{1}{x + 2} \right) dx$$

$$= \frac{1}{4} \left(\log |x - 2| - \log |x + 2| \right) + C$$

$$= \frac{1}{4} \log \left| \frac{x - 2}{x + 2} \right| + C. \quad \square$$

Example 2 gives

$$\int \frac{2x^2 + 3}{x(x-1)^2}\, dx = \int \left(\frac{3}{x} - \frac{1}{x-1} + \frac{5}{(x-1)^2} \right) dx$$

$$= 3 \log |x| - \log |x-1| - \frac{5}{x-1} + C. \quad \square$$

Example 3 gives

$$\int \frac{-2x}{(x+1)(x^2+1)}\, dx = \int \left(\frac{1}{x+1} - \frac{x+1}{x^2+1} \right) dx.$$

Since

$$\int \frac{dx}{x+1} = \log |x+1| + C_1$$

and

$$\int \frac{x+1}{x^2+1}\, dx = \frac{1}{2} \int \frac{2x}{x^2+1}\, dx + \int \frac{dx}{x^2+1}$$

$$= \frac{1}{2} \log (x^2+1) + \arctan x + C_2,$$

we have

$$\int \frac{-2x}{(x+1)(x^2+1)}\, dx = \log |x+1| - \frac{1}{2} \log (x^2+1) - \arctan x + C. \quad \square$$

Example 4 gives

$$\int \frac{dx}{x(x^2+x+1)} = \int \left(\frac{1}{x} - \frac{x+1}{x^2+x+1} \right) dx = \log |x| - \int \frac{x+1}{x^2+x+1}\, dx.$$

To compute the remaining integral, we note that

$$\int \frac{x+1}{x^2+x+1}\, dx = \frac{1}{2} \int \frac{2x+1}{x^2+x+1}\, dx + \frac{1}{2} \int \frac{dx}{x^2+x+1}.$$

Since

$$\frac{1}{2} \int \frac{2x+1}{x^2+x+1}\, dx = \frac{1}{2} \log (x^2+x+1) + C_1$$

and

$$\frac{1}{2} \int \frac{dx}{x^2+x+1} = \frac{1}{2} \int \frac{dx}{(x+\frac{1}{2})^2 + (\sqrt{3}/2)^2} = \frac{1}{\sqrt{3}} \arctan \left[\frac{2}{\sqrt{3}} \left(x + \frac{1}{2} \right) \right] + C_2,$$

we have

$$\int \frac{dx}{x(x^2+x+1)} = \log |x| - \frac{1}{2} \log (x^2+x+1) - \frac{1}{\sqrt{3}} \arctan \left[\frac{2}{\sqrt{3}} \left(x + \frac{1}{2} \right) \right] + C. \quad \square$$

Example 5 gives

$$\int \frac{3x^4 + x^3 + 20x^2 + 3x + 31}{(x + 1)(x^2 + 4)^2} dx = \int \left(\frac{2}{x + 1} + \frac{x}{x^2 + 4} - \frac{1}{(x^2 + 4)^2} \right) dx.$$

The first two fractions are easy to integrate:

$$\int \frac{2}{x + 1} dx = 2 \log |x + 1| + C_1,$$

$$\int \frac{x}{x^2 + 4} dx = \frac{1}{2} \int \frac{2x}{x^2 + 4} dx = \frac{1}{2} \log (x^2 + 4) + C_2.$$

To integrate the last fraction you can use the reduction formula in Exercise 16 at the end of the section. This gives

$$\int \frac{dx}{(x^2 + 4)^2} = \frac{1}{8} \left(\frac{x}{x^2 + 4} \right) + \frac{1}{8} \int \frac{dx}{x^2 + 4}$$

$$= \frac{1}{8} \left(\frac{x}{x^2 + 4} \right) + \frac{1}{16} \arctan \left(\frac{x}{2} \right) + C_3.$$

The integral we want is therefore

$$2 \log |x + 1| + \frac{1}{2} \log (x^2 + 4) - \frac{1}{8} \left(\frac{x}{x^2 + 4} \right) - \frac{1}{16} \arctan \left(\frac{x}{2} \right) + C. \quad \square$$

Example 6 gives

$$\int \frac{x^5 + 2}{x^2 - 1} dx = \int \left(x^3 + x - \frac{1}{2(x + 1)} + \frac{3}{2(x - 1)} \right) dx$$

$$= \frac{x^4}{4} + \frac{x^2}{2} - \frac{1}{2} \log |x + 1| + \frac{3}{2} \log |x - 1| + C. \quad \square$$

Exercises

Work out the following integrals.

1.* $\int \dfrac{7}{(x - 2)(x + 5)} dx.$

2. $\int \dfrac{x}{(x + 1)(x + 2)(x + 3)} dx.$

3.* $\int \dfrac{x^2 + 1}{x(x^2 - 1)} dx.$

4.* $\int \dfrac{2x^2 + 3}{x^2(x - 1)} dx.$

5. $\int \dfrac{x^5}{x - 2} dx.$

6.* $\int \dfrac{x^5}{(x - 2)^2} dx.$

7.* $\int \dfrac{x + 3}{x^2 - 3x + 2} dx.$

8. $\int \dfrac{x^2 + 3}{x^2 - 3x + 2} dx.$

9.* $\int \dfrac{dx}{(x - 1)^3}.$

10.* $\int \dfrac{x^2}{(x - 1)^2(x + 1)} dx.$

11. $\displaystyle\int \frac{x^3 + 4x^2 - 4x - 1}{(x^2 + 1)^2}\,dx.$

14. $\displaystyle\int \frac{x}{x^3 - 1}\,dx.$

12.* $\displaystyle\int \frac{2x - 1}{(x + 1)^2(x - 2)^2}\,dx.$

15.* $\displaystyle\int \frac{dx}{x^4 + 4}.$

13.* $\displaystyle\int \frac{dx}{x^4 - 16}.$

16. Verify the following reduction formula for $n > 1$:

$$\int_a^b \frac{dx}{(x^2 + c^2)^n} = \left[\frac{1}{2c^2(n - 1)}\frac{x}{(x^2 + c^2)^{n-1}}\right]_a^b + \frac{2n - 3}{2c^2(n - 1)}\int_a^b \frac{dx}{(x^2 + c^2)^{n-1}}.$$

Evaluate the following.

17.* $\displaystyle\int_0^4 \frac{dx}{x^2 + 16}.$

19.* $\displaystyle\int_0^1 \frac{x^3 + x + 2}{(x^2 + 1)^3}\,dx.$

18. $\displaystyle\int_0^4 \frac{dx}{(x^2 + 16)^2}.$

20. $\displaystyle\int_1^2 \frac{dx}{x^2 + 2x + 2}.$

Find the area below the graph of f.

21.* $\displaystyle f(x) = \frac{1}{x(x - 1)(x - 2)}, 3 \le x \le 5.$

27.* $\displaystyle f(x) = \frac{1}{(x^2 + 4)^2}, 0 \le x \le 2.$

22. $\displaystyle f(x) = \frac{1}{(x - 1)^2}, 2 \le x \le 3.$

28. $\displaystyle f(x) = \frac{x}{(x^2 + 4)^2}, 0 \le x \le 2.$

23.* $\displaystyle f(x) = \frac{1}{x^2 + 4}, 0 \le x \le 2.$

29.* $\displaystyle f(x) = \frac{1}{\sqrt{1 - x^2}}, 0 \le x \le \tfrac{1}{2}.$

24. $\displaystyle f(x) = \frac{x}{x^2 + 4}, 0 \le x \le 2.$

30. $\displaystyle f(x) = \frac{x}{\sqrt{1 - x^2}}, 0 \le x \le \tfrac{1}{2}.$

25.* $\displaystyle f(x) = \frac{1}{4 - x^2}, 0 \le x \le 1.$

31.* $\displaystyle f(x) = \frac{1}{\sqrt{4 - x^2}}, 0 \le x \le 1.$

26. $\displaystyle f(x) = \frac{x}{4 - x^2}, 0 \le x \le 1.$

32. $\displaystyle f(x) = \frac{x}{\sqrt{4 - x^2}}, 0 \le x \le 1.$

33.* (Optional) It is known that m parts of chemical A combine with n parts of chemical B to produce a compound C. Suppose that the rate at which C is produced varies directly with the product of the amounts of A and B present at that instant. Find the amount of C produced in t minutes from an initial mixing of A_0 pounds of A with B_0 pounds of B, given that

(a) $n = m$, $A_0 = B_0$, and A_0 pounds of C are produced in the first minute.
(b) $n = m$, $A_0 = \tfrac{1}{2}B_0$, and A_0 pounds of C are produced in the first minute.
(c) $n \neq m$, $A_0 = B_0$, and A_0 pounds of C are produced in the first minute.

HINT: Denote by $A(t)$, $B(t)$, and $C(t)$ the amounts of A, B, and C present at time t. Observe that

$$C'(t) = kA(t)B(t).$$

Note that

$$A_0 - A(t) = \frac{m}{m+n} C(t) \quad \text{and} \quad B_0 - B(t) = \frac{n}{m+n} C(t)$$

and thus

$$C'(t) = k \left[A_0 - \frac{m}{m+n} C(t) \right] \left[B_0 - \frac{n}{m+n} C(t) \right].$$

8.3   Integration by substitution

Integration by parts is based on the product differentiation formula

$$\frac{d}{dt}[f(t)g(t)] = f(t)\frac{d}{dt}[g(t)] + g(t)\frac{d}{dt}[f(t)].$$

Integration by *substitution* is based on the chain rule

$$\frac{d}{dt}[F(g(t))] = F'(g(t))g'(t).$$

If we denote F' by f, then we can write

$$\frac{d}{dt}[F(g(t))] = f(g(t))g'(t).$$

Suppose now that for each $t \in [c, d]$, g' is continuous at t and f is continuous at $g(t)$. Then

$$\int_c^d f(g(t))g'(t)\, dt = \int_c^d \frac{d}{dt}[F(g(t))]\, dt$$

$$= F(g(d)) - F(g(c))$$

$$= \int_{g(c)}^{g(d)} F'(x)\, dx$$

$$= \int_{g(c)}^{g(d)} f(x)\, dx. \quad \square$$

We summarize this result in a theorem.

Theorem

If for each $t \in [c, d]$, g' is continuous at t and f is continuous at $g(t)$, then

$$\boxed{\int_{g(c)}^{g(d)} f(x)\, dx = \int_c^d f(g(t))g'(t)\, dt.}$$

In practice we usually write $x(t)$ for $g(t)$. So doing, we obtain the substitution formula (the change-of-variables formula)

(8.3.1)
$$\boxed{\int_{x(c)}^{x(d)} f(x)\, dx = \int_c^d f(x(t))x'(t)\, dt.}$$

Problem. Evaluate

$$\int_1^4 \frac{dx}{1 + \sqrt{x}}$$

by the method of substitution.

SOLUTION.   Whatever substitution we make, we will end up with an integral of the form

$$\int_c^d \frac{x'(t)}{1 + \sqrt{x(t)}} \, dt \quad \text{with } x(c) = 1 \text{ and } x(d) = 4.$$

To eliminate the square-root sign we set

$$x(t) = t^2.$$

This gives

$$x'(t) = 2t.$$

The equations

$$x(c) = 1, \qquad x(d) = 4$$

are satisfied by setting $c = 1$, $d = 2$. Thus

$$\int_1^4 \frac{dx}{1 + \sqrt{x}} = \int_c^d \frac{x'(t)}{1 + \sqrt{x(t)}} \, dt$$

$$= \int_1^2 \frac{2t}{1 + t} \, dt$$

$$= \int_1^2 \left(2 - \frac{2}{1 + t} \right) dt$$

$$= \left[2t - 2 \log (1 + t) \right]_1^2$$

$$= (4 - 2 \log 3) - (2 - 2 \log 2)$$

$$= 2 + 2 \log \left(\frac{2}{3} \right). \quad \square$$

Problem. Evaluate

$$\int_0^{16} \frac{x^{1/2}}{4(1 + x^{3/4})} \, dx.$$

SOLUTION.   Substitution will lead to an integral of the form

$$\int_c^d \frac{[x(t)]^{1/2} x'(t)}{4(1 + [x(t)]^{3/4})} \, dt \quad \text{with } x(c) = 0 \text{ and } x(d) = 16.$$

To eliminate the fractional exponents we set

$$x(t) = t^4.$$

This gives

$$x'(t) = 4t^3.$$

The equations

$$x(c) = 0, \qquad x(d) = 16$$

are satisfied by setting

$$c = 0, \qquad d = 2.$$

Thus

$$\int_0^{16} \frac{x^{1/2}}{4(1 + x^{3/4})} \, dx = \int_c^d \frac{[x(t)]^{1/2} x'(t)}{4(1 + [x(t)]^{3/4})} \, dt$$

$$= \int_0^2 \frac{t^2 \cdot 4t^3}{4(1 + t^3)} \, dt$$

$$= \int_0^2 \frac{t^5}{1 + t^3} \, dt$$

$$= \int_0^2 \left(t^2 - \frac{t^2}{1 + t^3} \right) dt$$

$$= \left[\frac{t^3}{3} - \frac{1}{3} \log (1 + t^3) \right]_0^2$$

$$= \frac{8}{3} - \frac{1}{3} \log 9$$

$$= \frac{1}{3} (8 - \log 9). \quad \square$$

The method of substitution can also be used to compute indefinite integrals.

Problem. Compute

$$\int \frac{x}{(1 + 2x)^{3/2}} \, dx.$$

SOLUTION. We simplify the integrand† by setting

$$(1 + 2x)^{3/2} = t.$$

---

† The function being integrated.

Solving for x in terms of t, we have

$$x(t) = \tfrac{1}{2}(t^{2/3} - 1) \qquad \text{and} \qquad x'(t) = \tfrac{1}{3}t^{-1/3}.$$

Substitution now leads to the indefinite integral

$$\int \frac{x(t)x'(t)}{[1 + 2x(t)]^{3/2}} \, dt = \frac{1}{6} \int \frac{(t^{2/3} - 1)t^{-1/3}}{t} \, dt$$

$$= \frac{1}{6} \int (t^{-2/3} - t^{-4/3}) \, dt$$

$$= \frac{1}{6} (3t^{1/3} + 3t^{-1/3}) + C$$

$$= \frac{1}{2} (t^{1/3} + t^{-1/3}) + C.$$

With

$$t = (1 + 2x)^{3/2}$$

we have

$$t^{1/3} = (1 + 2x)^{1/2} \qquad \text{and} \qquad t^{-1/3} = (1 + 2x)^{-1/2}.$$

This gives

$$\int \frac{x}{(1 + 2x)^{3/2}} \, dx = \frac{1}{2} [(1 + 2x)^{1/2} + (1 + 2x)^{-1/2}] + C$$

$$= \frac{1 + x}{\sqrt{1 + 2x}} + C. \quad \square$$

Problem. Compute

$$\int \sqrt{1 - e^x} \, dx.$$

SOLUTION.   To eliminate the square-root sign we set

$$1 - e^x = t^2.$$

Solving for x in terms of t, we have

$$x(t) = \log (1 - t^2) \qquad \text{and} \qquad x'(t) = \frac{-2t}{1 - t^2} \cdot$$

This gives

$$\int \sqrt{1 - e^{x(t)}} \, x'(t) \, dt = \int t \left(\frac{-2t}{1 - t^2} \right) dt$$

$$= \int \frac{-2t^2}{1 - t^2} \, dt$$

$$= \int \left(2 - \frac{2}{1 - t^2} \right) dt$$

$$= 2 \int \left(1 + \frac{1}{t^2 - 1} \right) dt$$

$$= 2t + \log \left| \frac{t - 1}{t + 1} \right| + C.$$

Putting this back in terms of x we have

$$\int \sqrt{1 - e^x} \, dx = 2\sqrt{1 - e^x} + \log \left| \frac{\sqrt{1 - e^x} - 1}{\sqrt{1 - e^x} + 1} \right| + C. \quad \square$$

Exercises

Work out the following integrals by substitution.

1.* $\displaystyle\int \frac{dx}{1 - \sqrt{x}}.$

2. $\displaystyle\int_0^3 x \sqrt{1 + x} \, dx.$

3.* $\displaystyle\int \frac{\sqrt{x}}{1 + x} \, dx.$

4. $\displaystyle\int \frac{dx}{x(x^{1/3} - 1)}.$

5.* $\displaystyle\int \sqrt{1 + e^x} \, dx. \quad [x(t) = \log(t^2 - 1)]$

6. $\displaystyle\int x(1 + x)^{1/3} \, dx.$

7.* $\displaystyle\int_2^3 \frac{x^3}{(1 + x^2)^3} \, dx. \quad [x(t) = \sqrt{t - 1}]$

8. $\displaystyle\int x\sqrt{x + 1} \, dx.$

9.* $\displaystyle\int \frac{\sqrt{x}}{\sqrt{x} - 1} \, dx.$

10. $\displaystyle\int \frac{x}{\sqrt{x + 1}} \, dx.$

11.* $\displaystyle\int \frac{\sqrt{x - 1} + 1}{\sqrt{x - 1} - 1} \, dx.$

12. $\displaystyle\int \frac{1 - e^x}{1 + e^x} \, dx.$

13.* $\displaystyle\int \frac{dx}{\sqrt{1 + e^x}}.$

14. $\displaystyle\int \frac{dx}{1 + e^{-x}}.$

15.* $\displaystyle\int \frac{x}{\sqrt{x + 4}} \, dx.$

16. $\displaystyle\int \frac{x + 1}{x\sqrt{x - 2}} \, dx.$

17.* $\displaystyle\int_0^1 2x^2(4x + 1)^{-5/2} \, dx.$

18. $\displaystyle\int x^2 \sqrt{x - 1} \, dx.$

19.* $\displaystyle\int \frac{x}{(ax + b)^{3/2}} \, dx.$

20. $\displaystyle\int \frac{x}{\sqrt{ax + b}} \, dx.$

21. Prove that the integral is translation-invariant; that is, prove that, if f is continuous on $[a, b]$, then

$$\int_a^b f(x) \, dx = \int_{a+\alpha}^{b+\alpha} f(t - \alpha) \, dt$$

for each real α.

8.4   Integrals involving $\sqrt{a^2 \pm x^2}$ and $\sqrt{x^2 \pm a^2}$

Throughout we take $a > 0$. You are already familiar with the formula

$$\int \frac{dx}{\sqrt{a^2 - x^2}} = \arcsin\left(\frac{x}{a}\right) + C.$$

Here we add some new formulas to our table of integrals.

28. $\displaystyle\int \frac{dx}{\sqrt{x^2 + a^2}} = \sinh^{-1}\left(\frac{x}{a}\right) + C$

29. $\displaystyle\int \frac{dx}{\sqrt{x^2 - a^2}} = \cosh^{-1}\left(\frac{x}{a}\right) + C$

30. $\displaystyle\int \sqrt{a^2 - x^2}\, dx = \frac{x}{2}\sqrt{a^2 - x^2} + \frac{a^2}{2}\arcsin\left(\frac{x}{a}\right) + C$

31. $\displaystyle\int \sqrt{x^2 + a^2}\, dx = \frac{x}{2}\sqrt{x^2 + a^2} + \frac{a^2}{2}\sinh^{-1}\left(\frac{x}{a}\right) + C$

32. $\displaystyle\int \sqrt{x^2 - a^2}\, dx = \frac{x}{2}\sqrt{x^2 - a^2} - \frac{a^2}{2}\cosh^{-1}\left(\frac{x}{a}\right) + C$

A Derivation of Formula 28

To find

$$\int \frac{dx}{\sqrt{x^2 + a^2}}$$

we set

$$x = a \sinh t$$

and use the identity

$$a^2 \sinh^2 t + a^2 = a^2 \cosh^2 t.$$

Note that

$$\frac{x}{a} = \sinh t \qquad \text{and therefore} \qquad t = \sinh^{-1}\left(\frac{x}{a}\right).$$

We now have

$$\int \frac{dx}{\sqrt{x^2 + a^2}} = \int \frac{x'(t)}{\sqrt{[x(t)]^2 + a^2}}\, dt$$

$$= \int \frac{a \cosh t}{\sqrt{a^2 \sinh^2 t + a^2}}\, dt$$

$$= \int \frac{a \cosh t}{a \cosh t}\, dt$$

$$= \int 1 \, dt$$

$$= t + C$$

$$= \sinh^{-1}\left(\frac{x}{a}\right) + C. \quad \square$$

Formula 29 can be derived in a similar manner by setting

$$x = a \cosh t, \qquad t > 0.$$

A Derivation of Formula 30

To find

$$\int \sqrt{a^2 - x^2} \, dx$$

we set

$$x = a \sin t, \qquad t \in \left(-\frac{\pi}{2}, \frac{\pi}{2}\right)$$

and use the identity

$$a^2 - a^2 \sin^2 t = a^2 \cos^2 t.$$

Note that

$$t = \arcsin\left(\frac{x}{a}\right).$$

We now have

$$\int \sqrt{a^2 - x^2} \, dx = \int \sqrt{a^2 - [x(t)]^2} \, x'(t) \, dt$$

$$= \int \sqrt{a^2 - a^2 \sin^2 t} \, a \cos t \, dt$$

$$= \int \sqrt{a^2 \cos^2 t} \, a \cos t \, dt$$

$$= a^2 \int \cos^2 t \, dt$$

$$= a^2 \int \frac{1 + \cos 2t}{2} \, dt$$

$$= \frac{a^2}{2} t + \frac{a^2}{4} \sin 2t + C$$

$$= \frac{a^2}{2} t + \frac{a^2}{2} \sin t \cos t + C.$$

With

$$t = \arcsin\left(\frac{x}{a}\right)$$

we have

$$\sin t = \frac{x}{a} \quad \text{and} \quad \cos t = \frac{\sqrt{a^2 - x^2}}{a}. \qquad \text{(See Figure 8.4.1.)}$$

This gives

$$\frac{a^2}{2} t + \frac{a^2}{2} \sin t \cos t + C = \frac{a^2}{2} \arcsin\left(\frac{x}{a}\right) + \frac{a^2}{2}\left(\frac{x}{a}\right) \frac{\sqrt{a^2 - x^2}}{a} + C$$

$$= \frac{a^2}{2} \arcsin\left(\frac{x}{a}\right) + \frac{x}{2} \sqrt{a^2 - x^2} + C.$$

Another way to handle this integral is to write

$$\int \sqrt{a^2 - x^2}\, dx = \int \frac{\sqrt{a^2 - x^2}\sqrt{a^2 - x^2}}{\sqrt{a^2 - x^2}}\, dx = \int \frac{a^2}{\sqrt{a^2 - x^2}}\, dx - \int \frac{x^2}{\sqrt{a^2 - x^2}}\, dx.$$

The first integral on the right you already know:

$$\int \frac{a^2}{\sqrt{a^2 - x^2}}\, dx = a^2 \arcsin\left(\frac{x}{a}\right) + C_1.$$

We can compute the second integral by parts:

$$\int \frac{x^2}{\sqrt{a^2 - x^2}}\, dx = \int (-x)\left(\frac{-x}{\sqrt{a^2 - x^2}}\right) dx$$

$$= \int (-x)\frac{d}{dx}\left(\sqrt{a^2 - x^2}\right) dx$$

$$= -x\sqrt{a^2 - x^2} - \int \sqrt{a^2 - x^2}\, \frac{d}{dx}(-x)\, dx$$

$$= -x\sqrt{a^2 - x^2} + \int \sqrt{a^2 - x^2}\, dx.$$

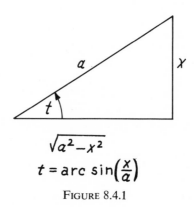

$$t = \arcsin\left(\frac{x}{a}\right)$$

FIGURE 8.4.1

Combining these results we have

$$\int \sqrt{a^2 - x^2}\, dx = a^2 \arcsin\left(\frac{x}{a}\right) + C_1 + x\sqrt{a^2 - x^2} - \int \sqrt{a^2 - x^2}\, dx$$

so that

$$2\int \sqrt{a^2 - x^2}\, dx = x\sqrt{a^2 - x^2} + a^2 \arcsin\left(\frac{x}{a}\right) + C_1$$

and

$$\int \sqrt{a^2 - x^2}\, dx = \frac{x}{2}\sqrt{a^2 - x^2} + \frac{a^2}{2}\arcsin\left(\frac{x}{a}\right) + C. \quad \square$$

Formula 31 can be derived by writing

$$\int \sqrt{x^2 + a^2}\, dx = \int \frac{\sqrt{x^2 + a^2}\sqrt{x^2 + a^2}}{\sqrt{x^2 + a^2}}\, dx$$

$$\int \frac{x^2}{\sqrt{x^2 + a^2}}\, dx + \int \frac{a^2}{\sqrt{x^2 + a^2}}\, dx$$

$$\int \frac{x^2}{\sqrt{x^2 + a^2}}\, dx + a^2 \sinh^{-1}\left(\frac{x}{a}\right).$$

The first integral can then be computed by parts. $\square$

The derivation of Formula 32 is left as an exercise.

Alternative Forms

Since

$$\sinh^{-1}\left(\frac{x}{a}\right) = \log\left(\frac{x}{a} + \sqrt{\left(\frac{x}{a}\right)^2 + 1}\right)$$

(by Theorem 6.6.1)

$$= \log\left(\frac{x + \sqrt{x^2 + a^2}}{a}\right)$$

$$= \log(x + \sqrt{x^2 + a^2}) - \log a$$

and

$$\cosh^{-1}\left(\frac{x}{a}\right) = \log\left(\frac{x}{a} + \sqrt{\left(\frac{x}{a}\right)^2 - 1}\right)$$

(by Theorem 6.6.1)

$$= \log\left(\frac{x + \sqrt{x^2 - a^2}}{a}\right)$$

$$= \log(x + \sqrt{x^2 - a^2}) - \log a,$$

we can combine Formulas 28 and 29 into

$$\int \frac{dx}{\sqrt{x^2 \pm a^2}} = \log (x + \sqrt{x^2 \pm a^2}) + C. \quad \dagger$$

Formulas 31 and 32 can in turn be summarized by the formula

$$\int \sqrt{x^2 \pm a^2}\, dx = \frac{x}{2}\sqrt{x^2 \pm a^2} \pm \frac{a^2}{2} \log (x + \sqrt{x^2 \pm a^2}) + C.$$

Exercises

Work out the following integrals.

1.* $\int_0^1 \sqrt{1 - x^2}\, dx.$

2. $\int_0^1 \sqrt{1 + x^2}\, dx.$

3.* $\int_1^2 \sqrt{x^2 - 1}\, dx.$

4. $\int_0^2 \sqrt{4 + x^2}\, dx.$

5.* $\int_0^{a/2} \frac{dx}{\sqrt{a^2 - x^2}}.$

6. $\int_0^2 x \sqrt{4 + x^2}\, dx.$

7.* $\int_0^2 x \sqrt{4 - x^2}\, dx.$

8. $\int \frac{x}{\sqrt{x^2 - 4}}\, dx.$

9.* $\int \frac{x}{\sqrt{4 - x^2}}\, dx.$

10. $\int \frac{x^2}{\sqrt{x^2 - 4}}\, dx.$

11.* $\int \frac{x^2}{\sqrt{4 - x^2}}\, dx.$

12. $\int \frac{x^2}{\sqrt{4 + x^2}}\, dx.$

13.* $\int \frac{e^x}{\sqrt{9 - e^{2x}}}\, dx.$

14. $\int \frac{dx}{\sqrt{(x + 1)^2 - 4}}.$

15.* $\int \frac{dx}{\sqrt{(x + 1)^2 + 4}}.$

16. $\int \frac{x}{\sqrt{(x + 1)^2 - 4}}\, dx.$

17.* $\int \frac{x}{\sqrt{(x + 1)^2 + 4}}\, dx.$

18. $\int \frac{dx}{\sqrt{(x - 1)^2 + 4}}.$

19.* $\int \frac{dx}{(a^2 - x^2)^{3/2}}.$ [set $x = a \sin t$]

20. $\int \frac{x}{(a^2 - x^2)^{3/2}}\, dx.$

21.* $\int \frac{x^2}{(a^2 - x^2)^{3/2}}\, dx.$

22. $\int \frac{x}{a^2 + x^2}\, dx.$

23.* $\int_2^3 \frac{dx}{x\sqrt{3x^2 - 2x - 1}}.$ $\left[\text{set } x = \frac{1}{t}\right]$

24. $\int \frac{dx}{x \sqrt{x^2 + 4x - 4}}.$

25.* $\int_1^2 \frac{dx}{x \sqrt{1 + 4x + 5x^2}}.$

26. $\int_0^1 \sqrt{2x + x^2}\, dx.$

27.* $\int \frac{\sqrt{1 - x^2}}{x^4}\, dx.$ $\left[\text{set } x = \frac{1}{t}\right]$

28. $\int \frac{\sqrt{x^2 - 1}}{x}\, dx.$

---

† The term log a has been absorbed in the constant C.

[For the remaining integrals set $x = a/t$.]

29.* $\displaystyle\int \frac{dx}{x\sqrt{a^2 - x^2}}$.

30. $\displaystyle\int \frac{dx}{x^2\sqrt{a^2 - x^2}}$.

31.* $\displaystyle\int \frac{dx}{x\sqrt{a^2 + x^2}}$.

32. $\displaystyle\int \frac{dx}{x^2\sqrt{a^2 + x^2}}$.

33.* $\displaystyle\int \frac{dx}{x^2\sqrt{x^2 - a^2}}$.

34. $\displaystyle\int \frac{dx}{x\sqrt{x^2 - a^2}}$.

8.5 Integrating powers of the trigonometric functions

Odd Powers of sin x and cos x

To find

$$\int \sin^{2n+1} x \, dx \qquad \text{and} \qquad \int \cos^{2n+1} x \, dx$$

you can use the fact

$$\sin^{2n+1} x = \sin^{2n} \sin x = (\sin^2 x)^n \sin x = (1 - \cos^2 x)^n \sin x$$

and

$$\cos^{2n+1} x = \cos^{2n} \cos x = (\cos^2 x)^n \cos x = (1 - \sin^2 x)^n \cos x.$$

Example

$$\int \cos^5 x \, dx = \int \cos^4 x \cos x \, dx = \int (\cos^2 x)^2 \cos x = \int (1 - \sin^2 x)^2 \cos x \, dx$$

$$= \int (1 - 2\sin^2 x + \sin^4 x) \cos x \, dx$$

$$= \int (\cos x - 2\sin^2 x \cos x + \sin^4 x \cos x) \, dx$$

$$= \sin x - \frac{2}{3} \sin^3 x + \frac{\sin^5 x}{5} + C. \quad \square$$

The same technique works in evaluating integrals of the form

$$\int \sin^n x \cos^m x \, dx$$

as long as at least one of the powers is odd.

Example

$$\int \sin^2 x \cos^3 x \, dx = \int \sin^2 x \cdot \cos^2 x \cdot \cos x \, dx$$

$$= \int \sin^2 x (1 - \sin^2 x) \cos x \, dx$$

$$= \int \sin^2 x \cos x - \sin^4 x \cos x \, dx$$

$$= \frac{\sin^3 x}{3} - \frac{\sin^5 x}{5} + C. \quad \square$$

Even Powers of sin x and cos x

To find

$$\int \sin^{2n} x \, dx \quad \text{and} \quad \int \cos^{2n} x \, dx$$

you can use the fact that

$$\sin^2 x = \tfrac{1}{2}(1 - \cos 2x) \quad \text{and} \quad \cos^2 x = \tfrac{1}{2}(1 + \cos 2x).$$

Example

$$\int \sin^6 x \, dx = \int (\sin^2 x)^3 = \tfrac{1}{8} \int (1 - \cos 2x)^3 \, dx$$

$$= \tfrac{1}{8} \int (1 - 3 \cos 2x + 3 \cos^2 2x - \cos^3 2x) \, dx.$$

Since

$$\int (1 - 3 \cos 2x) \, dx = x - \tfrac{3}{2} \sin 2x + C_1$$

$$\int 3 \cos^2 2x \, dx = \tfrac{3}{2} \int (1 + \cos 4x) \, dx = \tfrac{3}{2} x + \tfrac{3}{8} \sin 4x + C_2$$

and

$$\int - \cos^3 2x \, dx = - \int \cos^2 2x \cos 2x \, dx = - \int (1 - \sin^2 2x) \cos 2x \, dx$$

$$= - \frac{\sin 2x}{2} + \frac{\sin^3 2x}{6} + C_3,$$

we have

$$\int \sin^6 x \, dx = \tfrac{1}{8} [\tfrac{5}{2} x - 2 \sin 2x + \tfrac{3}{8} \sin 4x + \tfrac{1}{6} \sin^3 2x] + C. \quad \square$$

You can handle integrals of the form

$$\int \sin^{2n} x \cos^{2m} x \, dx$$

by changing the integrand into a combination of powers of only cos x or a combination of powers of only sin x.

Example

$$\int \sin^4 x \cos^2 x \, dx = \int \sin^4 x \, (1 - \sin^2 x) \, dx$$

$$= \int (\sin^4 x - \sin^6 x) \, dx, \quad \text{etc.} \quad \square$$

Powers of tan x and cot x

Integrals of the form

$$\boxed{\int \tan^n x \, dx}$$

can be handled noting that

$$\tan^n x = \tan^{n-2} x \tan^2 x$$
$$= \tan^{n-2} x \, (\sec^2 x - 1)$$
$$= \tan^{n-2} x \sec^2 x - \tan^{n-2} x.$$

A similar reduction formula works for integrals of the form

$$\boxed{\int \cot^n x \, dx.}$$

Example

$$\int \tan^6 x \, dx = \int (\tan^4 x \sec^2 x - \tan^4 x) \, dx$$

$$= \int (\tan^4 x \sec^2 x - \tan^2 x \sec^2 x + \tan^2 x) \, dx$$

$$= \int (\tan^4 x \sec^2 x - \tan^2 x \sec^2 x + \sec^2 x - 1) \, dx$$

$$= \frac{\tan^5 x}{5} - \frac{\tan^3 x}{3} + \tan x - x + C. \quad \square$$

Powers of sec x and cosec x

To handle integrals of the form

$$\boxed{\int \sec^n x \, dx \qquad \text{and} \qquad \int \operatorname{cosec}^n x \, dx}$$

we integrate by parts. In the case of the secant we have

$$\int \sec^n x \, dx = \int \sec^{n-2} x \sec^2 x \, dx$$

$$= \int \sec^{n-2} x \frac{d}{dx} (\tan x) \, dx$$

$$= \sec^{n-2} x \tan x - \int \tan x \frac{d}{dx} (\sec^{n-2} x) \, dx$$

$$= \sec^{n-2} x \tan x - (n - 2) \int \tan^2 x \sec^{n-2} x \, dx$$

$$= \sec^{n-2} x \tan x - (n - 2) \int \sec^n x \, dx + (n - 2) \int \sec^{n-2} x \, dx.$$

This gives

$$(n - 1) \int \sec^n x \, dx = \sec^{n-2} x \tan x + (n - 2) \int \sec^{n-2} x \, dx$$

and thus

$$\int \sec^n x \, dx = \frac{1}{n - 1} \sec^{n-2} x \tan x + \frac{n - 2}{n - 1} \int \sec^{n-2} x \, dx.$$

There is a similar reduction formula for powers of the cosecant:

$$\int \cosec^n x \, dx = - \frac{1}{n - 1} \cosec^{n-2} x \cot x + \frac{n - 2}{n - 1} \int \cosec^{n-2} x \, dx.$$

Example

$$\int \sec^5 x \, dx = \int \sec^3 x \sec^2 x \, dx$$

$$= \int \sec^3 x \frac{d}{dx} (\tan x) \, dx$$

$$= \sec^3 x \tan x - \int \tan x \frac{d}{dx} (\sec^3 x) \, dx$$

$$= \sec^3 x \tan x - \int \tan x \cdot 3 \sec^2 x \cdot \sec x \tan x \, dx$$

$$= \sec^3 x \tan x - 3 \int \tan^2 x \sec^3 x \, dx$$

$$= \sec^3 x \tan x - 3 \int (\sec^2 x - 1) \sec^3 x \, dx$$

$$= \sec^3 x \tan x - 3 \int \sec^5 x \, dx + 3 \int \sec^3 x \, dx$$

$$4 \int \sec^5 x \, dx = \sec^3 x \tan x + 3 \int \sec^3 x \, dx$$

$$\int \sec^5 x \, dx = \frac{1}{4} \sec^3 x \tan x + \frac{3}{4} \int \sec^3 x \, dx.$$

To go on, apply the same technique to

$$\int \sec^3 x \, dx.$$

So doing, you will eventually find that

$$\int \sec^5 x \, dx = \frac{1}{4} \sec^3 x \tan x + \frac{3}{8} \sec x \tan x + \frac{3}{8} \log|\sec x + \tan x| + C. \quad \square$$

Exercises

Work out the following integrals.

1.* $\int \sin^3 x \, dx.$

2. $\int \sin^2 x \, dx.$

3.* $\int_0^{\pi/4} \cos^2 x \, dx.$

4. $\int_0^{\pi/2} \cos^3 x \, dx.$

5.* $\int_0^{\pi} \sin^4 x \, dx.$

6. $\int \tan^2 (x + 1) \, dx.$

7.* $\int_0^{\pi/2} \cos^4 x \, dx.$

8. $\int \sec^2 (x + 1) \, dx.$

9.* $\int \sin^3 x \cos^2 x \, dx.$

10. $\int \sin^3 x \cos^3 x \, dx.$

11.* $\int \sin^2 x \cos^2 x \, dx.$

12. $\int \sin^5 x \, dx.$

13.* $\int \sec^3 x \, dx.$

14. $\int \tan^3 x \, dx.$

15.* $\int \cot^3 x \, dx.$

16. $\int \sin^5 x \cos^2 x \, dx.$

17.* $\int \operatorname{cosec}^3 x \, dx.$

18. $\int \sin^3 (3x) \, dx.$

19.* $\int \tan^4 x \, dx.$

20. $\int \sec^4 x \, dx.$

8.6   Rational expressions in sin x and cos x

There is a substitution which makes it possible to integrate all rational expressions of $\sin x$ and $\cos x$. The result is significant enough to be cast as a theorem.

Theorem 8.6.1

If $f(x)$ is a rational expression in $\sin x$ and $\cos x$, then the substitution

$$x(t) = 2 \arctan t$$

transforms the integral

$$\int f(x) \, dx$$

into the integral of a rational function of t.

PROOF.   Whatever substitution we apply, the end result will be an integral of the form

$$\int f(x(t))x'(t) \, dt.$$

All we need to prove is that, under the circumstances of the theorem, $f(x(t))x'(t)$ is a rational function of t.
With

$$\frac{x(t)}{2} = \arctan t, \qquad \qquad \text{(Figure 8.6.1)}$$

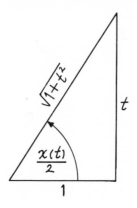

FIGURE 8.6.1

we have

$$\sin \frac{x(t)}{2} = \frac{t}{\sqrt{1 + t^2}} \quad \text{and} \quad \cos \frac{x(t)}{2} = \frac{1}{\sqrt{1 + t^2}}.$$

Since

$$\sin x(t) = 2 \sin \frac{x(t)}{2} \cos \frac{x(t)}{2} \quad \text{and} \quad \cos x(t) = \cos^2 \frac{x(t)}{2} - \sin^2 \frac{x(t)}{2},$$

we have

$$\sin x(t) = 2 \frac{t}{\sqrt{1 + t^2}} \frac{1}{\sqrt{1 + t^2}} = \frac{2t}{1 + t^2}$$

and

$$\cos x(t) = \left(\frac{1}{\sqrt{1 + t^2}}\right)^2 - \left(\frac{t}{\sqrt{1 + t^2}}\right)^2 = \frac{1 - t^2}{1 + t^2}.$$

Since $f(x)$ is rational in $\sin x$ and in $\cos x$ and each of these in turn is rational in t, the composition $f(x(t))$ is itself rational in t. Since

$$x'(t) = \frac{2}{1 + t^2}$$

is also rational in t, the product

$$f(x(t))x'(t)$$

is rational in t. □

In proving the theorem we noted that the substitution

$$\boxed{x(t) = 2 \arctan t}$$

had the following consequences:

$$\sin x(t) = \frac{2t}{1 + t^2}, \qquad \cos x(t) = \frac{1 - t^2}{1 + t^2}, \qquad x'(t) = \frac{2}{1 + t^2}.$$

Keep this in mind as you work the problems.

Problem. Find

$$\int \frac{dx}{1 + 2 \cos x}.$$

SOLUTION. The substitution

$$x(t) = 2 \arctan t$$

gives

$$\int \frac{dx}{1 + 2 \cos x} = \int \frac{x'(t)}{1 + 2 \cos x(t)}\, dt$$

$$= \int \frac{\dfrac{2}{1 + t^2}}{1 + 2\left(\dfrac{1 - t^2}{1 + t^2}\right)}\, dt$$

$$= -2 \int \frac{dt}{t^2 - 3}$$

$$= -\frac{1}{\sqrt{3}} \log \left| \frac{t - \sqrt{3}}{t + \sqrt{3}} \right| + C$$

$$= -\frac{1}{\sqrt{3}} \log \left| \frac{\tan (x/2) - \sqrt{3}}{\tan (x/2) + \sqrt{3}} \right| + C.$$

The last step follows from observing that

$$\frac{x}{2} = \arctan t \quad \text{implies} \quad \tan \frac{x}{2} = t. \quad \square$$

Since the remaining trigonometric functions

$$\tan x, \qquad \cot x, \qquad \sec x, \qquad \operatorname{cosec} x$$

can each be expressed rationally in terms of

$$\sin x \qquad \text{and} \qquad \cos x,$$

the substitution

$$x(t) = 2 \arctan t$$

works also for rational expressions involving these other functions.

Problem. Find

$$\int \frac{\sec x}{2 \tan x + \sec x - 1} \, dx.$$

SOLUTION. With

$$x(t) = 2 \arctan t,$$

we have

$$\int \frac{\sec x}{2 \tan x + \sec x - 1} \, dx = \int \frac{\dfrac{1}{\cos x}}{2 \dfrac{\sin x}{\cos x} + \dfrac{1}{\cos x} - 1} \, dx$$

$$= \int \frac{dx}{2 \sin x - \cos x + 1}$$

$$= \int \frac{x'(t)}{2 \sin x(t) - \cos x(t) + 1} \, dt$$

$$= \int \frac{\dfrac{2}{1 + t^2}}{2 \cdot \dfrac{2t}{1 + t^2} - \dfrac{1 - t^2}{1 + t^2} + 1} \, dt$$

$$= \int \frac{dt}{t^2 + 2t}$$

$$= \int \frac{dt}{t(t + 2)}$$

$$= \frac{1}{2} \int \left(\frac{1}{t} - \frac{1}{t + 2} \right) dt$$

$$= \frac{1}{2} \log \left| \frac{t}{t + 2} \right| + C$$

$$= \frac{1}{2} \log \left| \frac{\tan (x/2)}{\tan (x/2) + 2} \right| + C. \quad \square$$

Exercises

Work out the following integrals.

1.* $\displaystyle \int \frac{dx}{1 + \cos x}$.

2. $\displaystyle \int \frac{dx}{1 - \sin x}$.

3.* $\displaystyle \int \frac{dx}{1 - \cos x}$.

4. $\displaystyle \int_0^{\pi/2} \frac{dx}{3 + 2 \cos x}$.

5.* $\displaystyle\int_0^{\pi/2} \frac{dx}{3 + \cos x}$.

6. $\displaystyle\int \frac{\sin x}{2 - \sin x}\, dx.$

7.* $\displaystyle\int \frac{dx}{5 + 4\cos x}$.

8. $\displaystyle\int \frac{dx}{1 + \tan x}$.

9.* $\displaystyle\int \frac{dx}{5 \sec x - 3}$.

10. $\displaystyle\int \frac{\cos x}{1 - \cos x}\, dx.$

11.* $\displaystyle\int \frac{1 - \cos x}{1 + \sin x}\, dx.$

12. $\displaystyle\int \frac{1 + \sin x}{1 + \cos x}\, dx.$

13.* $\displaystyle\int \left(\frac{1 + \cos x}{1 + \sin x}\right)^2 dx.$

14. $\displaystyle\int \left(\frac{1 + \sin x}{1 - \cos x}\right)^2 dx.$

8.7   Approximate integration

The formula

$$\int_a^b f(x)\, dx = F(b) - F(a)$$

is of no computational use unless we can find an antiderivative F for which we can evaluate both $F(a)$ and $F(b)$. Here we take up some simple numerical methods for estimating

$$\int_a^b f(x)\, dx.$$

The methods described involve only simple arithmetic and lend themselves well to the electronic computer.

As usual, we suppose that f is continuous on $[a, b]$ and, for pictorial convenience, assume that f is positive. We begin by subdividing $[a, b]$ into n nonoverlapping subintervals each of length $(b - a)/n$:

$$[a, b] = [x_0, x_1] \cup \cdots \cup [x_{i-1}, x_i] \cup \cdots \cup [x_{n-1}, x_n],$$

with

$$x_i = a + \frac{i}{n}(b - a).$$

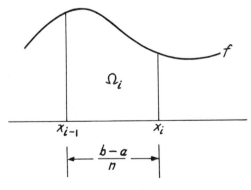

FIGURE 8.7.1

The region Ω_i pictured in Figure 8.7.1 can be approximated in several ways.

(1) By the left endpoint rectangle (Figure 8.7.2):

$$\text{area} = f(x_{i-1})(x_i - x_{i-1}) = f(x_{i-1})\left(\frac{b-a}{n}\right).$$

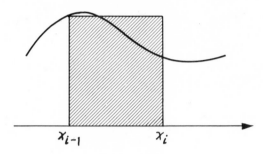

FIGURE 8.7.2

(2) By the right endpoint rectangle (Figure 8.7.3):

$$\text{area} = f(x_i)(x_i - x_{i-1}) = f(x_i)\left(\frac{b-a}{n}\right).$$

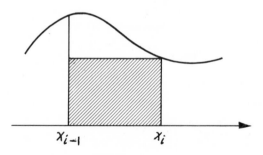

FIGURE 8.7.3

(3) By the midpoint rectangle (Figure 8.7.4):

$$\text{area} = f\left(\frac{x_i + x_{i-1}}{2}\right)(x_i - x_{i-1}) = f\left(\frac{x_i + x_{i-1}}{2}\right)\left(\frac{b-a}{n}\right).$$

(4) By a trapezoid (Figure 8.7.5):

$$\text{area} = \frac{1}{2}[f(x_i) + f(x_{i-1})](x_i - x_{i-1}) = \frac{1}{2}[f(x_i) + f(x_{i-1})]\left(\frac{b-a}{n}\right).$$

(5) By a parabolic region (Figure 8.7.6): take the parabola with vertical axis which passes through the three points indicated.

$$\text{area} = \left[f(x_{i-1}) + 4f\left(\frac{x_i + x_{i-1}}{2}\right) + f(x_i) \right] \left(\frac{x_i - x_{i-1}}{6}\right)$$

$$= \left[f(x_{i-1}) + 4f\left(\frac{x_i + x_{i-1}}{2}\right) + f(x_i) \right] \left(\frac{b - a}{6n}\right).$$

(See Exercises 16, 17, 18 of Section 7.3).

FIGURE 8.7.4

FIGURE 8.7.5

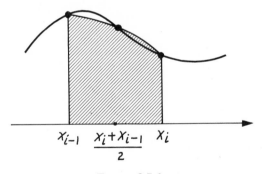

FIGURE 8.7.6

The approximations to Ω_i just considered yield the following estimates for

$$\int_a^b f(x)\, dx.$$

(1) The left endpoint estimate:

$$L_n = \frac{b-a}{n}[f(x_0) + f(x_1) + \cdots + f(x_{n-1})].$$

(2) The right endpoint estimate:

$$R_n = \frac{b-a}{n}[f(x_1) + f(x_2) + \cdots + f(x_n)].$$

(3) The midpoint estimate:

$$M_n = \frac{b-a}{n}\left[f\left(\frac{x_1 + x_0}{2}\right) + \cdots + f\left(\frac{x_n + x_{n-1}}{2}\right)\right].$$

(4) The trapezoidal estimate (*trapezoidal rule*):

$$T_n = \frac{b-a}{2n}[f(x_0) + 2f(x_1) + \cdots + 2f(x_{n-1}) + f(x_n)].$$

(5) The parabolic estimate (*Simpson's rule*):

$$S_n = \frac{b-a}{6n}\left\{f(x_0) + f(x_n) + 2[f(x_1) + \cdots + f(x_{n-1})]\right.$$
$$\left. + 4\left[f\left(\frac{x_1 + x_0}{2}\right) + \cdots + f\left(\frac{x_n + x_{n-1}}{2}\right)\right]\right\}.$$

As an example, we estimate

$$\log 2 = \int_1^2 \frac{dx}{x}$$

by each of these methods. Here we have

$$f(x) = \frac{1}{x}, \qquad [a, b] = [1, 2].$$

Taking $n = 5$, we obtain

$$L_5 = \frac{1}{5}\left(\frac{5}{5} + \frac{5}{6} + \frac{5}{7} + \frac{5}{8} + \frac{5}{9}\right) = \left(\frac{1}{5} + \frac{1}{6} + \frac{1}{7} + \frac{1}{8} + \frac{1}{9}\right),$$

$$R_5 = \frac{1}{5}\left(\frac{5}{6} + \frac{5}{7} + \frac{5}{8} + \frac{5}{9} + \frac{5}{10}\right) = \left(\frac{1}{6} + \frac{1}{7} + \frac{1}{8} + \frac{1}{9} + \frac{1}{10}\right),$$

$$M_5 = \frac{1}{5}\left(\frac{10}{11} + \frac{10}{13} + \frac{10}{15} + \frac{10}{17} + \frac{10}{19}\right) = 2\left(\frac{1}{11} + \frac{1}{13} + \frac{1}{15} + \frac{1}{17} + \frac{1}{19}\right),$$

$$T_5 = \frac{1}{10}\left(\frac{5}{5} + \frac{10}{6} + \frac{10}{7} + \frac{10}{8} + \frac{10}{9} + \frac{5}{10}\right) = \left(\frac{1}{10} + \frac{1}{6} + \frac{1}{7} + \frac{1}{8} + \frac{1}{9} + \frac{1}{20}\right),$$

$$S_5 = \frac{1}{30}\left[1 + \frac{5}{10} + 2\left(\frac{5}{6} + \frac{5}{7} + \frac{5}{8} + \frac{5}{9}\right) + 4\left(\frac{10}{11} + \frac{10}{13} + \frac{10}{15} + \frac{10}{17} + \frac{10}{19}\right)\right].$$

Carrying out the computations and rounding off to the nearest hundredth, we have the following estimates:

$$L_5 \overset{\text{approx}}{=} 0.75, \qquad R_5 \overset{\text{approx}}{=} 0.65, \qquad M_5 \overset{\text{approx}}{=} 0.69, \qquad T_5 \overset{\text{approx}}{=} 0.70, \qquad S_5 \overset{\text{approx}}{=} 0.69.$$

A look at a five-place logarithm table reveals that

$$0.6931 \leq \log 2 \leq 0.6932.$$

Rounding off to the nearest hundredth, we do have

$$\log 2 \overset{\text{approx}}{=} 0.69.$$

Exercises

(In each of the numerical computations below, round off your final answer to the nearest hundredth.)

1.* Find an approximate value for

$$\frac{\pi}{4} = \text{arc tan } 1 = \int_0^1 \frac{dx}{1 + x^2}$$

  (a) by applying the left endpoint estimate, $n = 4$.
  (b) by applying the right endpoint estimate, $n = 4$.
  (c) by applying the midpoint estimate, $n = 4$.
  (d) by applying the trapezoidal rule, $n = 4$.
  (e) by applying Simpson's rule, $n = 4$.

2. Find an approximate value for

$$\int_0^\pi \frac{\sin x}{1 + x} dx$$

  (a) by applying the left endpoint estimate, $n = 6$.
  (b) by applying the trapezoidal rule, $n = 6$.
  (c) by applying Simpson's rule, $n = 3$.

3.* Which of the estimates of this section are linear? That is, which of them have the property that

$$\text{estimate for } (\alpha f + \beta g) = \alpha(\text{estimate for } f) + \beta(\text{estimate for } g)?$$

4. Show that Simpson's rule gives the exact value of the integral of a cubic:

$$\int_a^b (Ax^3 + Bx^2 + Cx + D)\, dx.$$

[HINT: Take $n = 1$. You already know that Simpson's rule is exact for

$$\int_a^b (Bx^2 + Cx + D)\, dx$$

from Exercise 18 of Section 7.3.]

8.8   Additional problems

Work out the following integrals and check your answers by differentiation.

1. $\int 10^{nx}\, dx.$

2. $\int e^x \tan{(e^x)}\, dx.$

3. $\int \sqrt{2x+1}\, dx.$

4. $\int x\sqrt{2x+1}\, dx.$

5. $\int \tan\left(\dfrac{\pi}{n}x\right) dx.$

6. $\int \dfrac{dx}{\sqrt{x+1}-\sqrt{x}}.$

7. $\int \dfrac{dx}{a^2 x^2 + b^2}.$

8. $\int \sin 2x \cos x\, dx.$

9. $\int \dfrac{e^{-\sqrt{x}}}{\sqrt{x}}\, dx.$

10. $\int \sinh^2 x\, dx.$

11. $\int \sec^3{(2x)}\, dx.$

12. $\int \dfrac{dx}{\sqrt{1-e^{2x}}}$

13. $\int x2^x\, dx.$

14. $\int \sin^2\left(\dfrac{\pi}{n}x\right) dx.$

15. $\int \dfrac{dx}{x^3-1}.$

16. $\int \dfrac{dx}{a\sqrt{x}+b}.$

17. $\int (1-\sec x)^2\, dx.$

18. $\int \dfrac{\sin 3x}{2+\cos 3x}\, dx.$

19. $\int \dfrac{\sqrt{a-x}}{\sqrt{a+x}}\, dx.$

20. $\int \dfrac{\sqrt{a+x}}{\sqrt{a-x}}\, dx.$

21. $\int \dfrac{1-\sin 2x}{1+\sin 2x}\, dx.$

22. $\int \dfrac{\sqrt{a^2-x^2}}{x^2}\, dx.$

23. $\int \log\sqrt{x+1}\, dx.$

24. $\int \dfrac{x}{(x+1)^2}\, dx.$

25. $\int \dfrac{dx}{\cos x - \sin x}.$

26. $\int a^{2x}\, dx.$

27. $\int \log(ax+b)\, dx.$

28. $\int x\log(ax+b)\, dx.$

29. $\int e^x \sin \pi x\, dx.$

30. $\int \dfrac{\sin\sqrt{x}}{\sqrt{x}}\, dx.$

31. $\int \log(x\sqrt{x})\, dx.$

32. $\int \dfrac{x^2}{1+x^2}\, dx.$

33. $\int \sqrt{\dfrac{x^2}{9}-1}\, dx.$

34. $\int \dfrac{-x^2}{\sqrt{1-x^2}}\, dx.$

35. $\int (\tan x + \cot x)^2\, dx.$

36. $\int \dfrac{dx}{1+3\sin x}.$

37. $\int x\log\sqrt{x^2+1}\, dx.$

38. $\int \dfrac{x^3}{\sqrt{1+x^2}}\, dx.$

39. $\int x\tan^2{(\pi x)}\, dx.$

40. $\int \dfrac{dx}{2-\sqrt{x}}.$

41. $\int x \arctan (x - 3)\, dx.$

42. $\int \dfrac{2}{x(1 + x^2)}\, dx.$

43. $\int \sin 2x \cos 3x\, dx.$

44. $\int \dfrac{\cos^4 x}{\sin^2 x}\, dx.$

45. $\int \dfrac{x - 3}{x^2(x + 1)}\, dx.$

46. $\int \dfrac{\sqrt{x^2 + 4}}{x}\, dx.$

47. $\int 2x \sinh x\, dx.$

48. $\int \dfrac{dx}{2x^2 - 2x + 1}.$

49. $\int \dfrac{dx}{x\sqrt{9 - x^2}}.$

50. $\int \dfrac{dx}{e^x - 2e^{-x}}.$

51. $\int \dfrac{e^x}{\sqrt{e^x + 1}}\, dx.$

52. $\int e^{-x} \cosh x\, dx.$

53. $\int \sin^5 \left(\dfrac{x}{2}\right) dx.$

54. $\int \tanh^2 (2x)\, dx.$

55. $\int (\sin^2 x - \cos x)^2\, dx.$

56. $\int \dfrac{dx}{\sqrt{2x - x^2}}.$

57. $\int \log (1 - \sqrt{x})\, dx.$

58. $\int \dfrac{3}{\sqrt{2 - 3x - 4x^2}}\, dx.$

59. $\int \dfrac{\sin x}{\cos^2 x - 2\cos x + 3}\, dx.$

60. $\int \left[\dfrac{x}{\sqrt{a^2 - x^2}} - \arcsin \left(\dfrac{x}{a}\right)\right] dx.$

9

INTEGRATION AS AN AVERAGING PROCESS; APPLICATIONS

9.1 The average value of a function

We begin with a function f continuous on $[a, b]$ and ask ourselves, "What number if any should be called the *average value of f on $[a, b]$*?"

To get our bearings we first look at averages in a setting with which we are familiar. Suppose that a student takes N_1 tests, then N_2 tests. . . . , and finally N_n tests. If N is the total number of tests he takes, then

$$N = N_1 + N_2 + \cdots + N_n.$$

His average on the N tests has the following two properties:

(i) lowest of N grades $\leq$ average on N tests $\leq$ highest of N grades;

(ii) $\begin{pmatrix} \text{average on} \\ N \text{ tests} \end{pmatrix} \cdot N = \begin{pmatrix} \text{average on} \\ \text{first } N_1 \text{ tests} \end{pmatrix} \cdot N_1$

$$+ \begin{pmatrix} \text{average on} \\ \text{next } N_2 \text{ tests} \end{pmatrix} \cdot N_2 + \cdots + \begin{pmatrix} \text{average on} \\ \text{final } N_n \text{ tests} \end{pmatrix} \cdot N_n.$$

Property (i) is obvious; property (ii) holds since each side of that equation represents the total number of points scored.

Let's return now to the function f. In view of (i) and (ii), we make two requirements of the number which we shall call the average of f:

Requirement 1.   Minimum value of $f \leq$ average of $f \leq$ maximum value of f.

Requirement 2. If $P = \{x_0, x_1, \ldots, x_n\}$ is a partition of $[a, b,]$ then

$$\left(\begin{array}{c}\text{average of } f \\ \text{on } [a, b]\end{array}\right)(b-a) = \left(\begin{array}{c}\text{average of } f \\ \text{on } [x_0, x_1]\end{array}\right)(x_1 - x_0) + \cdots + \left(\begin{array}{c}\text{average of } f \\ \text{on } [x_{n-1}, x_n]\end{array}\right)(x_n - x_{n-1}).$$

To meet Requirements 1 and 2, there is only one way to define average and that is to set

$$\text{average value of } f \text{ on } [a, b] = \frac{1}{b-a} \int_a^b f(x)\, dx.$$

To see this, take an arbitrary partition

$$P = \{x_0, x_1, \ldots, x_n\} \quad \text{of} \quad [a, b].$$

For each subinterval $[x_{i-1}, x_i]$, Requirement 1 gives

$$m_i \leq \text{average of } f \text{ on } [x_{i-1}, x_i] \leq M_i,$$

where, as usual,

$$m_i = \text{minimum value of } f \text{ on } [x_{i-1}, x_i]$$

and

$$M_i = \text{maximum value of } f \text{ on } [x_{i-1}, x_i].$$

Multiplying by $(x_i - x_{i-1})$, we have

$$m_i(x_i - x_{i-1}) \leq \left(\begin{array}{c}\text{average of } f \\ \text{on } [x_{i-1}, x_i]\end{array}\right)(x_i - x_{i-1}) \leq M_i(x_i - x_{i-1}).$$

Summing from $i = 1$ to $i = n$, we get

$$L_f(P) \leq \left(\begin{array}{c}\text{average of } f \\ \text{on } [x_0, x_1]\end{array}\right)(x_1 - x_0) + \cdots + \left(\begin{array}{c}\text{average of } f \\ \text{on } [x_{n-1}, x_n]\end{array}\right)(x_n - x_{n-1}) \leq U_f(P).\dagger$$

Requirement 2 now gives

$$L_f(P) \leq \left(\begin{array}{c}\text{average of } f \\ \text{on } [a, b]\end{array}\right)(b-a) \leq U_f(P).$$

Since P was chosen arbitrarily, this inequality must hold for all partitions P.

There is only one number with this property and that is the integral of f on $[a, b]$. (See Section 4.2.) Thus we must have

$$\left(\begin{array}{c}\text{average of } f \\ \text{on } [a, b]\end{array}\right)(b-a) = \int_a^b f(x)\, dx$$

and

$$\text{average of } f \text{ on } [a, b] = \frac{1}{b-a} \int_a^b f(x)\, dx. \quad \square$$

---

† $L_f(P)$ and $U_f(P)$ are the lower and upper sums discussed in Section 4.2.

This sense of average provides a powerful and intuitive way of viewing the definite integral. Think for a moment in terms of area. If f is constant and positive on $[a, b]$, then Ω, the region below the graph, is a rectangle. Its area is given simply by the formula

$$\text{area of } \Omega = (\text{constant value of } f \text{ on } [a, b]) \cdot (b - a).$$

If f is now allowed to vary continuously on $[a, b]$, then we have

$$\text{area of } \Omega = \int_a^b f(x)\, dx.$$

In terms of average values, the formula becomes

$$\textit{area of } \Omega = (\textit{average value of } f \textit{ on } [a, b]) \cdot (b - a).$$

Area = (constant value of f) · $(b-a)$

FIGURE 9.1.1

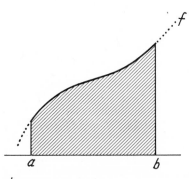

Area = $\int_a^b f(x)dx$ = (average value of f)·$(b-a)$

FIGURE 9.1.2

Think now in terms of motion. If an object moves along a line with constant speed $|v|$ during the time interval $[a, b]$, then

$$\text{the distance traveled} = (\text{constant value of } |v| \text{ on } [a, b]) \cdot (b - a).$$

If the speed $|v|$ is allowed to vary, then we have

$$\text{distance traveled} = \int_a^b |v(t)|\, dt.$$

In terms of average values, the formula becomes

distance traveled = (average value of $|v|$ on $[a, b]$)·$(b - a)$.

In general we have the identity

$$\int_a^b f(x)\, dx = (\text{average value of } f \text{ on } [a, b])\cdot(b - a).$$

Theorem   (*The first mean-value theorem for integrals*)

If f is continuous on $[a, b]$, then there is a number c in (a, b) such that

$$f(c)(b - a) = \int_a^b f(x)\, dx.$$

In other words, there exists a number c in (a, b) such that

$$f(c) = \text{the average value of } f \text{ on } [a, b].$$

PROOF.   Observe that

min value of f on $[a, b] \leq$ average value of f on $[a, b] \leq$ max value of f on $[a, b]$

and apply the intermediate-value theorem (Theorem 2.6.1).   □

For a geometric interpretation of this theorem in the case that f is positive we refer to Figure 9.1.3. The theorem says that somewhere in (a, b) there exists a number c such that the rectangle displayed has the same area as the region under the curve.

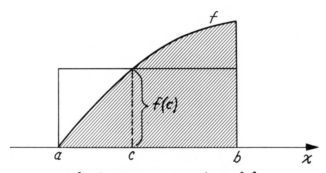

$f(c)$ is the average value of f:
the area of the rectangle = the area under the curve

FIGURE 9.1.3

Exercises

For the following, sketch the graph of f and find its average value on $[-1, 1]$.

1.* $f(x) = \alpha$.
2. $f(x) = \alpha x + \beta$.
3.* $f(x) = x^2$.
4. $f(x) = x^3$.
5.* $f(x) = \sqrt{1 + x}$.
6. $f(x) = \sqrt{1 - x^2}$.

7.* $f(x) = \sqrt{1 + x^2}$.
8. $f(x) = e^x$.
9.* $f(x) = \dfrac{1}{1 + x^2}$.
10. $f(x) = \dfrac{1}{\sqrt{1 + x^2}}$.

11.* Find the average value of the sine and cosine functions on $[c, c + 2\pi]$.

12. Let f be continuous on $[a, b]$. Compare

$$f(b)(b - a) \qquad \text{and} \qquad \int_a^b f(x)\, dx$$

if (a) f is constant on $[a, b]$; (b) f is increasing on $[a, b]$; (c) f is decreasing on $[a, b]$.

13. In Chapter 3, we viewed $[f(b) - f(a)]/(b - a)$ as the average rate of change of f on $[a, b]$ and $f'(x)$ as the rate of change at x. If our new sense of average is to be consistent with the old one, we must have

$$\frac{f(b) - f(a)}{b - a} = \text{average of } f' \text{ on } [a, b].$$

Prove that this is the case.

For the following, find the average slope of the graph of f on $[a, b]$.

14.* $f(x) = \alpha$.
15. $f(x) = mx + \beta$.
16.* $f(x) = \alpha x^2 + \beta x + \gamma$.

17. $f(x) = \log x$.
18.* $f(x) = e^x$.
19. $f(x) = \cos x$.

20.* A stone falls from rest in a vacuum for x seconds. (a) Compare its terminal velocity to its average velocity; (b) compare its average velocity during the first $x/2$ seconds to its average velocity during the next $x/2$ seconds.

21. Prove or disprove by a counter example: in each open interval (a, b) there is a number c such that

(a) $\dfrac{e^b - e^a}{b - a} = e^c$, \qquad (b) $\dfrac{\sin b - \sin a}{b - a} = \sin c$, \qquad (c) $\dfrac{\sin b - \sin a}{b - a} = \cos c$.

22. Show that

$$\text{the average of } f \text{ on } [a, b]$$

need not be

$$\sqrt{\text{the average of } f^2 \text{ on } [a, b]}.$$

23.* Find the average vertical and horizontal dimensions of the ellipse

$$\frac{x^2}{a^2} + \frac{y^2}{b^2} = 1.$$

24. Prove that two distinct continuous functions cannot take on the same average value on every interval.

25. Let f be continuous on $[a, b]$. Let $a < c < b$. Prove that

$$f(c) = \lim_{h \downarrow 0} (\text{average of } f \text{ on } [c - h, c + h]).$$

9.2 More on area

We begin with two functions f and g both continuous on an interval $[a, b]$. If f and g are both positive and if $f(x) \geq g(x)$ for all x in $[a, b]$ (see Figure 9.2.1), then the area between the graphs is given by the integral

$$\int_a^b [f(x) - g(x)]\, dx.$$

This you already know.

What we want now is a formula which applies also to the region depicted in Figure 9.2.2. Here neither f nor g remains positive. Moreover, neither function remains greater than the other.

FIGURE 9.2.1

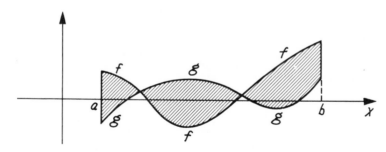

FIGURE 9.2.2

One way to proceed is to raise the entire region a fixed number of units so that both functions become positive. (See Figure 9.2.3.) The new boundaries are now of the form

$$F(x) = f(x) + C \qquad \text{and} \qquad G(x) = g(x) + C.$$

The area of the first part is

$$\int_a^s [F(x) - G(x)]\, dx = \int_a^s [f(x) - g(x)]\, dx = \int_a^s |f(x) - g(x)|\, dx;$$

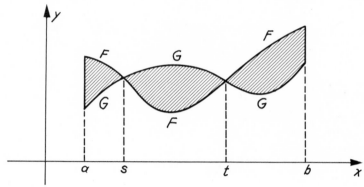

FIGURE 9.2.3

the area of the second part is

$$\int_{s}^{t} [G(x) - F(x)]\, dx = \int_{s}^{t} [g(x) - f(x)]\, dx = \int_{s}^{t} |f(x) - g(x)|\, dx;$$

the area of the third part is

$$\int_{t}^{b} [F(x) - G(x)]\, dx = \int_{t}^{b} [f(x) - g(x)]\, dx = \int_{t}^{b} |f(x) - g(x)|\, dx.$$

The total area is therefore the sum

$$\int_{a}^{s} |f(x) - g(x)|\, dx + \int_{s}^{t} |f(x) - g(x)|\, dx + \int_{t}^{b} |f(x) - g(x)|\, dx.$$

By the additivity of the integral, this sum is simply

$$\int_{a}^{b} |f(x) - g(x)|\, dx.$$

In short,

$$\boxed{\text{the area between the graphs} = \int_{a}^{b} |f(x) - g(x)|\, dx.}$$

The number $|f(x) - g(x)|$ gives the vertical separation between the two boundaries:

$$\boxed{\text{the area} = (\text{average vertical separation})\cdot(b - a).}$$

In Figures 9.2.4 and 9.2.5 we display regions in which the boundary curves are not functions of x but functions of y instead. In such cases the area is given by the integral

$$\boxed{\int_{c}^{d} |f(y) - g(y)|\, dy.}$$

This is simply

$$\boxed{(\text{the average horizontal separation})\cdot(d - c).}$$

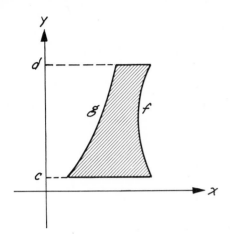

FIGURE 9.2.4

FIGURE 9.2.5

Problem. Find the area between

$$y = \cos x \qquad \text{and} \qquad y = \sin x, \qquad x \in [0, 2\pi].$$

SOLUTION. The region in question is displayed in Figure 9.2.6. The area is given by the integral

$$\int_0^{2\pi} |\cos x - \sin x|\, dx.$$

The easiest way to evaluate this integral is to note that

$$\cos x - \sin x \text{ is } \begin{cases} \geq 0, & \text{for } x \text{ in } \left[0, \dfrac{\pi}{4}\right] \\[2mm] \leq 0, & \text{for } x \text{ in } \left[\dfrac{\pi}{4}, \dfrac{5\pi}{4}\right] \\[2mm] \geq 0, & \text{for } x \text{ in } \left[\dfrac{5\pi}{4}, 2\pi\right] \end{cases}.$$

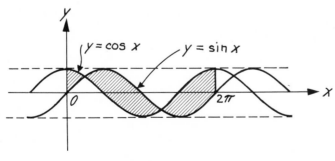

FIGURE 9.2.6

This means that

$$\text{area} = \int_0^{\pi/4} (\cos x - \sin x)\, dx + \int_{\pi/4}^{5\pi/4} (\sin x - \cos x)\, dx + \int_{5\pi/4}^{2\pi} (\cos x - \sin x)\, dx$$

$$= \Big[\sin x + \cos x \Big]_0^{\pi/4} + \Big[-\cos x - \sin x \Big]_{\pi/4}^{5\pi/4} + \Big[\sin x + \cos x \Big]_{5\pi/4}^{2\pi}$$

$$= (\sqrt{2} - 1) + 2\sqrt{2} + (1 + \sqrt{2}) = 4\sqrt{2}. \quad \square$$

Problem. Find the area of the region bounded by the curves

$$y = (x + 1)^3 \quad \text{and} \quad x + y - 2y^2 + 1 = 0.$$

SOLUTION. Both curves can be expressed as functions of y:

$$x = y^{1/3} - 1 \quad \text{and} \quad x = 2y^2 - y - 1.$$

The first curve is easy to draw. The second one can be written in the form

$$x = 2\left(y - \frac{1}{4} \right)^2 - \frac{9}{8}.$$

It is a parabola that has horizontal axis and opens to the right. The two curves intersect when $y = 0$ and when $y = 1$. (Check this out.) The region is pictured in Figure 9.2.7.

$$\text{area} = \int_0^1 |(y^{1/3} - 1) - (2y^2 - y - 1)|\, dy = \int_0^1 (y^{1/3} - 2y^2 + y)\, dy$$

$$= \left[\frac{3}{4} y^{4/3} - \frac{2}{3} y^3 + \frac{1}{2} y^2 \right]_0^1$$

$$= \frac{3}{4} - \frac{2}{3} + \frac{1}{2} = \frac{7}{12}. \quad \square$$

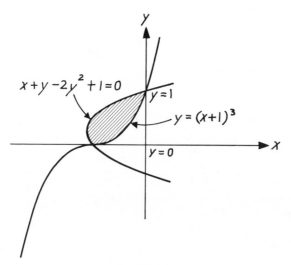

FIGURE 9.2.7

Exercises

Sketch the region that is bounded by the following curves and find the area.

1.* $y = x^2$, $y = 2x + 3$.
2. $y^2 - 27x = 0$, $x + y = 0$.
3.* $x - y^2 + 3 = 0$, $x - 2y = 0$.
4. $y = \sqrt{1 - x^2}$, $y = 1/\sqrt{1 - x^2}$, $-\frac{1}{2} \le x \le \frac{1}{2}$.
5.* $x^3 - 10y^2 = 0$, $x - y = 0$.
6. $a^2x = a^2y - y^2$, $4x - y = 0$.
7.* $3y - 3x + x^2 = 0$, $x - 2y = 0$.
8. $x + y^2 - 4 = 0$, $x + y = 2$.
9.* $x + y - y^3 = 0$, $x - y + y^2 = 0$.
10. $xy = 9$, $\sqrt{x} + \sqrt{y} = 4$.

11.* Find the area of the region enclosed by the ellipse

$$\frac{x^2}{a^2} + \frac{y^2}{b^2} = 1.$$

12. Find the area of the region that lies between the right-hand branch of the hyperbola

$$\frac{x^2}{a^2} - \frac{y^2}{b^2} = 1$$

and the vertical line

$$x = 2a.$$

13.* Find the area between

$$y = \sin 2x, \quad x \in [0, \pi] \quad \text{and} \quad y = \sin x, \quad x \in [0, \pi].$$

14. Find the area between

$$y = \sin^2 x, \quad x \in [0, 2\pi] \quad \text{and} \quad y = \cos^2 x, \quad x \in [0, 2\pi].$$

9.3 Volume

The Method of Parallel Cross Sections

We begin with a solid through which we pass a coordinate line l.   (See Figure 9.3.1.) As in the figure we suppose that the solid lies entirely between $x = a$ and $x = b$. By $A(x)$ we mean the area of the cross section that has coordinate x.

If the cross-sectional area is constant, as in the case of the solids displayed in Figure 9.3.2, the volume is simply

$$\text{(cross-sectional area)} \cdot \text{(thickness)}.$$

That is, we have

$$V = \text{(constant value of } A) \cdot (b - a).$$

FIGURE 9.3.1

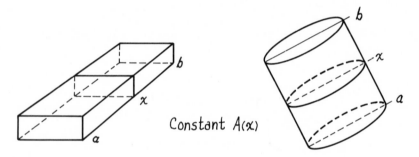

FIGURE 9.3.2

If the cross-sectional area is not constant but instead varies continuously (see, for example, Figure 9.3.1), then we bring the notion of average value into play and set

$$V = (\text{average value of } A \text{ on } [a, b]) \cdot (b - a).$$

In this manner, we obtain the formula

(9.3.1)
$$V = \int_a^b A(x)\, dx.$$

We justify this formula more thoroughly in the supplement to this section. Right now we carry out some computations.

Problem.   Find the volume of a cone that has base radius r and height h.

SOLUTION.   As a basis for the coordinate system we choose the line that passes through

the vertex of the cone and the center of the base. (See Figure 9.3.3.) The cross section
with coordinate x is a circular disk. Its radius $r(x)$ satisfies the equation

$$\frac{r(x)}{x} = \frac{r}{h}.$$

This you can see by similar triangles. Since

$$A(x) = \pi[r(x)]^2 \qquad \text{and} \qquad r(x) = \frac{r}{h}x,$$

we have

$$A(x) = \frac{\pi r^2}{h^2} \cdot x^2.$$

The volume of the cone is thus

$$\int_0^h \frac{\pi r^2}{h^2} x^2 \, dx = \frac{\pi r^2}{h^2}\left[\frac{x^3}{3}\right]_0^h = \frac{1}{3}\pi r^2 h.$$

In short, we have obtained the standard formula

$$\text{volume of cone} = \frac{1}{3}\pi r^2 h. \quad \square$$

The next result is more general and contains the cone as a special instance.

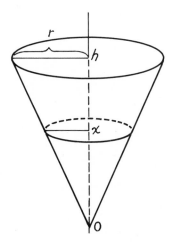

FIGURE 9.3.3

Solids of Revolution

Suppose that f is nonnegative and continuous on $[a, b]$. If we rotate the region below the
graph of f about the x-axis, we obtain a solid. (See Figure 9.3.4). The volume of this
solid is given by the formula

(9.3.2.)

$$V = \int_a^b \pi[f(x)]^2 \, dx.$$

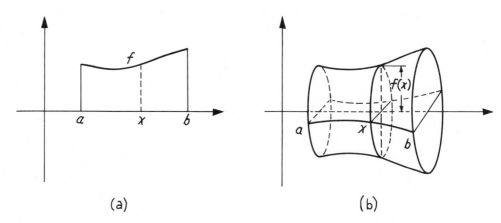

(a)   (b)

FIGURE 9.3.4

To see this, note that the cross section with coordinate x is a circular disk of radius $f(x)$. The cross-sectional area is thus

$$\pi[f(x)]^2.$$

The result follows from Formula 9.3.1.   □

As special instances of such solids of revolution we have the cone and the sphere.

Formula (9.3.2) Applied to the Cone

To generate a cone of base radius r and height h, we can take

$$f(x) = \frac{r}{h}x, \qquad 0 \le x \le h$$

and rotate the region below the graph about the x-axis. Formula (9.3.2) then gives

$$V = \pi \int_0^h \frac{r^2}{h^2} x^2 \, dx = \frac{1}{3}\pi r^2 h. \quad \square$$

Formula (9.3.2) Applied to the Sphere

A sphere of radius r can be obtained by rotating the region below the graph of

$$f(x) = \sqrt{r^2 - x^2}, \qquad -r \le x \le r$$

about the x-axis. Consequently, we have

$$\text{volume of sphere} = \pi \int_{-r}^r (r^2 - x^2) \, dx = \pi \left[r^2 x - \frac{x^3}{3} \right]_{-r}^r = \frac{4}{3}\pi r^3.$$

Incidentally, this result was obtained by Archimedes in the third century B.C.   □

Problem.   Find the volume of a triangular pyramid with base area B and height h.

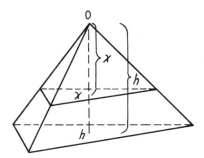

FIGURE 9.3.5

SOLUTION.   As in Figure 9.3.5 we choose the coordinate line so that it passes through the apex and is perpendicular to the base.

To the apex we assign coordinate 0, and to the base point coordinate h. The cross section at distance x from the apex ($0 \leq x \leq h$) is a triangle similar to the base triangle. The corresponding sides of these triangles are proportional, the factor of proportionality being x/h. This means that the areas are also proportional, but now the factor of proportionality is $(x/h)^2$. Thus we have

$$A(x) = \frac{Bx^2}{h^2},$$

and

$$V = \int_0^h A(x)\, dx = \frac{B}{h^2} \int_0^h x^2\, dx = \frac{1}{3}\, Bh.$$

This formula too was discovered in ancient times. It was known to Eudoxos of Cnidos (408–355 B.C.).   □

The Shell Method

This technique for computing volume is based on some simple properties of a cylinder. We begin by noting that a rectangle of dimensions $2\pi r \times h$ can be wrapped to form a cylindrical shell of base radius r and height h (Figure 9.3.6). Consequently such a cylindrical shell is said to have lateral area $2\pi rh$.

FIGURE 9.3.6

Suppose now that we have a solid cylinder of radius b and height h. Its volume is clearly $\pi b^2 h$. If from this cylinder of radius b we cut out a cylindrical core of radius a, then the resulting solid has volume

$$V = \pi b^2 h - \pi a^2 h. \qquad \text{(See Figure 9.3.7.)}$$

This formula can be rewritten as

$$V = \left(\frac{2\pi bh + 2\pi ah}{2}\right) \cdot (b - a).$$

Since the outer lateral area of our solid is $2\pi bh$ and the inner lateral area is $2\pi ah$, we have

$$V = (\text{average lateral area}) \cdot (\text{thickness}).$$

This is the idea which inspires the shell method.

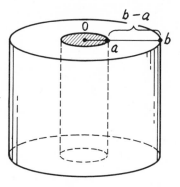

FIGURE 9.3.7

We begin with a function f nonnegative and continuous on the interval $[a, b]$. For convenience we assume that $a \geq 0$. If the region below the graph is now rotated about the y-axis, then a solid S is generated. (See Figure 9.3.8.) We want to compute the volume of this solid S. For each $x \in [a, b]$ we can inscribe a cylindrical shell of radius x and height $f(x)$. The lateral area of such a shell is $2\pi x f(x)$. If we knew that the lateral area were constant as x ranged from a to b, we could reasonably set

$$V = (\text{constant lateral area}) \cdot (\text{thickness}).$$

Since the lateral area need not be constant, we make use of the notion of average value and, as in the case of the cylinder, write

$$V = (\text{average lateral area}) \cdot (\text{thickness}).$$

Since the average lateral area is

$$\frac{1}{b - a} \int_a^b 2\pi x f(x) \, dx$$

and the thickness is $b - a$, we obtain the *shell-method formula*

(9.3.3)
$$\boxed{V = \int_a^b 2\pi x f(x) \, dx.}$$

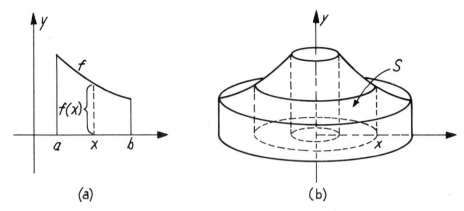

FIGURE 9.3.8

A more detailed justification of this formula appears in the supplement to this section.

Problem.   Use the shell method to find a formula for the volume of a cone.

SOLUTION.   A cone of base radius r and height h can be obtained by rotating the region below the graph of

$$f(x) = -\frac{h}{r}x + h, \qquad 0 \le x \le r$$

about the y-axis. (You can convince yourself of this by drawing your own diagram.) The shell method then gives

$$V = \int_0^r 2\pi x \left(-\frac{h}{r}x + h \right) dx.$$

A short computation yields the familiar formula

$$V = \frac{1}{3}\pi r^2 h. \quad \square$$

Problem.   Find the volume of the ring generated by revolving the circular disk

$$(x - c)^2 + y^2 \le r^2, \qquad c > r$$

about the y-axis. (See Figure 9.3.9.)

SOLUTION.   First we observe that the volume of this ring is twice that of the solid generated by revolving the region below the graph of

$$f(x) = \sqrt{r^2 - (x - c)^2}, \qquad c - r \le x \le c + r.$$

Thus we have

$$V = 2 \int_{c-r}^{c+r} 2\pi x \sqrt{r^2 - (x - c)^2} \, dx = 2\pi \int_{c-r}^{c+r} 2x \sqrt{r^2 - (x - c)^2} \, dx.$$

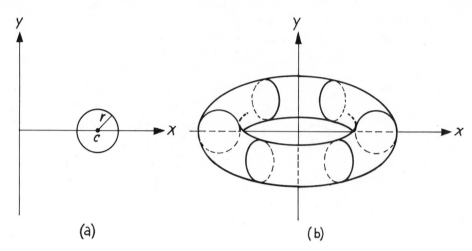

(a)   (b)

FIGURE 9.3.9

Since

$$\int_{c-r}^{c+r} 2x\sqrt{r^2 - (x - c)^2}\, dx$$

$$= \int_{c-r}^{c+r} 2(x - c)\sqrt{r^2 - (x - c)^2}\, dx + 2c \int_{c-r}^{c+r} \sqrt{r^2 - (x - c)^2}\, dx$$

and the first integral on the right is zero, we have

$$V = (2\pi c)\left(2 \int_{c-r}^{c+r} \sqrt{r^2 - (x - c)^2}\, dx \right) = (2\pi c)(\text{area of circle of radius } r)$$

$$= (2\pi c)(\pi r^2) = 2\pi^2 c r^2. \quad \square$$

Exercises

Sketch each region and find the volume generated by revolving it (i) about the x-axis, (ii) about the y-axis.

1.* The region below

$$y = x^2, \qquad x \in [0, 1].$$

2.   The region below

$$y = x^3, \qquad x \in [1, 2].$$

3.* The region below

$$f(x) = e^x, \qquad x \in [0, 1].$$

4.   The equilateral triangle with vertices

$$(0, 0), \qquad (a, 0), \qquad \left(\frac{a}{2}, \frac{\sqrt{3}a}{2}\right).$$

5.* The region between

$$y = \sqrt{x}, \qquad x \in [0, 1] \qquad \text{and} \qquad y = x^2, \qquad x \in [0, 1].$$

6. The region bounded

above by $y = \sqrt{1 - x^2}$ and   below by $y = \frac{1}{2}$.

7.* The region bounded by the ellipse

$$\frac{x^2}{a^2} + \frac{y^2}{b^2} = 1.$$

8. The region below

$$x^2 = y^3, \qquad x \in [0, 2].$$

9.* The region between

$y = \sinh x, \qquad x \in [0, 1]$ and $y = \cosh x, \qquad x \in [0, 1].$

10. The region bounded below by

$$y = \sin x, \qquad x \in [0, \pi]$$

and above by

$$y = x, \qquad x \in [0, \pi].$$

11.* Derive a formula for the volume of the frustrum of a cone in terms of its height h, the lower base radius R, and the upper base radius r. (See Figure 9.3.10.)

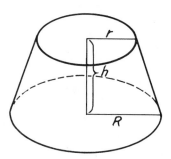

FIGURE 9.3.10

12. The base of a solid is the circle

$$x^2 + y^2 = r^2.$$

Find the volume of the solid given that the cross sections perpendicular to the x-axis are

(a) squares.   (b) equilateral triangles.

13.* The base of a solid is the region bounded by the ellipse

$$\frac{x^2}{a^2} + \frac{y^2}{b^2} = 1.$$

Find the volume of the solid, given that the cross sections perpendicular to the x-axis are (a) equilateral triangles, (b) isosceles right triangles each with hypotenuse on the xy-plane, (c) squares, (d) triangles of height 2.

14. The base of a solid is the bounded region between the graphs of

$$f(x) = x^2 \quad \text{and} \quad g(x) = -2x^2 + 3.$$

Find the volume of the solid, given that the cross sections perpendicular to the y-axis are (a) squares, (b) rectangles of height h, (c) equilateral triangles, (d) isosceles right triangles each with hypotenuse on the xy-plane.

15.* A hemispheric basin of radius r ft is being used to store water. To what percent of capacity is it filled when the water is (a) $r/2$ ft deep, (b) $r/3$ ft deep?

16. Find the volume of the solid generated by rotating the region between

$$\sqrt{x} + \sqrt{y} = 1 \quad \text{and} \quad x + y = 1$$

about the x-axis.

17.* Find $V'(x)$, given that $V(x)$ is the volume of the solid obtained by rotating the region below the graph of f on $[a, x]$ about (a) the x-axis, (b) the y-axis.

18. A sphere of radius r is cut by two parallel planes: in the one case, a units above the equator; in the other case, b units above the equator. Assume that $a < b$ and find the volume of that portion of the sphere that lies between the two planes.

19.* Find the volume of the solid generated by rotating the region below

$$y = \log x, \quad x \in [1, e]$$

(i) about the x-axis.   (ii) about the y-axis.

20. Find the volume of the solid obtained by rotating the region below

$$y = e^x, \quad x \in [0, 1]$$

(a) about the line $y = -1$.
(b) about the line $y = 3$.
(c) about the line $x = -1$.
(d) about the line $x = 1$.
(e) about the line $x = 2$.

21.* Find the volume of the intersection of two cylinders of radius r if the axes meet at right angles.

SUPPLEMENT TO SECTION 9.3

Further Justification of Formula 9.3.1

$$V = \int_a^b A(x) \, dx.$$

Let S be the solid in question and let $P = \{x_0, x_1, \ldots, x_n\}$ be a partition of $[a, b]$. For each subinterval $[x_{i-1}, x_i]$ let m_i and M_i be respectively the minimum and maximum values of A on $[x_{i-1}, x_i]$. Let S_i be that portion of the solid S that corresponds to the interval $[x_{i-1}, x_i]$ and let V_i be its volume. S_i contains a solid of cross-sectional area m_i and thickness $(x_i - x_{i-1})$, and is contained in a solid of cross-sectional area M_i and thickness $(x_i - x_{i-1})$. This suggests that

$$m_i(x_i - x_{i-1}) \leq V_i \leq M_i(x_i - x_{i-1}).$$

Adding up these inequalities from $i = 1$ to $i = n$ we get

(1) $$L_A(P) \leq V_1 + \cdots + V_n \leq U_A(P).$$

Since

$$S = S_1 \cup S_2 \cup \cdots \cup S_n$$

and the S_i do not overlap, V, the total volume of S, must satisfy

$$V = V_1 + \cdots + V_n.$$

Inequality (1) now implies that

$$L_A(P) \leq V \leq U_A(P).$$

Since this last inequality must hold for every partition P, we must have

$$V = \int_a^b A(x) \, dx. \quad \square$$

Further Justification of the Shell Method Formula

$$V = \int_a^b 2\pi x f(x) \, dx.$$

Let's try to define a function υ with the property that $\upsilon(x)$ corresponds to our intuitive idea of the volume contributed by the interval $[a, x]$. It is certainly natural to ask
(1) that υ be continuous on $[a, b]$, and
(2) that $\upsilon(a) = 0$.
As we show below, it is also natural to ask
(3) that $\upsilon'(x) = 2\pi x f(x)$ for each $x \in (a, b)$.

Requirements (2) and (3) mean that we must have

$$\upsilon(t) = \int_a^t 2\pi x f(x) \, dx \qquad \text{for each } t \in [a, b).$$

Requirement (1) means that the formula must also apply to b; namely, we must have

$$V = \upsilon(b) = \int_a^b 2\pi x f(x) \, dx.$$

To see how Requirement (3) comes about, we begin by supposing that

$$a < x < x + h \leq b.$$

(See Figure 9.3.11.) The volume contributed by the interval $[x, x + h]$ should be the volume contributed by the interval $[a, x + h]$ minus the volume contributed by the interval $[a, x]$. In other words, we should have

the contribution of $[x, x + h] = \upsilon(x + h) - \upsilon(x)$.

Now let

$$m_h = \text{minimum value of } f \text{ on } [x, x + h]$$

and

$$M_h = \text{maximum value of } f \text{ on } [x, x + h].$$

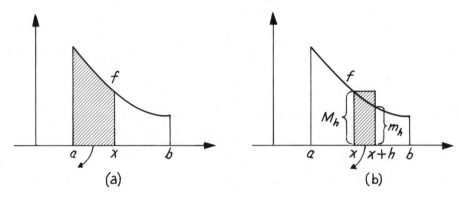

FIGURE 9.3.11

The solid corresponding to the interval $[x, x + h]$ contains
(i) a cylindrical shell of height m_h, inner radius x, and outer radius $x + h$, and is contained in
(ii) a cylindrical shell of height M_h, inner radius x, and outer radius $x + h$. Since shell (i) has volume

$$\pi(x + h)^2 m_h - \pi x^2 m_h = \pi(2x + h)h m_h$$

and shell (ii) has volume

$$\pi(x + h)^2 M_h - \pi x^2 M_h = \pi(2x + h)h M_h,$$

we should have

$$\pi(2x + h)h m_h \leq \mathcal{V}(x + h) - \mathcal{V}(x) \leq \pi(2x + h)h M_h$$

and thus

$$\pi(2x + h)m_h \leq \frac{\mathcal{V}(x + h) - \mathcal{V}(x)}{h} \leq \pi(2x + h)M_h.$$

Since f is continuous, we have

$$\lim_{h \downarrow 0} m_h = f(x) = \lim_{h \downarrow 0} M_h,$$

and consequently

$$\lim_{h \downarrow 0} \pi(2x + h)m_h = 2\pi x f(x) = \lim_{h \downarrow 0} \pi(2x + h)M_h.$$

The pinching theorem now gives

$$\lim_{h \downarrow 0} \frac{\mathcal{V}(x + h) - \mathcal{V}(x)}{h} = 2\pi x f(x).$$

A similar argument produces

$$\lim_{h \uparrow 0} \frac{\mathcal{V}(x + h) - \mathcal{V}(x)}{h} = 2\pi x f(x).$$

Combining these one-sided limits, we obtain

$$\lim_{h \to 0} \frac{\mho(x + h) - \mho(x)}{h} = 2\pi x f(x)$$

and thus Requirement (3).   □

9.4   Area in polar coordinates

Here we develop a technique for calculating the area of a region the boundary of which is given in polar coordinates.

As a start, we suppose that θ_1 and θ_2 are two real numbers satisfying

$$\theta_1 < \theta_2 \leq \theta_1 + 2\pi.$$

We take ρ as a function continuous and nonnegative on $[\theta_1, \theta_2]$ and ask for the area of the region Γ which is bounded by the rays

$$\theta = \theta_1, \qquad \theta = \theta_2$$

and the curve

$$r = \rho(\theta). \qquad\qquad \text{(See Figure 9.4.1)}$$

If ρ is a constant function, then Γ is simply the sector of a circle and its area is

$$\text{(the constant value of } \rho^2/2 \text{ on } [\theta_1, \theta_2]) \cdot (\theta_2 - \theta_1).$$

If ρ varies on $[\theta_1, \theta_2]$, then we bring the notion of average value into play and set

$$\text{area of } \Gamma = \left(\text{average value of } \frac{\rho^2}{2} \text{ on } [\theta_1, \theta_2] \right) \cdot \left(\theta_2 - \theta_1 \right).$$

In the language of integrals, we have

(9.4.1)

$$\boxed{\text{area of } \Gamma = \int_{\theta_1}^{\theta_2} \frac{[\rho(\theta)]^2}{2}\, d\theta.}$$

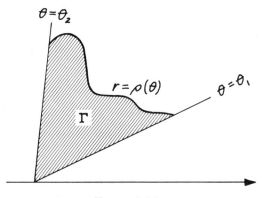

FIGURE 9.4.1

A more thorough justification of this formula appears in the supplement to this section.

Problem. Calculate the area of the region Γ pictured in Figure 9.4.2.

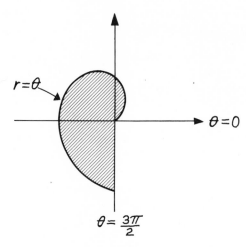

FIGURE 9.4.2

SOLUTION

$$\text{area of } \Gamma = \int_0^{3\pi/2} \frac{\theta^2}{2} \, d\theta = \left[\frac{\theta^3}{6}\right]_0^{3\pi/2} = \frac{9\pi^3}{16}. \quad \square$$

Problem. Calculate the area of the region enclosed by the cardioid

$$r = 1 - \cos\theta. \qquad\qquad \text{(Figure 7.6.11)}$$

SOLUTION

$$\text{Area} = \int_0^{2\pi} \frac{(1 - \cos\theta)^2}{2} \, d\theta$$

$$= \frac{1}{2} \int_0^{2\pi} (1 - 2\cos\theta + \cos^2\theta) \, d\theta$$

$$= \frac{1}{2} \left\{ \int_0^{2\pi} (1 - 2\cos\theta) \, d\theta + \int_0^{2\pi} \cos^2\theta \, d\theta \right\}.$$

Since

$$\int_0^{2\pi} (1 - 2\cos\theta) \, d\theta = \left[\theta - 2\sin\theta\right]_0^{2\pi} = 2\pi$$

and

$$\int_0^{2\pi} \cos^2\theta \, d\theta = \int_{0.}^{2\pi} \frac{1 + \cos 2\theta}{2} \, d\theta = \left[\frac{\theta}{2} + \frac{\sin 2\theta}{4}\right]_0^{2\pi} = \pi,$$

we have

$$\text{area} = \frac{3\pi}{2}. \quad \square$$

A slightly more complicated type of region is pictured in Figure 9.4.3. We can calculate the area of such a region Ω by taking the area up to $r = \rho_2(\theta)$ and subtracting from it the area up to $r = \rho_1(\theta)$. This gives the formula

$$\boxed{\text{area of } \Omega = \int_{\theta_1}^{\theta_2} \frac{[\rho_2(\theta)]^2 - [\rho_1(\theta)]^2}{2} \, d\theta.}$$

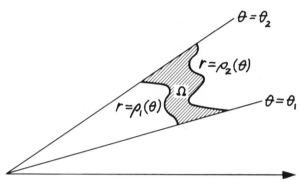

FIGURE 9.4.3

Exercises

Calculate the area of the region enclosed by the following curves. Take $a > 0$.

1.* $r = a \cos \theta$, $-\pi/2 \leq \theta \leq \pi/2$.
2. $r = a \cos 3\theta$, $-\pi/6 \leq \theta \leq \pi/6$.
3.* $r^2 = a^2 \cos 2\theta$, $-\pi/4 \leq \theta \leq \pi/4$.
4. $r = a(1 + \cos 3\theta)$, $-\pi/3 \leq \theta \leq \pi/3$.
5.* $r^2 = a^2 \sin^2 \theta$.
6. $r^2 = a^2 \sin^2 2\theta$.

Calculate the area of the region bounded by the following.

7.* $r = \tan 2\theta$ and the rays $\theta = 0$, $\theta = \pi/8$.
8. $r = \cos \theta$, $r = \sin \theta$, and the rays $\theta = 0$, $\theta = \pi/4$.
9.* $r = 2 \cos \theta$, $r = \cos \theta$, and the rays $\theta = 0$, $\theta = \pi/4$.
10. $r = 1 + \cos \theta$, $r = \cos \theta$, and the rays $\theta = 0$, $\theta = \pi$.
11.* $r = a(4 \cos \theta - \sec \theta)$ and the rays $\theta = 0$, $\theta = \pi/4$.
12.   The parabola $r = \frac{1}{2} \sec^2 (\theta/2)$ and the vertical line through the origin.

Find the area of the region bounded by the graphs of the following.

13.* $r = e^\theta$, $0 \leq \theta \leq \pi$; $r = \theta$, $0 \leq \theta \leq \pi$;   the rays $\theta = 0$ and $\theta = \pi$.

14. $r = e^\theta$, $2\pi \leq \theta \leq 3\pi$; $r = \theta$, $0 \leq \theta \leq \pi$;   the rays $\theta = 0$ and $\theta = \pi$.

15.* $r = e^\theta$, $0 \leq \theta \leq \pi$; $r = e^{\theta/2}$, $0 \leq \theta \leq \pi$;   the rays $\theta = 2\pi$ and $\theta = 3\pi$.

16. $r = e^\theta$, $0 \leq \theta \leq \pi$; $r = e^\theta$, $2\pi \leq \theta \leq 3\pi$;   the rays $\theta = 0$ and $\theta = \pi$.

SUPPLEMENT TO SECTION 9.4

Further Justification of Formula (9.4.1)

$$\text{Area of } \Gamma = \int_{\theta_1}^{\theta_2} \frac{[\rho(\theta)]^2}{2} \, d\theta.$$

Let $P = \{\phi_0, \phi_1, \ldots, \phi_n\}$ be a partition of $[\theta_1, \theta_2]$. Let r_i and R_i be respectively the minimum and maximum values of ρ on $[\phi_{i-1}, \phi_i]$. Let Γ_i be that portion of Γ which corresponds to the interval $[\phi_{i-1}, \phi_i]$ and let A_i be its area. Since Γ_i contains a circular sector of area

$$\frac{r_i^2}{2} (\phi_i - \phi_{i-1})$$

and is contained in a circular sector of area

$$\frac{R_i^2}{2} (\phi_i - \phi_{i-1}),$$

we expect

$$\frac{r_i^2}{2} (\phi_i - \phi_{i-1}) \leq A_i \leq \frac{R_i^2}{2} (\phi_i - \phi_{i-1}).$$

Summing from $i = 1$ to $i = n$, we obtain

$$L_f(P) \leq \text{area of } \Gamma \leq U_f(P),$$

where

$$f(\theta) = \frac{[\rho(\theta)]^2}{2}.$$

Since this last inequality must hold for every partition P of $[\theta_1, \theta_2]$, we must have

$$\text{area of } \Gamma = \int_{\theta_1}^{\theta_2} f(\theta) \, d\theta = \int_{\theta_1}^{\theta_2} \frac{[\rho(\theta)]^2}{2} \, d\theta. \quad \square$$

9.5   The least upper bound axiom; arc length

The Least Upper Bound Axiom

We begin with a set S of real numbers. As we mentioned in Chapter 1, a number M is called an *upper bound* for S iff

$$x \leq M \qquad \text{for all } \ x \in S.$$

Obviously, not all sets of real numbers have upper bounds. Those that do are said to be *bounded above*.

It is obvious that every set that has a largest element has an upper bound; if b is the largest element of S, then

$$x \leq b \qquad \text{for all} \quad x \in S$$

and therefore b is an upper bound for S. The converse is false: for example, the sets

$$(-\infty, 0) \qquad \text{and} \qquad \left\{ \frac{1}{2}, \frac{2}{3}, \frac{3}{4}, \ldots, \frac{n}{n+1}, \ldots \right\}$$

both have upper bounds (2 for instance) but neither has a largest element.

Let's return to the set $(-\infty, 0)$. While $(-\infty, 0)$ does not have a largest element, the set of its upper bounds, $[0, \infty)$, does have a least element, namely 0. A similar remark can be made about the second set. While the set of quotients

$$\frac{n}{n+1} = 1 - \frac{1}{n+1}$$

does not have a greatest element, the set of its upper bounds, $[1, \infty)$, does have a least element, namely 1. Along these lines there is a key *assumption* that we make about the real number system. It is called the *least upper bound axiom*.

The Least Upper Bound Axiom

Every nonempty set of real numbers that has an upper bound has a *least* upper bound.

The least upper bound of a set has a property that deserves particular attention. The idea is this: the fact that M is the least upper bound of the set S does not tell us that M is in S (it need not be) but it does tell us that we can approximate M as closely as we wish by members of S.

Theorem 9.5.1

If M is the least upper bound of the set S and ϵ is positive, then there is a number s in S such that

$$M - \epsilon < s \leq M.$$

PROOF.   Since all numbers in S are less than or equal to M, the right-hand side of the inequality causes no difficulty. All we have to show therefore is that there exists some number s in S such that

$$M - \epsilon < s.$$

Suppose on the contrary that no such number exists. We then have

$$x \leq M - \epsilon \qquad \text{for all} \quad x \in S$$

and so that $M - \epsilon$ becomes an upper bound for S. But this cannot happen for it makes

$M - \epsilon$ an upper bound that is less than M, and M is by assumption the *least* upper bound. $\square$

Similar observations can be made about lower bounds. In the first place, a number m is called a *lower bound* for S iff

$$m \le x \qquad \text{for all} \quad x \in S.$$

Sets that have lower bounds are said to be *bounded below*. Not all sets have lower bounds, but those that do, have *greatest lower bounds*. This need not be taken as an axiom. Using the least upper bound axiom we can prove it as a theorem.

> **Theorem**
>
> Every nonempty set of real numbers that has a lower bound has a *greatest* lower bound.

PROOF.   Suppose that S is nonempty and that it has a lower bound x. Then

$$x \le s \qquad \text{for each} \quad s \in S.$$

It follows that

$$-s \le -x \qquad \text{for each} \quad s \in S.$$

that is,

$$\{-s : s \in S\} \quad \text{has an upper bound} \quad -x.$$

From the least upper bound axiom we conclude that $\{-s : s \in S\}$ has a least upper bound. Call it x_0. Since

$$-s \le x_0 \qquad \text{for each} \quad s \in S,$$

we see that

$$-x_0 \le s \qquad \text{for each} \quad s \in S,$$

and thus $-x_0$ is a lower bound for S. We assert now that $-x_0$ is the greatest lower bound of the set S. To see this, we note that if there existed x_1 satisfying

$$-x_0 < x_1 \le s \qquad \text{for each} \quad s \in S,$$

then we would have

$$-s \le -x_1 < x_0 \qquad \text{for each} \quad s \in S,$$

and thus x_0 would not be the *least* upper bound of $\{-s : s \in S\}$. $\square$

As in the case of the least upper bound, the greatest lower bound of a set need not be in the set but it can be approximated as closely as we wish by members of the set. In short, we have the following theorem, the proof of which is left as an exercise.

> **Theorem 9.5.2**
>
> If m is the greatest lower bound of the set S and ϵ is positive, then there is a number s in S such that
>
> $$m \le s < m + \epsilon.$$

Arc Length Defined

We come now to the notion of arc length. In Figure 9.5.1 we have sketched a curve C which we assume is parametrized by a pair of continuously differentiable functions:†

$$C: \quad x(t), y(t), \quad t \in [a, b].$$

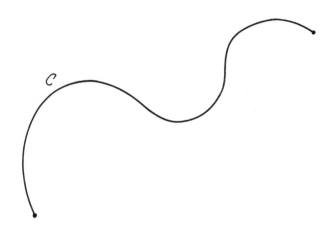

What is the length of this curve?

FIGURE 9.5.1

What we want to do is assign a length to the curve C. Here our experience in Chapter 4 can be used as a model.

To decide what should be meant by the area of a region Ω, we approximated Ω by the union of a finite number of rectangles. To decide what should be meant by the length of the curve C, we will approximate C by the union of a finite number of line segments.

Each point t in $[a, b]$ gives rise to a point $P = P(x(t), y(t))$ that lies on the curve C. By choosing a finite number of points in $[a, b]$,

$$a = t_0 < t_1 < \cdots < t_{i-1} < t_i < \cdots < t_{n-1} < t_n = b,$$

we obtain a finite number of points of C,

$$P_0, P_1, \cdots, P_{i-1}, P_i, \cdots, P_{n-1}, P_n.$$

We now join these points consecutively by line segments and call the resulting path,

$$L = \overline{P_0 P_1} \cup \cdots \cup \overline{P_{i-1} P_i} \cup \cdots \cup \overline{P_{n-1} P_n},$$

a polygonal path inscribed in the curve C. (See Figure 9.5.2.)

---

† By this we mean functions that have continuous first derivatives.

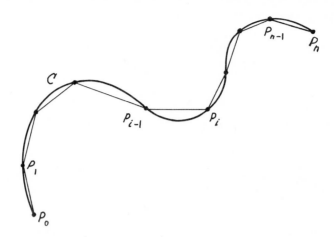

A polygonal path inscribed in the curve C

FIGURE 9.5.2

The length of such a polygonal path is the sum of the distances between consecutive vertices:

$$\text{length of } L = d(P_0, P_1) + \cdots + d(P_{i-1}, P_i) + \cdots + d(P_{n-1}, P_n).$$

The polygon L serves as an approximation to the curve C, but obviously a better approximation can be obtained by adding more vertices to L. At this point let's ask ourselves exactly what we require of the number that we shall call the length of C. Certainly we require that

$$l(L) \leq \text{the length of } C \qquad \text{for each } L \text{ inscribed in } C.$$

But that is not enough. There is another requirement that seems reasonable. If we can choose L to approximate C as closely as we wish, then we should be able to choose L so that $l(L)$ approximates the length of C as closely as we wish. Namely, for each positive ϵ there should exist a polygonal path L such that

$$(\text{length of } C) - \epsilon < l(L) \leq \text{length of } C.$$

Theorem 9.5.1 tells us that we can achieve this result by defining the length of C as the least upper bound of all the $l(L)$. This is in fact what we do:

Definition

$$\text{length of } C = \begin{cases} \text{the least upper bound of the} \\ \text{set of all lengths of polygonal} \\ \text{paths inscribed in } C. \end{cases}$$

Arc-Length Formulas

Now that we have explained what we mean by the length of a curve C it is time to describe a way in which to compute it. The basic result is easy to state. If C is parametrized by a pair of continuously differentiable functions

$$C: \quad x(t), y(t), t \in [a, b]$$

then

(9.5.3)

$$\text{length of } C = \int_a^b \sqrt{[x'(t)]^2 + [y'(t)]^2} \, dt.$$

Obviously this is not something to be taken on faith. It has to be proven. We will do so but not until Chapter 13. Right now we assume that the result is true and carry out some computations.

Example. If C is a circle of radius r, say

$$C: \quad x(t) = r \cos t, \quad y(t) = r \sin t, \quad t \in [0, 2\pi],$$

the formula yields

$$l(C) = \int_0^{2\pi} \sqrt{r^2 \sin^2 t + r^2 \cos^2 t} \, dt = \int_0^{2\pi} r \, dt = 2\pi r,$$

which is reassuring.   □

Example. In the case of the astroid

$$C: \quad x(t) = a \cos^3 t, \quad y(t) = a \sin^3 t,$$

shown in Figure 9.5.3, we have

$$[x'(t)]^2 + [y'(t)]^2 = 9a^2 \sin^2 t \cos^2 t,$$

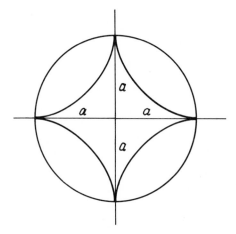

FIGURE 9.5.3

so that

$$l(C) = 4 \int_0^{\pi/2} 3a \sin t \cos t \, dt = 12a \left[\frac{\sin^2 t}{2} \right]_0^{\pi/2} = 6a.$$

This is a little less than the circumference of the circumscribed circle.   □

Suppose now that the curve C is actually the graph of a continuously differentiable function

$$y = f(x), \qquad x \in [a, b].$$

As a parametrization for C we can take

$$x(t) = t, \qquad y(t) = f(t), \qquad t \in [a, b].$$

Since

$$x'(t) = 1 \qquad \text{and} \qquad y'(t) = f'(t),$$

the arc length formula reduces to

$$l(C) = \int_a^b \sqrt{1 + [f'(t)]^2} \, dt.$$

Replacing t by x we can write

(9.5.4) $$\boxed{\text{length of the graph of } f = \int_a^b \sqrt{1 + [f'(x)]^2} \, dx.}$$

Example.   In the case of the function

$$f(x) = x^2, \qquad x \in [0, 1]$$

the graph is a parabolic arc from $(0, 0)$ to $(1, 1)$. The length of this arc is given by

$$\int_0^1 \sqrt{1 + [f'(x)]^2} \, dx = \int_0^1 \sqrt{1 + 4x^2} \, dx = 2 \int_0^1 \sqrt{x^2 + \left(\frac{1}{2}\right)^2} \, dx$$

$$= \left[x \sqrt{x^2 + \left(\frac{1}{2}\right)^2} + \left(\frac{1}{2}\right)^2 \log \left| x + \sqrt{x^2 + \left(\frac{1}{2}\right)^2} \right| \right]_0^1$$

$$= \frac{\sqrt{5}}{2} + \frac{1}{4} \log (2 + \sqrt{5}). \quad \square$$

Curves given in polar coordinates can also be measured in a similar manner. If C is given by a polar equation

$$r = \rho(\theta), \qquad \theta_1 \leq \theta \leq \theta_2,$$

then we have the parametric representation

$$x(\theta) = \rho(\theta) \cos \theta, \qquad y(\theta) = \rho(\theta) \sin \theta, \qquad \theta_1 \leq \theta \leq \theta_2.$$

With

$$x'(\theta) = -\rho(\theta) \sin \theta + \rho'(\theta) \cos \theta \qquad \text{and} \qquad y'(\theta) = \rho(\theta) \cos \theta + \rho'(\theta) \sin \theta,$$

we find, after simplification, that

$$[x'(\theta)]^2 + [y'(\theta)]^2 = [\rho(\theta)]^2 + [\rho'(\theta)]^2.$$

Consequently, we have the formula

$$l(C) = \int_{\theta_1}^{\theta_2} \sqrt{[\rho(\theta)]^2 + [\rho'(\theta)]^2} \, d\theta.$$

Example. As a polar equation for the circle of radius ρ we have simply

$$r = \rho.$$

Since in this case ρ is a constant, its derivative is zero. The circumference of the circle is therefore

$$\int_0^{2\pi} \sqrt{\rho^2} \, d\theta = \int_0^{2\pi} \rho \, d\theta = 2\pi\rho. \quad \square$$

Example. In the case of the cardioid

$$r = 1 - \cos\theta, \qquad\qquad \text{(Figure 7.6.11)}$$

we have

$$\rho(\theta) = 1 - \cos\theta.$$

Here

$$[\rho(\theta)]^2 + [\rho'(\theta)]^2 = 1 - 2\cos\theta + \cos^2\theta + \sin^2\theta = 2(1 - \cos\theta).$$

In view of the identity

$$\frac{1 - \cos\theta}{2} = \sin^2\frac{\theta}{2},$$

we have

$$[\rho(\theta)]^2 + [\rho'(\theta)]^2 = 4\sin^2\frac{\theta}{2}.$$

The length of the cardioid is therefore

$$\int_0^{2\pi} \sqrt{[\rho(\theta)]^2 + [\rho'(\theta)]^2} \, d\theta = \int_0^{2\pi} 2\sin\left(\frac{\theta}{2}\right) d\theta = 4\int_0^{2\pi} \frac{1}{2}\sin\left(\frac{\theta}{2}\right) d\theta$$

$$= 4\left[-\cos\left(\frac{\theta}{2}\right)\right]_0^{2\pi} = 8. \quad \square$$

Exercises

Find the length of the graph of f.

1.* $f(x) = mx + b$, $x \in [c, d]$.

2. $f(x) = x^{3/2}$, $x \in [0, 44]$.

3.* $f(x) = \dfrac{\sqrt{x}}{3}(x - 3)$, $x \in [0, 3]$.

4. $f(x) = 2e^{x/2}$, $x \in [0, \log 8]$.

5.* $f(x) = \log(\sec x)$, $x \in \left[-\dfrac{\pi}{4}, \dfrac{\pi}{4}\right]$.

6. $f(x) = \cosh x$, $x \in [0, \log 2]$.

7.* $f(x) = e^x$, $x \in [0, \frac{1}{2}\log 3]$.

8. $f(x) = \dfrac{1}{3}(x^2 + 2)^{3/2}$, $x \in [0, 1]$.

9.* $f(x) = \dfrac{2}{3}(x - 1)^{3/2}$, $x \in [1, 2]$.

10. $f(x) = \dfrac{x^2}{2}$, $x \in [0, 1]$.

11.* $f(x) = \dfrac{x}{2}\sqrt{3 - x^2} + \dfrac{3}{2}\arcsin\left(\dfrac{x}{\sqrt{3}}\right)$, $x \in [0, 1]$.

Find the length of the following curves.

12. $x(t) = at^2$, $y(t) = 2at$, $t \in [0, b]$.

13.* $x(t) = t - 1$, $y(t) = \dfrac{t^2}{2}$, $t \in [0, 1]$.

14. $x(t) = t^2$, $y(t) = t^3$, $t \in [0, 1]$.

15.* $x(t) = e^t \sin t$, $y(t) = e^t \cos t$, $t \in [0, \pi]$.

16. $x(t) = \cos t + t \sin t$, $y(t) = \sin t - t \cos t$, $t \in [0, \pi]$.

17.* $r = e^\theta$, $0 \le \theta \le 4\pi$.   (logarithmic spiral)

18. $r = ae^\theta$, $-2\pi \le \theta \le 2\pi$.

19.* $r = e^{2\theta}$, $0 \le \theta \le 2\pi$.

20. $r = a\theta$, $0 \le \theta \le 2\pi$.   (spiral of Archimedes)

21.   Prove Theorem 9.5.2.

22.   At time t a particle has position

$$x(t) = 1 - \cos t, \qquad y(t) = t - \sin t.$$

Find the total distance traveled between $t = 0$ and $t = 2\pi$.

23.* At time t a particle has position

$$x(t) = 1 + \arctan t, \qquad y(t) = 1 - \log\sqrt{1 + t^2}.$$

Find the total distance traveled between $t = 0$ and $t = 1$.

24.* Let f be a positive nonconstant function with the property that for every interval $[a, b]$ the length of the graph equals the area of the region under the graph. Find f, given that $f(0) = 1$.

25.   Show that a homogeneous, flexible, inelastic rope hanging from two fixed points assumes the shape of a catenary:

$$f(x) = a \cosh\left(\dfrac{x}{a}\right).$$

[HINT: Refer to Figure 9.5.4. That part of the rope which corresponds to the interval $[0, x]$ is subject to the following forces:
(1) its weight, which is proportional to its length;
(2) a horizontal pull at 0, $p(0)$;
(3) a tangential pull at x, $p(x)$.
Balancing the vertical forces, we have

$$k\int_0^x \sqrt{1 + [f'(t)]^2}\, dt = p(x)\sin\theta. \qquad \text{(weight = vertical pull at } x\text{)}$$

Balancing the horizontal forces, we have

$$p(0) = p(x) \cos \theta. \qquad \text{(pull at 0 = horizontal pull at } x\text{)}$$

Note also that

$$f'(x) = \tan \theta.]$$

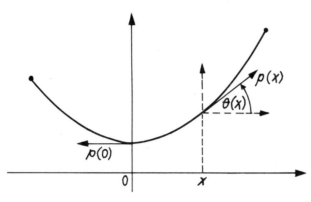

FIGURE 9.5.4

SUPPLEMENT TO SECTION 9.5

The arc length formulas can be arrived at from average value considerations. Take for example the case of a function f that is continuously differentiable on a closed interval $[a, b]$.

If the slope of the graph of f is constant, then the graph is a line segment. (See Figure 9.5.5.) The length of this line segment is simply the distance between the end points:

$$\sqrt{(b - a)^2 + [f(b) - f(a)]^2}.$$

We can rewrite this expression as

$$\sqrt{1 + \left[\frac{f(b) - f(a)}{b - a}\right]^2} \cdot (b - a)$$

and thus as

$$\sqrt{1 + [\text{slope}]^2} \cdot (b - a).$$

In other words, if the slope of the graph is constant, the length of the graph is simply

$$(\text{the constant value of } \sqrt{1 + [\text{slope}]^2}) \cdot (b - a).$$

If the slope varies (Figure 9.5.6) the formula should be modified to read

$$(\text{the average value of } \sqrt{1 + [\text{slope}]^2}) \cdot (b - a).$$

This is simply the integral we obtained before:

$$\int_a^b \sqrt{1 + [f'(x)]^2} \, dx. \quad \square$$

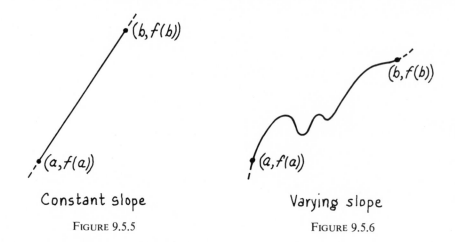

Constant slope

FIGURE 9.5.5

Varying slope

FIGURE 9.5.6

9.6   Area of a surface of revolution

Let f be a nonnegative function with derivative f' continuous on $[a, b]$. By revolving the graph of f from $x = a$ to $x = b$ about the x-axis, we obtain a surface of revolution. (See Figure 9.6.1.) The area of such a surface is commonly defined to be

$$2\pi \int_a^b f(x)\sqrt{[f'(x)]^2 + 1}\ dx.$$

(a)

(b)

FIGURE 9.6.1

Below we describe a simple way in which to arrive at this definition.

To begin with, for each $x \in [a, b]$ we let $s(x)$ be the length of the graph of f from a to x. (Figure 9.6.2) If we let l be the length of the graph from a to b, then as x ranges from a to b, s ranges from 0 to l. For each number $s \in [0, l]$, we define $h(s)$ as the height of that point of the graph of f which is at an arc distance s from the point $(a, f(a))$. (Figure 9.6.3)

FIGURE 9.6.2

FIGURE 9.6.3

If h is constant on $[0, l]$, the surface is cylindrical and it satisfies

$$\text{surface area} = 2\pi(\text{constant height}) \cdot l$$

$$= 2\pi(\text{constant value of } h \text{ on } [0, l]) \cdot (l - 0).$$

If h is not constant, then we use the notion of average value and write

$$\text{surface area} = 2\pi(\text{average value of } h \text{ on } [0, l]) \cdot (l - 0).$$

In the language of integrals, we have

$$\boxed{\text{surface area} = 2\pi \int_0^l h(s)\, ds.}\qquad †$$

Now we apply the change-of-variables formula (8.3.1). Since $s(x)$ is the length of the graph from a to x, we have

$$s(x) = \int_0^x \sqrt{[f'(t)]^2 + 1}\; dt. \qquad\qquad \text{(By 9.5.4)}$$

Also

$$s'(x) = \sqrt{[f'(x)]^2 + 1}, \qquad s(a) = 0, \qquad s(b) = l.$$

---

† If you want further justification for this formula, see the supplement to this section.

Consequently,

$$2\pi \int_0^l h(s)\,ds = 2\pi \int_a^b h(s(x))s'(x)\,dx = 2\pi \int_a^b h(s(x))\sqrt{[f'(x)]^2 + 1}\,dx.$$

Since $h(s(x)) = f(x)$, we have the formula

(9.6.1)

$$\text{surface area} = 2\pi \int_a^b f(x)\sqrt{[f'(x)]^2 + 1}\,dx. \quad \Box$$

Problem. Find a formula for the slant surface area of a cone.

SOLUTION.   A cone of base radius r and height h can be generated by rotating the graph of

$$f(x) = \frac{r}{h}\,x, \qquad x \in [0, h]$$

about the x-axis. (See Figure 9.6.4.) For such a cone we have

$$\text{slant surface area} = 2\pi \int_0^h f(x)\sqrt{[f'(x)]^2 + 1}$$

$$= 2\pi \int_0^h \frac{r}{h}\,x\,\sqrt{\frac{r^2}{h^2} + 1}\,dx$$

$$= \frac{2\pi r\sqrt{r^2 + h^2}}{h^2} \int_0^h x\,dx$$

$$= \pi r\sqrt{r^2 + h^2}. \quad \Box$$

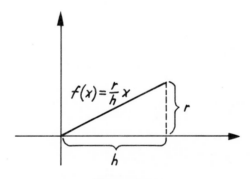

$$f(x) = \frac{r}{h}x$$

FIGURE 9.6.4

Problem. Find the area of the surface generated by revolving the graph of

$$f(x) = \sin x, \qquad x \in \left[0, \frac{\pi}{2}\right].$$

about the x-axis.

SOLUTION.   In this case, we have

$$f(x) = \sin x, \qquad f'(x) = \cos x,$$

and thus

$$\text{surface area} = 2\pi \int_0^{\pi/2} \sin x \sqrt{\cos^2 x + 1}\, dx$$

$$= -2\pi \int_0^{\pi/2} \sqrt{\cos^2 x + 1}\, \frac{d}{dx}(\cos x)\, dx$$

$$= -2\pi \left[\frac{\cos x}{2} \sqrt{\cos^2 x + 1} + \frac{1}{2} \log (\cos x + \sqrt{\cos^2 x + 1}) \right]_0^{\pi/2}$$

$$= 2\pi \left[\frac{1}{2} \sqrt{2} + \frac{1}{2} \log (1 + \sqrt{2}) \right]$$

$$= \pi[\sqrt{2} + \log (1 + \sqrt{2})]. \quad \square$$

Suppose now that the graph of f is given parametrically, say

$$\text{graph of } f: \quad x(t), y(t), \qquad t \in [a, b].$$

Again we let l be the total length of the graph. For each $s \in [0, l]$, we let $h(s)$ be the height of that point of the graph that is at an arc distance s from $(x(a), y(a))$. (See Figure 9.6.5.) Arguing as before, we arrive at the formula

$$\text{surface area} = 2\pi \int_0^l h(s)\, ds.$$

If this time we let $s(t)$ be the arc distance from $(x(a), y(a))$ to $(x(t), y(t))$, then we have

$$s(t) = \int_a^t \sqrt{[x'(\mu)]^2 + [y'(\mu)]^2}\, d\mu \qquad \text{(By 9.5.3)} \qquad s'(t) = \sqrt{[x'(t)]^2 + [y'(t)]^2},$$

$$s(a) = 0, \qquad s(b) = l, \qquad h(s(t)) = y(t),$$

and consequently,

(9.6.2)
$$\boxed{\text{surface area} = 2\pi \int_a^b y(t) \sqrt{[x'(t)]^2 + [y'(t)]^2}\, dt.}$$

The details here have been purposely omitted. It is a good exercise to fill them in. $\quad \square$

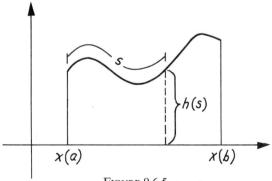

FIGURE 9.6.5

Problem.   Derive the formula for the surface area of a sphere.

SOLUTION.   We can generate a sphere of radius r by rotating the arc

$$x(t) = r \cos t, \qquad y(t) = r \sin t, \qquad t \in [0, \pi]$$

about the x-axis. Formula (9.6.2) then gives

$$\text{surface area} = 2\pi \int_0^\pi y(t)\sqrt{[x'(t)]^2 + [y'(t)]^2}\, dt = 2\pi \int_0^\pi r \sin t\sqrt{r^2(\sin^2 t + \cos^2 t)}\, dt$$

$$= 2\pi r^2 \int_0^\pi \sin t\, dt = 2\pi r^2 \left[-\cos t \right]_0^\pi = 4\pi r^2. \quad \square$$

Exercises

Find the area of the surface that results when the indicated curve is rotated about the x-axis.

1.* $f(x) = r, \ x \in [0, 1]$.

2. $f(x) = \sqrt{x}, \ x \in [1, 2]$.

3.* $f(x) = \sec \dfrac{1}{2} \pi x, \ x \in \left[-\dfrac{1}{2}, \dfrac{1}{2} \right]$.

4. $f(x) = 2\sqrt{1 - x}, \ x \in [-1, 0]$.

5.* $f(x) = \dfrac{1}{3} x^3, \ x \in [0, 2]$.

6. $f(x) = |x - 3|, \ x \in [0, 6]$.

7.* $4y = x^3, \ x \in [0, 1]$.

8. $y^2 = 9x, \ x \in [0, 4]$.

9.* $x(t) = 2t, \ y(t) = 3t, \ t \in [0, 1]$.

10. $x(t) = t^2, \ y(t) = 2t, \ t \in [0, \sqrt{3}]$.

11.* $x^2 + y^2 = r^2, \ x \in \left[-\dfrac{r}{2}, \dfrac{r}{2} \right]$.

12. $y = \cos x, \ x \in \left[-\dfrac{\pi}{2}, \dfrac{\pi}{2} \right]$.

13.* $y = \cosh x, \ x \in [0, 1]$.

14. $y = \sin \pi x, \ x \in [0, 1]$.

15.* $x(t) = a \cos^3 t, \ y(t) = a \sin^3 t, \ t \in \left[0, \dfrac{\pi}{2} \right]$.

16. $x(t) = e^t \sin t, \ y(t) = e^t \cos t, \ t \in \left[0, \dfrac{\pi}{2} \right]$.

17.* $r = e^\theta, \ \theta \in \left[0, \dfrac{\pi}{2} \right]$.

18. $r = \rho(\theta), \ \theta \in [\theta_1, \theta_2]$.

19.* Find a formula for the lateral surface area of the frustrum of a cone (Figure 9.3.10).

20. Find the area of the surface that results when the catenary

$$y = a \cosh \frac{x}{a}, \qquad x \in [-a, a]$$

is rotated about (i) the x-axis; (ii) the y-axis.

21.* Find the area of the ellipsoid obtained by rotating the ellipse

$$\frac{x^2}{a^2} + \frac{y^2}{b^2} = 1$$

(i) about its major axis; (ii) about its minor axis.

SUPPLEMENT TO SECTION 9.6

Further Justification for Setting surface area $= 2\pi \int_0^l h(s) \, ds.$

Let $P = \{s_0, s_1, \ldots, s_n\}$ be a partition of $[0, l]$. Set

$$m_i = \text{minimum value of } h \text{ on } [s_{i-1}, s_i],$$
$$M_i = \text{maximum value of } h \text{ on } [s_{i-1}, s_i].$$

The surface area S_i contributed by the ith interval $[s_{i-1}, s_1]$ should certainly satisfy the inequality

$$2\pi m_i(s_i - s_{i-1}) \le S_i \le 2\pi M_i(s_i - s_{i-1}).$$

Summing from $i = 1$ to $i = n$ and requiring

$$\text{surface area} = S_1 + S_2 + \cdots + S_n,$$

we are led to

$$L_{2\pi h}(P) \le \text{surface area} \le U_{2\pi h}(P).$$

Since this inequality must hold for every partition P, we have

$$\text{surface area} = \int_0^l 2\pi h(s) \, ds = 2\pi \int_0^l h(s) \, ds. \quad \square$$

9.7   (Optional) The notion of work

Suppose that an object moves a distance s in a fixed direction. Suppose that during the motion a constant force f is applied to the object in the direction of the motion. The work done by such a force is then defined by the physicist as

$$W = f \cdot s.$$
$$[\text{work} = \text{force} \cdot \text{distance}]$$

If the force is measured in pounds and the distance in feet, the units of work are called foot-pounds. Thus if a constant force of 500 lbs is applied to pushing a car 60 ft, the work done by the pushing force is 30,000 ft-lbs.

If we coordinatize the line along which the motion takes place, assigning coordinate a to the initial point and coordinate b to the terminal point $(b > a)$, then we have

$$\text{work} = (\text{constant force}) \cdot (b - a).$$

In other words,

$$\text{work} = (\text{constant value of } f \text{ on } [a, b]) \cdot (b - a).$$

If f, the force applied, is allowed to vary, then we replace the constant value of f by its average value, and define

$$\text{work} = (\text{average value of } f \text{ on } [a, b]) \cdot (b - a).$$

Thus, in the case of a variable force, we have

(9.7.1)

$$\text{work} = \int_a^b f(x)\, dx.$$

Stretching a Spring

A simple instance of a variable force is offered by the behavior of a steel spring. According to Hooke's law (Robert Hooke, 1635–1703), a spring stretched x units beyond its natural length exerts a force which is proportional to x. Thus we have

$$f(x) = kx,$$

the proportionality constant k depending upon the spring and the units used.

Problem. A certain spring exerts a force of $\frac{1}{2}$ lb when stretched $\frac{1}{3}$ ft beyond its natural length. What is the work done in stretching the spring $\frac{1}{10}$ ft beyond its natural length? What is the work done in stretching it an additional $\frac{1}{10}$ ft?

SOLUTION. We know that the force function is of the form

$$f(x) = kx.$$

Since $f(\frac{1}{3}) = \frac{1}{2}$, we have

$$k \cdot \tfrac{1}{3} = \tfrac{1}{2},$$

so that $k = \frac{3}{2}$. Thus, for this particular spring, the force function is

$$f(x) = \tfrac{3}{2}x.$$

The work done in the initial stretching is given by

$$W_1 = \int_0^{1/10} \frac{3}{2} x\, dx = \frac{3}{2}\left[\frac{x^2}{2}\right]_0^{1/10} = \frac{3}{400} \text{ ft-lbs.}$$

The work done in the next stretching is given by

$$W_2 = \int_{1/10}^{2/10} \frac{3}{2} x\, dx = \frac{3}{2}\left[\frac{x^2}{2}\right]_{1/10}^{2/10} = \frac{9}{400} \text{ ft-lbs.} \quad \square$$

Emptying Out A Tank

To lift an object, one must counteract the force of gravity. Consequently, the work done in lifting an object is given by the simple formula

$$\text{work} = (\text{weight of the object}) \cdot (\text{distance lifted}).$$

Problem. A tank containing a liquid that weighs σ lbs per cu ft is being pumped out from above. (See Figure 9.7.1) What is the work done in lowering the level of the liquid from a ft below the top of the tank to b ft below the top of the tank?

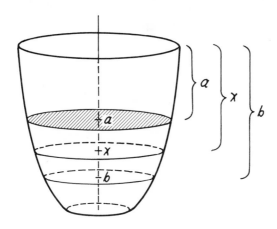

FIGURE 9.7.1

SOLUTION.   For each $x \in [a, b]$, we let

$A(x)$ = cross-sectional area x ft below the top of the tank,

$s(x)$ = distance that the x-level must be lifted.

If all the cross sections had the same area A, then the volume of the liquid to be lifted would be

$$A(b - a).$$

Its total weight would be

$$\sigma A(b - a).$$

If this weight all had to be lifted the same distance s, the work required would be

$$(\text{weight}) \cdot (\text{distance lifted}) = \sigma A(b - a) \cdot s = \sigma As(b - a).$$

In other words, if the function As were constant, we would have

$$\text{work} = \sigma \cdot (\text{constant value of } As) \cdot (b - a).$$

Since the function As is not necessarily constant, we set

$$\text{work} = \sigma \cdot (\text{average value of } As \text{ on } [a, b]) \cdot (b - a).$$

As an integral, we have

(9.7.2)
$$\text{work} = \sigma \int_a^b A(x)s(x)\, dx.$$

Problem.   A hemispherical water tank of radius 10 ft is being pumped out. Find the work done in lowering the water level from 2 ft below the top of the tank to 4 ft below the top of the tank, (a) given that the pump is placed right on top of the tank, (b) given that the pump is placed 3 ft above the tank.

SOLUTION.   As standard weight for water we take 62.5 lbs per cu ft. Referring to Figure 9.7.2, we see that the cross section x ft from the top is a circular disk of radius $\sqrt{100 - x^2}$. Thus

$$A(x) = \pi(100 - x^2).$$

In the case of (a), we have

$$s(x) = x,$$

and consequently,

$$\text{work} = 62.5 \int_2^4 \pi(100 - x^2)x \, dx = 33{,}750\pi \text{ ft-lbs.}$$

In the case of (b), we have

$$s(x) = x + 3,$$

and consequently,

$$\text{work} = 62.5 \int_2^4 \pi(100 - x^2)(x + 3) \, dx = 67{,}750\pi \text{ ft-lbs.} \quad \square$$

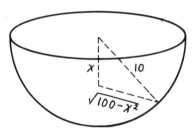

FIGURE 9.7.2

Exercises

1.* A weight of 2 lbs stretches a certain spring 4 ft beyond its natural length. Find the work done in stretching the spring (a) 1 ft beyond its natural length, (b) $1\frac{1}{2}$ ft beyond its natural length.

2. A certain spring has natural length l. Given that W is the work done in stretching the spring from l ft to $l + a$ ft, find the work done in stretching the spring (a) from l ft to $l + 2a$ ft, (b) from l ft to $l + na$ ft, (c) from $l + a$ ft to $l + 2a$ ft, (d) from $l + a$ ft to $l + na$ ft.

3.* Find the natural length of a heavy metal spring, given that the work done in stretching it from a length of 2 ft to a length of 3 ft is one-half the work done in stretching it from a length of 3 ft to a length of 4 ft.

4. A vertical cylindrical tank of radius 2 ft and height 6 ft is full of water. Find the work done in pumping out the water (a) to the top of the tank, (b) to a level 5 ft above the top of the tank. (Assume that water weighs 62.5 lbs per cu ft.)

5.* A horizontal cylindrical tank of radius 3 ft and length 8 ft is half full of oil weighing 60 lbs per cu ft. What is the work done in pumping out the oil (a) to the top of the tank, (b) to a level 4 ft above the top of the tank?

6. A conical container (vertex down) of radius r ft and height h ft is full of a liquid weighing σ lbs per cu ft. Find the work done in pumping out the top $h/2$ ft of liquid (a) to the top of the tank, (b) to a level k feet above the top of the tank.

7.* A rope of length l feet that weighs σ lbs per cu ft is lying on the ground. What is the work done in lifting the rope so that it hangs from a beam (a) l feet high, (b) $2l$ feet high?

8. An 800-lb steel beam hangs from a 50-ft cable which weighs 6 lbs per ft. Find the work done in winding 20 ft of the cable about a steel drum.

9.8 Additional problems

Find the areas bounded by the following curves. In each case draw the figure.

1.* $y^2 = 2x, x^2 = 3y$.

2. $y^2 = 6x, x^2 + 4y = 0$.

3.* $y = 4 - x^2, y = x + 2$.

4. $y = 4 - x^2, x + y + 2 = 0$.

5.* $y^2 = x, y = x^3$.

6. $x + y = 2y^2, y = x^3$.

13.* $xy = a^2$, the x-axis, $x = a$, and $x = 2a$.

7.* $4y = x^2 - x^4, x + y + 1 = 0$.

8. $4y = x^4 - x^2, y = 2$.

9.* $r^2 = 4 \sin 2\theta$.

10. $r = 2 + \sin 3\theta$.

11.* $r = a(\sin 2\theta + \cos 2\theta)$.

12. $r = \sec \theta + \tan \theta$ and the rays $\theta = 0, \theta = \pi/4$.

14.* Find the area bounded by the parabola $y = 6 + 4x - x^2$ and the chord joining $(-2, -6)$ to $(4, 6)$.

15.* Find the area bounded by the semicubical parabola $y^3 = x^2$ and the chord joining $(-1, 1)$ to $(8, 4)$.

The square with one vertex at the origin and opposite vertex at $(1, 1)$ is divided into two parts by each of the following curves. In each instance, find the ratio of the larger area to the smaller area.

16.* $y^2 = x^3$.

17. $y = x^3$.

18.* $\sqrt{x} + \sqrt{y} = 1$.

19. $y = x^n, n > 0$.

20.* $y = \sin(\pi x/2)$.

21. $y = xe^{x-1}$.

The region bounded by the following curves is revolved about the x-axis. Find the volume of the solid generated.

22.* $ay^2 = x^3, y = 0, x = a$.

23. $y^2 = (2 - x)^3, y = 0, x = 0, x = 1$.

24.* $\sqrt{x} + \sqrt{y} = \sqrt{a}, x = 0, y = 0$.

25. $x^{2/3} + y^{2/3} = a^{2/3}$.

26.* $(x/a)^2 + (y/b)^{2/3} = 1$.

27. $a^2y^2 = x^2(a^2 - x^2)$.

The region bounded by the following curves is rotated about the y-axis. Find the volume of the solid generated.

28.* $y = x^3, y = 0, x = 2$.

29. $y^2 = 9 - x, x = 0$.

30.* $(x/a)^2 + (y/b)^{2/3} = 1$.

31. $x^2 = 16 - y, y = 0$.

32.   A load of weight W is lifted from the bottom of a shaft h feet deep. Find the work done if the rope used to hoist the load weighs σ pounds per foot.

33.* A wedge is cut from a cylinder of radius r by two planes, one perpendicular to the axis of the cylinder and the other passing through a diameter of the section made by the first plane and inclined to this plane at an angle θ. Find the volume of the wedge.

34.* Find the average value of $\sin^2 x$ between $x = 0$ and $x = \pi$.

Find the length of each curve.

35.* $y^2 = x^3$ from $x = 0$ to $x = 5/9$.　　　37.* $ay^2 = x^3$ from $x = 0$ to $x = 5a$.

36. $9y^2 = 4(1 + x^2)^3$ from $x = 0$ to $x = 3$.　38. $y = \log(1 - x^2)$ from $x = 0$ to $x = 1/2$.

39.* $x^{2/3} + y^{2/3} = a^{2/3}$.

40. $y = \log(\operatorname{cosec} x)$ from $x = \pi/6$ to $x = \pi/2$.

41.* $(x/a)^{2/3} + (y/b)^{2/3} = 1$ in the first quadrant.

Find the area of the surface generated by revolving the indicated curve about the x-axis.

42.* $y^2 = 2px$ from $x = 0$ to $x = 4p$.

43. $y^2 = 4x$ from $x = 0$ to $x = 24$.

44.* $6a^2xy = x^4 + 3a^4$ from $x = a$ to $x = 2a$.

45. $3x^2 + 4y^2 = 3a^2$.

46.* $y = \dfrac{x^3}{6} + \dfrac{1}{2x}$ from $x = 1$ to $x = 3$.

47.* $y^2 + 4x = 2 \log y$ from $y = 1$ to $y = 2$.

SEQUENCES AND SERIES

10.1 Sequences of real numbers

So far our attention has been fixed on functions defined on an interval or on the union of intervals. Here we study functions that are defined on the set of positive integers.

Definition

A function that takes on real values and is defined on the set of positive integers is called a *sequence of real numbers* or, more briefly, a *sequence*.

Thus the functions defined for each positive integer by

$$a(n) = n - 1, \qquad b(n) = \frac{n^2 - 1}{n}, \qquad c(n) = \sqrt{\log n}, \qquad d(n) = \frac{e^n}{n}$$

are all sequences of real numbers. The notions developed for functions in general carry over to sequences. For example, a sequence is said to be bounded (bounded above, bounded below) iff its range is bounded (bounded above, bounded below). If a and b are sequences, then their linear combination $\alpha a + \beta b$ and their product ab, defined by setting

$$(\alpha a + \beta b)(n) = \alpha a(n) + \beta b(n) \qquad \text{and} \qquad (ab)(n) = a(n) \cdot b(n),$$

are also sequences. If the sequence b does not take on the value 0, then the reciprocal $1/b$ is a sequence and so is the quotient a/b:

$$\frac{1}{b}(n) = \frac{1}{b(n)} \qquad \text{and} \qquad \frac{a}{b}(n) = \frac{a(n)}{b(n)}.$$

The number $a(n)$, called *the nth term of the sequence a*, is usually abbreviated as a_n. The sequence itself can then be denoted by

$$\{a_1, a_2, a_3, \cdots\}$$

or even by

$$\{a_n\}.$$

For instance, the sequence of reciprocals defined by

$$a(n) = \frac{1}{n} \quad \text{for each positive integer} \quad n$$

can be defined by simply setting

$$a_n = \frac{1}{n}$$

or by writing

$$\left\{1, \frac{1}{2}, \frac{1}{3}, \cdots\right\},$$

or even by writing

$$\left\{\frac{1}{n}\right\}.$$

In our abbreviated notation, we have

$$\alpha\{a_n\} + \beta\{b_n\} = \{\alpha a_n + \beta b_n\}, \qquad \{a_n\}\{b_n\} = \{a_n b_n\}$$

and, provided that none of the b_n are zero,

$$\frac{1}{\{b_n\}} = \left\{\frac{1}{b_n}\right\} \quad \text{and} \quad \frac{\{a_n\}}{\{b_n\}} = \left\{\frac{a_n}{b_n}\right\}.$$

We illustrate the notation by some trivial assertions.

(1) $$5\left\{1, \frac{1}{2}, \frac{1}{4}, \frac{1}{8}, \cdots\right\} = \left\{5, \frac{5}{2}, \frac{5}{4}, \frac{5}{8}, \cdots\right\}$$

or, equivalently,

$$5\left\{\frac{1}{2^{n-1}}\right\} = \left\{\frac{5}{2^{n-1}}\right\}.$$

(2) $$\{1, 2, 3, \cdots\} + \left\{1, \frac{1}{2}, \frac{1}{3}, \cdots\right\} = \left\{2, 2\frac{1}{2}, 3\frac{1}{3}, \cdots\right\}$$

or, equivalently,

$$\{n\} + \left\{\frac{1}{n}\right\} = \left\{n + \frac{1}{n}\right\}.$$

(3) $$\frac{\{n\}}{\{n+1\}} = \left\{\frac{n}{n+1}\right\}.$$

(4) The sequence $\left\{\dfrac{1}{n}\right\}$ is bounded below by 0 and bounded above by 1:

$$0 \leq \frac{1}{n} \leq 1 \qquad \text{for all } n.$$

(5) The sequence $\{2^n\}$ is bounded below by 2:

$$2 \leq 2^n \qquad \text{for all } n.$$

It is not bounded above: there is no fixed number M which satisfies

$$2^n \leq M \qquad \text{for all } n.$$

(6) The sequence

$$a_n = (-1)^n 2^n,$$

can be written

$$\{-2, 4, -8, 16, -32, 64, \cdots\}.$$

It is unbounded in both senses.   □

Definition

A sequence $\{a_n\}$ is said to be
  (i) *increasing*   iff $a_n < a_{n+1}$ for each positive integer n,
  (ii) *nondecreasing* iff $a_n \leq a_{n+1}$ for each positive integer n,
  (iii) *decreasing*   iff $a_n > a_{n+1}$ for each positive integer n,
  (iv) *nonincreasing* iff $a_n \geq a_{n+1}$ for each positive integer n.
If any of these four properties holds, the sequence is said to be *monotonic*.

The sequences

$$\left\{1, \frac{1}{2}, \frac{1}{3}, \cdots\right\}, \quad \left\{1, 1, \frac{1}{2}, \frac{1}{2}, \frac{1}{3}, \frac{1}{3}, \cdots\right\}, \quad \{2, 4, 8, 16 \cdots\}, \quad \{2, 2, 4, 4, 8, 8, 16, 16 \cdots\}$$

are all monotonic, but

$$\left\{1, \frac{1}{2}, 1, \frac{1}{3}, 1, \frac{1}{4}, \cdots\right\}$$

is not.

The next examples are less trivial.

Example.   The sequence

$$a_n = \frac{n}{n+1}$$

is increasing. It is bounded below by $\dfrac{1}{2}$ and above by 1.

PROOF. Since

$$a_n = \frac{n}{n+1} = \frac{1}{1+1/n} < \frac{1}{1+1/(n+1)} = \frac{n+1}{(n+1)+1} = a_{n+1}$$

we have

$$a_n < a_{n+1}.$$

This tells us that the sequence is increasing. The bounds are obvious.   □

Example. The sequence $a_n = 2^n/n!$ is nonincreasing.

PROOF. Since

$$a_{n+1} = \frac{2^{n+1}}{(n+1)!} = \frac{2}{n+1} \cdot \frac{2^n}{n!} = \frac{2}{n+1} a_n,$$

we see that

$$a_n > a_{n+1} \qquad \text{for all } n \geq 2.$$

Since $a_1 = a_2 = 2$, we have

$$a_n \geq a_{n+1} \qquad \text{for all } n.   □$$

Example. The sequence $\{|c|^n\}$ is bounded if $|c| \leq 1$ and unbounded if $|c| > 1$.

PROOF. The first statement is obvious. For the second we suppose that $|c| > 1$. To show the unboundedness, we take an arbitrary positive number M and show that there exists a positive integer k for which

$$|c|^k \geq M.$$

A suitable k is one that satisfies

$$k \geq \frac{\log M}{\log |c|},$$

for then we have

$$k \log |c| \geq \log M, \qquad \log |c|^k \geq \log M,$$

and consequently

$$|c|^k \geq M.   □$$

Since sequences are defined on the set of positive integers and not on an interval, they are not directly susceptible to the methods of calculus. Fortunately, we can often get around this difficulty by dealing initially, not with the sequence itself, but with a function which is defined on all of $[1, \infty)$ and agrees with the given sequence on the integers.

We illustrate this idea in the next two examples. In the first example, we study the sequence

$$a_n = \frac{e^n}{n}$$

by directing our attention first to the function

$$f(x) = \frac{e^x}{x}.$$

Example. The sequence

$$a_n = \frac{e^n}{n}$$

is an increasing sequence that is unbounded above.

PROOF. We begin by setting

$$f(x) = \frac{e^x}{x}.$$

It is not hard to see that

$$f'(x) = \frac{xe^x - e^x}{x^2} = \frac{e^x(x-1)}{x^2}.$$

Since

$$f'(x) \quad \text{is} \quad \begin{cases} 0, & \text{at } x = 1 \\ \text{positive,} & \text{for } x > 1 \end{cases},$$

the function f increases on $[1, \infty)$. Obviously then the sequence

$$a_n = \frac{e^n}{n}$$

is itself increasing. To see the unboundedness of the sequence observe that

$$e^n > \frac{n^p}{p!} \quad \text{for each positive integer } p.$$

(See Exercise 12, Section 5.2). Setting $p = 2$, we have

$$e^n > \frac{n^2}{2!}$$

and thus

$$\frac{e^n}{n} > \frac{n}{2}. \quad \square$$

Example. The sequence

$$a_n = (n + 2)^{1/(n+2)}$$

is a decreasing sequence.

PROOF. We could compare a_n with a_{n+1} directly, but it is easier to consider the function

$$f(x) = x^{1/x}$$

instead. Since

$$f(x) = e^{(1/x) \log x},$$

we have

$$f'(x) = e^{(1/x) \log x} \frac{d}{dx} \left(\frac{1}{x} \log x \right) = x^{1/x} \cdot \left(\frac{1 - \log x}{x^2} \right).$$

For $x > e, f'(x) < 0$. This tells us that f decreases on $[e, \infty)$. Since $3 > e, f$ decreases on $[3, \infty)$. It follows that $\{a_n\}$ is a decreasing sequence. $\square$

Exercises

Discuss the boundedness and monotonicity of the sequence whose nth term is given by the following.

1.* $\dfrac{2}{n}$.

2. $\dfrac{(-1)^n}{n}$.

3.* $\sqrt{n}$.

4. $\dfrac{n + (-1)^n}{n}$.

5.* $\dfrac{n}{2^n}$.

6. $\dfrac{n - 1}{n}$.

7.* $\dfrac{n^2}{n + 1}$.

8. $\dfrac{n + 1}{n^2}$.

9.* $\dfrac{4n}{\sqrt{4n^2 + 1}}$.

10. $\dfrac{4^n}{2^n + 100}$.

11.* $\dfrac{2^n}{4^n + 1}$.

12.* $\dfrac{10^{10}\sqrt{n}}{n + 1}$.

13.* $(-1)^n \sqrt{n}$.

14. $\dfrac{n + 1}{n}$.

15.* $\log \left(\dfrac{2n}{n + 1} \right)$.

16. $\left(-\dfrac{1}{2} \right)^n$.

17.* $\dfrac{(n + 1)^2}{n^2}$.

18. $\sqrt{4 - \dfrac{1}{n}}$.

19.* $\dfrac{2^n - 1}{2^n}$.

20. $(0.9)^n$.

21.* $\dfrac{1}{n} - \dfrac{1}{n + 1}$.

22. $\dfrac{\log (n + 1)}{n}$.

23.* $\log \left(\dfrac{n + 1}{n} \right)$.

24. $\dfrac{\sqrt{n + 1}}{\sqrt{n}}$.

25.* $\dfrac{n^2}{3^n}$.

26. $\dfrac{1 - (\frac{1}{2})^n}{(\frac{1}{2})^n}$.

27.* $\sinh \dfrac{1}{n}$.

28. $\cos n\pi$.

29. Show that linear combinations and products of bounded sequences are bounded.

30. Show that the sequence

$$a_n = (c^n + d^n)^{1/n} \qquad \text{with} \qquad 0 < c < d$$

is bounded and monotonic.

10.2   The limit of a sequence

The gist of

$$\lim_{x \to c} f(x) = l$$

is that we can make $f(x)$ as close as we wish to the number l simply by requiring that x be sufficiently close to c. The gist of

$$\lim_{n \to \infty} a_n = l$$

(read "the limit of a_n as n tends to infinity is l") is that we can make a_n as close as we wish to the number l simply by requiring that n be sufficiently large.

Definition of Limit

$$\lim_{n \to \infty} a_n = l \quad \text{iff} \quad \begin{cases} \text{for each } \epsilon > 0 \text{ there exists an integer } k > 0 \text{ such that,} \\ \quad\quad \text{if} \quad n \geq k, \quad\quad \text{then} \quad\quad |a_n - l| < \epsilon. \end{cases}$$

Example

$$\lim_{n \to \infty} \frac{1}{n} = 0.$$

PROOF. We take $\epsilon > 0$ and note that if $k > 1/\epsilon$, then $1/k < \epsilon$. Consequently, for $n \geq k$, we have

$$\frac{1}{n} \leq \frac{1}{k} < \epsilon \quad \text{and thus} \quad \left| \frac{1}{n} - 0 \right| < \epsilon. \quad \square$$

Example

$$\lim_{n \to \infty} \frac{2n - 1}{n} = 2.$$

PROOF. Let $\epsilon > 0$. We must show that there exists an integer k such that

$$\left| \frac{2n - 1}{n} - 2 \right| < \epsilon \quad \text{for all} \quad n \geq k.$$

Since

$$\left| \frac{2n - 1}{n} - 2 \right| = \left| \frac{2n - 1 - 2n}{n} \right| = \left| -\frac{1}{n} \right| = \frac{1}{n},$$

again we need only choose $k > 1/\epsilon$. $\quad \square$

Example.   For the decimal fractions

$$b_n = 0.\overset{n}{\overbrace{33 \ldots 3}}$$

we have

$$\lim_{n \to \infty} b_n = \frac{1}{3}.$$

PROOF.   Let $\epsilon > 0$. We have

$$\left| b_n - \frac{1}{3} \right| = \left| 0.\overbrace{33 \ldots 3}^{n} - \frac{1}{3} \right| = \left| \frac{\overbrace{0.99 \ldots 9}^{n} - 1}{3} \right| = \frac{1}{3} \cdot \frac{1}{10^n} < \frac{1}{10^n}.$$

By choosing k such that $1/10^k < \epsilon$, we ensure that

$$\left| b_n - \frac{1}{3} \right| < \epsilon \qquad \text{for all} \quad n \geq k. \quad \square$$

Limit Theorems

The limit process for sequences is so similar to the limit process you have already studied that you will probably find that you can prove most of the limit theorems on your own. In any case, it is a good idea to try to come up with your own proofs and refer to the given proofs only if necessary.

Uniqueness Theorem

If

$$\lim_{n \to \infty} a_n = l \qquad \text{and} \qquad \lim_{n \to \infty} a_n = m,$$

then

$$l = m.$$

PROOF.   If $l \neq m$, then

$$\frac{|l - m|}{2} > 0.$$

From

$$\lim_{n \to \infty} a_n = l \qquad \text{and} \qquad \lim_{n \to \infty} a_n = m,$$

we conclude that there exists k_1 such that

$$\text{if} \quad n \geq k_1, \qquad \text{then} \quad |a_n - l| < \frac{|l - m|}{2}$$

and there exists k_2 such that

$$\text{if} \quad n \geq k_2, \qquad \text{then} \quad |a_n - m| < \frac{|l - m|}{2}.$$

For $n \geq \max\{k_1, k_2\}$ we have

$$|a_n - l| + |a_n - m| < |l - m|.$$

But by the triangle inequality we have

$$|a_n - l| + |a_n - m| = |l - a_n| + |a_n - m| \geq |l - m|.$$

Combining the last two statements, we obtain

$$|l - m| < |l - m|.$$

The hypothesis $l \neq m$ has led to an absurdity. We conclude that $l = m$. ☐

Definition

A sequence that has a limit is said to be *convergent*. A sequence that has no limit is said to be *divergent*.

Instead of writing

$$\lim_{n \to \infty} a_n = l,$$

we shall use the simpler notation

$$a_n \to l. \qquad\qquad \text{(read ``}a_n \text{ converges to } l\text{'')}$$

Theorem 10.2.1

A convergent sequence is bounded.

PROOF.   Suppose that

$$a_n \to l$$

and take any positive number: 1, for instance.

Using 1 as ϵ, we see that there must exist k such that

$$|a_n - l| < 1 \qquad \text{for all} \quad n \geq k.$$

This means that

$$|a_n| < 1 + |l| \qquad \text{for all} \quad n \geq k,$$

and consequently

$$|a_n| \leq \max\{|a_1|, |a_2|, \cdots, |a_{k-1}|, 1 + |l|\} \qquad \text{for all} \quad n.$$

This proves that $\{a_n\}$ is bounded. ☐

Since convergent sequences are bounded, unbounded sequences are divergent. The following sequences,

$$\left\{\frac{n}{2}\right\}, \quad \{\sqrt{\log n}\}, \quad \left\{\frac{n}{\cos(n+1)}\right\}, \quad \left\{\frac{e^n}{n}\right\},$$

being unbounded, are all divergent. Boundedness does not imply convergence. As a counterexample, take the oscillating sequence

$$\{1, 0, 1, 0, \cdots\}.$$

This sequence is certainly bounded (above by 1 and below by 0), but obviously it does not converge.

Boundedness together with monotonicity does imply convergence.

Theorem 10.2.2

A bounded, nondecreasing sequence converges to the least upper bound of its range; a bounded, nonincreasing sequence converges to the greatest lower bound of its range.

PROOF. Suppose that $\{a_n\}$ is bounded and nondecreasing. Let ϵ be an arbitrary positive number. If

$$l = \text{lub } \{a_n : n \text{ a positive integer}\},$$

then there must exist a_k such that

$$l - \epsilon < a_k.$$

(Otherwise $l - \epsilon$ would be an upper bound less than l.) By the monotonicity, we see that

$$\text{if} \quad n \geq k, \quad \text{then} \quad a_k \leq a_n.$$

Thus we have

$$l - \epsilon < a_n \leq l \quad \text{for all} \quad n \geq k.$$

It follows that $|a_n - l| < \epsilon$ and

$$a_n \to l.$$

The nonincreasing case can be handled in a similar manner. □

Example. Take the sequence

$$\{(3^n + 4^n)^{1/n}\}.$$

Since

$$3 = (3^n)^{1/n} < (3^n + 4^n)^{1/n} < (2 \cdot 4^n)^{1/n} = 2^{1/n} \cdot 4 \leq 8,$$

the sequence is bounded. Note that

$$(3^n + 4^n)^{(n+1)/n} = (3^n + 4^n)^{1/n}(3^n + 4^n) = (3^n + 4^n)^{1/n}3^n + (3^n + 4^n)^{1/n}4^n$$
$$> 3 \cdot 3^n + 4 \cdot 4^n = 3^{n+1} + 4^{n+1}.$$

Taking the $(n + 1)$st root of both extremes, we get

$$(3^n + 4^n)^{1/n} > (3^{n+1} + 4^{n+1})^{1/n+1}.$$

This tells us that the sequence is a decreasing one. Being bounded, it must be convergent. (Later you will be asked to show that the limit is 4.) □

Theorem

If $a_n \rightarrow l$ and $b_n \rightarrow m$, then

  (i) $a_n + b_n \rightarrow l + m$,
  (ii) $\alpha a_n \rightarrow \alpha l$ for each real α,
  (iii) $a_n b_n \rightarrow lm$.

If, in addition, $m \neq 0$ and b_n is never 0, then

  (iv) $\dfrac{1}{b_n} \rightarrow \dfrac{1}{m}$ and   (v) $\dfrac{a_n}{b_n} \rightarrow \dfrac{l}{m}$.

PROOF.   Parts (i) and (ii) are left as exercises. To prove (iii), we set $\epsilon > 0$. For each n,

$$|a_n b_n - lm| = |(a_n b_n - a_n m) + (a_n m - lm)|$$
$$\leq |a_n|\,|b_n - m| + |m|\,|a_n - l|.$$

Since $\{a_n\}$ is convergent, $\{a_n\}$ is bounded; that is, there exists $M > 0$ such that

$$|a_n| \leq M \qquad \text{for all } n.$$

Since $|m| < |m| + 1$, we have

(1) $$|a_n b_n - lm| \leq M|b_n - m| + (|m| + 1)|a_n - l|.$$

Since $b_n \rightarrow m$, we know that there exists k_1 such that

$$\text{if}\quad n \geq k_1, \qquad \text{then}\quad |b_n - m| < \frac{\epsilon}{2M}.$$

Since $a_n \rightarrow l$, we know that there exists k_2 such that

$$\text{if}\quad n \geq k_2, \qquad \text{then}\quad |a_n - l| < \frac{\epsilon}{2(|m| + 1)}.$$

For $n \geq \max\{k_1, k_2\}$ both conditions hold, and consequently

$$M|b_n - m| + (|m| + 1)|a_n - l| < \frac{\epsilon}{2} + \frac{\epsilon}{2} = \epsilon.$$

Applying (1), we conclude that

$$\text{if}\quad n \geq \max\{k_1, k_2\}, \qquad \text{then}\quad |a_n b_n - lm| < \epsilon.$$

This proves that

$$a_n b_n \rightarrow lm.$$

To prove (iv) once again we set $\epsilon > 0$. In the first place

$$\left| \frac{1}{b_n} - \frac{1}{m} \right| = \left| \frac{m - b_n}{b_n m} \right| = \frac{|b_n - m|}{|b_n|\,|m|}$$

Since $b_n \to m$ and $|m|/2 > 0$, there exists k_1 such that

$$\text{if} \quad n \geq k_1, \quad \text{then} \quad |b_n - m| < \frac{|m|}{2}.$$

This tells us that for $n \geq k_1$ we have

$$|b_n| > \frac{|m|}{2} \quad \text{and thus} \quad \frac{1}{|b_n|} < \frac{2}{|m|}.$$

Thus for $n \geq k_1$ we have

$$(2) \qquad\qquad \left| \frac{1}{b_n} - \frac{1}{m} \right| \leq \frac{2}{|m|^2} |b_n - m|.$$

Since $b_n \to m$, there exists k_2 such that

$$\text{if} \quad n \geq k_2, \quad \text{then} \quad |b_n - m| < \frac{\epsilon |m|^2}{2}.$$

Thus for $n \geq k_2$ we have

$$\frac{2}{|m|^2} |b_n - m| < \epsilon.$$

Combining this inequality with (2), we see that

$$\text{if} \quad n \geq \max\{k_1, k_2\}, \quad \text{then} \quad \left| \frac{1}{b_n} - \frac{1}{m} \right| < \epsilon.$$

This proves that

$$\frac{1}{b_n} \to \frac{1}{m}.$$

The proof of (v) is now easy:

$$\frac{a_n}{b_n} = a_n \cdot \frac{1}{b_n} \to l \cdot \frac{1}{m} = \frac{l}{m}. \quad \square$$

We are now in a position to handle any rational sequence

$$a_n = \frac{\alpha_k n^k + \alpha_{k-1} n^{k-1} + \cdots + \alpha_0}{\beta_j n^j + \beta_{j-1} n^{j-1} + \cdots + \beta_0}.$$

To determine the behavior of such a sequence we need only divide both numerator and denominator by the highest power of n that occurs.

Example

$$\frac{3n^4 - 2n^2 + 1}{n^5 - 3n^3} = \frac{\dfrac{3}{n} - \dfrac{2}{n^3} + \dfrac{1}{n^5}}{1 - \dfrac{3}{n^2}} \to \frac{0}{1} = 0. \quad \square$$

Example

$$\frac{1 - 4n^7}{n^7 + 12n} = \frac{\dfrac{1}{n^7} - 4}{1 + \dfrac{12}{n^6}} \to \frac{-4}{1} = -4. \quad \Box$$

Example

$$\frac{n^4 - 3n^2 + n + 2}{n^3 + 7n} = \frac{1 - \dfrac{3}{n^2} + \dfrac{1}{n^3} + \dfrac{2}{n^4}}{\dfrac{1}{n} + \dfrac{7}{n^3}} .$$

Since the numerator tends to 1 and the denominator tends to 0, the sequence is unbounded. It can therefore not converge. $\Box$

Theorem

$$a_n \to l \quad \text{iff} \quad a_n - l \to 0 \quad \text{iff} \quad |a_n - l| \to 0.$$

The proof is left as an exercise. $\Box$

The Pinching Theorem for Sequences

Suppose that

$$a_n \le b_n \le c_n \qquad \text{for all } n \text{ sufficiently large.}$$

If

$$a_n \to l \quad \text{and} \quad c_n \to l$$

then

$$b_n \to l.$$

Once again the proof is left as an exercise. $\Box$

As an immediate and obvious consequence of the pinching theorem we have the following corollary.

Corollary

Suppose that

$$|b_n| \le |a_n| \qquad \text{for all } n \text{ sufficiently large.}$$

If $|a_n| \to 0$, then $|b_n| \to 0.$

Example

$$\frac{\cos \pi n}{n} \to 0$$

since

$$\left| \frac{\cos \pi n}{n} \right| \le \frac{1}{n} \quad \text{and} \quad \frac{1}{n} \to 0. \quad \square$$

Example

$$\sqrt{4 + \left(\frac{1}{n}\right)^2} \to 2$$

since

$$2 \le \sqrt{4 + \left(\frac{1}{n}\right)^2} \le \sqrt{4 + 4\left(\frac{1}{n}\right) + \left(\frac{1}{n}\right)^2} = 2 + \frac{1}{n}$$

and

$$2 + \frac{1}{n} \to 2. \quad \square$$

Example

$$\lim_{n \to \infty} \left(1 + \frac{1}{n}\right)^n = e.$$

PROOF.   You have seen already that

$$\left(1 + \frac{1}{n}\right)^n \le e \le \left(1 + \frac{1}{n}\right)^{n+1}.$$

From this it follows that

$$\left| \left(1 + \frac{1}{n}\right)^n - e \right| \le \left| \left(1 + \frac{1}{n}\right)^n - \left(1 + \frac{1}{n}\right)^{n+1} \right|$$

$$= \left(1 + \frac{1}{n}\right)^n \left| 1 - \left(1 + \frac{1}{n}\right) \right| = \left(1 + \frac{1}{n}\right)^n \left(\frac{1}{n}\right) \le \frac{e}{n}.$$

In short we have the estimate

$$\left| \left(1 + \frac{1}{n}\right)^n - e \right| \le \frac{e}{n}.$$

Since

$$\frac{e}{n} \to 0$$

we have

$$\left| \left(1 + \frac{1}{n}\right)^n - e \right| \to 0 \quad \text{and therefore} \quad \left(1 + \frac{1}{n}\right)^n \to e. \quad \square$$

The sequences

$$\left\{\cos\frac{\pi}{n}\right\}, \quad \left\{\log\left(\frac{n}{n+1}\right)\right\}, \quad \left\{e^{1/n}\right\}, \quad \left\{\tan\sqrt{\frac{\pi^2 n^2 - 8}{16n^2}}\right\}$$

are all of the form

$$\{f(c_n)\}$$

with f a continuous function. Such sequences are easy to deal with. The basic idea is this: when a continuous function is applied to a convergent sequence, the result is itself a convergent sequence. More precisely we have the following theorem.

Theorem

Suppose that

$$c_n \to c$$

and that, for each n, c_n is in the domain of f. If f is continuous at c, then

$$f(c_n) \to f(c).$$

PROOF.   We assume that f is continuous at c and take $\epsilon > 0$. From the continuity of f at c we know that there exists $\delta > 0$ such that

$$\text{if} \quad |x - c| < \delta, \quad \text{then} \quad |f(x) - f(c)| < \epsilon.$$

Since $c_n \to c$, we know that there exists a positive integer k such that

$$\text{if} \quad n \geq k, \quad \text{then} \quad |c_n - c| < \delta.$$

It follows therefore that

$$\text{if} \quad n \geq k, \quad \text{then} \quad |f(c_n) - f(c)| < \epsilon. \quad \square$$

Examples

(1) Since

$$\frac{\pi}{n} \to 0$$

and the cosine function is continuous at 0,

$$\cos\frac{\pi}{n} \to \cos 0 = 1. \quad \square$$

(2) Since

$$\frac{n}{n+1} = \frac{1}{1 + 1/n} \to 1$$

and the logarithm function is continuous at 1,

$$\log\left(\frac{n}{n+1}\right) \to \log 1 = 0. \quad \square$$

(3) Since

$$\frac{1}{n} \to 0$$

and the exponential function is continuous at 0,

$$e^{1/n} \to e^0 = 1. \quad \square$$

(4) Since

$$\frac{\pi^2 \cdot n^2 - 8}{16n^2} = \frac{\pi^2 - 8/n^2}{16} \to \frac{\pi^2}{16}$$

and the function $f(x) = \tan \sqrt{x}$ is continuous at $\pi^2/16$,

$$\tan \sqrt{\frac{\pi^2 n^2 - 8}{16n^2}} \to \tan \sqrt{\frac{\pi^2}{16}} = \tan \frac{\pi}{4} = 1. \quad \square$$

(5) Since

$$\frac{2n+1}{n} + \left(5 - \frac{1}{n^2}\right) \to 7$$

and the square-root function is continuous at 7, we have

$$\sqrt{\frac{2n+1}{n} + \left(5 - \frac{1}{n^2}\right)} \to \sqrt{7}. \quad \square$$

(6) For each $x > 0$,

$$x^{1/n} \to 1.$$

To see this, we note that

$$\frac{1}{n} \log x \to 0.$$

Since the exponential function is continuous at 0,

$$x^{1/n} = e^{(1/n)\log x} \to e^0 = 1. \quad \square$$

(7) Since the absolute-value function is everywhere continuous,

$$a_n \to l \quad \text{implies} \quad |a_n| \to |l|. \quad \square$$

Exercises

State whether or not the indicated sequence converges and if it does, find the limit.

1.* $\dfrac{2}{n}$.

2. $\dfrac{(-1)^n}{n}$.

3.* $\sqrt{n}$.

4. $\dfrac{n-1}{n}$.

5.* $\dfrac{n+(-1)^n}{n}$.

6. $\sin\dfrac{\pi}{2n}$.

7.* $\dfrac{n^2}{n+1}$.

8. $\dfrac{n+1}{n^2}$.

9.* $\dfrac{4n}{\sqrt{n^2+1}}$.

10. $\dfrac{4^n}{2^n+10^6}$.

11.* $\dfrac{2^n}{4^n+1}$.

12. $\dfrac{10^{10}\sqrt{n}}{n+1}$.

13.* $(-1)^n\sqrt{n}$.

14. 2^n.

15.* $\log\left(\dfrac{2n}{n+1}\right)$.

16. $\left(-\dfrac{1}{2}\right)^n$.

17.* $\dfrac{n^4-1}{n^4+n-6}$.

18. $\dfrac{n^5}{17n^4+12}$.

19.* $\dfrac{(n+1)^2}{n^2}$.

20. $\sqrt{4-\dfrac{1}{n}}$.

21.* $\dfrac{2^n-1}{2^n}$.

22. $\dfrac{n^2}{\sqrt{2n^4+1}}$.

23.* $\dfrac{1}{n}-\dfrac{1}{n+1}$.

24. $\cos n\pi$.

25.* $(0.9)^n$.

26. $(0.9)^{-n}$.

27.* $\log n - \log(n+1)$.

28.* $\dfrac{\sqrt{n+1}}{2\sqrt{n}}$.

29. $\dfrac{\sqrt{n}\sin(e^n\pi)}{n+1}$.

30.* $\left(1+\dfrac{2}{n}\right)^n$.

31. Prove that a bounded nonincreasing sequence converges to the greatest lower bound of its range.

32. Show that
$$\left(1+\frac{1}{n}\right)^{n+1}\to e.$$

33. Prove the pinching theorem for sequences.

10.3 Some important limits

The following limits occur so frequently that it is actually worth remembering them:

(10.3.1) $\qquad\qquad x^{1/n}\to 1 \qquad\qquad$ for each $\ x>0$.

(10.3.2) $\qquad\qquad x^n\to 0 \qquad\qquad$ for $\ |x|<1$.

(10.3.3) $\qquad\qquad \dfrac{x^n}{n!}\to 0 \qquad\qquad$ for each real $\ x$.

(10.3.4) $\qquad\qquad \dfrac{1}{n^\alpha}\to 0 \qquad\qquad$ for each $\ \alpha>0$.

(10.3.5)
$$\frac{\log n}{n} \to 0.$$

(10.3.6)
$$n^{1/n} \to 1.$$

(10.3.7)
$$\frac{n^{\alpha}}{e^n} \to 0 \qquad \text{for each} \quad \alpha > 0.$$

(10.3.8)
$$\left(1 + \frac{x}{n}\right)^n \to e^x \quad \text{for each real} \quad x.$$

PROOF OF (10.3.1). Given in the last section. □

PROOF OF (10.3.2). Suppose that $|x| < 1$. Let $\epsilon > 0$. By (10.3.1),

$$\epsilon^{1/n} \to 1.$$

Thus there exists an integer $k > 0$ such that

$$|x| < \epsilon^{1/k}. \qquad \text{(Explain)}$$

This means that

$$|x^k| = |x|^k < \epsilon,$$

and thus

$$\text{if} \quad n \geq k, \quad \text{then} \quad |x^n| < \epsilon. \quad \square$$

PROOF OF (10.3.3). Choose an integer k such that

$$k > |x|.$$

For $n > k$,

$$n! = \underbrace{[n(n-1) \cdots (k+1)]}_{n - k \text{ terms}} k! > (k^{n-k})(k!) = (k^n)(k^{-k})(k!).$$

Consequently

$$\frac{|x^n|}{n!} = \frac{|x|^n}{n!} < \frac{|x|^n}{(k^n)(k^{-k})(k!)} = \left(\frac{|x|}{k}\right)^n \frac{k^k}{k!}.$$

Since $\dfrac{|x|}{k} < 1$,

$$\left(\frac{|x|}{k}\right)^n \to 0 \quad \text{and therefore} \quad \left(\frac{|x|}{k}\right)^n \frac{k^k}{k!} \to 0.$$

It follows that

$$\frac{|x^n|}{n!} \to 0. \quad \square$$

PROOF OF (10.3.4).   Since $\alpha > 0$, there exists an odd positive integer p such that

$$\frac{1}{p} < \alpha.$$

Obviously

$$0 < \frac{1}{n^\alpha} = \left(\frac{1}{n}\right)^\alpha \leq \left(\frac{1}{n}\right)^{1/p}.$$

Since

$$\frac{1}{n} \to 0 \quad \text{and} \quad f(x) = x^{1/p} \text{ is continuous at } 0,$$

we have

$$\left(\frac{1}{n}\right)^{1/p} \to 0 \quad \text{and thus} \quad \frac{1}{n^\alpha} \to 0. \quad \square$$

PROOF OF (10.3.5)

$$\frac{\log n}{n} = \frac{1}{n} \int_1^n \frac{dt}{t} \leq \frac{1}{n} \int_1^n \frac{dt}{\sqrt{t}} = \frac{2}{n}\left[\sqrt{t}\right]_1^n = \frac{2}{n}(\sqrt{n} - 1) = 2\left(\frac{1}{\sqrt{n}} - \frac{1}{n}\right) \to 0. \quad \square$$

PROOF OF (10.3.6).   We have

$$n^{1/n} = e^{(1/n)\log n}.$$

Since $(1/n) \log n \to 0$ and the exponential function is continuous at 0,

$$n^{1/n} \to e^0 = 1. \quad \square$$

PROOF OF (10.3.7).   Let p be a positive integer greater than α. Obviously

$$\frac{n^\alpha}{e^n} \leq \frac{n^p}{e^n}.$$

Since

$$e^n > \frac{n^{p+1}}{(p + 1)!}, \qquad \text{(Exercise 12, Section 5.2)}$$

we have

$$\frac{n^p}{e^n} < \frac{(p + 1)!}{n}.$$

Thus

$$\frac{n^\alpha}{e^n} < \frac{(p + 1)!}{n}.$$

Since $(p + 1)!$ is fixed,

$$\frac{(p + 1)!}{n} \to 0, \quad \text{and consequently} \quad \frac{n^\alpha}{e^n} \to 0. \quad \square$$

PROOF OF (10.3.8).   For $x = 0$, the result is obvious. For $x \neq 0$,

$$\log \left(1 + \frac{x}{n}\right)^n = n \log \left(1 + \frac{x}{n}\right) = x \left[\frac{\log (1 + x/n) - \log 1}{x/n}\right].$$

The crux here is to recognize the bracketed expression as a difference quotient for the logarithm function.   Once we see this, we can easily obtain

$$\lim_{n \to \infty} \left[\frac{\log (1 + x/n) - \log 1}{x/n}\right] = \lim_{h \to 0} \left[\frac{\log (1 + h) - \log 1}{h}\right] = 1.$$

This tells us that

$$\log \left(1 + \frac{x}{n}\right)^n \to x,$$

and consequently

$$\left(1 + \frac{x}{n}\right)^n = e^{\log(1+x/n)^n} \to e^x. \quad \square$$

Exercises

State whether or not the indicated sequence converges and, if it does, find the limit.

1.* $2^{2/n}$.

2.* $e^{-\alpha/n}$.

3.* $\left(\dfrac{2}{n}\right)^n$.

4. $\dfrac{n}{2^n}$.

5.* $\dfrac{\log (n + 1)}{n}$.

6. $\log \left(\dfrac{n + 1}{n}\right)$.

7.* $\dfrac{\log_{10} n}{n}$.

8.* $n^{\alpha/n}, \alpha > 0$.

9.* $\dfrac{3^n}{4^n}$.

10. $\dfrac{3^{n+1}}{4^{n-1}}$.

11.* $n^{1/(n+2)}$.

12. $(n + 2)^{1/n}$.

13.* $\dfrac{n^2}{3^n}$.

14. $(n + 2)^{1/(n+2)}$.

15.* $\displaystyle\int_0^n e^{-x}\, dx$.

16. $\displaystyle\int_{-n}^0 e^{2x}\, dx$.

17.* $\displaystyle\int_0^n e^{-nx}\, dx$.

18. $\displaystyle\int_{-1/n}^{1/n} \sin x^3\, dx$.

19.* $\displaystyle\int_{-1+1/n}^{1-1/n} \frac{dx}{\sqrt{1 - x^2}}$.

20. $\displaystyle\int_n^{n+1} e^{-x^2}\, dx$.

21.* $\displaystyle\int_{1/n}^1 \frac{dx}{\sqrt{x}}$.

22.* $\left(1 - \dfrac{1}{n}\right)^n$.

23. $n^2 \sin n\pi$.

24.* $n^2 \sin \dfrac{\pi}{n}$.

25.   Show that

$$\lim_{n \to \infty} (\sqrt{n + 1} - \sqrt{n}) = 0.$$

26. Show that

$$\text{if } \quad 0 < c < d, \qquad \text{then} \quad (c^n + d^n)^{1/n} \to d.$$

27.* Find

$$\lim_{n \to \infty} \left(2n \sin \frac{\pi}{n} \right).$$

What is the geometric significance of this limit?

[HINT: Think of a regular polygon of n sides inscribed in the unit circle.]

Find the following limits.

28.* $\displaystyle \lim_{n \to \infty} \frac{1 + 2 + \cdots + n}{n^2}.$ $\left[\text{HINT: } 1 + 2 + \cdots + n = \frac{n(n+1)}{2}. \right]$

29. $\displaystyle \lim_{n \to \infty} \frac{1^2 + 2^2 + \cdots + n^2}{(1+n)(2+n)}.$ $\left[\text{HINT: } 1^2 + 2^2 + \cdots + n^2 = \frac{n(n+1)(n+2)}{6}. \right]$

30.* $\displaystyle \lim_{n \to \infty} \frac{1^3 + 2^3 + \cdots + n^3}{2n^4 + n - 1}.$ $\left[\text{HINT: } \quad 1^3 + 2^3 + \cdots + n^3 = \frac{n^2(n+1)^2}{4}. \right]$

31. A sequence $\{a_n\}$ is said to be a *Cauchy sequence* [after the French mathematician Augustin-Louis (baron de) Cauchy, 1789–1857] iff

> for each $\epsilon > 0$ there exists a positive integer k such that
> $a_n - a_m < \epsilon$ for all $m, n > k$.

Show that

> every convergent sequence is a Cauchy sequence. †

32. Let

$$m_n = \frac{1}{n} (a_1 + a_2 + \cdots + a_n)$$

be the sequence of arithmetic means. (a) Prove that

$$\text{if} \quad \{a_n\} \text{ is increasing,} \qquad \text{then} \quad \{m_n\} \text{ is increasing.}$$

(b) (*Optional*) Prove that

$$\text{if} \quad a_n \to 0, \qquad \text{then} \quad m_n \to 0.$$

HINT: Choose an integer $j > 0$ such that if

$$n \geq j, \qquad \text{then} \quad a_n < \frac{\epsilon}{2}.$$

---

† It is also true that every Cauchy sequence is convergent, but this is much more difficult to prove.

Then for $n \geq j$, we have

$$|m_n| < \frac{|a_1 + a_2 + \cdots + a_j|}{n} + \frac{\epsilon}{2}\left(\frac{n - j}{n}\right).$$

(*Optional*) State whether or not the indicated sequence converges and, if it does, find the limit.

33.* $\left(\dfrac{n + 1}{n + 2}\right)^n$.

34. $\left(1 + \dfrac{1}{n}\right)^{n^2}$.

35.* $\left(1 + \dfrac{1}{n^2}\right)^n$.

36. $2^{n^2} \cdot n^{-n}$.

37.* $\left(t + \dfrac{x}{n}\right)^n$, $\quad t > 0, \quad x > 0$.

38. $\displaystyle\int_{-n}^{n} \frac{dx}{1 + x^2}$.

10.4   Some comments on notation

On indexing sequences

In indexing sequences it is not necessary to begin with the index 1. For example, the sequence

$$\{1, \tfrac{1}{2}, \tfrac{1}{4}, \cdots\}$$

indicated by

$$\{a_1, a_2, a_3, \cdots\} \qquad \text{with } a_n = (\tfrac{1}{2})^{n-1}$$

can also be indicated by

$$\{b_0, b_1, b_2, \cdots\} \qquad \text{with } b_n = (\tfrac{1}{2})^n,$$

or more generally by

$$\{c_p, c_{p+1}, c_{p+2}, \cdots\} \qquad \text{with } c_n = (\tfrac{1}{2})^{n-p}.$$

A review of $\sum$-notation for finite sums

The symbol $\sum$ is the capital Greek letter "sigma." We use the expression

(1) $$\sum_{k=0}^{n} a_k$$

(read "the sum of the a sub k from k equals 0 to n") to indicate the sum

$$a_0 + a_1 + \cdots + a_n.$$

More generally, if $n \geq m$, we use

(2) $$\sum_{k=m}^{n} a_k$$

to indicate the sum

$$a_m + a_{m+1} + \cdots + a_n.$$

In (1) and (2) the letter "k" is being used as a "dummy" variable. That is, it can be replaced by any letter not already engaged. For instance,

$$\sum_{i=3}^{7} a_i, \quad \sum_{j=3}^{7} a_j, \quad \sum_{k=3}^{7} a_k$$

can all be used to indicate the sum

$$a_3 + a_4 + a_5 + a_6 + a_7.$$

Translating

$$(a_0 + \cdots + a_n) + (b_0 + \cdots + b_n) = (a_0 + b_0) + \cdots + (a_n + b_n),$$
$$\alpha(a_0 + \cdots + a_n) = \alpha a_0 + \cdots + \alpha a_n,$$
$$(a_0 + \cdots + a_m) + (a_{m+1} + \cdots + a_n) = a_0 + \cdots + a_n$$

into the $\sum$-notation, we have

$$\sum_{k=0}^{n} a_k + \sum_{k=0}^{n} b_k = \sum_{k=0}^{n} (a_k + b_k), \quad \alpha \sum_{k=0}^{n} a_k = \sum_{k=0}^{n} \alpha a_k,$$

$$\sum_{k=0}^{m} a_k + \sum_{k=m+1}^{n} a_k = \sum_{k=0}^{n} a_k.$$

At times it is convenient to change indices. In doing this, note that

$$\sum_{k=j}^{n} a_k = \sum_{k=0}^{n-j} a_{k+j}.$$

[Both are abbreviations for $a_j + a_{j+1} + \cdots + a_n$.]

10.5 Infinite series

To place our discussion on a solid footing, we begin by establishing the basic terminology. Our starting point is an arbitrary real sequence

$$\{a_0, a_1, a_2, \cdots\}.$$

Definition

(1) The *infinite series*

$$\sum_{k=0}^{\infty} a_k$$

is the sequence

$$\{a_0, a_0 + a_1, a_0 + a_1 + a_2, \cdots\}.$$

(2) The number a_k is called the kth *term of the series,* and the number

$$s_n = a_0 + a_1 + \cdots + a_n = \sum_{k=0}^{n} a_k$$

is called the *n*th *partial sum.*

---

(3) To say that the series $\sum_{k=0}^{\infty} a_k$ *converges* to the number l is to say that the sequence $\{s_n\}$ converges to the number l. To say that the series $\sum_{k=0}^{\infty} a_k$ *diverges* is to say that the sequence $\{s_n\}$ diverges.

(4) If the series $\sum_{k=0}^{\infty} a_k$ converges to the number l, then l is called *the sum of the series* and we write

$$\sum_{k=0}^{\infty} a_k = l \qquad \text{or} \qquad a_0 + a_1 + a_2 + \cdots = l.$$

Example The series

$$\sum_{k=0}^{\infty} 2^k$$

diverges. To see this, note that the nth partial sum is given by

$$s_n = 1 + 2 + \cdots + 2^n.$$

Since the sequence $\{s_n\}$ is unbounded, it cannot converge (Theorem 10.2.1). □

Example

$$\sum_{k=0}^{\infty} \frac{1}{(k+1)(k+2)} = 1.$$

To show this, we must show that

$$s_n = \sum_{k=0}^{n} \frac{1}{(k+1)(k+2)} \to 1.$$

Since

$$\frac{1}{(k+1)(k+2)} = \frac{1}{k+1} - \frac{1}{k+2},$$

it follows that

$$s_n = \frac{1}{1 \cdot 2} + \frac{1}{2 \cdot 3} + \cdots + \frac{1}{(n+1)(n+2)}$$

$$= \left(\frac{1}{1} - \frac{1}{2}\right) + \left(\frac{1}{2} - \frac{1}{3}\right) + \cdots + \left(\frac{1}{n+1} - \frac{1}{n+2}\right).$$

The sum on the right telescopes to give

$$s_n = 1 - \frac{1}{n+2}.$$

It is now obvious that $s_n \to 1$. □

Example. The series

$$\sum_{k=1}^{\infty} (-1)^k$$

diverges. Here

$$s_n = -1 \quad \text{for } n \text{ odd} \quad \text{and} \quad s_n = 0 \quad \text{for } n \text{ even.}$$

Consequently $\{s_n\}$ does not converge. □

The next example has many applications.

Example (*The geometric series*)

(i)   If $|x| < 1$,   then $\displaystyle\sum_{k=0}^{\infty} x^k = \frac{1}{1-x}\,.$

(ii)   If $|x| \geq 1$,   then $\displaystyle\sum_{k=0}^{\infty} x^k$ diverges.

PROOF. The nth partial sum of the geometric series

$$\sum_{k=0}^{\infty} x^k$$

is the number

(1) $$s_n = 1 + x + \cdots + x^n.$$

Multiplication by x gives

$$xs_n = x + x^2 + \cdots + x^{n+1}.$$

We now subtract the second equation from the first one and obtain

$$(1 - x)s_n = 1 - x^{n+1}.$$

For $x \neq 1$ this gives

(2) $$s_n = \frac{1 - x^{n+1}}{1 - x}$$

If $|x| < 1$, then $x^{n+1} \to 0$ and thus

$$s_n \to \frac{1}{1-x}\,.$$

This proves (i). For $x = 1$, we use (1) and see that

$$s_n = n + 1.$$

Consequently the series diverges. For $|x| \geq 1$, $x \neq 1$, we use (2). Since in this instance $\{x^{n+1}\}$ diverges, $\{s_n\}$ diverges. □

As a special case of the geometric series, we have

$$\sum_{k=0}^{\infty} \frac{1}{2^k} = \frac{1}{1 - \frac{1}{2}} = 2.$$

By beginning the summation at $k = 1$, instead of at $k = 0$, we get

$$\boxed{\sum_{k=1}^{\infty} \frac{1}{2^k} = 1.}$$

The partial sums of this series

$$s_1 = \tfrac{1}{2}$$

$$s_2 = \tfrac{1}{2} + \tfrac{1}{4} = \tfrac{3}{4}$$

$$s_3 = \tfrac{1}{2} + \tfrac{1}{4} + \tfrac{1}{8} = \tfrac{7}{8}$$

$$s_4 = \tfrac{1}{2} + \tfrac{1}{4} + \tfrac{1}{8} + \tfrac{1}{16} = \tfrac{15}{16}$$

$$s_5 = \tfrac{1}{2} + \tfrac{1}{4} + \tfrac{1}{8} + \tfrac{1}{16} + \tfrac{1}{32} = \tfrac{31}{32}$$

etc.

are illustrated in Figure 10.5.1.   Each new partial sum lies halfway between the previous one and the number 1.

FIGURE 10.5.1

In a sense, the geometric series gives rise to our decimal system. To see how this comes about, take the geometric series and consider the case $x = \tfrac{1}{10}$. Here

$$\sum_{k=0}^{\infty} \frac{1}{10^k} = \frac{1}{1 - \frac{1}{10}} = \frac{10}{9} \quad \text{and} \quad \sum_{k=1}^{\infty} \frac{1}{10^k} = \frac{1}{9}.$$

The nth partial sum in this last instance is

$$s_n = \frac{1}{10} + \frac{1}{10^2} + \cdots + \frac{1}{10^n}.$$

Take now the series

$$\sum_{k=1}^{\infty} \frac{a_k}{10^k} \quad \text{with } a_k \in \{0, 1, 2, \ldots, 9\}.$$

The partial sums here are

$$t_n = \frac{a_1}{10} + \frac{a_2}{10^2} + \cdots + \frac{a_n}{10^n} \leq 9 \left(\frac{1}{10} + \frac{1}{10^2} + \cdots + \frac{1}{10^n} \right) = 9s_n.$$

Since $\{s_n\}$ converges, $\{s_n\}$ is bounded. This tells us that $\{t_n\}$ is bounded. Since $\{t_n\}$ is nondecreasing, $\{t_n\}$ is itself convergent; that is, the series

$$\sum_{k=1}^{\infty} \frac{a_k}{10^k}$$

converges. The sum of this series is what we mean by the decimal fraction

$$0.a_1 a_2 a_3 \cdots . \quad \square$$

The geometric series arises naturally in many settings. Here is a simple example.

Problem.   At what time between 2 and 3 o'clock is the minute hand directly over the hour hand?

SOLUTION.   The hour hand travels $\frac{1}{12}$ as fast as the minute hand. At 2 o'clock the minute hand points to 12 and the hour hand points to 2. By the time the minute hand reaches 2 the hour hand points to $2 + \frac{1}{6}$. By the time the minute hand reaches $2 + \frac{1}{6}$, the hour hand points to $2 + 1/6 + 1/(6 \cdot 12)$. By the time the minute hand reaches

$$2 + \frac{1}{6} + \frac{1}{6 \cdot 12},$$

the hour hand points to

$$2 + \frac{1}{6} + \frac{1}{6 \cdot 12} + \frac{1}{6 \cdot 12^2}$$

and so on. In general, by the time the minute hand reaches

$$2 + \frac{1}{6} + \frac{1}{6 \cdot 12} + \cdots + \frac{1}{6 \cdot 12^{n-1}} = 2 + \frac{1}{6} \sum_{k=0}^{n-1} \frac{1}{12^n},$$

the hour hand points to

$$2 + \frac{1}{6} + \frac{1}{6 \cdot 12} + \cdots + \frac{1}{6 \cdot 12^{n-1}} + \frac{1}{6 \cdot 12^n} = 2 + \frac{1}{6} \sum_{k=0}^{n} \frac{1}{12^k}.$$

The two hands coincide when both of them point to the limiting value

$$2 + \frac{1}{6} \sum_{k=0}^{\infty} \frac{1}{12^k} = 2 + \frac{1}{6} \left(\frac{1}{1 - \frac{1}{12}} \right) = 2 + \frac{2}{11}.$$

This happens at

$$2 + \tfrac{2}{11} \text{ o'clock.}\dagger \quad \square$$

$\dagger$ This particular problem can also be solved without infinite series. See if you can figure out how.

We will return to the geometric series later. Right now we turn our attention to some results about series in general. First we prove something that is essentially obvious:

If

$$\sum_{k=0}^{\infty} a_k = l \quad \text{and} \quad \sum_{k=0}^{\infty} b_k = m,$$

then

(i)

$$\sum_{k=0}^{\infty} (a_k + b_k) = l + m,$$

and

(ii)

$$\sum_{k=0}^{\infty} \alpha a_k = \alpha l \quad \text{for each real } \alpha.$$

PROOF. Let

$$s_n = \sum_{k=0}^{n} a_k, \qquad t_n = \sum_{k=0}^{n} b_k,$$

$$u_n = \sum_{k=0}^{n} (a_k + b_k), \qquad v_n = \sum_{k=0}^{n} \alpha a_k.$$

Note that

$$u_n = s_n + t_n \quad \text{and} \quad v_n = \alpha s_n.$$

Since $s_n \to l$ and $t_n \to m$, we have

$$u_n \to l + m \quad \text{and} \quad v_n \to \alpha l. \quad \square$$

Theorem 10.5.1

If $\sum_{k=0}^{\infty} a_k$ converges, then $a_k \to 0$.

PROOF. For each n, set

$$s_n = \sum_{k=0}^{n} a_k.$$

To say that $\sum_{k=0}^{\infty} a_k$ converges to some number l is to say that

$$s_n \to l.$$

Obviously we must also have

$$s_{n-1} \to l.$$

Since $a_n = s_n - s_{n-1}$, we have

$$a_n \to l - l = 0. \quad \square$$

Caution: The converse of Theorem 10.5.1 is false. There are divergent series $\sum_{k=0}^{\infty} a_k$ for which $a_k \to 0$.

Example. In the case of

$$\sum_{k=1}^{\infty} \frac{1}{\sqrt{k}}$$

we have

$$a_k = \frac{1}{\sqrt{k}} \to 0$$

but

$$s_n = 1 + \frac{1}{\sqrt{2}} + \frac{1}{\sqrt{3}} + \cdots + \frac{1}{\sqrt{n}} > \frac{n}{\sqrt{n}} = \sqrt{n}.$$

Being unbounded, $\{s_n\}$ cannot converge. $\square$

Exercises

Each of the series below converges. Find its sum.

1.* $\displaystyle\sum_{k=3}^{\infty} \frac{1}{(k+1)(k+2)}$.

6. $\displaystyle\sum_{k=0}^{\infty} \frac{67}{1000^k}$.

11.* $\displaystyle\sum_{k=0}^{\infty} \left(\frac{25}{10^k} - \frac{6}{100^k}\right)$.

2. $\displaystyle\sum_{k=0}^{\infty} \frac{1}{(k+3)(k+4)}$.

7.* $\displaystyle\sum_{k=0}^{\infty} \frac{(-1)^k}{5^k}$.

12. $\displaystyle\sum_{k=3}^{\infty} \frac{1}{2^{k-1}}$.

3.* $\displaystyle\sum_{k=0}^{\infty} \frac{1}{(k+2)(2k+2)}$.

8. $\displaystyle\sum_{k=0}^{\infty} \left(\frac{3}{4}\right)^k$.

13.* $\displaystyle\sum_{k=0}^{\infty} \frac{1}{2^{k+3}}$.

4. $\displaystyle\sum_{k=0}^{\infty} \frac{3}{10^k}$.

9.* $\displaystyle\sum_{k=0}^{\infty} \frac{3^k + 4^k}{5^k}$.

14. $\displaystyle\sum_{k=0}^{\infty} \frac{2^{k+3}}{3^k}$.

5.* $\displaystyle\sum_{k=0}^{\infty} \frac{12}{100^k}$.

10. $\displaystyle\sum_{k=0}^{\infty} \frac{1 - 2^k}{3^k}$.

In the following, write each decimal fraction as an infinite series and express the sum as the quotient of two integers.

15.* 0.777 . . . .

18. 0.8989 . . . .

21.* $0.62\widehat{45}45$ . . . .

16. 0.999 . . . .

19.* $0.\widehat{112}\widehat{112}112$ . . . .

22. $0.112\widehat{019}019$ . . . .

17.* 0.2424 . . . .

20. $0.\widehat{315}\widehat{315}\widehat{315}$ . . . .

23. Using series, show that every repeating decimal represents a rational number (the quotient of two integers).

24. Show that

$$\sum_{k=0}^{\infty} a_k = l \quad \text{iff} \quad \sum_{k=j+1}^{\infty} a_k = l - (a_0 + \cdots + a_j).$$

Use the geometric series to prove the following.

25. $\displaystyle\frac{1}{1+x} = \sum_{k=0}^{\infty} (-1)^k x^k \qquad \text{for} \qquad |x| < 1.$

26. $\dfrac{1}{1+x^2} = \displaystyle\sum_{k=0}^{\infty} (-1)^k x^{2k}$ for $|x| < 1$.

27. Find a series expansion for

(a)* $\dfrac{x}{1+x}$ valid for $|x| < 1$.

(b) $\dfrac{x}{1+x^2}$ valid for $|x| < 1$.

(c)* $\dfrac{1}{1-x^2}$ valid for $|x| < 1$.

(d) $\dfrac{1}{1+4x^2}$ valid for $|x| < \dfrac{1}{2}$.

28. At what time between 4 and 5 o'clock is the minute hand directly above the hour hand? Express your answer as a geometric series.

29.* How much money must a man deposit at 5% interest (compounded annually) if he wishes to enable his descendants to withdraw $100 a year in perpetuity? Express your answer as a geometric series.

30. A ball dropped from a height of h feet is known to rebound to a height of σh feet where σ is a positive constant less than 1. Find the total distance traveled by the ball if it is dropped initially from a height of h_0 feet.

10.6 Series with nonnegative terms

The easiest series to handle are those with nonnegative terms. To determine whether or not such series converge, the following simple theorem is fundamental.

Theorem 10.6.1

A series with nonnegative terms converges iff the sequence of partial sums is bounded.

PROOF. If the sequence of partial sums is not bounded, it cannot converge (Theorem 10.2.1). Suppose that the sequence of partial sums is bounded. Since the terms are nonnegative, the sequence of partial sums is nondecreasing. By Theorem 10.2.2 it must converge.   □

To decide upon the boundedness or unboundedness of a sequence of partial sums, it is sometimes useful to compare it to a sequence of integrals.

The Integral Test

If the function f is continuous, decreasing, and positive on the interval $[1, \infty)$, then the series $\sum_{k=1}^{\infty} f(k)$ converges   iff   the sequence $\{\int_1^n f(x)\,dx\}$ converges.

PROOF. To visualize the proof, see Figure 10.6.1. Since f decreases on the interval $[1, n]$,

$$f(2) + \cdots + f(n)   \text{ is a lower sum for } f \text{ on } [1, n]$$

FIGURE 10.6.1

and

$$f(1) + \cdots + f(n-1) \quad \text{is an upper sum for } f \text{ on } [1, n].$$

Consequently

$$f(2) + \cdots + f(n) \le \int_1^n f(x)\, dx \quad \text{and} \quad \int_1^n f(x)\, dx \le f(1) + \cdots + f(n-1).$$

If the sequence $\{\int_1^n f(x)\, dx\}$ converges, it is bounded. By the first inequality the series itself must be bounded and therefore convergent. Suppose now that the sequence $\{\int_1^n f(x)\, dx\}$ diverges. Since f is positive,

$$\int_1^n f(x)\, dx < \int_1^{n+1} f(x)\, dx.$$

This tells us that the sequence of integrals is monotonic. Being divergent and monotonic, it must be unbounded. By the second inequality, the series itself must be unbounded and therefore divergent.　□

Applying the integral test

Example. *(The harmonic series)*

$$\boxed{\sum_{k=1}^{\infty} \frac{1}{k} \quad \text{diverges.}}$$

PROOF.　Set $f(x) = 1/x$ and note that

$$f(k) = \frac{1}{k}.$$

Here

$$\int_1^n f(x)\, dx = \int_1^n \frac{dx}{x} = \log n.$$

Since the sequence $\{\log n\}$ diverges, the series diverges.　□

　More generally, we have the following result:

Example. *(The p-series)*

$$\boxed{\sum_{k=1}^{\infty} \frac{1}{k^p} \quad \text{converges} \quad \text{iff} \quad p > 1.}$$

PROOF. Set $f(x) = 1/x^p$ and note that

$$f(k) = \frac{1}{k^p}.$$

For $p \neq 1$,

$$\int_1^n f(x)\, dx = \int_1^n \frac{dx}{x^p} = \left[\frac{x^{1-p}}{1-p}\right]_1^n = \frac{1}{1-p}(n^{1-p} - 1).$$

If $p > 1$, then $\{n^{1-p}\}$ converges and thus the sequence of integrals converges. If $p < 1$, then $\{n^{1-p}\}$ diverges and the sequence of integrals diverges. The case $p = 1$ gives the harmonic series which, as you saw in the last example, diverges. $\square$

Example. To show that

$$\sum_{k=1}^\infty \frac{1}{k \log (k+1)} \quad \text{diverges,}$$

we set

$$f(x) = \frac{1}{x \log (x+1)}.$$

Since f is continuous, decreasing, and positive, we can use the integral test:

$$\int_1^n \frac{dx}{x \log (x+1)} > \int_1^n \frac{dx}{(x+1) \log (x+1)}$$

$$= [\log (\log (x+1))]_1^n$$

$$= \log (\log (n+1)) - \log (\log 2).$$

Since $\{\log (\log (n+1))\}$ diverges, the sequence of integrals diverges. $\square$

REMARK ON NOTATION. You have seen for each $j \geq 0$

$$\sum_{k=0}^\infty a_k \quad \text{converges} \qquad \text{iff} \qquad \sum_{k=j+1}^\infty a_k \quad \text{converges.}$$

(Exercise 24, Section 10.5.) This tells you that, in determining whether or not a series converges, it is immaterial where we begin the indexing. Where such detailed indexing is unnecessary, we can omit it and speak simply of the series

$$\sum a_k.$$

For instance, it makes sense to say that

$$\sum \frac{1}{k^2} \quad \text{converges} \qquad \text{and} \qquad \sum \frac{1}{k} \quad \text{diverges.}$$

Much of the work on series with nonnegative terms is based on comparison with series of known behavior. The basic comparison theorem is extremely simple.

Basic Comparison Theorem

Let $\sum a_k$ be a series with nonnegative terms.

(i) $\sum a_k$ converges if there exists a convergent series $\sum c_k$ with nonnegative terms such that

$$a_k \leq c_k \qquad \text{for all } k \text{ sufficiently large};$$

(ii) $\sum a_k$ diverges if there exists a divergent series $\sum d_k$ with nonnegative terms such that

$$d_k \leq a_k \qquad \text{for all } k \text{ sufficiently large}.$$

PROOF.   The proof is just a matter of noting that in the first instance

$$\sum a_k \quad \text{and} \quad \sum c_k \quad \text{are both bounded,}$$

and in the second instance

$$\sum a_k \quad \text{and} \quad \sum d_k \quad \text{are both unbounded.}$$

The details are left to you. $\square$

Comparison with the geometric series

$$\sum q^k$$

and with the *p*-series

$$\sum \frac{1}{k^p}$$

leads to two important tests for convergence: the root test and the ratio test.

The Root Test

Let $\sum a_k$ be a series with nonnegative terms and suppose that

$$(a_k)^{1/k} \longrightarrow \rho.$$

If $\rho < 1$, $\sum a_k$ converges. If $\rho > 1$, $\sum a_k$ diverges. If $\rho = 1$, the test is inconclusive.

PROOF.   We suppose first that $\rho < 1$ and choose $\epsilon > 0$ so small that

$$\rho + \epsilon < 1.$$

Since $(a_k)^{1/k} \longrightarrow \rho$, we have

$$(a_k)^{1/k} < \rho + \epsilon \qquad \text{for all } k \text{ sufficiently large.}$$

Thus

$$a_k < (\rho + \epsilon)^k \qquad \text{for all } k \text{ sufficiently large.}$$

Since

$$\sum (\rho + \epsilon)^k \quad \text{converges}$$

(a geometric series with $0 < \rho + \epsilon < 1$), we know by the comparison theorem that

$$\sum a_k \quad \text{converges.}$$

We suppose now that $\rho > 1$ and choose $\epsilon > 0$ so small that

$$\rho - \epsilon > 1.$$

Since $(a_k)^{1/k} \to \rho$, we have

$$\rho - \epsilon < (a_k)^{1/k} \qquad \text{for all } k \text{ sufficiently large.}$$

Thus

$$(\rho - \epsilon)^k < a_k \qquad \text{for all } k \text{ sufficiently large.}$$

Since

$$\sum (\rho - \epsilon)^k \quad \text{diverges}$$

(a geometric series with $\rho - \epsilon > 1$), the comparison theorem tells us that

$$\sum a_k \quad \text{diverges.}$$

To see the inconclusiveness of the root test in the case of $\rho = 1$, we need only observe that the series $\sum (1/k^2)$ converges and the series $\sum (1/k)$ diverges but in both instances

$$(a_k)^{1/k} \to 1. \quad \square$$

Applying the root test

Example. In the case of

$$\sum \frac{1}{(\log k)^k},$$

we have

$$(a_k)^{1/k} = \frac{1}{\log k} \to 0.$$

The series converges. $\square$

Example. In the case of

$$\sum \frac{2^k}{k^3},$$

we have

$$(a_k)^{1/k} = 2 \left(\frac{1}{k}\right)^{3/k} = 2 \left[\left(\frac{1}{k}\right)^{1/k}\right]^3 \to 2 \cdot 1^3 = 2.$$

The series diverges. $\square$

Example. In the case of

$$\sum \left(1 - \frac{1}{k}\right)^k,$$

we have

$$(a_k)^{1/k} = 1 - \frac{1}{k} \to 1.$$

Here the root test is inconclusive. Since $a_k = (1 - 1/k)^k$ tends to $1/e$ and not to 0, we know by Theorem (10.5.1) that actually the series diverges. □

The Ratio Test

Let $\sum a_k$ be a series with positive terms and suppose that

$$\frac{a_{k+1}}{a_k} \to \lambda.$$

If $\lambda < 1$, $\sum a_k$ converges. If $\lambda > 1$, $\sum a_k$ diverges. If $\lambda = 1$, the test is inconclusive.

PROOF. We suppose first that $\lambda < 1$ and choose $\epsilon > 0$ so small that

$$\lambda + \epsilon < 1.$$

Since

$$\frac{a_{k+1}}{a_k} \to \lambda,$$

we know that there exists $m > 0$ such that

$$\text{if} \quad k \geq m, \quad \text{then} \quad \frac{a_{k+1}}{a_k} < \lambda + \epsilon.$$

This gives us

$$a_{m+1} < (\lambda + \epsilon)a_m, \qquad a_{m+2} < (\lambda + \epsilon)a_{m+1} < (\lambda + \epsilon)^2 a_m,$$

and more generally,

$$a_{m+j} < (\lambda + \epsilon)^j a_m.$$

In other words, for $k > m$ we have

$$a_k < (\lambda + \epsilon)^{k-m}a_m = \frac{a_m}{(\lambda + \epsilon)^m}(\lambda + \epsilon)^k.$$

Since $\lambda + \epsilon < 1$,

$$\sum \frac{a_m}{(\lambda + \epsilon)^m}(\lambda + \epsilon)^k = \frac{a_m}{(\lambda + \epsilon)^m}\sum (\lambda + \epsilon)^k \quad \text{converges.}$$

By the comparison theorem,

$$\sum a_k \quad \text{converges.}$$

The proof of the rest of the theorem is left to the exercises. □

Applying the ratio test

Example.   The convergence of the series

$$\sum \frac{1}{k!}$$

is easy to verify by the ratio test:

$$\frac{a_{k+1}}{a_k} = \frac{1}{(k+1)!} \cdot \frac{k!}{1} = \frac{1}{k+1} \to 0. \quad \square$$

Example.   In the case of

$$\sum \frac{k}{10^k},$$

we have

$$\frac{a_{k+1}}{a_k} = \frac{k+1}{10^{k+1}} \cdot \frac{10^k}{k} = \frac{1}{10} \frac{k+1}{k} \to \frac{1}{10}.$$

The series therefore converges. $\square$

Example.   In the case of

$$\sum \frac{k^k}{k!},$$

we have

$$\frac{a_{k+1}}{a_k} = \frac{(k+1)^{k+1}}{(k+1)!} \cdot \frac{k!}{k^k} = \left(\frac{k+1}{k}\right)^k = \left(1 + \frac{1}{k}\right)^k \to e.$$

Since $e > 1$, the series diverges. $\square$

Example.   For the series

$$\sum \frac{1}{2k+1}$$

the ratio test is inconclusive:

$$\frac{a_{k+1}}{a_k} = \frac{1}{2(k+1)+1} \cdot \frac{2k+1}{1} = \frac{2k+1}{2k+3} = \frac{2+1/k}{2+3/k} \to 1.$$

The integral test shows that the series diverges. $\square$

Exercises

In the following, indicate whether the series converges or diverges.

1.* $\sum \dfrac{k}{k^3 + 1}$.

6. $\sum \left(\dfrac{k}{2k + 1}\right)^k$.

11.* $\sum \dfrac{2^{k-1}}{(k + 1)(k + 2)}$.

2. $\sum \dfrac{1}{3k + 2}$.

7.* $\sum \dfrac{1}{(2k + 1)^2}$.

12. $\sum \dfrac{1}{k^2 + 1}$.

3.* $\sum \dfrac{1}{k^k}$.

8. $\sum \dfrac{\log k}{k}$.

13.* $\sum \dfrac{1}{1 + 2 \log k}$.

4. $\sum \dfrac{e^k}{k!}$.

9.* $\sum \dfrac{1}{\sqrt{k + 1}}$.

14. $\sum \left(\dfrac{1}{2}\right)^{-k}$.

5.* $\sum \dfrac{1}{k2^k}$.

10. $\sum \dfrac{1}{\log k \cdot \log (k + 1)}$.

15.* $\sum k \left(\dfrac{2}{3}\right)^k$.

16. $\sum \dfrac{k}{(k + 1)(2k + 1)(4k + 1)}$.

17.* $\sum \dfrac{k!}{10^k}$.

23.* $\sum \dfrac{1}{k} \left(\dfrac{1}{\log k}\right)^{3/2}$.

28. $\sum k^{-(1+1/k)}$.

18. $\sum \dfrac{k!}{10^{4k}}$.

24. $\sum \dfrac{1}{k} \left(\dfrac{1}{\log k}\right)^{1/2}$.

29.* $\sum \dfrac{11}{1 + 100^{-k}}$.

19.* $\sum \dfrac{k^2}{e^k}$.

25.* $\sum \dfrac{1}{\sqrt{k^3 - 1}}$.

30. $\sum \dfrac{\log k}{e^k}$.

20. $\sum \dfrac{\sqrt{k}}{k^2 + 1}$.

26. $\sum \left(\dfrac{k}{k + 100}\right)^k$.

31.* $\sum \dfrac{1}{1 + \sqrt{k}}$.

21.* $\sum \dfrac{2^k k!}{k^k}$.

27.* $\sum \dfrac{(k!)^2}{(2k)!}$.

32. $\sum \dfrac{\log k}{k^2}$.

22. $\sum \dfrac{k!}{(k + 2)!}$.

33. Complete the proof of the ratio test.
    (a) Prove that if $\lambda > 1$, then $\sum a_k$ diverges.
    (b) Prove that if $\lambda = 1$, the ratio test is inconclusive.
    [HINT: Consider $\sum (1/k)$ and $\sum (1/k^2)$.]

34. Let $\sum a_k$ be a series with nonnegative terms and let $\{c_k\}$ be a sequence of positive numbers which converges to some positive number c. Show that

$$\sum a_k \text{ converges} \quad \text{iff} \quad \sum c_k a_k \text{ converges.}$$

$\Bigg[$ HINT: There exists an integer n such that

$$\dfrac{c}{2} < c_k < \dfrac{3c}{2} \quad \text{for } k \geq n. \Bigg]$$

10.7   Absolute convergence; alternating series

In this section we consider series which have both positive and negative terms.

Absolute Convergence

Let $\sum a_k$ be a series with both positive and negative terms. One way to show that $\sum a_k$ converges is to show that $\sum |a_k|$ converges.

Theorem

If $\sum |a_k|$ converges, then $\sum a_k$ converges.

PROOF.   For each k,

$$-|a_k| \leq a_k \leq |a_k|$$

and therefore

$$0 \leq a_k + |a_k| \leq 2|a_k| \ .$$

If $\sum |a_k|$ converges, then $\sum 2|a_k| = 2 \sum |a_k|$ converges, and therefore, by the comparison test,

$$\sum (a_k + |a_k|) \quad \text{converges.}$$

Since

$$a_k = (a_k + |a_k|) - |a_k|,$$

we can conclude that

$$\sum a_k \quad \text{converges.} \quad \square$$

A series $\sum a_k$ for which $\sum |a_k|$ converges is called *absolutely convergent*. The theorem we just proved says that

---

if $\sum a_k$ converges absolutely, then $\sum a_k$ converges.

As you will see a little later, the converse is false: There are series that converge but do not converge absolutely.

Here are some examples that should help you get the feeling of these ideas.

Example

$$1 - \frac{1}{2^2} + \frac{1}{3^2} - \frac{1}{4^2} + \frac{1}{5^2} - \frac{1}{6^2} + \cdots .$$

If we replace each of the terms by its absolute value, we obtain the series

$$1 + \frac{1}{2^2} + \frac{1}{3^2} + \frac{1}{4^2} + \frac{1}{5^2} + \frac{1}{6^2} + \cdots .$$

This is a *p*-series with $p = 2$. It is therefore convergent. This means that the initial series is absolutely convergent and thus convergent. □

Example

$$1 - \frac{1}{2} - \frac{1}{2^2} + \frac{1}{2^3} - \frac{1}{2^4} - \frac{1}{2^5} + \frac{1}{2^6} - \frac{1}{2^7} - \frac{1}{2^8} + \cdots .$$

If we replace each of the terms by its absolute value, we obtain the series

$$1 + \frac{1}{2} + \frac{1}{2^2} + \frac{1}{2^3} + \frac{1}{2^4} + \frac{1}{2^5} + \frac{1}{2^6} + \frac{1}{2^7} + \frac{1}{2^8} + \cdots .$$

This is a convergent geometric series. The initial series is therefore absolutely convergent and thus convergent. □

Example

$$1 - \frac{1}{2} + \frac{1}{3} - \frac{1}{4} + \frac{1}{5} - \frac{1}{6} + \cdots .$$

If we replace each of the terms by its absolute value, we obtain the series

$$1 + \frac{1}{2} + \frac{1}{3} + \frac{1}{4} + \frac{1}{5} + \frac{1}{6} + \cdots .$$

This is the harmonic series. Since the harmonic series diverges, the initial series is not absolutely convergent. It is however, convergent. (See the next theorem.) □

Alternating Series

A series in which successive terms have opposite signs is called an *alternating series*. As examples of alternating series we have

$$1 - \frac{1}{2} + \frac{1}{3} - \frac{1}{4} + \frac{1}{5} - \frac{1}{6} + \cdots$$

$$1 - \frac{1}{\sqrt{2}} + \frac{1}{\sqrt{3}} - \frac{1}{\sqrt{4}} + \frac{1}{\sqrt{5}} - \frac{1}{\sqrt{6}} + \cdots$$

$$1 - \frac{2}{\log 2} + \frac{3}{\log 3} - \frac{4}{\log 4} + \frac{5}{\log 5} - \frac{6}{\log 6} + \cdots .$$

The series

$$1 - \frac{1}{2} - \frac{1}{3} + \frac{1}{4} - \frac{1}{5} - \frac{1}{6} + \cdots$$

is not an alternating series because there are consecutive terms with the same sign.

> **Theorem on Alternating Series**
>
> Let $\{a_k\}$ be a decreasing sequence of positive numbers.
>
> If $a_k \to 0$,   then $\sum_{k=0}^{\infty} (-1)^k a_k$ converges.

PROOF.   First we look at the even partial sums, s_{2m}. Since

$$s_{2m} = (a_0 - a_1) + (a_2 - a_3) + \cdots + (a_{2m-2} - a_{2m-1}) + a_{2m}$$

is the sum of positive numbers, the even partial sums are all positive. Since

$$s_{2m+2} = s_{2m} - (a_{2m+1} - a_{2m+2}) \qquad \text{and} \qquad a_{2m+1} - a_{2m+2} > 0,$$

we have

$$s_{2m+2} < s_{2m}.$$

This means that the sequence of even partial sums is decreasing. Being bounded below by 0, it is convergent; say,

$$s_{2m} \to l.$$

Now

$$s_{2m+1} = s_{2m} - a_{2m+1}.$$

Since $a_{2m+1} \to 0$, we also have

$$s_{2m+1} \to l.$$

With both the even and the odd partial sums tending to l, it is obvious that all the partial sums must tend to l. $\square$

The theorem we just proved makes it clear that each of the following series converges:

$$1 - \frac{1}{2} + \frac{1}{3} - \frac{1}{4} + \frac{1}{5} - \frac{1}{6} + \cdots$$

$$1 - \frac{1}{\sqrt{2}} + \frac{1}{\sqrt{3}} - \frac{1}{\sqrt{4}} + \frac{1}{\sqrt{5}} - \frac{1}{\sqrt{6}} + \cdots$$

$$1 - \frac{1}{2!} + \frac{1}{3!} - \frac{1}{4!} + \frac{1}{5!} - \frac{1}{6!} + \cdots.$$

Of these only the last one is absolutely convergent.

Exercises

Test the following series for (a) convergence, (b) absolute convergence.

1.* $1 + (-1) + 1 + \cdots + (-1)^k + \cdots.$

2. $\dfrac{1}{4} - \dfrac{1}{6} + \dfrac{1}{8} - \dfrac{1}{10} + \cdots + \dfrac{(-1)^k}{2k} + \cdots.$

3.* $\dfrac{1}{2} - \dfrac{2}{3} + \dfrac{3}{4} - \dfrac{4}{5} + \cdots + (-1)^k \dfrac{k}{k+1} + \cdots .$

4. $\dfrac{1}{2 \log 2} - \dfrac{1}{3 \log 3} + \dfrac{1}{4 \log 4} - \dfrac{1}{5 \log 5} + \cdots + (-1)^k \dfrac{1}{k \log k} + \cdots .$

5.* $\sum (-1)^k \dfrac{\log k}{k} .$ 12. $\sum \sin \left(\dfrac{k\pi}{4} \right) .$

6. $\sum (-1)^k \dfrac{k}{\log k} .$ 13.* $\sum \sin \left(\dfrac{\pi}{4k^2} \right) .$

7.* $\sum \left(\dfrac{1}{k} - \dfrac{1}{k!} \right) .$ 14. $\sum \dfrac{(-1)^k}{\sqrt{k} + \sqrt{k+1}} .$

8. $\sum \dfrac{k^3}{2^k} .$ 15.* $\sum (-1)^k \dfrac{k}{k^2 + 1} .$

9.* $\sum (-1)^k \dfrac{1}{2k + 1} .$ 16. $\sum \dfrac{(-1)^k}{\sqrt{k(k+1)}} .$

10. $\sum (-1)^k \dfrac{(k!)^2}{(2k)!} .$ 17.* $\sum (-1)^k k \left(\dfrac{1}{2} \right)^k .$

11.* $\sum \dfrac{k!}{(-2)^k} .$ 18. $\sum \left(\dfrac{1}{\sqrt{k}} - \dfrac{1}{\sqrt{k+1}} \right) .$

19.* $\dfrac{1}{2} - \dfrac{1}{3} - \dfrac{1}{4} + \dfrac{1}{5} - \dfrac{1}{6} - \dfrac{1}{7} + \cdots + \dfrac{1}{3k+2} - \dfrac{1}{3k+3} - \dfrac{1}{3k+4} + \cdots .$

20. $\dfrac{2 \cdot 3}{4 \cdot 5} - \dfrac{5 \cdot 6}{7 \cdot 8} + \dfrac{8 \cdot 9}{10 \cdot 11} - \dfrac{11 \cdot 12}{13 \cdot 14} + \cdots + (-1)^k \dfrac{(3k+2)(3k+3)}{(3k+4)(3k+5)} + \cdots .$

21. *An Estimate For Alternating Series.* Let

$$\sum_{k=0}^{\infty} (-1)^k a_k = a_0 - a_1 + a_2 - a_3 + a_4 - a_5 + a_6 - \cdots$$

be an alternating series which satisfies the conditions of the last theorem. Show that if

$$\sum_{k=0}^{\infty} (-1)^k a_k = l$$

then s_n, the nth partial sum of the series, satisfies the inequality

$$|s_n - l| < a_{n+1}.$$

[HINT: For n even,

$$s_{n+1} < l < s_n$$

and for n odd,

$$s_n < l < s_{n+1}.]$$

22.   (*Optional*) In Section 10 of this chapter we prove that if

$$|x| < |x_1| \qquad \text{and} \qquad \sum a_k x_1^k \quad \text{converges}$$

then

$$\sum a_k x^k \quad \text{converges absolutely.}$$

See if you can show this now.

10.8   Taylor polynomials and Taylor series

Taylor Polynomials

We begin with a function f that is differentiable at 0. The linear function that best approximates f at 0 is the function

$$P_1(x) = f(0) + f'(0)x.$$

At 0 it has the same value as f and also the same derivative:

$$P_1(0) = f(0), \qquad P_1'(0) = f'(0).$$

If f has two derivatives at 0, then we can get a better approximation by using the quadratic polynomial

$$P_2(x) = f(0) + f'(0)x + f''(0)\frac{x^2}{2!} \, .$$

Here, as you can check,

$$P_2(0) = f(0), \qquad P_2'(0) = f'(0), \qquad \text{and} \qquad P_2''(0) = f''(0).$$

If f has three derivatives at 0, then we can use the cubic polynomial

$$P_3(x) = f(0) + f'(0)x + \frac{f''(0)}{2!} x^2 + \frac{f'''(0)}{3!} x^3,$$

and thereby take the third derivative into account. Here

$$P_3(0) = f(0), \quad P_3'(0) = f'(0), \quad P_3''(0) = f''(0), \qquad \text{and} \qquad P_3'''(0) = f'''(0).$$

More generally, for a function f with n derivatives at 0, we can use the polynomial

$$P_n(x) = f(0) + f'(0)x + \frac{f''(0)}{2!} x^2 + \cdots + \frac{f^{(n)}(0)}{n!} x^n.$$

This is the polynomial of degree n whose first n derivatives agree with those of f at 0:

$$P_n(0) = f(0), P_n'(0) = f'(0), P_n''(0) = f''(0), \ldots, P_n^{(n)}(0) = f^{(n)}(0).$$

The polynomials $P_1(x), P_2(x), \ldots, P_n(x)$ that we have just described are called *Taylor polynomials*, after the English mathematician Brook Taylor (1685–1731). The groundwork for all that we discuss here was laid by Taylor in 1712.

The fact that the Taylor polynomials

$$P_k(x) = f(0) + f'(0)x + \frac{f''(0)}{2!} x^2 + \cdots + \frac{f^{(k)}(0)}{k!} x^k$$

approximate $f(x)$ is of little practical use unless we know something about the accuracy of the approximations. The key to this question of accuracy is Taylor's Theorem.

Taylor's Theorem

Let I be an interval containing the number 0. If f has n continuous derivatives on I, then for each x in I

$$f(x) = f(0) + f'(0)x + \frac{f''(0)}{2!} x^2 + \cdots + \frac{f^{(n-1)}(0)}{(n-1)!} x^{n-1} + R_n,$$

where the remainder R_n is given by the formula

$$R_n = \frac{1}{(n-1)!} \int_0^x f^{(n)}(t)(x-t)^{n-1} \, dt.$$

PROOF.   Integration by parts (see Exercise 26 at the end of the section) gives

$$f'(0)x = \int_0^x f'(t) \, dt - \int_0^x f''(t)(x-t) \, dt$$

$$\frac{f''(0)}{2!} x^2 = \int_0^x f''(t)(x-t) \, dt - \frac{1}{2!} \int_0^x f'''(t)(x-t)^2 \, dt$$

$$\frac{f'''(0)}{3!} x^3 = \frac{1}{2!} \int_0^x f'''(t)(x-t)^2 \, dt - \frac{1}{3!} \int_0^x f^{(iv)}(t)(x-t)^3 \, dt$$

$$\cdot$$
$$\cdot$$
$$\cdot$$

$$\frac{f^{(n-1)}(0)}{(n-1)!} x^{n-1} = \frac{1}{(n-2)!} \int_0^x f^{(n-1)}(t)(x-t)^{(n-2)} \, dt - \frac{1}{(n-1)!} \int_0^x f^{(n)}(t)(x-t)^{n-1} \, dt.$$

We now add these equations. The sum on the left is simply

$$f'(0)x + \frac{f''(0)}{2!} x^2 + \frac{f'''(0)}{3!} x^3 + \cdots + \frac{f^{(n-1)}(0)}{(n-1)!} x^{n-1}.$$

The sum on the right telescopes to

$$\int_0^x f'(t) \, dt - \frac{1}{(n-1)!} \int_0^x f^{(n)}(t)(x-t)^{n-1} \, dt = f(x) - f(0) - R_n.$$

The result is now obvious.   □

Taylor's formula can be written

$$f(x) = P_{n-1}(x) + R_n,$$

where

$$R_n = \frac{1}{(n-1)!} \int_0^x f^{(n)}(t)(x-t)^{n-1}\, dt.$$

For most purposes it is convenient to write the remainder term, R_n, in the manner of Lagrange:†

(10.8.1)
$$R_n = \frac{f^{(n)}(c)}{n!} x^n,$$

where c is some number between 0 and x. [So as not to obscure the main ideas by too many technical arguments we have placed the proof of Lagrange's form of the remainder in the supplement to this section. It's not that the argument is difficult, it's just that it is distracting.]

Taylor Series

If we adopt the conventions that $0! = 1$ and that the 0th derivative of f is f itself, then we can write Taylor's formula in the form

$$f(x) = \sum_{k=0}^{n-1} \frac{f^{(k)}(0)}{k!} x^k + R_n.$$

Of special interest is the case in which the function has derivatives of all orders. In this case Taylor's formula is valid for all positive integers n. If it happens that $R_n \to 0$, then

$$f(x) = \lim_{n \to \infty} \sum_{k=0}^{n-1} \frac{f^{(k)}(0)}{k!} x^k$$

and we have the Taylor-series expansion

$$f(x) = \sum_{k=0}^{\infty} \frac{f^{(k)}(0)}{k!} x^k.$$

It is time for some examples.

Example.   For all real x,

(10.8.2)
$$e^x = \sum_{k=0}^{\infty} \frac{x^k}{k!} = 1 + x + \frac{x^2}{2!} + \frac{x^3}{3!} + \cdots.$$

PROOF.   Let x be a fixed real number. Setting

$$f(t) = e^t,$$

---

† Joseph Louis Lagrange, French mathematician (1736–1813).

we find that

$$f^{(k)}(t) = e^t \quad \text{for all } k.$$

This tells us that for all k

$$f^{(k)}(0) = e^0 = 1.$$

The coefficients in (10.8.2) are thus the Taylor coefficients. To verify that the Taylor series does indeed converge to e^x, we must verify that

$$R_n \to 0.$$

Let M be the maximum value of the exponential function on the interval joining 0 and x. For all t in that interval

$$|f^{(n)}(t)| = e^t \leq M.$$

Using Lagrange's form of the remainder, we have

$$|R_n| = \frac{|e^c|}{n!} |x|^n \leq M \frac{|x|^n}{n!}.$$

Since

$$\frac{|x|^n}{n!} \to 0 \qquad\qquad\qquad \text{[by 10.3.3]}$$

we have

$$R_n \to 0. \quad \square$$

Example.   For all real x

$$(10.8.3) \quad \boxed{\sin x = \sum_{k=0}^{\infty} \frac{(-1)^k}{(2k+1)!} x^{2k+1} = x - \frac{x^3}{3!} + \frac{x^5}{5!} - \frac{x^7}{7!} + \cdots}$$

and

$$(10.8.4) \quad \boxed{\cos x = \sum_{k=0}^{\infty} \frac{(-1)^k}{(2k)!} x^{2k} = 1 - \frac{x^2}{2!} + \frac{x^4}{4!} - \frac{x^6}{6!} + \cdots .}$$

PROOF.   We focus on the sine function and leave the cosine as an exercise. We take x as a fixed real number and let

$$f(t) = \sin t.$$

Differentiating, we find

$$f'(t) = \cos t, \qquad f''(t) = -\sin t,$$
$$f'''(t) = -\cos t, \qquad f^{(\text{iv})}(t) = \sin t.$$

More generally,

$$f^{(2k)}(t) = (-1)^k \sin t, \qquad f^{(2k+1)}(t) = (-1)^k \cos t.$$

Since

$$f^{(2k)}(0) = 0 \quad \text{and} \quad f^{(2k+1)}(0) = (-1)^k,$$

we see that the coefficients in (10.8.3) are actually the Taylor coefficients. Since for all t, $|f^{(n)}(t)| \leq 1$, Lagrange's form of the remainder gives

$$|R_n| = \frac{|f^{(n)}(c)|}{n!} |x|^n \leq \frac{|x|^n}{n!}.$$

Since $|x|^n/n! \to 0$, we have

$$R_n \to 0.$$

This tells us that the series does converge to $\sin x$. $\square$

Some Numerical Calculations

The fact that the Taylor polynomial

$$P_{n-1}(x) = f(0) + f'(0)x + \frac{f''(0)}{2!} x^2 + \cdots + \frac{f^{(n-1)}(x)}{(n-1)!} x^{n-1}$$

approximates $f(x)$ to within R_n enables us to calculate certain functional values as accurately as we wish. Below we give some sample calculations. For ready reference we list some values of $n!$ and of its reciprocal $1/n!$.

$n!$
$2! = 2$
$3! = 6$
$4! = 24$
$5! = 120$
$6! = 720$
$7! = 5,040$
$8! = 40,320$

Table 10.8.5

$\dfrac{1}{n!}$
$0.50000 = \dfrac{1}{2!} = 0.50000$
$0.16666 < \dfrac{1}{3!} < 0.16667$
$0.04166 < \dfrac{1}{4!} < 0.04167$
$0.00833 < \dfrac{1}{5!} < 0.00834$
$0.00138 < \dfrac{1}{6!} < 0.00139$
$0.00019 < \dfrac{1}{7!} < 0.00020$

Table 10.8.6

Problem. Find a numerical estimate for e that is accurate within 0.001.

SOLUTION. You are already familiar with the series expansion

$$e^x = 1 + x + \frac{x^2}{2!} + \frac{x^3}{3!} + \cdots + \frac{x^{n-1}}{(n-1)!} + \cdots.$$

Taking $x = 1$, we have

$$e = 1 + 1 + \frac{1}{2!} + \frac{1}{3!} + \cdots + \frac{1}{(n-1)!} + \cdots .$$

To estimate e within 0.001, we need only consider the expansion to the point where

$$|R_n| < 0.001.$$

Since

$$|R_7| = \frac{e^c}{7!} < \frac{e}{7!} < 3(0.0002) = 0.0006,$$

we see that

$$P_6(1) = 1 + 1 + \frac{1}{2!} + \frac{1}{3!} + \frac{1}{4!} + \frac{1}{5!} + \frac{1}{6!} = \frac{1957}{720}$$

differs from e by less than 0.0006. To turn this into a decimal estimate for e, we note that

$$2.7180 < \frac{1957}{720} < 2.7181.$$

Within the prescribed limits of accuracy we can take $e = 2.718$. □

Problem. Find a numerical estimate for $e^{0.2}$ that is accurate within 0.001.

SOLUTION. Here we take

$$1 + 0.2 + \frac{(0.2)^2}{2!} + \frac{(0.2)^3}{3!} + \cdots + \frac{(0.2)^{n-1}}{(n-1)!} + \cdots$$

to the point where

$$|R_n| < 0.001.$$

Since

$$|R_4| = |e^c| \frac{|0.2|^4}{4!} \leq \frac{e^{0.2}16}{240,000} < \frac{3 \cdot 16}{240,000} < 0.001,$$

we can conclude that

$$1 + 0.2 + \frac{(0.2)^2}{2!} + \frac{(0.2)^3}{3!} = \frac{7326}{6000} = 1.221$$

differs from $e^{0.2}$ by less than 0.001. □

Problem. Find a numerical estimate for sin (0.5) that is accurate within 0.001.

SOLUTION. Recall the series expansion

$$\sin x = x - \frac{x^3}{3!} + \frac{x^5}{5!} - \frac{x^7}{7!} + \cdots$$

and the remainder estimate

$$|R_n| \leq \frac{|x|^n}{n!}.$$

For $x = 0.5$, we have

$$|R_5| \leq \frac{(0.5)^5}{5!} < \frac{1}{32}(0.00834) < 0.001.$$

It follows that

the coefficient of x^4 is 0

$$P_4(0.5) = P_3(0.5) = 0.5 - \frac{(0.5)^3}{3!} = \frac{23}{48}$$

approximates sin (0.5) within 0.001. $\square$

Exercises

Find the Taylor polynomial $P_5(x)$ for each of the following functions.

1.* e^{-x}.	3.* $\sinh x$.	5.* arc sin x.	7.* $\tan x$.
2. e^{2x}.	4. arc tan x.	6. $(1 + x)^{-1}$.	8. $x^2 \tan x$.

Find the Taylor polynomial $P_4(x)$ for each of the following functions.

9.* $\cosh x$.	11.* $\sec x$.	13.* $\log(1 + x)$.	15.* $\log \cos x$.
10. $x \sinh x$.	12. $x - \cos x$.	14. $\sqrt{1 + x}$.	16. $\sqrt{\cos x}$.

Use Taylor polynomials to find a numerical estimate that is accurate within 0.01.

17.* $\sqrt{e}$.	19.* $\cos 1$.	21.* arc sin (0.9).	23.* e^2.
18. $\sin(0.3)$.	20. $\cos(0.5)$.	22. $\sin 1$.	24. e^{-1}.

25. Show that

$$\cos x = \sum_{k=0}^{\infty} \frac{(-1)^k}{(2k)!} x^{2k} \qquad \text{for all real } x.$$

26. Verify the identity

$$\frac{f^{(k)}(0)}{k!} x^k = \frac{1}{(k-1)!} \int_0^x f^{(k)}(t)(x-t)^{(k-1)}\, dt - \frac{1}{k!} \int_0^x f^{(k+1)}(t)(x-t)^k\, dt$$

by computing the second integral by parts.

$$\left[\text{HINT: } f^{(k+1)}(t)(x-t)^k = \frac{d}{dt}[f^{(k)}(t)](x-t)^k. \right]$$

27. (Optional) Show that e is irrational. [HINT: (1) Use the expansion

$$e = \sum_{k=0}^{\infty} \frac{1}{k!}$$

and show that the qth partial sum

$$s_q = \sum_{k=0}^{q} \frac{1}{k!}$$

satisfies the inequality

$$0 < q!(e - s_q) < \frac{1}{q}.$$

(2) Show that $q!s_q$ is an integer and argue that, if e were of the form p/q, then we would have $q!(e - s_q)$ as a positive integer less than 1.]

Here is a more general version of Taylor's theorem:

> Let $\mathcal{I}$ be an interval containing the number a. If g has n continuous derivatives on $\mathcal{I}$, then for each $x \in \mathcal{I}$
>
> (10.8.7)
> $$g(x) = g(a) + g'(a)(x - a) + \cdots + \frac{g^{(n-1)}(a)}{(n - 1)!}(x - a)^{n-1} + R_n,$$
>
> where
>
> $$R_n = \frac{1}{(n - 1)!} \int_a^x g^{(n)}(s)(x - s)^{n-1}\, ds.$$

In this more general setting the Lagrange form of the remainder takes the form

> $$R_n = \frac{g^{(n)}(c)}{n!}(x - a)^n \qquad \text{with } c \text{ between } a \text{ and } x.$$

If $R_n \to 0$,

> $$g(x) = \sum_{k=0}^{\infty} \frac{g^{(k)}(a)}{k!}(x - a)^k = g(a) + g'(a)(x - a) + \cdots + \frac{g^{(n)}(a)}{n!}(x - a)^n + \cdots.$$

This is called the Taylor-series expansion of $g(x)$ in powers of $(x - a)$.

28.   Verify the expansion

$$e^x = e^a\left[1 + (x - a) + \frac{(x - a)^2}{2!} + \frac{(x - a)^3}{3!} + \cdots\right].$$

Expand

29.* $\sin x$ in powers of $(x - a)$.
30. $\cos x$ in powers of $(x - a)$.
31.* $\sinh x$ in powers of $(x - a)$.
32. $\cosh x$ in powers of $(x - a)$.
33.* $\log x$ in powers of $(x - a)$.

34. (*Optional*)   Prove the more general version of Taylor's theorem.   [HINT: Set

$$f(x - a) = g(x).$$

Note that

$$f'(x - a) = g'(x), \ldots, f^{(n)}(x - a) = g^{(n)}(x)$$

and that

$$f(0) = g(a), f'(0) = g'(a), \ldots, f^{(n)}(0) = g^{(n)}(a).]$$

SUPPLEMENT TO SECTION 10.8

Before proving the validity of Lagrange's form of the remainder, we prove a simple extension of the first mean-value theorem for integrals.

Theorem 10.8.8

If f and g are continuous on $[a, b]$ and g keeps a constant sign on $[a, b]$, then

$$\int_a^b f(t)g(t) \, dt = f(c) \int_a^b g(t) \, dt$$

for some number c in the interval $[a, b]$.

PROOF.   Let

$$m_f = \text{minimum value of } f \text{ on } [a, b]$$

and

$$M_f = \text{maximum value of } f \text{ on } [a, b].$$

For each number t in $[a, b]$

$$m_f \leq f(t) \leq M_f$$

and, if g remains nonnegative,

$$m_f g(t) \leq f(t)g(t) \leq M_f g(t).$$

(If g remains nonpositive, the inequality is reversed and the rest of the argument must be adjusted accordingly.)

By integrating the last inequality from a to b, we get

$$\int_a^b m_f g(t) \, dt \leq \int_a^b f(t)g(t) \, dt \leq \int_a^b M_f g(t) \, dt$$

and therefore

$$m_f \int_a^b g(t) \, dt \leq \int_a^b f(t)g(t) \, dt \leq M_f \int_a^b g(t) \, dt.$$

If $\int_a^b g(t) \, dt = 0$, then $\int_a^b f(t)g(t) = 0$ and the result holds. If $\int_a^b g(t) \, dt \neq 0$, then

$$m_f \leq \frac{\int_a^b f(t)g(t) \, dt}{\int_a^b g(t) \, dt} \leq M_f$$

and since f, being continuous skips no values, there must exist c in $[a, b]$ such that

$$f(c) = \frac{\int_a^b f(t)g(t)\,dt}{\int_a^b g(t)\,dt} \;.$$

Obviously then

$$\int_a^b f(t)g(t) = f(c) \int_a^b g(t)\,dt. \quad \square$$

Lagrange's form of the remainder is now easy to obtain. For $x > 0$,

$$R_n = \frac{1}{(n-1)!} \int_0^x f^{(n)}(t)(x-t)^{n-1}\,dt = \frac{f^{(n)}(c)}{(n-1)!} \int_0^x (x-t)^{n-1}\,dt$$

Here is where we use the last theorem.

$$= \frac{f^{(n)}(c)}{(n-1)!} \left[-\frac{(x-t)^n}{n} \right]_0^x$$

$$= \frac{f^{(n)}(c)}{n!} x^n.$$

For $x < 0$,

$$R_n = \frac{1}{(n-1)!} \int_0^x f^{(n)}(t)(x-t)^{n-1}\,dt = \frac{1}{(n-1)!} \int_x^0 f^{(n)}(t) \left[-(x-t)^{n-1} \right] dt$$

$$= \frac{f^{(n)}(c)}{(n-1)!} \int_x^0 \left[-(x-t)^{n-1} \right] dt$$

$$= \frac{f^{(n)}(c)}{(n-1)!} \left[\frac{(x-t)^n}{n} \right]_x^0$$

$$= \frac{f^{(n)}(c)}{n!} x^n. \quad \square$$

10.9   The logarithm and the arc tangent; computing π

Taylor-series expansions for $\log(1 + x)$ and arc tan x can be derived by the method of the last section. It is, however, easier to follow the method described below.

A series for log $(1 + x)$

In proving the convergence of the geometric series we noted that for $x \neq 1$,

$$\frac{1 - x^n}{1 - x} = 1 + x + \cdots + x^{n-1}.$$

We can rewrite this identity as

$$\frac{1}{1 - x} = 1 + x + x^2 + \cdots + x^{n-1} + \frac{x^n}{1 - x} \;.$$

Setting $x = -t$, we have

$$\frac{1}{1+t} = 1 + (-t) + (-t)^2 + \cdots + (-t)^{n-1} + \frac{(-t)^n}{1+t}.$$

It follows that

$$\log (1 + x) = \int_0^x \frac{dt}{1+t} = x - \frac{x^2}{2} + \frac{x^3}{3} - \cdots + (-1)^{n-1}\frac{x^n}{n} + T_n(x),$$

where

$$T_n(x) = (-1)^n \int_0^x \frac{t^n}{1+t}\,dt.$$

Below we show that

$$T_n(x) \to 0 \quad \text{if} \quad -1 < x \le 1.$$

For $0 \le x \le 1$, we have

$$|T_n(x)| = \int_0^x \frac{t^n}{1+t}\,dt \le \int_0^x t^n\,dt = \frac{x^{n+1}}{n+1} \to 0.$$

For $-1 < x < 0$, we have

$$|T_n(x)| = \left| \int_0^x \frac{t^n}{1+t}\,dt \right| \le \int_x^0 \frac{|t|^n}{|1+t|}\,dt = \int_x^0 \frac{(-t)^n}{1+t}\,dt$$

$$\le \int_x^0 \frac{(-t)^n}{1+x}\,dt = \frac{1}{1+x}\left[\frac{(-x)^{n+1}}{n+1} \right] \to 0.$$

You have now seen that

$$T_n(x) \to 0 \quad \text{for } -1 < x \le 1,$$

It follows that

$$(10.9.1) \qquad \boxed{\log (1 + x) = x - \frac{x^2}{2} + \frac{x^3}{3} - \frac{x^4}{4} + \cdots \qquad \text{for } -1 < x \le 1.}$$

There is no hope of extending the result to $x = -1$ since $\log 0$ is not defined.
Using $x = 1$, we get

$$\log 2 = 1 - \frac{1}{2} + \frac{1}{3} - \frac{1}{4} + \cdots.$$

This intrigued some of the early enthusiasts of the calculus.

A series for arc tan x

The development here is so similar to the one we just used for $\log (1 + x)$ that we can leave out some of the details. We begin with

$$\frac{1}{1+t^2} = \frac{1}{1-(-t^2)} = 1 + (-t^2) + (-t^2)^2 + \cdots + (-t^2)^{n-1} + \frac{(-t^2)^n}{1+t^2}.$$

Since

$$\text{arc tan } x = \int_0^x \frac{dt}{1 + t^2},$$

we have

$$\text{arc tan } x = x + (-1)\frac{x^3}{3} + (-1)^2\frac{x^5}{5} + \cdots + (-1)^{n-1}\frac{x^{2n-1}}{2n - 1} + S_n(x),$$

where

$$S_n(x) = (-1)^n \int_0^x \frac{t^{2n}}{1 + t^2}\, dt.$$

If $x \in [-1, 1]$, then $S_n(x) \to 0$. (See Exercise 8.)   It follows that

(10.9.2)
$$\boxed{\text{arc tan } x = x - \frac{x^3}{3} + \frac{x^5}{5} - \frac{x^7}{7} + \cdots \qquad \text{for } -1 \leq x \leq 1.}$$

This series was known to the Scottish mathematician James Gregory in 1671, but the discovery was not published until 1712.

Since

$$\text{arc tan } 1 = \frac{\pi}{4},$$

we have

$$\frac{\pi}{4} = 1 - \frac{1}{3} + \frac{1}{5} - \frac{1}{7} + \frac{1}{9} - \cdots.$$

G. W. Leibniz, a German mathematician, seems to have found this formula in 1673. It is an elegant formula for π, but it converges too slowly to be efficient for computational purposes.

Computing π

A more convenient way to compute π is to use the identity

(10.9.3)
$$\frac{\pi}{4} = 4 \text{ arc tan } \frac{1}{5} - \text{arc tan } \frac{1}{239}.$$

This identity was discovered in 1706 by John Machin, a Scotsman. It can be verified by repeated application of the addition formula

$$\tan (A + B) = \frac{\tan A + \tan B}{1 - \tan A \tan B}.$$

(See Exercises 10, 11, 12.)

The arc tangent series (10.9.2) gives

$$\text{arc tan } \tfrac{1}{5} = \tfrac{1}{5} - \tfrac{1}{3}(\tfrac{1}{5})^3 + \tfrac{1}{5}(\tfrac{1}{5})^5 - \tfrac{1}{7}(\tfrac{1}{5})^7 + \cdots$$

and

$$\text{arc tan } \tfrac{1}{239} = \tfrac{1}{239} - \tfrac{1}{3}(\tfrac{1}{239})^3 + \tfrac{1}{5}(\tfrac{1}{239})^5 - \tfrac{1}{7}(\tfrac{1}{239})^7 + \cdots.$$

Note that the even partial sums increase and the odd ones decrease. Using the inequalities

$$\tfrac{1}{5} - \tfrac{1}{3}(\tfrac{1}{5})^3 \leq \text{arc tan } \tfrac{1}{5} \leq \tfrac{1}{5} - \tfrac{1}{3}(\tfrac{1}{5})^3 + \tfrac{1}{5}(\tfrac{1}{5})^5,$$

$$\tfrac{1}{239} - \tfrac{1}{3}(\tfrac{1}{239})^3 \leq \text{arc tan } \tfrac{1}{239} \leq \tfrac{1}{239},$$

together with (10.9.3) and a little arithmetic, you can verify that

$$3.14 < \pi < 3.147.$$

By using six terms of the series for arc tan $\tfrac{1}{5}$ and still only two of the series for arc tan $\tfrac{1}{239}$, one can show that

$$3.14159262 < \pi < 3.14159267.$$

Greater accuracy can of course be obtained by taking more terms into account. We shall not pursue this any further but instead simply give the value of π to twenty decimal places:

$$\pi = 3.14159\ 26535\ 89793\ 23846\ldots.$$

Exercises

Find the approximate value (within 0.01).

1.* log (1.1).   3.* log (0.9).   5.* arc tan (0.4).

2. log (1.2).   4. log (1.4).   6. arc tan (0.5).

7.* Let $a > 0$. Find a series expansion for log $(a + x)$ which is valid for $-a < x \leq a$.

8. Prove that

$$\text{if } x \in [-1, 1], \quad \text{then} \quad (-1)^n \int_0^x \frac{t^{2n}}{1 + t^2}\, dt \to 0.$$

9.* Evaluate

$$\sum_{k=1}^{\infty} \frac{1}{k(k + 1)(k + 2)}.$$

$$\left[\text{HINT:} \right.$$

$$\frac{1}{k(k + 1)(k + 2)} = \frac{1}{2}\left(\frac{1}{k} - \frac{1}{k + 1}\right) - \frac{1}{2}\left(\frac{1}{k + 1} - \frac{1}{k + 2}\right). \left.\right]$$

Verify that

$$\pi/4 = 4 \text{ arc tan } \tfrac{1}{5} - \text{arc tan } \tfrac{1}{239}$$

by the three-step computation of Exercises 10 through 12.

10. First, compute tan $(2 \text{ arc tan } \tfrac{1}{5})$.

11.* Then, compute tan $(4 \text{ arc tan } \tfrac{1}{5})$.

12. Finally, compute tan $(4 \text{ arc tan } \tfrac{1}{5} - \text{arc tan } \tfrac{1}{239})$.

10.10   Power series

You have seen how certain functions can be expanded in Taylor series

$$\sum_{k=0}^{\infty} \frac{f^{(k)}(0)}{k!} \, x^k.$$

Such series are special instances of series of the form

$$\sum_{k=0}^{\infty} a_k x^k.$$

The latter are called *power series*. In this section we study power series in general.

Power series have some interesting properties and they raise some interesting questions. A natural question to ask is: What power series are actually Taylor series? We will be able to give a complete answer to this question a little later.

As before, when it is immaterial where we begin the summation, we will dispense with detailed indexing. For example, to indicate a power series we will often simply write

$$\sum a_k x^k.$$

We launch our discussion with a definition.

Definition

A power series $\sum a_k x^k$ is said to converge
(i) at x_1 iff $\sum a_k x_1^k$ converges.
(ii) on the set S iff $\sum a_k x^k$ converges for each $x \in S$.

For determining at what numbers a power series converges, the following theorem is fundamental.

Theorem 10.10.1

If $\sum a_k x^k$ converges at x_1, $x_1 \neq 0$, then it converges absolutely at all x with $|x| < |x_1|$.
If $\sum a_k x^k$ diverges at x_1, then it diverges at all x with $|x| > |x_1|$.

PROOF.   If $\sum a_k x_1^k$ converges, then $a_k x_1^k \to 0$. In particular, for k sufficiently large,

$$|a_k x_1^k| \leq 1$$

and thus

$$|a_k x^k| = |a_k x_1^k| \left|\frac{x}{x_1}\right|^k \leq \left|\frac{x}{x_1}\right|^k.$$

For x satisfying $|x| < |x_1|$, we have

$$\left|\frac{x}{x_1}\right| < 1.$$

The convergence of

$$\sum |a_k x^k|$$

follows by comparison with the geometric series. This proves the first statement.

Suppose now that
$$\sum a_k x_1^k \quad \text{diverges.}$$
By the previous argument, there cannot exist x with $|x_1| < |x|$ such that
$$\sum a_k x^k \quad \text{converges.}$$
The existence of such an x would imply the absolute convergence of
$$\sum a_k x_1^k.$$
This proves the second statement.   □

From the theorem we just proved you can see that for a power series there are exactly three possibilities:

(i) *The series may converge only at 0.* This is what happens with
$$\sum k^k x^k.$$
(The kth term, $k^k x^k$, tends to 0 only if $x = 0$.)

(ii) *It may converge everywhere absolutely.* This is what happens with the exponential series
$$\sum \frac{x^k}{k!}.$$

(iii) The only remaining possibility is that *there exists a positive number r such that the series converges absolutely for $|x| < r$ and diverges for $|x| > r$.*
This is what happens with the geometric series
$$\sum x^k.$$
In this instance, there is absolute convergence for $|x| < 1$ and divergence for $|x| > 1$.

Associated with each case there is a *radius of convergence*:
In case (i), we say that the radius of convergence is 0.
In case (ii), we say that the radius of convergence is ∞.
In case (iii), we say that the radius of convergence is r. The three cases are pictured in Figure 10.10.1.

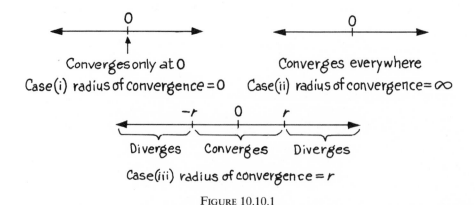

FIGURE 10.10.1

In general the behavior of a power series at $-r$ and at r is not predictable. The series

$$\sum x^k, \quad \sum \frac{1}{k} x^k, \quad \sum \frac{(-1)^k}{k} x^k, \quad \sum \left(\frac{1}{k}\right)^2 x^k$$

all have radius of convergence 1, but the intervals of convergence are respectively

$$(-1, 1), \quad [-1, 1), \quad (-1, 1], \quad [-1, 1].$$

It turns out that, in the interior of its interval of convergence, a power series represents an infinitely differentiable function. As a first step toward proving this, we have the following theorem.

Theorem 10.10.2

If

$$\sum a_k x^k \quad \text{converges on } (-c, c),$$

then

$$\sum \frac{d}{dx} (a_k x^k) = \sum k a_k x^{k-1} \quad \text{converges on } (-c, c).$$

PROOF.   The convergence of $\sum a_k x^k$ on $(-c, c)$ indicates that we have either case (ii) or case (iii). In either event, we can conclude that $\sum a_k x^k$ converges absolutely on $(-c, c)$. We take $t \in (-c, c)$ and choose $\epsilon > 0$ such that

$$|t| < |t| + \epsilon < |c|.$$

Since $|t| + \epsilon$ is within the interval of convergence,

$$\sum |a_k(|t| + \epsilon)^k| \quad \text{converges.}$$

Exercise 33 consists of showing that for all k sufficiently large

$$|kt^{k-1}| \leq (|t| + \epsilon)^k.$$

Using this inequality, we find that

$$|ka_k t^{k-1}| \leq |a_k(|t| + \epsilon)^k|.$$

Since $\sum |a_k(|t| + \epsilon)^k|$ converges, it follows that

$$\sum |ka_k t^{k-1}| \quad \text{converges.} \quad \square$$

Repeated application of this theorem shows that the series

$$\sum \frac{d^2}{dx^2} (a_k x^k) = \sum k(k - 1)a_k x^{k-2}$$

$$\sum \frac{d^3}{dx^3} (a_k x^k) = \sum k(k - 1)(k - 2)a_k x^{k-3}$$

$$\text{etc.}$$

also converge on $(-c, c)$. For example, since the geometric series

$$\sum x^k = 1 + x + x^2 + x^3 + x^4 + \cdots + x^n + \cdots$$

converges on $(-1, 1)$, we know now that the series

$$\sum \frac{d}{dx}(x^k) = \sum kx^{k-1} = 1 + 2x + 3x^2 + 4x^3 + \cdots + nx^{n-1} + \cdots$$

$$\sum \frac{d^2}{dx^2}(x^k) = \sum k(k-1)x^{k-2} = 2 + 6x + 12x^2 + \cdots + n(n-1)x^{n-2} + \cdots, \quad \text{etc.}$$

also converge on $(-1, 1)$. $\square$

Suppose now that

$$\sum a_k x^k \quad \text{converges on } (-c, c).$$

Then, as you just saw,

$$\sum ka_k x^{k-1} \quad \text{also converges on } (-c, c).$$

Using the first series, we can define a function f on $(-c, c)$ by setting

$$f(x) = \sum a_k x^k \quad \text{for all } x \text{ in } (-c, c).$$

Using the second series, we can also define a function g by setting

$$g(x) = \sum ka_k x^{k-1} \quad \text{for all } x \text{ in } (-c, c).$$

The crucial point is that

$$f'(x) = g(x)$$

For emphasis we cast this as a theorem.

The Differentiability of Power-Series Theorem.

If

$$f(x) = \sum_{k=0}^{\infty} a_k x^k \quad \text{for all } x \text{ in } (-c, c),$$

then f is differentiable on $(-c, c)$ and

$$f'(x) = \sum_{k=1}^{\infty} ka_k x^{k-1} \quad \text{for all } x \text{ in } (-c, c).$$

By applying this theorem to f', you will see that f' is itself differentiable. This in turn implies that f'' is differentiable, and so on. In short, f has derivatives of all orders.

We can summarize this way:

> In the interior of its interval of convergence a power series defines an infinitely differentiable function, the derivatives of which can be obtained by differentiating term by term.

The term-by-term differentiation refers to the fact that

$$\frac{d}{dx}\left(\sum a_k x^k\right) = \sum \frac{d}{dx}(a_k x^k).$$

For a proof of the differentiability theorem we refer to the supplement at the end of the section. Right now we give some examples.

Example. You already know that

$$\frac{d}{dx}(e^x) = e^x.$$

You can see this directly by differentiating the exponential series:

$$\frac{d}{dx}(e^x) = \frac{d}{dx}\left(\sum_{k=0}^{\infty}\frac{x^k}{k!}\right) = \sum_{k=0}^{\infty}\frac{d}{dx}\left(\frac{x^k}{k!}\right) = \sum_{k=1}^{\infty}\frac{x^{k-1}}{(k-1)!} = \sum_{k=0}^{\infty}\frac{x^k}{k!} = e^x. \quad \square$$

Example. You know that

$$\sin x = x - \frac{x^3}{3!} + \frac{x^5}{5!} - \frac{x^7}{7!} + \frac{x^9}{9!} - \cdots$$

and

$$\cos x = 1 - \frac{x^2}{2!} + \frac{x^4}{4!} - \frac{x^6}{6!} + \frac{x^8}{8!} - \cdots.$$

The relations

$$\frac{d}{dx}(\sin x) = \cos x, \qquad \frac{d}{dx}(\cos x) = -\sin x$$

can be easily verified by differentiating the series term by term:

$$\frac{d}{dx}(\sin x) = 1 - \frac{3x^2}{3!} + \frac{5x^4}{5!} - \frac{7x^6}{7!} + \frac{9x^8}{9!} - \cdots$$

$$= 1 - \frac{x^2}{2!} + \frac{x^4}{4!} - \frac{x^6}{6!} + \frac{x^8}{8!} - \cdots = \cos x,$$

$$\frac{d}{dx}(\cos x) = -\frac{2x}{2!} + \frac{4x^3}{4!} - \frac{6x^5}{6!} + \frac{8x^7}{8!} - \cdots = -x + \frac{x^3}{3!} - \frac{x^5}{5!} + \frac{x^7}{7!} - \cdots$$

$$= -\left(x - \frac{x^3}{3!} + \frac{x^5}{5!} - \frac{x^7}{7!} + \cdots\right) = -\sin x. \quad \square$$

Example. We can sum the series

$$\sum_{n=1}^{\infty}\frac{x^n}{n}, \qquad x \in (-1, 1)$$

by setting

$$g(x) = \sum_{n=1}^{\infty}\frac{x^n}{n}, \qquad x \in (-1, 1)$$

and noting that

$$g'(x) = \sum_{n=1}^{\infty} \frac{nx^{n-1}}{n} = \sum_{n=1}^{\infty} x^{n-1} = \sum_{n=0}^{\infty} x^n = \frac{1}{1-x} \cdot$$

Since

$$g(0) = 0 \quad \text{and} \quad g'(x) = \frac{1}{1-x},$$

we must have

$$g(x) = \log \left| \frac{1}{1-x} \right| \cdot \quad \square$$

Power series can also be integrated term by term.

Term-By-Term Integration Theorem

If

$$f(x) = \sum a_k x^k \quad \text{converges on } (-c, c),$$

then

$$g(x) = \sum \frac{a_k x^{k+1}}{k+1} \quad \text{also converges on } (-c, c)$$

and

$$\int f(x)\, dx = g(x) + C.$$

PROOF.   If $\sum a_k x^k$ converges on $(-c, c)$, then $\sum |a_k x^k|$ converges on $(-c, c)$. Since

$$\left| \frac{a_k x^k}{k+1} \right| \leq |a_k x^k|,$$

we know by comparison that

$$\sum \left| \frac{a_k x^k}{k+1} \right| \quad \text{also converges on } (-c, c).$$

It follows that

$$x \sum \frac{a_k x^k}{k+1} = \sum \frac{a_k x^{k+1}}{k+1} \quad \text{converges on } (-c, c).$$

With

$$f(x) = \sum a_k x^k \quad \text{and} \quad g(x) = \sum \frac{a_k x^{k+1}}{k+1},$$

we know from the differentiability theorem that

$$g'(x) = f(x)$$

and therefore

$$\int f(x)\,dx = g(x) + C. \quad \Box$$

The idea of term-by-term integration can also be expressed by writing

$$\int \left(\sum a_k x^k\right) dx = \left(\sum \frac{a_k x^{k+1}}{k+1}\right) + C.$$

For definite integrals, we have

$$\int_a^b \left(\sum a_k x^k\right) dx = \sum \left(\int_a^b \frac{a_k x^k}{k+1}\,dx\right),$$

so long, of course, as $[a, b]$ is contained in the interval of convergence.

Here are some examples of term-by-term integration.

Example. By integrating

$$\frac{1}{1+x} = \frac{1}{1-(-x)} = \sum_{k=0}^{\infty} (-1)^k x^k, \qquad |x| < 1$$

we get

$$\log(1 + x) = \int \left(\sum_{k=0}^{\infty} (-1)^k x^k\right) dx = \left(\sum_{k=0}^{\infty} \frac{(-1)^k x^{k+1}}{k+1}\right) + C, \qquad |x| < 1.$$

The constant C is 0 as you can tell from the fact that the series on the right and $\log(1 + x)$ are both 0 at $x = 0$. $\Box$

Example. The arc tangent series can also be obtained by term-by-term integration:

$$\frac{1}{1+x^2} = \frac{1}{1-(-x^2)} = \sum_{k=0}^{\infty} (-1)^k x^{2k}$$

and therefore

$$\text{arc tan } x = \int \left(\sum_{k=0}^{\infty} (-1)^k x^{2k}\right) dx = \left(\sum_{k=0}^{\infty} \frac{(-1)^k x^{2k+1}}{2k+1}\right) + C.$$

The constant C is once again 0, this time because the series on the right and arc tan x are both 0 at $x = 0$. $\Box$

Term-by-term integration can be a useful technique even if at the beginning there are no series in sight. Suppose that you are trying to evaluate an integral

$$\int_a^b f(x)\,dx$$

and that you cannot find an antiderivative. If you know that $f(x)$ has a convergent power series expansion, then you can evaluate the integral in question by first forming the series and then integrating term by term.

Example.   We can apply these ideas to

$$\int_0^1 e^{-x^2}\,dx.$$

Since

$$e^y = 1 + y + \frac{y^2}{2!} + \frac{y^3}{3!} + \frac{y^4}{4!} + \cdots,$$

we have

$$e^{-x^2} = 1 - x^2 + \frac{x^4}{2!} - \frac{x^6}{3!} + \frac{x^8}{4!} - \cdots.$$

Term-by-term integration gives

$$\int_0^1 e^{-x^2}\,dx = \left[x - \frac{x^3}{3} + \frac{x^5}{5\cdot 2!} - \frac{x^7}{7\cdot 3!} + \frac{x^9}{9\cdot 4!} - \cdots \right]_0^1$$

$$= 1 - \frac{1}{3} + \frac{1}{5\cdot 2!} - \frac{1}{7\cdot 3!} + \frac{1}{9\cdot 4!} - \cdots.$$

This last series is an alternating series of the type we have discussed. It is not hard to see that

$$1 - \frac{1}{3} + \frac{1}{5\cdot 2!} - \frac{1}{7\cdot 3!} \le \int_0^1 e^{-x^2}\,dx \le 1 - \frac{1}{3} + \frac{1}{5\cdot 2!} - \frac{1}{7\cdot 3!} + \frac{1}{9\cdot 4!}$$

and therefore

$$0.74 < \int_0^1 e^{-x^2}\,dx < 0.75.$$

Greater accuracy can of course be obtained by using more terms. $\square$

It is time to relate Taylor series

$$\sum_{k=0}^{\infty} \frac{f^{(k)}(0)}{k!} x^k$$

to power series in general. The relation is very simple:

On its interval of convergence a power series is the Taylor series of its sum.

To see this, all you have to do is differentiate

$$f(x) = a_0 + a_1 x + a_2 x^2 + \cdots + a_k x^k + \cdots$$

term by term. By doing this you will find that

$$f^{(k)}(0) = k! a_k \quad \text{and therefore} \quad a_k = \frac{f^{(k)}(0)}{k!}. \quad \square$$

There is one more loose end to tie up. We have talked at some length about the radius of convergence of a power series, but we have not given any attention to the problem of actually finding the radius of convergence of a given series.

There is no difficulty if the series converges only at 0. Then $r = 0$. There is also no difficulty if the series converges everywhere. Then $r = \infty$. The only series that present a problem are those that converge at some nonzero numbers and diverge at others. Such is the case with

$$\sum_{k=0}^{\infty} \frac{(k+1)x^k}{2^k 3^k} = 1 + \frac{2x}{2 \cdot 3} + \frac{3x^2}{2^2 \cdot 3^2} + \frac{4x^3}{2^3 \cdot 3^3} + \cdots.$$

Problem.   Find the radius of convergence of

$$\sum_{k=0}^{\infty} \frac{(k+1)x^k}{2^k 3^k} = 1 + \frac{2x}{2 \cdot 3} + \frac{3x^2}{2^2 \cdot 3^2} + \frac{4x^3}{2^3 \cdot 3^3} + \cdots.$$

SOLUTION.   As the kth term we have

$$b_k = \frac{(k+1)x^k}{2^k 3^k}.$$

Because of the special behavior of power series in general (Theorem 10.10.1) the series we want to test is really $\sum |b_k|$. Here

$$|b_k| = (k+1)\left(\frac{|x|}{6}\right)^k.$$

Since

$$|b_k|^{1/k} = (k+1)^{1/k} \frac{|x|}{6} \to \frac{|x|}{6},$$

the root test shows that $\sum |b_k|$ converges

$$\text{if } \frac{|x|}{6} < 1 \qquad \text{(that is, if } |x| < 6)$$

and diverges

$$\text{if } \frac{|x|}{6} > 1 \qquad \text{(that is, if } |x| > 6).$$

The radius of convergence is therefore 6.   □

In working out the last problem we used the root test. In another instance another tool may be preferable. Probably the only way to develop some proficiency in this matter is to get some practice. That, incidentally, is why we devote the first twenty exercises of this section to the subject. The main thing to remember is that, in a search for the radius of convergence, you are looking for absolute convergence. What counts is the behavior of $\sum |a_k x^k|$. The terms being nonnegative, you have at your disposal all the tools developed in Section 10.6.

Exercises

Find the radius of convergence.

1.* $\sum k x^k$.

2. $\sum \frac{1}{k} x^k$.

3.* $\sum \frac{x^k}{(2k)!}$.

4. $\sum k^k x^k$.

5.* $\sum (-k)^{2k} x^{2k}$.

6. $\sum \frac{(-1)^k}{\sqrt{k}} x^k$.

7.* $\sum \frac{1}{k 2^k} x^k$.

8. $\sum \frac{1}{k^2 2^k} x^k$.

9.* $\sum \frac{1}{k(k+1)} x^k$.

10. $\sum \frac{k^2}{1+k^2} x^k$.

11.* $\sum \frac{2^k}{\sqrt{k}} x^k$.

12. $\sum \frac{1}{\log k} x^k$.

13.* $\sum \frac{k-1}{k} x^k$.

14. $\sum k a^k x^k$.

15.* $\sum \frac{k}{10^k} x^k$.

16. $\sum \frac{(-1)^k}{k^k} x^k$.

17.* $\sum \frac{(-1)^k a^k}{k^2} x^k$.

18. $\sum \frac{x^k}{(\log k)^k}$.

19.* $\sum \frac{2^{1/k} \pi^k}{k(k+1)(k+2)} x^k$.

20. $\sum \left(1 + \frac{1}{k}\right)^{k^2} x^k$.

Find the approximate value. (within 0.01)

21.* $\int_0^1 e^{-x^3} \, dx$.

22. $\int_0^1 \sin x^2 \, dx$.

23.* $\int_0^1 \sin \sqrt{x} \, dx$.

24.* $\int_0^1 \arctan x^2 \, dx$.

25. $\int_0^1 x^4 e^{-x^2} \, dx$.

26.* $\int_1^2 \frac{1 - \cos x}{x} \, dx$.

27. $\int_0^{1/9} e^x \log (1 + x) \, dx$.

28. $\int_0^1 x \sin \sqrt{x} \, dx$.

29. Find a series for $\sec^2 x$ by differentiating the series for $\tan x$.

30. Find a series for $\log (\cos x)$ by integrating the series for $\tan x$.

31. Find a series for $\log (1 - x)$ by integration.

32. Show that, if $\sum a_k x^k$ and $\sum b_k x^k$ both converge to the same sum on some interval, then

$$a_k = b_k \qquad \text{for each } k.$$

33. Show that if $\epsilon > 0$, then

$$|k t^{k-1}| < (|t| + \epsilon)^k \qquad \text{for all } k \text{ sufficiently large.}$$

[HINT: $k^{1/k} |t|^{(k-1)/k} = k^{1/k} |t|^{1-(1/k)} \rightarrow |t|$.]

SUPPLEMENT TO SECTION 10.10

Proof of the Differentiability of Power Series

We begin by setting

$$f(x) = \sum_{k=0}^{\infty} a_k x^k \qquad \text{and} \qquad g(x) = \sum_{k=1}^{\infty} k a_k x^{k-1}.$$

Taking x from $(-c, c)$, we want to show that

$$\lim_{h \to 0} \frac{f(x+h) - f(x)}{h} = g(x).$$

With $x + h$ in $(-c, c)$, $h \neq 0$, we have

$$\left| g(x) - \frac{f(x+h) - f(x)}{h} \right| = \left| \sum_{k=1}^{\infty} k a_k x^{k-1} - \sum_{k=0}^{\infty} \frac{a_k(x+h)^k - a_k x^k}{h} \right|$$

$$= \left| \sum_{k=1}^{\infty} k a_k x^{k-1} - \sum_{k=1}^{\infty} a_k \left[\frac{(x+h)^k - x^k}{h} \right] \right|.$$

By the mean-value theorem we know that there exists t_k between x and $x + h$ such that

$$\frac{(x+h)^k - x^k}{h} = k t_k^{k-1}.$$

Using this result, we have

$$\left| g(x) - \frac{f(x+h) - f(x)}{h} \right| = \left| \sum_{k=1}^{\infty} k a_k x^{k-1} - \sum_{k=1}^{\infty} k a_k t_k^{k-1} \right|$$

$$= \left| \sum_{k=1}^{\infty} k a_k (x^{k-1} - t_k^{k-1}) \right| = \left| \sum_{k=2}^{\infty} k a_k (x^{k-1} - t_k^{k-1}) \right|.$$

Again by the mean-value theorem we know that there exists p_{k-1} between x and t_k such that

$$\frac{x^{k-1} - t_k^{k-1}}{x - t_k} = (k-1)(p_{k-1})^{k-2}.$$

Now

$$|x^{k-1} - t_k^{k-1}| = |x - t_k| \, |(k-1)(p_{k-1})^{k-2}|.$$

Since $|x - t_k| < |h|$ and

$$|p_{k-1}| \leq |\alpha|, \qquad \text{where} \qquad |\alpha| = \max \{ |x|, |x+h| \},$$

we have

$$|x^{k-1} - t_k^{k-1}| \leq |h| \, |(k-1)\alpha^{k-2}|.$$

Thus

$$\left| g(x) - \frac{f(x+h) - f(x)}{h} \right| \leq |h| \sum_{k=2}^{\infty} |k(k-1)a_k \alpha^{k-2}|.$$

Since the series on the right converges, we have

$$\lim_{h \to 0} \left(|h| \sum_{k=2}^{\infty} |k(k-1)a_k \alpha^{k-2}| \right) = 0,$$

so that

$$\lim_{h \to 0} \left| g(x) - \frac{f(x + h) - f(x)}{h} \right| = 0$$

and

$$\lim_{h \to 0} \frac{f(x + h) - f(x)}{h} = g(x). \quad \square$$

10.11 Problems on the binomial series

Through a collection of problems we invite you to derive on your own the basic properties of one of the most celebrated series of all — the *binomial series*.

Beginning with the binomial $1 + x$ (2 terms) and a real number α, form the function

$$\boxed{f(x) = (1 + x)^\alpha.}$$

Problem 1. Show that

$$\frac{f^{(k)}(0)}{k!} = \frac{\alpha[\alpha - 1][\alpha - 2] \cdots [\alpha - (k - 1)]}{k!}.$$

The number you just obtained is the coefficient of x^k in the expansion of $(1 + x)^\alpha$. It is called the kth *binomial coefficient* and it is usually denoted by $\binom{\alpha}{k}$:

$$\boxed{\binom{\alpha}{k} = \frac{\alpha[\alpha - 1][\alpha - 2] \cdots [\alpha - (k - 1)]}{k!}.} \quad †$$

Problem 2. Show that the binomial series

$$\sum \binom{\alpha}{k} x^k$$

has radius of convergence 1. [HINT: Use the ratio test.]

From Problem 2 you know that the binomial series converges on the open interval $(-1, 1)$ and defines there an infinitely differentiable function. The next thing to show is that this function (the one defined by the series) is actually $(1 + x)^\alpha$. To do this, you first need some other results.

Problem 3. Verify the identity

$$(k + 1) \binom{\alpha}{k + 1} + k \binom{\alpha}{k} = \alpha \binom{\alpha}{k}.$$

Problem 4. Use the identity of Problem 3 to show that the sum of the binomial series

$$\phi(x) = \sum_{k=0}^{\infty} \binom{\alpha}{k} x^k, \qquad x \in (-1, 1)$$

---

† By special definition $\binom{\alpha}{0} = 1$.

satisfies the differential equation

$$(1 + x)\phi'(x) = \alpha\phi(x).$$

You are now in a position to prove the main result.

Problem 5. Show that for all x in $(-1, 1)$

$$(1 + x)^\alpha = \sum_{k=0}^{\infty} \binom{\alpha}{k} x^k.$$

To get a better feeling for what the series looks like it is a good idea to expand it a few terms:

(10.11.1)

$$(1 + x)^\alpha = 1 + \alpha x + \frac{\alpha(\alpha - 1)}{2!} x^2 + \frac{\alpha(\alpha - 1)(\alpha - 2)}{3!} x^3$$
$$+ \frac{\alpha(\alpha - 1)(\alpha - 2)(\alpha - 3)}{4!} x^4 + \cdots .$$

Problem 6. Using (10.11.1) as a model expand each of the following in powers of x up to x^4.

(a)* $\sqrt{1 + x}$.   (b) $\dfrac{1}{\sqrt{1 + x}}$.   (c)* $\sqrt{1 + x^2}$.   (d) $\dfrac{1}{\sqrt{1 - x^2}}$.

Problem 7. Use series to find the approximate value. (within 0.01)

(a)* $\sqrt{98}$. [HINT: $\sqrt{98} = (100 - 2)^{1/2} = 10(1 - \frac{1}{50})^{1/2}$.]

(b) $\sqrt[3]{9}$.   (c)* $\sqrt[4]{620}$.   (d) $\sqrt[5]{36}$.   (e) $17^{-1/4}$.

10.12 A short table of series; additional problems

A Short Table of Series

For ready reference we list below some of the more important series expansions.

1. $\dfrac{1}{1 - x} = 1 + x + x^2 + \cdots + x^n + \cdots , \qquad -1 < x < 1.$

2. $e^x = 1 + x + \dfrac{x^2}{2!} + \cdots + \dfrac{x^n}{n!} + \cdots , \qquad$ all x.

3. $\sin x = x - \dfrac{x^3}{3!} + \dfrac{x^5}{5!} - \cdots + (-1)^n \dfrac{x^{2n+1}}{(2n + 1)!} + \cdots , \qquad$ all x.

4. $\cos x = 1 - \dfrac{x^2}{2!} + \dfrac{x^4}{4!} - \cdots + (-1)^n \dfrac{x^{2n}}{(2k)!} + \cdots , \qquad$ all x.

5. $\sinh x = x + \dfrac{x^3}{3!} + \dfrac{x^5}{5!} + \cdots + \dfrac{x^{2n+1}}{(2n + 1)!} + \cdots , \qquad$ all x.

6. $\cosh x = 1 + \dfrac{x^2}{2!} + \dfrac{x^4}{4!} + \cdots + \dfrac{x^{2n}}{(2n)!} + \cdots$,   all x.

7. $\arctan x = x - \dfrac{x^3}{3} + \dfrac{x^5}{5} - \cdots + (-1)^n \dfrac{x^{2n+1}}{2n+1} + \cdots$, $-1 \le x \le 1$.

8. $\arcsin x = x + \dfrac{1}{2 \cdot 3} x^3 + \dfrac{1 \cdot 3}{2 \cdot 4 \cdot 5} x^5 + \cdots + \dfrac{1 \cdot 3 \cdot 5 \cdots (2n-1)}{2 \cdot 4 \cdots (2n)(2n+1)} x^{2n+1} + \cdots$,

$$-1 \le x \le 1.$$

9. $\log(1 + x) = x - \dfrac{x^2}{2} + \dfrac{x^3}{3} - \cdots + (-1)^n \dfrac{x^{n+1}}{n+1} + \cdots$, $-1 < x \le 1$.

10. $(1 + x)^\alpha = 1 + \alpha x + \dfrac{\alpha[\alpha - 1]}{2!} x^2 + \cdots + \dfrac{\alpha[\alpha - 1] \cdots [\alpha - (n-1)]}{n!} x^n + \cdots$,

$$-1 < x < 1.$$

Additional problems

State whether or not the indicated sequence converges, and if it does, find the limit.

1.* $3^{1/n}$.

2. $n2^{1/n}$.

3.* $\dfrac{n^2 + 5n + 1}{n^3 + 1}$.

4. $\dfrac{(n+1)(n+2)}{(n+3)(n+4)}$.

5.* $\left(\dfrac{n}{1+n}\right)^{1/n}$.

6. $\cos n\pi \sin n\pi$.

7.* $\cos \dfrac{\pi}{n} \sin \dfrac{\pi}{n}$.

8. $\dfrac{n^\pi}{1 - n^\pi}$.

9.* $\left(2 + \dfrac{1}{n}\right)^n$.

10. $|x|^{(3n+1)/n}$.

11.* $\dfrac{\log[n(n+1)]}{n}$.

12. $\left[\log\left(1 + \dfrac{1}{n}\right)\right]^n$.

13.* $\dfrac{\pi}{n} \log \dfrac{n}{\pi}$.

14. $\dfrac{\pi}{n} e^{\pi/n}$.

15.* $\dfrac{n}{\pi} \sin n\pi$.

16. $\dfrac{\pi}{n} \cos \dfrac{\pi}{n}$.

Sum the following series.

17.* $\displaystyle\sum_{k=0}^{\infty} \left(\dfrac{1}{4}\right)^k$.

18. $\displaystyle\sum_{k=0}^{\infty} \left(\dfrac{3}{4}\right)^{k+1}$.

19.* $\displaystyle\sum_{k=0}^{\infty} (-1)^k \left(\dfrac{1}{2}\right)^k$.

20. $\displaystyle\sum_{k=0}^{\infty} \dfrac{(\log 2)^k}{k!}$.

21.* $\displaystyle\sum_{k=1}^{\infty} \left(\dfrac{1}{k} - \dfrac{1}{k+1}\right)$.

22. $\displaystyle\sum_{k=2}^{\infty} \left(\dfrac{1}{k^2} - \dfrac{1}{(k+1)^2}\right)$.

23.* $\displaystyle\sum_{k=0}^{\infty} \dfrac{1}{(2k)!}$.

24. $\displaystyle\sum_{k=1}^{\infty} \dfrac{(-1)^{k-1}}{k} \left(\dfrac{1}{2}\right)^k$.

Test the following series for (a) convergence, (b) absolute convergence.

25.* $1 + \dfrac{1}{3} + \dfrac{1}{5} + \cdots + \dfrac{1}{2n+1} + \cdots$.

26. $\dfrac{1}{1 \cdot 3} + \dfrac{1}{3 \cdot 5} + \dfrac{1}{5 \cdot 7} + \cdots + \dfrac{1}{(2n+1)(2n+3)} + \cdots$.

27.* $\dfrac{1}{2 \cdot 3} + \dfrac{1}{3 \cdot 4} + \dfrac{1}{4 \cdot 5} + \cdots + \dfrac{1}{(n+1)(n+2)} + \cdots$.

28. $\dfrac{1}{2 \log 2} + \dfrac{1}{3 \log 3} + \dfrac{1}{4 \log 4} + \cdots + \dfrac{1}{n \log n} + \cdots$.

29.* $1 - \dfrac{1}{3} + \dfrac{1}{5} - \cdots + (-1)^n \dfrac{1}{2n+1} + \cdots$.

30. $100 - \dfrac{100^2}{2!} + \dfrac{100^3}{3!} - \cdots + (-1)^{n+1} \dfrac{100^n}{n!} + \cdots$.

31.* $1 - \dfrac{2}{3} + \dfrac{3}{3^2} - \cdots + (-1)^{n-1} \dfrac{n}{3^{n-1}} + \cdots$.

32. $\dfrac{3}{4} + 2\left(\dfrac{3}{4}\right)^2 + 3\left(\dfrac{3}{4}\right)^3 + \cdots + n\left(\dfrac{3}{4}\right)^n + \cdots$.

33.* $\dfrac{1}{\sqrt{2 \cdot 3}} - \dfrac{1}{\sqrt{3 \cdot 4}} + \dfrac{1}{\sqrt{4 \cdot 5}} - \cdots + \dfrac{(-1)^{n-1}}{\sqrt{(n+1)(n+2)}} + \cdots$.

34. $\dfrac{1}{5} - \dfrac{1}{\sqrt{5}} + \dfrac{1}{\sqrt[3]{5}} - \cdots + \dfrac{(-1)^{n-1}}{\sqrt[n]{5}} + \cdots$.

Find the radius of convergence and specify exactly for what x the series converges.

35.* $\sum \dfrac{x^{2k+1}}{2k+1}$.
36. $\sum \dfrac{k!}{2} x^k$.
37.* $\sum \dfrac{k!}{2} x^{k!}$.
38. $\sum \dfrac{x^k}{2^{k!}}$.

Expand in powers of x.

39.* a^x .
40. $e^{\sin x}$.
41.* $\log (1 + x^2)$.
42. $\sqrt{1 + \sin x}$.

$$\left[\text{HINT FOR EXERCISE 42:} \quad \sqrt{1 + \sin x} = \sin \frac{x}{2} + \cos \frac{x}{2} \quad \text{for } x \text{ close to } 0. \right]$$

43. Verify the expansion

$$\log \left(\frac{1+x}{1-x}\right) = 2\left[x + \frac{x^3}{3} + \frac{x^5}{5} + \cdots\right].$$

Use the first three nonzero terms of the series to find a fractional approximation to $\log 2$. [HINT: Use $x = \frac{1}{3}$.]

44. Deduce a series expansion for

$$\frac{1}{(1-x)^2}$$

from the geometric series.

45.* Find a series expansion for $\tanh^{-1} x$ by integrating the series of its derivative.

46.* Use power series to find

(a) $\lim\limits_{x \to 0} \dfrac{\sinh x}{\sin x}$.

(b) $\lim\limits_{x \to 0} \dfrac{\sin x - \sinh x}{\cos x - \cosh x}$.

Find the approximate value. (within 0.01)

47.* $\displaystyle\int_0^{1/2} \dfrac{dx}{1 + x^4}$.
48. $e^{2/3}$.
49.* $\sqrt[3]{60}$.
50. $\displaystyle\int_0^{1/2} x \sin x^4 \, dx$.

L'HOSPITAL'S RULE; IMPROPER INTEGRALS

11.1 Limits as $x \to \pm \infty$

Now that you are familiar with convergence for sequences, limits as $x \to \infty$ should present no difficulties. To say that

$$\lim_{x \to \infty} f(x) = l$$

[read "the limit of $f(x)$ as x tends to infinity is l"] is to say that we can make the difference between $f(x)$ and l as small as we wish simply by requiring that x be sufficiently large. More precisely,

$$\lim_{x \to \infty} f(x) = l \quad \text{iff} \quad \begin{cases} \text{for each } \epsilon > 0 \text{ there exists } K > 0 \text{ such that,} \\ \text{if } x \geq K, \quad \text{then } |f(x) - l| < \epsilon. \end{cases}$$

Here are some simple examples:

$$\lim_{x \to \infty} \frac{1}{x} = 0, \quad \lim_{x \to \infty} \frac{x-1}{2x+5} = \lim_{x \to \infty} \frac{1 - 1/x}{2 + 5/x} = \frac{1}{2} \quad \lim_{x \to \infty} e^{1/x} = 1.$$

It is easy to interpret the idea geometrically. To say that $\lim_{x \to \infty} f(x) = A$ (see Figure 11.1.1) is to say that, as x becomes arbitrarily large, the graph of f approaches the horizontal line $y = A$. The line itself is called a *horizontal asymptote*.

It is obvious that limits as $x \to \infty$ are unique (if they exist) and that the usual rules for computation hold. For example, if

$$\lim_{x \to \infty} f(x) = l \quad \text{and} \quad \lim_{x \to \infty} g(x) = m,$$

FIGURE 11.1.1

then

(i) $$\lim_{x \to \infty} \alpha f(x) + \beta g(x) = \alpha l + \beta m;$$

(ii) $$\lim_{x \to \infty} f(x)g(x) = lm;$$

(iii) $$\lim_{x \to \infty} \frac{f(x)}{g(x)} = \frac{l}{m} \quad \text{if} \quad m \neq 0.$$

Moreover, the pinching theorem is valid; namely, if

$$h(x) \leq f(x) \leq g(x) \qquad \text{for all} \quad x \text{ sufficiently large}$$

and

$$\lim_{x \to \infty} h(x) = l = \lim_{x \to \infty} g(x),$$

then

$$\lim_{x \to \infty} f(x) = l.$$

We illustrate these ideas by carrying out some computations.

Problem.   Find

$$\lim_{x \to \infty} \frac{\sin^2 x}{x^2}.$$

SOLUTION.   For $x \neq 0$,

$$0 \leq \frac{\sin^2 x}{x^2} \leq \frac{1}{x^2}. \qquad\qquad \text{(since } |\sin x| \leq 1\text{)}$$

Since obviously

$$\lim_{x \to \infty} \frac{1}{x^2} = 0,$$

we have

$$\lim_{x \to \infty} \frac{\sin^2 x}{x^2} = 0. \quad \square$$

Problem. Find

$$\lim_{x \to \infty} \frac{x(e^{-x} + 1)}{2x - 1}.$$

SOLUTION. For x different from 0 and $\frac{1}{2}$,

$$\frac{x(e^{-x} + 1)}{2x - 1} = \frac{e^{-x} + 1}{2 - 1/x}.$$

Since

$$\lim_{x \to \infty} (e^{-x} + 1) = 1 \quad \text{and} \quad \lim_{x \to \infty} \left(2 - \frac{1}{x}\right) = 2,$$

we have

$$\lim_{x \to \infty} \frac{x(e^{-x} + 1)}{2x - 1} = \frac{1}{2}. \quad \square$$

Problem. Find

$$\lim_{x \to \infty} \frac{x + \log x}{x \log x}.$$

SOLUTION. For x different from 0 and 1,

$$\frac{x + \log x}{x \log x} = \frac{x}{x \log x} + \frac{\log x}{x \log x} = \frac{1}{\log x} + \frac{1}{x}.$$

Since obviously

$$\lim_{x \to \infty} \frac{1}{\log x} = 0 \quad \text{and} \quad \lim_{x \to \infty} \frac{1}{x} = 0,$$

we have

$$\lim_{x \to \infty} \frac{x + \log x}{x \log x} = 0. \quad \square$$

There is a simple relation between limits at ∞ and one-sided limits at 0. Setting $x = 1/t$, it is easy to see that

$$\boxed{\lim_{x \to \infty} f(x) = l \quad \text{iff} \quad \lim_{t \downarrow 0} f\left(\frac{1}{t}\right) = l.}$$

We'll use this idea in the next section.

Limits as $x \to -\infty$ are defined by setting

$$\lim_{x \to -\infty} f(x) = l \qquad \text{iff} \qquad \begin{cases} \text{for each } \epsilon > 0 \text{ there exist } K < 0 \text{ such that,} \\ \quad \text{if } x \le K, \qquad \text{then } |f(x) - l| < \epsilon. \end{cases}$$

The behavior of such limits is entirely analogous to the case $x \to \infty$. As simple examples, we have

$$\lim_{x \to -\infty} e^x = 0, \qquad \lim_{x \to -\infty} \frac{3 - x}{2 + x} = \lim_{x \to -\infty} \frac{3/x - 1}{2/x + 1} = -1.$$

In the case of

$$h(x) = \begin{cases} 1, & x > 0 \\ -1, & x < 0 \end{cases}$$

we have

$$\lim_{x \to \infty} h(x) = 1 \qquad \text{but} \qquad \lim_{x \to -\infty} h(x) = -1. \quad \square$$

Exercises

Find the following limits.

1.* $\displaystyle \lim_{x \to \infty} \frac{3}{x}$.

2. $\displaystyle \lim_{x \to \infty} \frac{x}{x^2 + 1}$.

3.* $\displaystyle \lim_{x \to \infty} \frac{x - 1}{x + 1}$.

4.* $\displaystyle \lim_{x \to \infty} \frac{2 \sin x}{x}$.

5. $\displaystyle \lim_{x \to \infty} \log\left(\frac{2x}{x + 1}\right)$.

6.* $\displaystyle \lim_{x \to \infty} 10^{1/x}$.

7.* $\displaystyle \lim_{x \to \infty} \frac{x^2 e^{-x}}{2 - x^2}$.

8. $\displaystyle \lim_{x \to \infty} \frac{(x - a)(x - b)}{(ax + b)^2}$.

9.* $\displaystyle \lim_{x \to \infty} \frac{(ax - b)^2}{(a - x)(b - x)}$.

10.* $\displaystyle \lim_{x \to \infty} \sin\frac{1}{x}$.

11. $\displaystyle \lim_{x \to \infty} \left(1 - \sin\frac{1}{x}\right)^2$.

12.* $\displaystyle \lim_{x \to \infty} x \sin\frac{1}{x}$.

13.* $\displaystyle \lim_{x \to \infty} \int_0^x \frac{dt}{1 + t^2}$.

14. $\displaystyle \lim_{x \to \infty} \int_e^x \frac{dt}{t(\log t)^2}$.

15.* $\displaystyle \lim_{x \to \infty} \left(x - x \cos\frac{1}{x}\right)$.

16. (i) Prove that if f is increasing and bounded on $[a, \infty)$, then f has a limit as x tends to ∞.

(ii) Prove that if f is decreasing and bounded on $[a, \infty)$, then f has a limit as x tends to ∞.

17. Prove that if f is continuous on $[a, \infty)$ and has a finite limit as x tends to ∞, then f is bounded on $[a, \infty)$.

11.2 L'Hospital's rule $\left(\frac{0}{0}\right)$

Here we are concerned with limits of quotients

$$\frac{f(x)}{g(x)},$$

where numerator and denominator both tend to 0. For convenience we will dispense with the formality of writing

$$\lim_{x \to c} f(x) = 0, \qquad \lim_{x \to \infty} f(x) = 0, \qquad \text{etc.}$$

and write instead

$$\text{as} \quad x \to c, \qquad f(x) \to 0$$

$$\text{as} \quad x \to \infty, \qquad f(x) \to 0, \qquad \text{etc.}$$

L'Hospital's rule $\left(\frac{0}{0}\right)$

Suppose that

as $x \downarrow c, x \uparrow c, x \to c, x \to \infty$, or $x \to -\infty$, $\quad f(x) \to 0$ and $g(x) \to 0$.

If $\qquad\qquad \dfrac{f'(x)}{g'(x)} \to l, \qquad$ then $\qquad \dfrac{f(x)}{g(x)} \to l.$

We will prove the validity of L'Hospital's rule a little later. First we demonstrate its usefulness.

Problem. Find

$$\lim_{x \to \pi/2} \frac{\cos x}{\pi - 2x}.$$

SOLUTION. As $x \to \pi/2$, both numerator and denominator tend to 0 and it is not at all obvious what happens to the quotient

$$\frac{\cos x}{\pi - 2x}.$$

To see whether we can apply L'Hospital's rule we will examine the quotient of the derivatives. Since

$$\frac{\dfrac{d}{dx}(\cos x)}{\dfrac{d}{dx}(\pi - 2x)} = \frac{-\sin x}{-2} = \frac{\sin x}{2}$$

and

$$\frac{\sin x}{2} \to \frac{1}{2} \qquad \text{as} \quad x \to \frac{\pi}{2},$$

we have

$$\frac{\dfrac{d}{dx}(\cos x)}{\dfrac{d}{dx}(\pi - 2x)} \to \frac{1}{2}.$$

It follows from L'Hospital's rule that

$$\frac{\cos x}{\pi - 2x} \to \frac{1}{2}.$$

We can express this all on one line:

$$\lim_{x \to \pi/2} \frac{\cos x}{\pi - 2x} = \lim_{x \to \pi/2} \frac{\dfrac{d}{dx}(\cos x)}{\dfrac{d}{dx}(\pi - 2x)} = \lim_{x \to \pi/2} \frac{\sin x}{2} = \frac{1}{2}. \quad \square$$

Problem. Find

$$\lim_{x \downarrow 0} \frac{x}{\sin \sqrt{x}}.$$

SOLUTION. As $x \downarrow 0$, both numerator and denominator tend to 0. Since

$$\frac{\dfrac{d}{dx}(x)}{\dfrac{d}{dx}(\sin \sqrt{x})} = \frac{2\sqrt{x}}{\cos \sqrt{x}} \to 0 \quad \text{as} \quad x \downarrow 0,$$

it follows from L'Hospital's rule that

$$\frac{x}{\sin \sqrt{x}} \to 0 \quad \text{as} \quad x \downarrow 0.$$

For short we write

$$\lim_{x \downarrow 0} \frac{x}{\sin \sqrt{x}} = \lim_{x \downarrow 0} \frac{\dfrac{d}{dx}(x)}{\dfrac{d}{dx}(\sin \sqrt{x})} = \lim_{x \downarrow 0} \frac{2\sqrt{x}}{\cos \sqrt{x}} = 0. \quad \square$$

Sometimes it is necessary to differentiate numerator and denominator more than once. The next problem gives such an instance.

Problem. Find

$$\lim_{x \to 0} \frac{1 - \cos 2x}{x^2}.$$

SOLUTION. As $x \to 0$, both numerator and denominator tend to 0. Trying to apply L'Hospital's rule, we form the quotient

$$\frac{\dfrac{d}{dx}(1 - \cos 2x)}{\dfrac{d}{dx}(x^2)} = \frac{2 \sin 2x}{2x} = \frac{\sin 2x}{x}.$$

Since numerator and denominator still tend to 0, we differentiate again. Doing so, we obtain

$$\frac{\dfrac{d^2}{dx^2}(1 - \cos 2x)}{\dfrac{d^2}{dx^2}(x^2)} = \frac{\dfrac{d}{dx}(\sin 2x)}{\dfrac{d}{dx}(x)} = \frac{2\cos 2x}{1}.$$

Since this last quotient tends to 2, we can conclude that

$$\frac{\sin 2x}{x} \to 2 \quad \text{and therefore} \quad \frac{1 - \cos 2x}{x^2} \to 2.$$

For short we can write

$$\lim_{x \to 0} \frac{1 - \cos 2x}{x^2} = \lim_{x \to 0} \frac{\sin 2x}{x} = \lim_{x \to 0} \frac{2\cos 2x}{1} = 2. \quad \square$$

Problem. Find

$$\lim_{x \downarrow 0} (1 + x)^{1/x}.$$

SOLUTION. As the expression stands, it is not amenable to L'Hospital's rule. To make it so, we take its logarithm. This gives

$$\lim_{x \downarrow 0} \log (1 + x)^{1/x} = \lim_{x \downarrow 0} \frac{\log (1 + x)}{x} \underset{\text{differentiating}}{\Big/} = \lim_{x \downarrow 0} \frac{1}{1 + x} = 1.$$

Since the log of $(1 + x)^{1/x}$ tends to 1, $(1 + x)^{1/x}$ must itself tend to e. $\square$

To prove the validity of L'Hospital's rule, we need first a generalization of the mean-value theorem.

The Cauchy mean-value theorem

Suppose that f and g are differentiable on (a, b) and continuous on $[a, b]$. If g' is never 0 in (a, b), then there is a number c in (a, b) such that

$$\frac{f'(c)}{g'(c)} = \frac{f(b) - f(a)}{g(b) - g(a)}.$$

PROOF. We can prove this by applying the mean-value theorem to the function

$$G(x) = [g(b) - g(a)][f(x) - f(a)] - [g(x) - g(a)][f(b) - f(a)].$$

Since

$$G(a) = 0 \quad \text{and} \quad G(b) = 0,$$

there exists (by the mean-value theorem) a number c in (a, b) such that

$$G'(c) = 0.$$

Since in general

$$G'(x) = [g(b) - g(a)]f'(x) - g'(x)[f(b) - f(a)],$$

we must have

$$[g(b) - g(a)]f'(c) - g'(c)[f(b) - f(a)] = 0,$$

and therefore

$$[g(b) - g(a)]f'(c) = g'(c)[f(b) - f(a)].$$

Since g' is never 0 in (a, b),

$$g'(c) \neq 0 \qquad \text{and} \qquad g(b) - g(a) \neq 0.$$

───────── Explain

We can therefore divide by these numbers and obtain

$$\frac{f'(c)}{g'(c)} = \frac{f(b) - f(a)}{g(b) - g(a)} . \quad \square$$

Now let's prove L'Hospital's rule for the case $x \downarrow c$; namely, let's assume that, as $x \downarrow c$,

$$f(x) \to 0, \qquad g(x) \to 0, \qquad \text{and} \qquad \frac{f'(x)}{g'(x)} \to l$$

and let's show that

$$\frac{f(x)}{g(x)} \to l.$$

The fact that

$$\frac{f'(x)}{g'(x)} \to l \qquad \text{as} \quad x \downarrow c$$

assures us that both f' and g' exist on a set of the form $(c, c + h]$ and g' is not zero there. By setting $f(c) = 0$ and $g(c) = 0$, we ensure that f and g are both continuous on $[c, c + h]$. We can now apply the Cauchy mean-value theorem and conclude that there exists a number c_h between c and $c + h$ such that

$$\frac{f'(c_h)}{g'(c_h)} = \frac{f(c + h) - f(c)}{g(c + h) - g(c)} = \frac{f(c + h)}{g(c + h)} .$$

The result is now obvious. $\square$

We close this section by showing the validity of L'Hospital's rule for the case $x \to \infty$.

The key here is to set $x = 1/t$:

$$\lim_{x \to \infty} \frac{f'(x)}{g'(x)} = \lim_{t \downarrow 0} \frac{f'(1/t)}{g'(1/t)}$$

$$= \lim_{t \downarrow 0} \frac{-t^2 f'(1/t)}{-t^2 g'(1/t)}$$

by L'Hospital's rule for the case $t \downarrow 0$ $\quad = \lim_{t \downarrow 0} \frac{f(1/t)}{g(1/t)}$

$$= \lim_{x \to \infty} \frac{f(x)}{g(x)}. \quad \square$$

Exercises

Calculate the following limits.

1.* $\displaystyle \lim_{x \downarrow 0} \frac{\sin x}{\sqrt{x}}$.

2. $\displaystyle \lim_{x \to 1} \frac{\log x}{1 - x}$.

3.* $\displaystyle \lim_{x \to 0} \frac{e^x - 1}{\log (1 + x)}$.

4.* $\displaystyle \lim_{x \to a} \frac{x - a}{x^n - a^n}$.

5. $\displaystyle \lim_{x \to \pi/2} \frac{\cos x}{\sin 2x}$.

6.* $\displaystyle \lim_{x \to 0} \frac{e^x - 1}{x(1 + x)}$.

7.* $\displaystyle \lim_{x \to 0} \frac{1 - \cos x}{3x}$.

8. $\displaystyle \lim_{x \to 1} \frac{x^{1/2} - x^{1/4}}{x - 1}$.

9.* $\displaystyle \lim_{x \to 0} \frac{e^x - e^{-x}}{\sin x}$.

10.* $\displaystyle \lim_{x \to 0} \frac{a^x - (a + 1)^x}{x}$.

11. $\displaystyle \lim_{x \to 0} \frac{\tan \pi x}{e^x - 1}$.

12.* $\displaystyle \lim_{x \to 0} \frac{x + \sin \pi x}{x - \sin \pi x}$.

13.* $\displaystyle \lim_{x \to 0} \frac{\sqrt{a + x} - \sqrt{a - x}}{x}$.

14. $\displaystyle \lim_{x \to 0} \frac{1 + x - e^x}{x(e^x - 1)}$.

15.* $\displaystyle \lim_{x \to 0} \frac{x - \tan x}{x - \sin x}$.

16.* $\displaystyle \lim_{x \to 0} \frac{\log(\sec x)}{x^2}$.

17. $\displaystyle \lim_{x \uparrow 1} \frac{\sqrt{1 - x^2}}{\sqrt{1 - x^3}}$.

18.* $\displaystyle \lim_{x \to 0} \left(\frac{1}{\sin x} - \frac{1}{x} \right)$.

19.* $\displaystyle \lim_{x \to 1} \left(\frac{1}{\log x} - \frac{x}{x - 1} \right)$.

20. $\displaystyle \lim_{x \to \infty} \left(1 + \frac{1}{x} \right)^x$.

21.* $\displaystyle \lim_{x \to 0} (e^x + x)^{1/x}$.

22.* $\displaystyle \lim_{x \to \pi/4} \frac{\sec^2 x - 2 \tan x}{1 + \cos 4x}$.

23. $\displaystyle \lim_{x \downarrow 0} \frac{\sqrt{x}}{\sqrt{x} + \sin \sqrt{x}}$.

24.* $\displaystyle \lim_{x \to 0} \frac{x e^{nx} - x}{1 - \cos nx}$.

25.* $\displaystyle \lim_{x \to 0} \frac{x - \arcsin x}{\sin^3 x}$.

26. $\displaystyle \lim_{x \to \pi/2} \frac{\log(\sin x)}{(\pi - 2x)^2}$.

27.* $\displaystyle \lim_{x \to 0} \frac{\sinh x - \sin x}{\sin^3 x}$.

11.3 Infinite limits; L'Hospital's rule $\left(\frac{\infty}{\infty}\right)$

It is convenient at times to allow infinite limits. Here is the basic idea. We write

$$\lim_{x \to c} f(x) = \infty$$

iff we can make $f(x)$ as large as we wish simply by requiring that x be sufficiently close to c. More formally, we have

$$\lim_{x \to c} f(x) = \infty \quad \text{iff} \quad \begin{cases} \text{for each } M > 0 \text{ there exists } \delta > 0 \text{ such that,} \\ \text{if } 0 < |x - c| < \delta, \qquad \text{then } f(x) \ge M. \end{cases}$$

Here are some examples.

Examples

$$\lim_{x \to c} \frac{1}{|x - c|} = \infty, \qquad \lim_{x \to c} \frac{1}{(\sqrt{x} - \sqrt{c})^2} = \infty, \qquad \lim_{x \to c} \frac{1}{\sin^2(x - c)} = \infty. \quad \square$$

One-sided infinite limits

$$\lim_{x \downarrow c} f(x) = \infty \qquad \text{and} \qquad \lim_{x \uparrow c} f(x) = \infty$$

are defined in a similar manner. We won't bother to spell out the details. The idea must be obvious. It must also be obvious to you that all these notions can be extended to allow for a limit of $- \infty$.

Geometrically limits of the form

$$\lim_{x \to c} f(x) = \pm \infty, \qquad \lim_{x \downarrow c} f(x) = \pm \infty, \qquad \lim_{x \uparrow c} f(x) = \pm \infty$$

signal the presence of a *vertical asymptote*. We give some pictorial examples in Figures 11.3.1–11.3.4.

There still remain limits of the form

$$\lim_{x \to \pm \infty} f(x) = \pm \infty$$

to discuss. There are four possibilities here but we will spell out details only for one of them:

$$\lim_{x \to \infty} f(x) = \infty.$$

We leave the others to your imagination. By writing

$$\lim_{x \to \infty} f(x) = \infty$$

we mean that we can make $f(x)$ as large as we wish simply by requiring that x be sufficiently large:

$$\lim_{x \to \infty} f(x) = \infty \quad \text{iff} \quad \begin{cases} \text{for each } M > 0 \text{ there exists } K > 0 \text{ such that,} \\ \qquad \text{if } x \ge K, \qquad \text{then } f(x) \ge M. \end{cases}$$

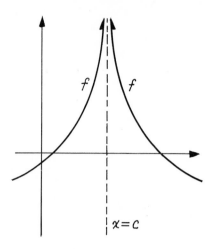

$$\lim_{x \to c} f(x) = \infty$$

FIGURE 11.3.1

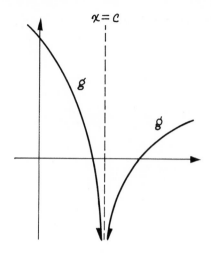

$$\lim_{x \to c} g(x) = -\infty$$

FIGURE 11.3.2

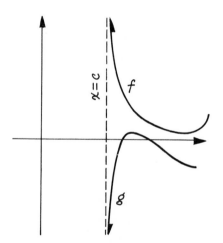

$$\lim_{x \downarrow c} f(x) = \infty, \ \lim_{x \downarrow c} g(x) = -\infty$$

FIGURE 11.3.3

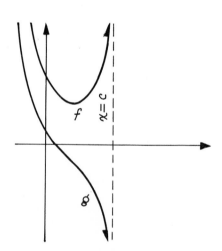

$$\lim_{x \uparrow c} f(x) = \infty, \ \lim_{x \uparrow c} g(x) = -\infty$$

FIGURE 11.3.4

As simple examples you can take

$$\lim_{x \to \infty} x = \infty, \qquad \lim_{x \to \infty} e^x = \infty$$

$$\lim_{x \to \infty} \log x = \infty, \qquad \lim_{x \to \infty} \left(x + \frac{1}{x}\right) = \infty.$$

To illustrate these ideas further we calculate some limits which are not quite so obvious.

Problem. Find

$$\lim_{x \to \infty} x(2 + \sin x).$$

SOLUTION.   Since the sine function is bounded below by -1, we know that for $x > 0$,

$$x \le x(2 + \sin x).$$

Since

$$\lim_{x \to \infty} x = \infty,$$

it is clear that

$$\lim_{x \to \infty} x(2 + \sin x) = \infty. \quad \square$$

Problem. Find

$$\lim_{x \to \infty} \frac{1 - x^2}{2x + 1}.$$

SOLUTION

$$\lim_{x \to \infty} \frac{1 - x^2}{2x + 1} = \lim_{x \to \infty} \frac{1/x^2 - 1}{2/x + 1/x^2} = -\infty. \quad \square$$

Problem. Find

$$\lim_{x \to \infty} \log\left(\frac{x}{x^2 + 1}\right).$$

SOLUTION.   It's not hard to see that

$$\lim_{x \to \infty} \frac{x}{x^2 + 1} = \lim_{x \to \infty} \frac{1}{x + 1/x} = 0$$

and consequently

$$\lim_{x \to \infty} \log\left(\frac{x}{x^2 + 1}\right) = -\infty. \quad \square$$

Problem. Find

$$\lim_{x \to \infty} x \sin \frac{1}{x}.$$

SOLUTION

$$\lim_{x \to \infty} x \sin \frac{1}{x} = \lim_{x \to \infty} \frac{\sin 1/x}{1/x} = \lim_{t \downarrow 0} \frac{\sin t}{t} = 1. \quad \square$$

Problem. Find

$$\lim_{x \to 0} \left(\frac{1}{x} - \frac{1}{x^2} \right).$$

SOLUTION

$$\lim_{x \to 0} \left(\frac{1}{x} - \frac{1}{x^2} \right) = \lim_{x \to 0} \frac{x - 1}{x^2} = -\infty. \quad \square$$

We come now to limits of quotients

$$\frac{f(x)}{g(x)},$$

where numerator and denominator both tend to ∞. We take l as a fixed real number.

L'Hospital's Rule $\left(\frac{\infty}{\infty} \right)$

Suppose that

as $x \uparrow c, x \downarrow c, x \to c, x \to \infty$, or $x \to -\infty$, $f(x) \to \infty$ and $g(x) \to \infty$.

If $$\frac{f'(x)}{g'(x)} \to l, \qquad \text{then} \qquad \frac{f(x)}{g(x)} \to l.$$

While the proof of L'Hospital's rule in this setting is a little more complicated than it was in the $\left(\frac{0}{0} \right)$ case,† the application of the rule is much the same.

Problem. Calculate

$$\lim_{x \to \infty} \frac{\log x}{x}.$$

SOLUTION.   Both numerator and denominator tend to ∞ with x. L'Hospital's rule gives

$$\lim_{x \to \infty} \frac{\log x}{x} = \lim_{x \to \infty} \frac{\dfrac{d}{dx} (\log x)}{\dfrac{d}{dx} (x)} = \lim_{x \to \infty} \frac{1}{x} = 0. \quad \square$$

Problem. Calculate

$$\lim_{x \to \infty} \frac{x^n}{e^x}.$$

SOLUTION.   Here we differentiate n times:

$$\lim_{x \to \infty} \frac{x^n}{e^x} = \lim_{x \to \infty} \frac{nx^{n-1}}{e^x} = \lim_{x \to \infty} \frac{n(n-1)x^{n-2}}{e^x} = \cdots = \lim_{x \to \infty} \frac{n!}{e^x} = 0. \quad \square$$

---

† We omit the proof.

Problem. Calculate

$$\lim_{x \downarrow 0} x^x.$$

SOLUTION. We begin by taking the logarithm of x^x. It is not hard to see that

$$\lim_{x \downarrow 0} \log x^x = \lim_{x \downarrow 0} x \log x = \lim_{t \to \infty} \frac{\log 1/t}{t} = \lim_{t \to \infty} \left(-\frac{\log t}{t} \right) = 0.$$

Since $\log x^x$ tends to 0, x^x must tend to 1. $\square$

Exercises

Calculate the following limits.

1.* $\lim_{x \to \pi/2} \tan x.$

2. $\lim_{x \downarrow 0} \log \frac{1}{x}.$

3.* $\lim_{x \to \infty} \frac{x^3 - 1}{2 - x}.$

4.* $\lim_{x \to \infty} \frac{x^3}{1 - x^3}.$

5. $\lim_{x \to \infty} x^2 \sin \frac{1}{x}.$

6.* $\lim_{x \to \infty} \frac{\log x}{\sqrt{x}}.$

7.* $\lim_{x \uparrow \pi/2} \frac{\tan 5x}{\tan x}.$

8. $\lim_{x \to 0} x \log|\sin x|.$

9.* $\lim_{x \downarrow 0} x^{2x}.$

10.* $\lim_{x \to 0} x (\log|x|)^2.$

11. $\lim_{x \to \infty} x \sin \frac{\pi}{x}.$

12.* $\lim_{x \downarrow 0} \frac{\log x}{\cot x}.$

13.* $\lim_{x \to \infty} \frac{\sqrt{1 + x^2}}{x}.$

14. $\lim_{x \to \infty} \log \left(\frac{x^2 - 1}{x^2 + 1} \right)^3.$

15.* $\lim_{x \downarrow 0} x^{\sin x}.$

16.* $\lim_{x \to 0} |\sin x|^x.$

17. $\lim_{x \to 0} \left[\frac{1}{\log (1 + x)} - \frac{1}{x} \right].$

18.* $\lim_{x \to 1} \left[\frac{x}{x - 1} - \frac{1}{\log x} \right].$

19.* $\lim_{x \to 1} x^{1/(x-1)}.$

20. $\lim_{x \to \infty} \left(\cos \frac{1}{x} \right)^x.$

21.* $\lim_{x \to \infty} (x^2 + a^2)^{(1/x)^2}.$

22.* $\lim_{x \to 0} \left[\frac{1}{\sin^2 x} - \frac{1}{x^2} \right].$

23. $\lim_{x \to \pi/2} |\sec x|^{\cos x}.$

24.* $\lim_{x \to \infty} \frac{1}{x} \int_0^x e^{t^2} \, dt.$

25. Show that the Taylor series

$$\sum_{n=0}^{\infty} \frac{f^{(n)}(0)}{n!} x^n$$

of the function

$$f(x) = \begin{cases} e^{-1/x^2}, & x \neq 0 \\ 0, & x = 0 \end{cases}$$

is identically zero and hence does not represent the function.

11.4   Improper integrals

We begin with a function f continuous on an unbounded interval $[a, \infty)$. For each number $b > a$ we can form the integral

$$\int_a^b f(x)\, dx.$$

If, as b tends to ∞, this integral tends to a finite limit l,

$$\lim_{b \to \infty} \int_a^b f(x)\, dx = l,$$

then we write

$$\int_a^\infty f(x)\, dx = l$$

and call

$$\int_a^\infty f(x)\, dx$$

a *convergent improper integral.* Otherwise we say that

$$\int_a^\infty f(x)\, dx$$

is a *divergent improper integral.* Improper integrals of the form

$$\int_{-\infty}^b f(x)\, dx$$

are introduced in a similar manner.

Examples

(1) $\displaystyle \int_1^\infty e^{-x}\, dx = \frac{1}{e}.$ 　　　　　　　　　(2) $\displaystyle \int_1^\infty \frac{dx}{x}$ 　　diverges.

(3) $\displaystyle \int_1^\infty \frac{dx}{x^2} = 1.$ 　　　　　　　　　　(4) $\displaystyle \int_1^\infty \cos \pi x\, dx$ 　　diverges.

VERIFICATION.

(1) 　　$\displaystyle \int_1^\infty e^{-x}\, dx = \lim_{b \to \infty} \int_1^b e^{-x}\, dx = \lim_{b \to \infty} \left[-e^{-x} \right]_1^b = \lim_{b \to \infty} \left(\frac{1}{e} - \frac{1}{e^b} \right) = \frac{1}{e}.$

(2) 　　$\displaystyle \int_1^\infty \frac{dx}{x} = \lim_{b \to \infty} \int_1^b \frac{dx}{x} = \lim_{b \to \infty} \log(b) = \infty.$

(3) $$\int_1^\infty \frac{dx}{x^2} = \lim_{b\to\infty} \int_1^b \frac{dx}{x^2} = \lim_{b\to\infty}\left[-\frac{1}{x}\right]_1^b = \lim_{b\to\infty}\left(1 - \frac{1}{b}\right) = 1.$$

(4) Note first that

$$\int_1^b \cos \pi x \, dx = \left[\frac{1}{\pi}\sin \pi x\right]_1^b = \frac{1}{\pi}\sin \pi b.$$

As b tends to ∞, $\sin \pi b$ oscillates between -1 and 1. The integral

$$\int_1^b \cos \pi x \, dx$$

oscillates between $-1/\pi$ and $1/\pi$. It does not converge. $\square$

The usual formulas for area and volume are extended to the unbounded case by means of improper integrals.

Example. If Ω is the region below the graph of

$$f(x) = \frac{1}{x^p}, \qquad x \geq 1 \qquad\qquad \text{(Figure 11.4.1)}$$

then we have

$$\text{area of } \Omega = \begin{cases} \dfrac{1}{p-1}, & \text{if } p > 1 \\[2mm] \infty, & \text{if } p \leq 1 \end{cases}.$$

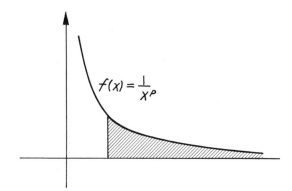

$$f(x) = \frac{1}{x^p}$$

FIGURE 11.4.1

This comes about from setting

$$\text{area of } \Omega = \lim_{b\to\infty} \int_1^b \frac{dx}{x^p} = \int_1^\infty \frac{dx}{x^p}.$$

For $p \neq 1$, we have

$$\int_1^\infty \frac{dx}{x^p} = \lim_{b \to \infty} \int_1^b \frac{dx}{x^p} = \lim_{b \to \infty} \frac{1}{1-p}(b^{1-p} - 1) = \begin{cases} \dfrac{1}{p-1}, & \text{if } p > 1 \\ \infty, & \text{if } p < 1 \end{cases}.$$

For $p = 1$, we have

$$\int_1^\infty \frac{dx}{x^p} = \int_1^\infty \frac{dx}{x} = \infty,$$

as you have seen already.   □

Example.   From the last example you know that the region below the graph of

$$f(x) = \frac{1}{x}, \qquad x \geq 1$$

has infinite area. Suppose that this region (with infinite area) is revolved about the x-axis. (See Figure 11.4.2.) What is the volume of the resulting solid? It may surprise you somewhat but the volume is not infinite. In fact, it is π:

$$V = \pi \int_1^\infty \frac{dx}{x^2} = \pi \cdot 1 = \pi.$$

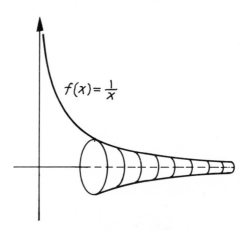

FIGURE 11.4.2

This result should not be disquieting. You have seen this kind of thing before:

$$\sum_{n=1}^\infty \frac{1}{n} \quad \text{diverges} \qquad \text{but} \qquad \sum_{n=1}^\infty \frac{1}{n^2} \quad \text{converges.}   □$$

Suppose now that f is continuous on $(-\infty, \infty)$. The *improper integral*

$$\int_{-\infty}^\infty f(x)\,dx$$

is said to *converge* iff both

$$\int_{-\infty}^{0} f(x)\, dx \qquad \text{and} \qquad \int_{0}^{\infty} f(x)\, dx$$

converge. If

$$\int_{-\infty}^{0} f(x)\, dx = l \qquad \text{and} \qquad \int_{0}^{\infty} f(x)\, dx = m,$$

then we set

$$\int_{-\infty}^{\infty} f(x)\, dx = l + m.$$

Improper integrals can also arise on bounded intervals. Suppose that f is continuous on the half-open interval $[a, b)$ but unbounded there. See Figure 11.4.3. If

$$\lim_{\epsilon \downarrow 0} \int_{a}^{b-\epsilon} f(x)\, dx = l, \quad (l \text{ finite}),$$

then we write

$$\int_{a}^{b-} f(x)\, dx = l$$

and call

$$\int_{a}^{b-} f(x)\, dx$$

a *convergent improper integral*. Otherwise we say that

$$\int_{a}^{b-} f(x)\, dx$$

is a *divergent improper integral*.

Functions continuous but unbounded on intervals of the form $(a, b]$ lead to limits of the form

$$\lim_{\epsilon \downarrow 0} \int_{a+\epsilon}^{b} f(x)\, dx$$

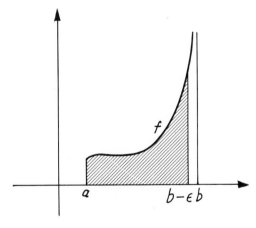

FIGURE 11.4.3

and thus to improper integrals

$$\int_{a+}^{b} f(x)\, dx.$$

Examples

(1) $\displaystyle\int_{0}^{1-} (1-x)^{-2/3}\, dx = 3.$ (2) $\displaystyle\int_{0+}^{1} \frac{dx}{x}$ diverges.

Verification

(1)
$$\int_{0}^{1-} (1-x)^{-2/3}\, dx = \lim_{\epsilon \downarrow 0} \int_{0}^{1-\epsilon} (1-x)^{-2/3}\, dx$$

$$= \lim_{\epsilon \downarrow 0} \left[-3(1-x)^{1/3} \right]_{0}^{1-\epsilon}$$

$$= \lim_{\epsilon \downarrow 0} 3(1 - \epsilon^{1/3})$$

$$= 3. \quad \square$$

(2)
$$\int_{0+}^{1} \frac{dx}{x} = \lim_{\epsilon \downarrow 0} \int_{\epsilon}^{1} \frac{dx}{x} = \lim_{\epsilon \downarrow 0} (-\log \epsilon) = \infty. \quad \square$$

Exercises

Evaluate the improper integrals that converge.

1.* $\displaystyle\int_{1}^{\infty} \frac{dx}{x^2}.$

2. $\displaystyle\int_{0}^{\infty} e^{px}\, dx, \quad p > 0.$

3.* $\displaystyle\int_{0}^{\infty} e^{-px}\, dx, \quad p > 0.$

4.* $\displaystyle\int_{0}^{\infty} \frac{dx}{1+x^2}.$

5. $\displaystyle\int_{0}^{\infty} \frac{dx}{4+x^2}.$

6.* $\displaystyle\int_{0+}^{1} \frac{dx}{\sqrt{x}}.$

7.* $\displaystyle\int_{0+}^{8} \frac{dx}{x^{2/3}}.$

8. $\displaystyle\int_{0+}^{1} \frac{dx}{x^2}.$

9.* $\displaystyle\int_{0}^{1-} \frac{dx}{\sqrt{1-x^2}}.$

10.* $\displaystyle\int_{0}^{1-} \frac{dx}{\sqrt{1-x}}.$

11. $\displaystyle\int_{0}^{2-} \frac{x}{\sqrt{4-x^2}}\, dx.$

12.* $\displaystyle\int_{0}^{a-} \frac{dx}{\sqrt{a^2-x^2}}.$

13.* $\displaystyle\int_{e}^{\infty} \frac{\log x}{x}\, dx.$

14. $\displaystyle\int_{e}^{\infty} \frac{dx}{x \log x}.$

15.* $\displaystyle\int_{e}^{\infty} \frac{dx}{x(\log x)^2}.$

16.* $\displaystyle\int_{0+}^{1} x \log x\, dx.$

17. $\displaystyle\int_{-\infty}^{\infty} \frac{dx}{1+x^2}.$

18.* $\displaystyle\int_{2}^{\infty} \frac{dx}{x^2-1}.$

19.* $\displaystyle\int_{-\infty}^{0} x e^x\, dx.$

20. $\displaystyle\int_{0}^{\infty} \frac{dx}{\cosh x}.$

21.* $\displaystyle\int_{0}^{3} \frac{dx}{\sqrt[3]{3x-1}}.$

22.* $\displaystyle\int_{1}^{\infty} \frac{dx}{x(x+1)}.$

23. $\displaystyle\int_{3+}^{5} \frac{x}{\sqrt{x^2-9}}\, dx.$

24.* $\displaystyle\int_{1}^{\infty} \frac{x}{(1+x^2)^2}\, dx.$

25.* Let Ω be the region under the curve

$$y = e^{-x}, \qquad x \geq 0.$$

(a) Sketch Ω. (b) Find the area of Ω. (c) Find the volume of the solid obtained by rotating Ω about the x-axis. (d) Find the volume obtained by rotating Ω about the y-axis. (e) Find the surface area of the solid in part (c).

26. Find the area of the region bounded above by $xy = 1$, below by $y(x^2 + 1) = x$, and to the left by $x = 1$.

27.* Let Ω be the region below the curve

$$y = x^{-1/4}, \qquad 0 < x \leq 1.$$

(a) Sketch Ω. (b) Find the area of Ω. (c) Find the volume of the solid obtained by rotating Ω about the x-axis. (d) Find the volume of the solid obtained by rotating Ω about the y-axis.

28. (*A comparison test*) Let f and g be continuous functions satisfying

$$0 \leq f(x) \leq g(x) \qquad \text{for all} \quad x \in [a, \infty).$$

Show that

(a) if $\displaystyle\int_a^\infty g(x)\,dx$ converges,   then $\displaystyle\int_a^\infty f(x)\,dx$ converges.

(b) if $\displaystyle\int_a^\infty f(x)\,dx$ diverges,   then $\displaystyle\int_a^\infty g(x)\,dx$ diverges.

Use the comparison test of exercise 28 to determine which of the following integrals converge.

29.* $\displaystyle\int_1^\infty \frac{dx}{\sqrt{1 + x^3}}.$

30. $\displaystyle\int_1^\infty e^{-x^2}\,dx.$

31.* $\displaystyle\int_0^\infty (1 + x^5)^{-1/6}\,dx.$

32.* $\displaystyle\int_\pi^\infty \frac{\sin^2 2x}{x^2}\,dx.$

33. $\displaystyle\int_1^\infty \frac{\log x}{x^2}\,dx.$

34.* $\displaystyle\int_e^\infty \frac{dx}{\sqrt{x + 1}\,\log x}.$

12

VECTORS

12.1 Cartesian space coordinates

To introduce a Cartesian coordinate system in space we begin with a plane Cartesian coordinate system $O\text{-}xy$. Through the point O, which we continue to call the origin, we pass a third line, perpendicular to the other two. This third line we call the z-axis. We coordinatize it using the same scale as before, assigning z-coordinate 0 to the origin O.

For later convenience we orient the z-axis so that $O\text{-}xyz$ forms a "right-handed" system. That is, if the index finger of the right hand points along the positive x-axis and the middle finger along the positive y-axis, then the thumb will point along the positive z-axis. (See Figure 12.1.1.)

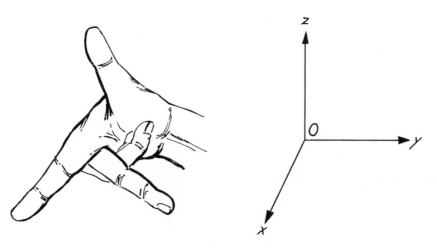

FIGURE 12.1.1

Now we take an arbitrary point P of space, and describe how we assign to it Cartesian coordinates. Through P we pass three planes: the first perpendicular to the x-axis, the second perpendicular to the y-axis, and the third perpendicular to the z-axis. We will say that the point P has *coordinates* (x_0, y_0, z_0) provided that the first plane intersects the x-axis at the point with linear coordinate x_0, the second plane intersects the y-axis at the point with linear coordinate y_0, and the third plane intersects the z-axis at the point with linear coordinate z_0. (See Figure 12.1.2.)

To indicate that P has coordinates (x_0, y_0, z_0), we will write $P(x_0, y_0, z_0)$. In Figure 12.1.3 we have plotted several points.

FIGURE 12.1.2

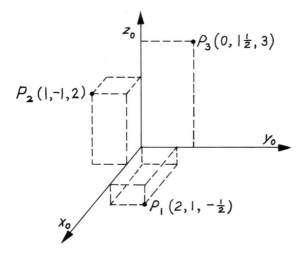

FIGURE 12.1.3

The Distance Formula

To find the distance $d(P_1, P_2)$ between $P_1(x_1, y_1, z_1)$ and $P_2(x_2, y_2, z_2)$ is an easy matter. Applying the Pythagorean theorem (see Figure 12.1.4) to triangle P_1SP_2, we get

$$[d(P_1, P_2)]^2 = [d(P_1, S)]^2 + [d(S, P_2)]^2.$$

From triangle P_1QS we get

$$[d(P_1, S)]^2 = [d(P_1, Q)]^2 + [d(Q, S)]^2 = (x_2 - x_1)^2 + (y_2 - y_1)^2.$$

Obviously

$$[d(S, P_2)]^2 = (z_2 - z_1)^2.$$

Combining these three equations, we get

$$[d(P_1, P_2)]^2 = (x_2 - x_1)^2 + (y_2 - y_1)^2 + (z_2 - z_1)^2.$$

and thus the distance formula

$$d(P_1, P_2) = \sqrt{(x_2 - x_1)^2 + (y_2 - y_1)^2 + (z_2 - z_1)^2}.$$

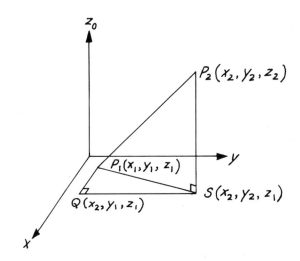

FIGURE 12.1.4

Symmetry

You are already familiar with two kinds of symmetry: symmetry with respect to a line and symmetry with respect to a point. In space we can also speak of symmetry with respect to a plane. The idea is obvious.

Exercises

1. Sketch a right-handed coordinate system and plot the following points.

(a) $A(1, 0, 0)$.   (d) $D(1, 1, 1)$.   (g) $G(-1, 1, 2)$.
(b) $B(0, 1, 0)$.   (e) $E(-1, -1, -1)$.   (h) $H(1, -2, 1)$.
(c) $C(0, 0, 1)$.   (f) $F(1, -1, 1)$.   (i) $I(-2, 1, -1)$.

2. Find the distance $d(P, Q)$.

(a)* $P(1, 0, 0)$ and $Q(0, 1, 0)$.
(b) $P(-1, 1, 2)$ and $Q(1, -2, 1)$.
(c)* $P(4, 2, 5)$ and $Q(1, 4, -1)$.
(d) $P(-1, -\sqrt{3}, -3)$ and $Q(3, \sqrt{3}, 0)$.
(e)* $P(x_1, x_2, 0)$ and $Q(y_1, y_2, 0)$.

3.* Find an equation for the sphere of radius r centered at

(a) the origin.   (b) $Q(a_1, a_2, a_3)$.

4. Find an equation for the plane through $Q(a_1, a_2, a_3)$ that is parallel to

(a)* the xy-plane.   (b) the xz-plane.   (c)* the yz-plane.

5. Given $P = P(1, -1, 2)$ find the point symmetric to

(i)* P with respect to the origin.
(ii) P with respect to the xy-plane.
(iii)* P with respect to the xz-plane.
(iv) P with respect to the yz-plane.
(v)* P with respect to $Q(1, 1, 2)$.
(vi) P with respect to $R(-1, -1, 2)$.

12.2 Displacements and forces

Our purpose here is to motivate the notion of vector. A quick reading of this section will do.

A displacement along a coordinate line can be specified by a real number and depicted by an arrow. For a displacement of a_1 units we can use the number a_1 and an arrow that begins at some number x and ends at $x + a_1$. If $a_1 > 0$ (and we follow convention), the arrow will point to the right and if $a_1 < 0$, the arrow will point to the left. (See Figure 12.2.1).

Displacement a_1

FIGURE 12.2.1

Displacements in the xy-plane are more interesting because instead of having two possible directions there are now an infinite number of directions. (See Figure 12.2.2.)

The most general displacements take place in space. Here ordered triples of real numbers come into play. A displacement of a_1 units in x-coordinate, a_2 units in y-coordinate, and a_3 units in z-coordinate can be indicated by an arrow that begins at some point $Q(x, y, z)$ and ends at $R(x + a_1, y + a_2, z + a_3)$. (See Figure 12.2.3.)

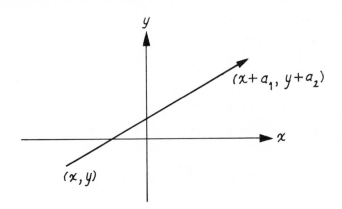

A displacement (a_1, a_2) in the $xy-$ plane

FIGURE 12.2.2

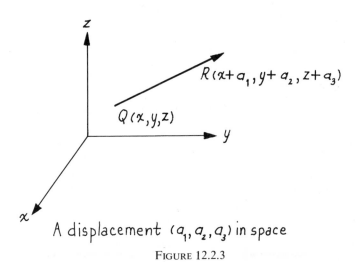

A displacement (a_1, a_2, a_3) in space

FIGURE 12.2.3

We can follow one displacement by another. A displacement (a_1, a_2, a_3) followed by a displacement (b_1, b_2, b_3) results in a total displacement $(a_1 + b_1, a_2 + b_2, a_3 + b_3)$. We can express this by writing

$$(a_1, a_2, a_3) + (b_1, b_2, b_3) = (a_1 + b_1, a_2 + b_2, a_3 + b_3).$$

We can picture the first displacement by an arrow that begins at some point $P(x, y, z)$ and ends at $Q(x + a_1, y + a_2, z + a_3)$ (see Figure 12.2.4), the second displacement by an arrow that begins at $Q(x + a_1, y + a_2, z + a_3)$ and ends at $R(x + a_1 + b_1, y + a_2 + b_2, z + a_3 + b_3)$ and the resultant displacement by an arrow that begins at $P(x, y, z)$ and ends at $R(x + a_1 + b_1, y + a_2 + b_2, z + a_3 + b_3)$. The three arrows then form a triangular pattern that is easy to remember.

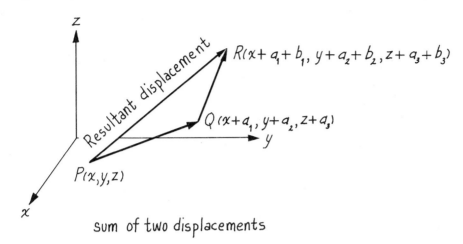

sum of two displacements

FIGURE 12.2.4

From a displacement (a_1, a_2, a_3) and a real number α, we can form a new displacement $(\alpha a_1, \alpha a_2, \alpha a_3)$. We can call this new displacement α times the initial one and write

$$\alpha(a_1, a_2, a_3) = (\alpha a_1, \alpha a_2, \alpha a_3).$$

It is not hard to see that the effect of multiplying a displacement by a number α is to change its magnitude by a factor of $|\alpha|$, keeping the same direction if $\alpha > 0$ and reversing it if $\alpha < 0$. We illustrate this idea in Figure 12.2.5. The displacement

$$2(a_1, a_2, a_3) = (2a_1, 2a_2, 2a_3)$$

is twice as long as

$$(a_1, a_2, a_3)$$

but has the same direction; the displacement

$$-(a_1, a_2, a_3) = (-a_1, -a_2, -a_3)$$

has the same length as

$$(a_1, a_2, a_3)$$

but the opposite direction; the displacement

$$-2(a_1, a_2, a_3) = (-2a_1, -2a_2, -2a_3)$$

is twice as long as

$$(a_1, a_2, a_3)$$

and has the opposite direction.

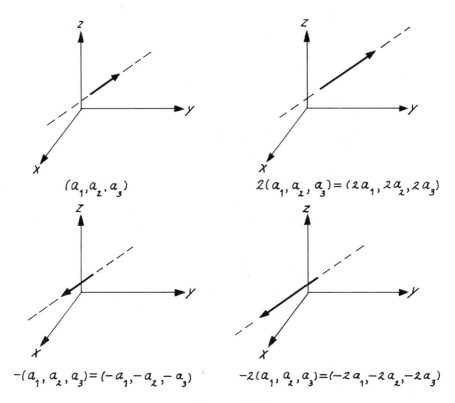

$$(a_1, a_2, a_3)$$

$$2(a_1, a_2, a_3) = (2a_1, 2a_2, 2a_3)$$

$$-(a_1, a_2, a_3) = (-a_1, -a_2, -a_3)$$

$$-2(a_1, a_2, a_3) = (-2a_1, -2a_2, -2a_3)$$

FIGURE 12.2.5

This same pattern

$$(a_1, a_2, a_3) + (b_1, b_2, b_3) = (a_1 + b_1, a_2 + b_2, a_3 + b_3)$$
$$\alpha(a_1, a_2, a_3) = (\alpha a_1, \alpha a_2, \alpha a_3)$$

arises naturally in other settings; for example, in the analysis of forces. To specify a force completely, we need to know its components along the x, y, and z axes. If these are respectively a_1, a_2, a_3, then the force is totally specified by the ordered triple (a_1, a_2, a_3). (See Figure 12.2.6.) If two forces

$$F_1 = (a_1, a_2, a_3) \qquad \text{and} \qquad F_2 = (b_1, b_2, b_3)$$

are applied simultaneously at the same point, the effect is identical to the effect produced by the single force

$$F_3 = (a_1 + b_1, a_2 + b_2, a_3 + b_3).$$

We speak of F_3 as the resultant or total force and write

$$F_1 + F_2 = F_3$$

$$(a_1, a_2, a_3) + (b_1, b_2, b_3) = (a_1 + b_1, a_2 + b_2, a_3 + b_3).$$

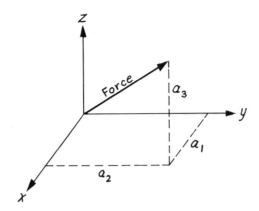

FIGURE 12.2.6

Pictorially we have the usual force diagram. (See Figure 12.2.7.) It is a parallelogram with the sides representing

$$F_1 = (a_1, a_2, a_3) \qquad \text{and} \qquad F_2 = (b_1, b_2, b_3)$$

and the diagonal representing

$$F_3 = F_1 + F_2 = (a_1 + b_1, a_2 + b_2, a_3 + b_3).$$

For any force $F = (a_1, a_2, a_3)$ and a real number α, the force αF is defined by the equation

$$\alpha F = (\alpha a_1, \alpha a_2, \alpha a_3).$$

Thus once again we have

$$\alpha(a_1, a_2, a_3) = (\alpha a_1, \alpha a_2, \alpha a_3).$$

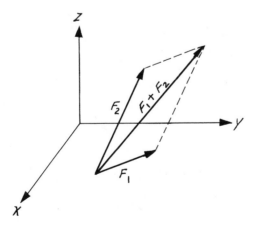

FIGURE 12.2.7

12.3   Vectors

The algebra of number triples which we introduced in the last section to discuss displacements and forces is so prodigiously rich in applications that it has found a firm place in the world of science and engineering and has generated much mathematics. It is to this mathematics that we now turn.

Definition.

Ordered triples of real numbers subject to the operation of addition

$$(a_1, a_2, a_3) + (b_1, b_2, b_3) = (a_1 + b_1, a_2 + b_2, a_3 + b_3)$$

and multiplication by scalars (real numbers)

$$\alpha(a_1, a_2, a_3) = (\alpha a_1, \alpha a_2, \alpha a_3)$$

are called *vectors*.

Two vectors are called *equal* iff they are identical; namely

$$(a_1, a_2, a_3) = (b_1, b_2, b_3) \qquad \text{iff} \qquad a_1 = b_1, a_2 = b_2, a_3 = b_3.$$

Geometrically we can depict vectors by arrows. To depict the vector (a_1, a_2, a_3) we can choose any initial point $Q = Q(x, y, z)$ and use the arrow

$$\overrightarrow{QR} \qquad \text{with} \quad R = R(x + a_1, y + a_2, z + a_3). \quad \text{(See Figure 12.3.1)}$$

Most of the time we will choose the origin as the initial point and use the arrow

$$\overrightarrow{OP} \qquad \text{with} \quad P = P(a_1, a_2, a_3).\dagger \qquad\qquad \text{(See Figure 12.3.2)}$$

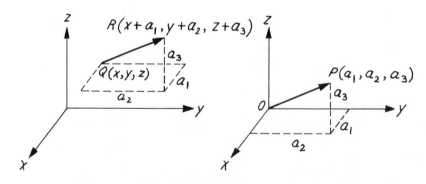

Representations of (a_1, a_2, a_3)

FIGURE 12.3.1   FIGURE 12.3.2

---

† The ordered triple (0,0,0) will not be represented by an arrow but simply by the origin.

We will use boldface letters to denote vectors. Thus for

$$\mathbf{a} = (a_1, a_2, a_3) \quad \text{and} \quad \mathbf{b} = (b_1, b_2, b_3)$$

we have

$$\mathbf{a} + \mathbf{b} = (a_1 + b_1, a_2 + b_2, a_3 + b_3)$$

and if α is a scalar (a real number)

$$\alpha\mathbf{a} = (\alpha a_1, \alpha a_2, \alpha a_3).$$

For the zero vector $(0, 0, 0)$ we will use the symbol $\mathbf{0}$. Obviously

$$0\mathbf{a} = \mathbf{0} \quad \text{for each vector } \mathbf{a}.$$

By the vector $-\mathbf{b}$ we mean $(-1)\mathbf{b}$; that is,

$$-(b_1, b_2, b_3) = (-b_1, -b_2, -b_3).$$

By $\mathbf{a} - \mathbf{b}$ we mean $\mathbf{a} + (-\mathbf{b})$; that is,

$$(a_1, a_2, a_3) - (b_1, b_2, b_3) = (a_1 - b_1, a_2 - b_2, a_3 - b_3).$$

Problem. Given

$$\mathbf{a} = (1, -1, 2), \quad \mathbf{b} = (2, 3, -1), \quad \mathbf{c} = (8, 7, 1)$$

find

(a) $\mathbf{a} - \mathbf{b}$.   (c) $3\mathbf{a} - 7\mathbf{b}$.
(b) $2\mathbf{a} + \mathbf{b}$.   (d) $2\mathbf{a} + 3\mathbf{b} - \mathbf{c}$.

SOLUTION

(a) $\mathbf{a} - \mathbf{b} = (1, -1, 2) - (2, 3, -1)$
$\qquad = (1 - 2, -1 - 3, 2 + 1)$
$\qquad = (-1, -4, 3).$
(b) $2\mathbf{a} + \mathbf{b} = 2(1, -1, 2) + (2, 3, -1)$
$\qquad = (2, -2, 4) + (2, 3, -1)$
$\qquad = (4, 1, 3).$
(c) $3\mathbf{a} - 7\mathbf{b} = 3(1, -1, 2) - 7(2, 3, -1)$
$\qquad = (3, -3, 6) - (14, 21, -7)$
$\qquad = (-11, -24, 13).$
(d) $2\mathbf{a} + 3\mathbf{b} - \mathbf{c} = 2(1, -1, 2) + 3(2, 3, -1) - (8, 7, 1)$
$\qquad = (2, -2, 4) + (6, 9, -3) - (8, 7, 1)$
$\qquad = (0, 0, 0)$
$\qquad = \mathbf{0}. \quad \square$

The addition of vectors can be visualized as the "addition" of arrows by the parallelogram law (as in the case of forces). If you picture $\mathbf{a}$, $\mathbf{b}$, and $\mathbf{a} + \mathbf{b}$ all as arrows emanating from the same point, say the origin, then $\mathbf{a} + \mathbf{b}$ acts as the diagonal of the parallelogram generated by $\mathbf{a}$ and $\mathbf{b}$. (See Figure 12.3.3.)

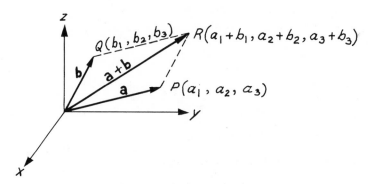

FIGURE 12.3.3

The addition of vectors can also be visualized as the "tail-to-head" addition of arrows (as in the case of displacements). If, instead of starting **b** at the origin, you start **b** at the tip of **a**, then **a** + **b** goes from the tail of **a** to the tip of **b**. (See Figure 12.3.4.) These two pictorial representations of vector addition lead to the same result.

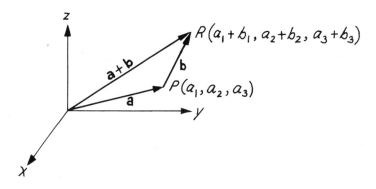

FIGURE 12.3.4

Definition 12.3.1

Two nonzero vectors **a** and **b** are said to be *parallel* provided that

$$\mathbf{a} = k\mathbf{b} \quad \text{for some real number} \quad k.$$

If $k > 0$, **a** and **b** are said to have the *same direction;* if $k < 0$, they are said to have *opposite directions.*

In the case of

$$\mathbf{a} = (2, -2, 6), \quad \mathbf{b} = (1, -1, 3), \quad \mathbf{c} = (-1, 1, -3)$$

we have

$$\mathbf{a} = 2\mathbf{b} \quad \text{and} \quad \mathbf{a} = -2\mathbf{c}.$$

This tells us that **a** and **b** are parallel and have the same direction but **a** and **c**, though parallel, have opposite directions. (See Figure 12.3.5.)

Definition 12.3.1 did not include the zero vector **0**. By special convention, **0** is called *parallel* to *every vector*. We will come back to this idea later.

Definition 12.3.2

The norm of a vector $\mathbf{a} = (a_1, a_2, a_3)$ is the number

$$\|\mathbf{a}\| = \sqrt{a_1^2 + a_2^2 + a_3^2}.$$

The norm of **a** is also called the *length* or *magnitude* of **a**. The reason for this is simple: if we represent the vector **a** by an arrow, say

$$\overrightarrow{QR} \quad \text{with} \quad Q = Q(x, y, z) \quad \text{and} \quad R = R(x + a_1, y + a_2, z + a_3),$$

then $\|\mathbf{a}\|$ gives the length of $\overrightarrow{QR}$.

The norm properties of vectors are very similar to the absolute value properties of real numbers. In particular, we have

---

(1) $\|\mathbf{a}\| \geq 0$ and $\|\mathbf{a}\| = 0$ iff $\mathbf{a} = \mathbf{0}$.

(2) $\|\alpha\mathbf{a}\| = |\alpha|\|\mathbf{a}\|$.

(3) $\|\mathbf{a} + \mathbf{b}\| \leq \|\mathbf{a}\| + \|\mathbf{b}\|$.   (the triangle inequality)

Property (1) is obvious. Property (2) is easy to verify:

$$\|\alpha\mathbf{a}\| = \sqrt{(\alpha a_1)^2 + (\alpha a_2)^2 + (\alpha a_3)^2} = |\alpha|\sqrt{a_1^2 + a_2^2 + a_3^2} = |\alpha|\|\mathbf{a}\|.$$

$$\mathbf{a} = (2, -2, 6) \qquad \mathbf{b} = (1, -1, 3) \qquad \mathbf{c} = (-1, 1, -3)$$

Some parallel vectors

FIGURE 12.3.5

We will not formally verify Property (3), the triangle inequality, until the next section where we will have "dot products" at our disposal. A proof at this time would be laborious.

Geometrically the meaning of the triangle inequality is clear. (See Figure 12.3.6.) It says simply that the length of a side of a triangle cannot exceed the sum of the lengths of the other two sides.

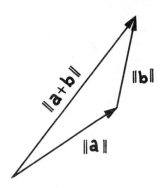

FIGURE 12.3.6

Problem.   Given

$$\mathbf{a} = (1, -2, 3) \quad \text{and} \quad \mathbf{b} = (-4, 1, 0),$$

find

(a) $\|\mathbf{a}\|$.   (c) $\|\mathbf{a} + \mathbf{b}\|$.   (e) $\|-7\mathbf{a}\|$.

(b) $\|\mathbf{b}\|$.   (d) $\|\mathbf{a} - \mathbf{b}\|$.   (f) $\|2\mathbf{a} - 3\mathbf{b}\|$.

SOLUTION

(a) $\quad \|\mathbf{a}\| = \sqrt{1^2 + (-2)^2 + (3)^2} = \sqrt{1 + 4 + 9} = \sqrt{14}.$

(b) $\quad \|\mathbf{b}\| = \sqrt{(-4)^2 + 1^2 + 0^2} = \sqrt{16 + 1 + 0} = \sqrt{17}.$

(c) $\quad \|\mathbf{a} + \mathbf{b}\| = \|(-3, -1, 3)\| = \sqrt{(-3)^2 + (-1)^2 + (3)^2} = \sqrt{9 + 1 + 9}$
$\qquad\qquad = \sqrt{19}.$

(d) $\quad \|\mathbf{a} - \mathbf{b}\| = \|(5, -3, 3)\| = \sqrt{(5)^2 + (-3)^2 + (3)^2} = \sqrt{25 + 9 + 9} = \sqrt{43}.$

(e) $\quad \|-7\mathbf{a}\| = |-7|\|\mathbf{a}\| = 7\sqrt{14}.$

(f) $\quad \|2\mathbf{a} - 3\mathbf{b}\| = \|2(1, -2, 3) - 3(-4, 1, 0)\| = \|(14, -7, 6)\|$
$\qquad\qquad = \sqrt{(14)^2 + (-7)^2 + (6)^2} = \sqrt{196 + 49 + 36} = \sqrt{281}. \quad \square$

To multiply a nonzero vector by a nonzero scalar α is to change its length by a factor of $|\alpha|$,

$$\|\alpha\mathbf{a}\| = |\alpha|\,\|\mathbf{a}\|,$$

keeping the same direction if $\alpha > 0$ and reversing the direction if $\alpha < 0$. The vector obtained from $\mathbf{a}$ simply by reversing its direction is the vector $(-1)\mathbf{a} = -\mathbf{a}$. (See Figure 12.3.7.)

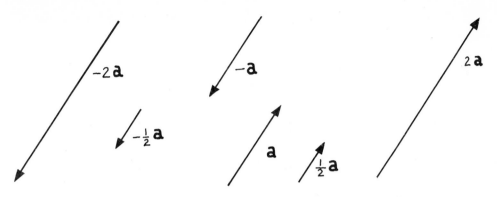

FIGURE 12.3.7

Recall that $\mathbf{a} - \mathbf{b}$ is the vector $\mathbf{a} + (-\mathbf{b})$. We can arrive at a pictorial representation of $\mathbf{a} - \mathbf{b}$ by forming $-\mathbf{b}$ and adding it to $\mathbf{a}$. (See Figure 12.3.8.)

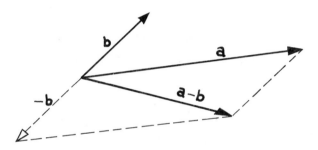

FIGURE 12.3.8

We can obtain the same result more easily by noting that $\mathbf{a} - \mathbf{b}$ is the vector we must add to $\mathbf{b}$ to obtain $\mathbf{a}$. (See Figure 12.3.9.)

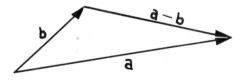

FIGURE 12.3.9

We single out for special attention the vectors

$$\mathbf{i} = (1, 0, 0), \qquad \mathbf{j} = (0, 1, 0), \qquad \mathbf{k} = (0, 0, 1).$$

These vectors all have norm 1 and, if pictured as emanating from the origin, lie along the positive coordinate axes. They are called *unit coordinate vectors*. (See Figure 12.3.10.)

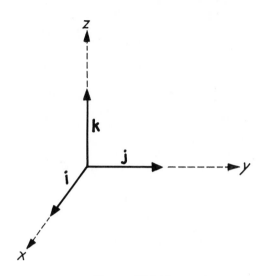

FIGURE 12.3.10

Each vector can be expressed as a linear combination of the unit coordinate vectors:

$$\text{for} \quad \mathbf{a} = (a_1, a_2, a_3) \qquad \text{we have} \quad \mathbf{a} = a_1\mathbf{i} + a_2\mathbf{j} + a_3\mathbf{k}.$$

VERIFICATION

$$\begin{aligned}(a_1, a_2, a_3) &= (a_1, 0, 0) + (0, a_2, 0) + (0, 0, a_3)\\ &= a_1(1, 0, 0) + a_2(0, 1, 0) + a_3(0, 0, 1)\\ &= a_1\mathbf{i} + a_2\mathbf{j} + a_3\mathbf{k}. \quad \square\end{aligned}$$

If

$$\mathbf{a} = a_1\mathbf{i} + a_2\mathbf{j} + a_3\mathbf{k},$$

the numbers a_1, a_2, a_3 are called the *scalar components* of $\mathbf{a}$ or more simply the *components* of $\mathbf{a}$. The vectors $a_1\mathbf{i}$, $a_2\mathbf{j}$, $a_3\mathbf{k}$ are called the *vector components* of $\mathbf{a}$.

Problem. Given that

$$\mathbf{a} = 3\mathbf{i} - \mathbf{j} + \mathbf{k} \qquad \text{and} \qquad \mathbf{b} = 2\mathbf{i} + 3\mathbf{j} - \mathbf{k},$$

(1) express $2\mathbf{a} - \mathbf{b}$ as a linear combination of $\mathbf{i}, \mathbf{j}, \mathbf{k}$.

(2) compute $\|2\mathbf{a} - \mathbf{b}\|$.

(3) find the vector $\mathbf{c}$ that has length 1 and the same direction as $2\mathbf{a} - \mathbf{b}$.

SOLUTION

(1)
$$\begin{aligned}2\mathbf{a} - \mathbf{b} &= 2(3\mathbf{i} - \mathbf{j} + \mathbf{k}) - (2\mathbf{i} + 3\mathbf{j} - \mathbf{k})\\ &= 6\mathbf{i} - 2\mathbf{j} + 2\mathbf{k} - 2\mathbf{i} - 3\mathbf{j} + \mathbf{k}\\ &= 4\mathbf{i} - 5\mathbf{j} + 3\mathbf{k}.\end{aligned}$$

(2) $$\|2\mathbf{a} - \mathbf{b}\| = \|4\mathbf{i} - 5\mathbf{j} + 3\mathbf{k}\|$$
$$= \sqrt{16 + 25 + 9}$$
$$= \sqrt{50}$$
$$= 5\sqrt{2}.$$

(3) If $\mathbf{c}$ has the same direction as $2\mathbf{a} - \mathbf{b}$ then

$$\mathbf{c} = k(2\mathbf{a} - \mathbf{b}) \qquad \text{with} \quad k > 0.$$

Taking norms, we have

$$1 = \|\mathbf{c}\| = \|k(2\mathbf{a} - \mathbf{b})\| = |k|\|2\mathbf{a} - \mathbf{b}\| = k5\sqrt{2}.$$

Therefore

$$k = \frac{1}{5\sqrt{2}}$$

and

$$\mathbf{c} = \frac{1}{5\sqrt{2}}(2\mathbf{a} - \mathbf{b}). \quad \square$$

Exercises

For the first six exercises we shall refer to the following vectors:

$$\mathbf{V}_1 = (1, -1, 2) \qquad \mathbf{V}_4 = (1, 0, -3) \qquad \mathbf{V}_7 = 3\mathbf{j} + 12\mathbf{k}$$
$$\mathbf{V}_2 = (0, 1, 4) \qquad \mathbf{V}_5 = (0, -\tfrac{1}{2}, 2) \qquad \mathbf{V}_8 = -\tfrac{1}{3}\mathbf{i} + \tfrac{1}{3}\mathbf{j} - \tfrac{2}{3}\mathbf{k}.$$
$$\mathbf{V}_3 = (0, -2, -8) \qquad \mathbf{V}_6 = (2, -2, 4)$$

1.* Which vectors are parallel to $\mathbf{V}_1$?
2. Which have the same direction as $\mathbf{V}_1$?
3.* Which have direction opposite to that of $\mathbf{V}_1$?
4. Which are parallel to $\mathbf{V}_2$?
5.* Which have the same direction as $\mathbf{V}_2$?
6. Which have direction opposite to that of $\mathbf{V}_2$?

7. Simplify the following linear combinations.
   (a)* $2(3, -1, 0) - (2, 1, 4)$.
   (b) $(6\mathbf{j} - \mathbf{k}) + (3\mathbf{i} - \mathbf{j} + 2\mathbf{k})$.
   (c)* $\tfrac{1}{2}(2\mathbf{i} - 5\mathbf{k}) - 3\mathbf{j} + 6(\tfrac{1}{2}\mathbf{j} - \mathbf{k})$.
8. Compute the norm of the following vectors.
   (a)* $\mathbf{i} + \mathbf{j}$.
   (b) $\mathbf{i} - \mathbf{j}$.
   (c)* $6\mathbf{i} + 2\mathbf{j} - \mathbf{k}$.
   (d) $\tfrac{1}{2}(\mathbf{i} + 4\mathbf{j}) - (\tfrac{3}{2}\mathbf{i} + \mathbf{k})$.
   (e)* $(\mathbf{i} - \mathbf{j}) + 2(\mathbf{j} - \mathbf{i}) + (\mathbf{k} - \mathbf{j})$.

9.* For each of the parallelograms below label the diagonals indicated:

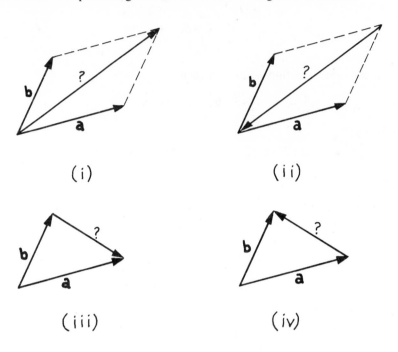

10. (*Important*) Prove the following version of the triangle inequality:

$$\big|\, \|\mathbf{a}\| - \|\mathbf{b}\| \,\big| \le \|\mathbf{a} - \mathbf{b}\|.$$

[HINT: Apply the previously stated triangle inequality to

$$\mathbf{a} = (\mathbf{a} - \mathbf{b}) + \mathbf{b}.]$$

11.* Given that

$$\mathbf{a} = (1, 1, 1), \quad \mathbf{b} = (-1, 3, 2), \quad \mathbf{c} = (-3, 0, 1), \quad \mathbf{d} = (4, -1, 1),$$

(a) express $\mathbf{a} + 2\mathbf{b} + 3\mathbf{c} + 4\mathbf{d}$ as a linear combination of $\mathbf{i}, \mathbf{j}, \mathbf{k}$.
(b) find scalars A, B, C such that

$$\mathbf{d} = A\mathbf{a} + B\mathbf{b} + C\mathbf{c}.$$

12. Find α given that

$$3\mathbf{i} + \mathbf{j} - \mathbf{k} \quad \text{and} \quad \alpha\mathbf{i} - 4\mathbf{j} + 4\mathbf{k}$$

are parallel.

13.* Find α given that

$$3\mathbf{i} + \mathbf{j} \quad \text{and} \quad \alpha\mathbf{j} - \mathbf{k}$$

have the same length.

14.   Solve for α:

$$\|\alpha\mathbf{i} + (\alpha - 1)\mathbf{j} + (\alpha + 1)\mathbf{k}\| = 2.$$

15.* Find the vector with norm 2 which has
   (a) the same direction as $\mathbf{i} + 2\mathbf{j} - \mathbf{k}$.
   (b) direction opposite to that of $3\mathbf{j} + 2\mathbf{k}$.

12.4   The dot product

We come now to a notion that is widely used in geometry and in physics.

> **Definition 12.4.1**
>
> For vectors $\mathbf{a} = (a_1, a_2, a_3)$ and $\mathbf{b} = (b_1, b_2, b_3)$ we define
>
> $$\mathbf{a} \cdot \mathbf{b} = a_1 b_1 + a_2 b_2 + a_3 b_3.$$

The number $\mathbf{a} \cdot \mathbf{b}$, read "a dot b", is called the *dot product* of $\mathbf{a}$ and $\mathbf{b}$.

Examples.   If

$$\mathbf{a} = (2, -1, 3) \qquad \text{and} \qquad \mathbf{b} = (-3, 1, 4),$$

then

$$\mathbf{a} \cdot \mathbf{b} = (2)(-3) + (-1)(1) + (3)(4) = -6 - 1 + 12 = 5.$$

If

$$\mathbf{a} = \mathbf{j} - \mathbf{k} \qquad \text{and} \qquad \mathbf{b} = 4\mathbf{i} - \tfrac{1}{2}\mathbf{j} + 2\mathbf{k},$$

then

$$\mathbf{a} \cdot \mathbf{b} = (\mathbf{j} - \mathbf{k}) \cdot (4\mathbf{i} - \tfrac{1}{2}\mathbf{j} + 2\mathbf{k}) = (0)(4) + (1)(-\tfrac{1}{2}) + (-1)(2) = -\tfrac{5}{2}. \quad \square$$

The dot product is also called the *scalar product* or *inner product*. We'll generally call it the dot product and speak of "dotting" $\mathbf{a}$ with $\mathbf{b}$. If we dot a vector with itself, we obtain the square of the norm of the vector:

$$\mathbf{a} \cdot \mathbf{a} = \|\mathbf{a}\|^2.$$

$$[\mathbf{a} \cdot \mathbf{a} = a_1 a_1 + a_2 a_2 + a_3 a_3 = a_1^2 + a_2^2 + a_3^2 = \|\mathbf{a}\|^2].$$

Consequently

$$\mathbf{a} \cdot \mathbf{a} \geq 0 \qquad \text{and} \qquad \mathbf{a} \cdot \mathbf{a} = 0 \quad \text{iff} \quad \mathbf{a} = 0.$$

For a geometric interpretation of $\mathbf{a} \cdot \mathbf{b}$ we form the triangle with vertices $P(x, y, z)$, $Q(x + a_1, y + a_2, z + a_3)$, $R(x + b_1, y + b_2, z + b_3)$. See Figure 12.4.1. Since the sides of the triangle have lengths $\|\mathbf{a}\|$, $\|\mathbf{b}\|$, and $\|\mathbf{a} - \mathbf{b}\|$, the law of cosines gives

$$\|\mathbf{a} - \mathbf{b}\|^2 = \|\mathbf{a}\|^2 + \|\mathbf{b}\|^2 - 2\|\mathbf{a}\|\|\mathbf{b}\| \cos \theta.$$

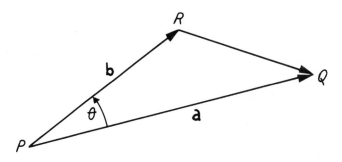

FIGURE 12.4.1

Consequently

$$2\|\mathbf{a}\| \|\mathbf{b}\| \cos \theta = \|\mathbf{a}\|^2 + \|\mathbf{b}\|^2 - \|\mathbf{a} - \mathbf{b}\|^2$$
$$= a_1^2 + a_2^2 + a_3^2 + b_1^2 + b_2^2 + b_3^2 - (a_1 - b_1)^2 - (a_2 - b_2)^2 - (a_3 - b_3)^2$$
$$= 2(a_1 b_1 + a_2 b_2 + a_3 b_3)$$
$$= 2(\mathbf{a} \cdot \mathbf{b}),$$

so that we have

(12.4.2) $\mathbf{a} \cdot \mathbf{b} = \|\mathbf{a}\| \|\mathbf{b}\| \cos \theta.$

The number θ (which in the figure is the angle between $\overrightarrow{PQ}$ and $\overrightarrow{PR}$) we take to satisfy $0 < \theta < \pi$ and call it the *angle between* $\mathbf{a}$ and $\mathbf{b}$. It can be obtained from the relation

$$\cos \theta = \frac{\mathbf{a} \cdot \mathbf{b}}{\|\mathbf{a}\| \|\mathbf{b}\|}$$

unless either $\mathbf{a}$ or $\mathbf{b}$ is the zero vector, in which case the angle is not defined.

If $\mathbf{a} \cdot \mathbf{b} = 0$, which happens if $\theta = \pi/2$ or if one of the vectors is the zero vector, we call $\mathbf{a}$ and $\mathbf{b}$ perpendicular.† To indicate that $\mathbf{a}$ and $\mathbf{b}$ are perpendicular we will sometimes write $\mathbf{a} \perp \mathbf{b}$. Obviously the coordinate vectors $\mathbf{i}, \mathbf{j}, \mathbf{k}$ are mutually perpendicular.

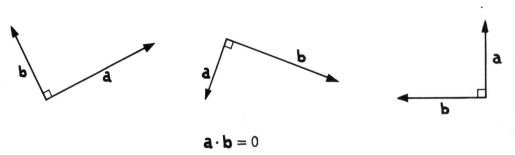

$\mathbf{a} \cdot \mathbf{b} = 0$

FIGURE 12.4.2

---

† This makes the zero vector both parallel and perpendicular to every vector. There is however no contradiction since we never apply the notion of angle to the zero vector.

Problem. Find the angle between

$$\mathbf{a} = 2\mathbf{i} + \mathbf{j} - 3\mathbf{k} \qquad \text{and} \qquad \mathbf{b} = \mathbf{i} - \mathbf{j} + \mathbf{k}.$$

SOLUTION

$$\cos\theta = \frac{\mathbf{a}\cdot\mathbf{b}}{\|\mathbf{a}\|\,\|\mathbf{b}\|} = \frac{(2)(1) + (1)(-1) + (-3)(1)}{\sqrt{2^2 + 1^2 + (-3)^2}\sqrt{1^2 + (-1)^2 + (1)^2}} = \frac{2 - 1 - 3}{\sqrt{14}\sqrt{3}} = -\frac{\sqrt{2}}{\sqrt{21}}$$

$$\theta = \text{arc cos}\left(-\frac{\sqrt{2}}{\sqrt{21}}\right). \quad \Box$$

Problem. Find α given that

$$\mathbf{i} + 2\mathbf{j} \qquad \text{and} \qquad 3\mathbf{i} - \alpha\mathbf{j} + \mathbf{k}$$

are perpendicular.

SOLUTION.   For the two vectors to be perpendicular, their dot product

$$(\mathbf{i} + 2\mathbf{j})\cdot(3\mathbf{i} - \alpha\mathbf{j} + \mathbf{k}) = (1)(3) + (2)(-\alpha) + (0)(1) = 3 - 2\alpha$$

must be zero. This requires

$$3 - 2\alpha = 0$$

and hence

$$\alpha = \frac{3}{2}. \quad \Box$$

In using the dot product, it is handy to note the following properties:

$$\mathbf{a}\cdot\mathbf{b} = \mathbf{b}\cdot\mathbf{a} \qquad\qquad \text{(the dot product is commutative)}$$

$$\alpha\mathbf{a}\cdot\beta\mathbf{b} = \alpha\beta(\mathbf{a}\cdot\mathbf{b}) \qquad\qquad \text{(scalars can be factored out)}$$

$$\mathbf{a}\cdot(\mathbf{b} + \mathbf{c}) = \mathbf{a}\cdot\mathbf{b} + \mathbf{a}\cdot\mathbf{c} \qquad\qquad \text{(the dot distributes over addition)}$$

$$|\mathbf{a}\cdot\mathbf{b}| \leq \|\mathbf{a}\|\,\|\mathbf{b}\|. \qquad\qquad \text{(Schwarz's inequality)}$$

The first three properties follow easily from the definition. Schwarz's inequality is obvious from the relation

$$\mathbf{a}\cdot\mathbf{b} = \|\mathbf{a}\|\,\|\mathbf{b}\|\cos\theta$$

together with the observation that

$$|\cos\theta| \leq 1.$$

Problem. Show that

$$(\mathbf{a} + \mathbf{b})\cdot\mathbf{c} = \mathbf{a}\cdot\mathbf{c} + \mathbf{b}\cdot\mathbf{c}.$$

SOLUTION

$$(\mathbf{a} + \mathbf{b})\cdot\mathbf{c} = \mathbf{c}\cdot(\mathbf{a} + \mathbf{b}) \quad \text{(by commutativity)}$$
$$= \mathbf{c}\cdot\mathbf{a} + \mathbf{c}\cdot\mathbf{b} \quad \text{(by distributivity)}$$
$$= \mathbf{a}\cdot\mathbf{c} + \mathbf{b}\cdot\mathbf{c}. \quad \text{(by commutativity)} \quad \square$$

We are now in a position to verify the triangle inequality

$$\|\mathbf{a} + \mathbf{b}\| \le \|\mathbf{a}\| + \|\mathbf{b}\|.$$

VERIFICATION

$$\|\mathbf{a} + \mathbf{b}\|^2 = (\mathbf{a} + \mathbf{b})\cdot(\mathbf{a} + \mathbf{b})$$
$$= \mathbf{a}\cdot\mathbf{a} + \mathbf{b}\cdot\mathbf{a} + \mathbf{a}\cdot\mathbf{b} + \mathbf{b}\cdot\mathbf{b}$$
$$= \|\mathbf{a}\|^2 + 2(\mathbf{a}\cdot\mathbf{b}) + \|\mathbf{b}\|^2$$
$$\le \|\mathbf{a}\|^2 + 2\|\mathbf{a}\|\,\|\mathbf{b}\| + \|\mathbf{b}\|^2$$
$$= (\|\mathbf{a}\| + \|\mathbf{b}\|)^2$$

so that

$$\|\mathbf{a} + \mathbf{b}\| \le \|\mathbf{a}\| + \|\mathbf{b}\|. \quad \square$$

We go back now to the formula

$$\mathbf{a}\cdot\mathbf{b} = \|\mathbf{a}\|\,\|\mathbf{b}\| \cos\theta.$$

For $\mathbf{a} \ne \mathbf{0}$, the number

$$\|\mathbf{b}\| \cos\theta = \frac{\mathbf{a}\cdot\mathbf{b}}{\|\mathbf{a}\|} \qquad \text{(See Figure 12.4.3)}$$

measures the "advance" of $\mathbf{b}$ in the direction of $\mathbf{a}$. It is called the (*scalar*) *component* of $\mathbf{b}$ in the direction of $\mathbf{a}$.

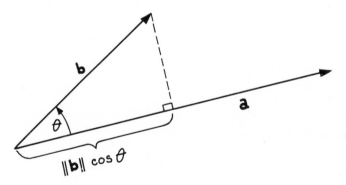

FIGURE 12.4.3

In abbreviated form we write

$$\text{comp}_a\mathbf{b} = \frac{\mathbf{a}\cdot\mathbf{b}}{\|\mathbf{a}\|} = \|\mathbf{b}\| \cos\theta.$$

Note that

$$\text{comp}_a\mathbf{b} \quad \text{is} \quad \begin{cases} \text{positive,} & \text{if } 0 \le \theta < \dfrac{\pi}{2}\,. \\[2mm] \text{zero,} & \text{if } \theta = \dfrac{\pi}{2}\,. \\[2mm] \text{and negative,} & \text{if } \dfrac{\pi}{2} < \theta \le \pi. \end{cases}$$

(See Figure 12.4.4.)

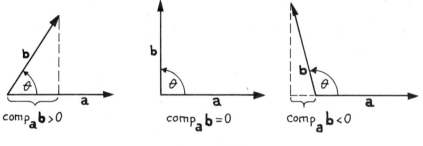

FIGURE 12.4.4

Problem. Given

$$\mathbf{a} = \mathbf{j} - 2\mathbf{i} + \mathbf{k} \quad \text{and} \quad \mathbf{b} = 4\mathbf{i} - 3\mathbf{j} + \mathbf{k},$$

compute the component of each vector in the direction of the other.

SOLUTION. We begin by rewriting $\mathbf{a}$ as

$$\mathbf{a} = -2\mathbf{i} + \mathbf{j} + \mathbf{k}.$$

Now

$$\begin{aligned} \mathbf{a}\cdot\mathbf{b} = \mathbf{b}\cdot\mathbf{a} &= -8 - 3 + 1 = -10 \\ \|\mathbf{a}\| &= \sqrt{4 + 1 + 1} = \sqrt{6} \\ \|\mathbf{b}\| &= \sqrt{16 + 9 + 1} = \sqrt{26}. \end{aligned}$$

Therefore

$$\text{comp}_\mathbf{a}\mathbf{b} = \frac{\mathbf{a} \cdot \mathbf{b}}{\|\mathbf{a}\|} = -\frac{10}{\sqrt{6}}$$

$$\text{comp}_\mathbf{b}\mathbf{a} = \frac{\mathbf{b} \cdot \mathbf{a}}{\|\mathbf{b}\|} = -\frac{10}{\sqrt{26}} \cdot \quad \square$$

If

$$\mathbf{b} = b_1\mathbf{i} + b_2\mathbf{j} + b_3\mathbf{k},$$

then

$$\text{comp}_\mathbf{i}\mathbf{b} = \frac{\mathbf{i} \cdot \mathbf{b}}{\|\mathbf{i}\|} = \frac{b_1}{1} = b_1$$

$$\text{comp}_\mathbf{j}\mathbf{b} = \frac{\mathbf{j} \cdot \mathbf{b}}{\|\mathbf{j}\|} = \frac{b_2}{1} = b_2$$

$$\text{comp}_\mathbf{k}\mathbf{b} = \frac{\mathbf{k} \cdot \mathbf{b}}{\|\mathbf{k}\|} = \frac{b_3}{1} = b_3.$$

These results agree with our previous use of the word "component."†

We can also speak of the *direction cosines* of a nonzero vector $\mathbf{b} = b_1\mathbf{i} + b_2\mathbf{j} + b_3\mathbf{k}$. These are the cosines of the angles α, β, γ that $\mathbf{b}$ makes with the coordinate vectors $\mathbf{i}, \mathbf{j}, \mathbf{k}$. Obviously we have

$$\cos \alpha = \frac{\mathbf{i} \cdot \mathbf{b}}{\|\mathbf{i}\| \, \|\mathbf{b}\|} = \frac{b_1}{\|\mathbf{b}\|}$$

$$\cos \beta = \frac{\mathbf{j} \cdot \mathbf{b}}{\|\mathbf{j}\| \, \|\mathbf{b}\|} = \frac{b_2}{\|\mathbf{b}\|}$$

$$\cos \gamma = \frac{\mathbf{k} \cdot \mathbf{b}}{\|\mathbf{k}\| \, \|\mathbf{b}\|} = \frac{b_3}{\|\mathbf{b}\|},$$

so that $\mathbf{b}$ can be written

$$\boxed{\mathbf{b} = \|\mathbf{b}\| \, (\cos \alpha \, \mathbf{i} + \cos \beta \, \mathbf{j} + \cos \gamma \, \mathbf{k}).}$$

If $\mathbf{b}$ is a unit vector (that is, if $\|\mathbf{b}\| = 1$), then we have simply

$$\mathbf{b} = \cos \alpha \, \mathbf{i} + \cos \beta \, \mathbf{j} + \cos \gamma \, \mathbf{k}.$$

Namely, in the case of a unit vector the components are the direction cosines.

Problem.   Find the vector $\mathbf{a}$ given it has norm 3 and direction angles

$$\alpha = \frac{\pi}{4}, \qquad \beta = \frac{2\pi}{3}, \qquad \gamma = \frac{\pi}{6} \cdot$$

---

† At the end of Section 12.3.

SOLUTION

$$\mathbf{b} = \|\mathbf{b}\|(\cos \alpha \ \mathbf{i} + \cos \beta \ \mathbf{j} + \cos \gamma \ \mathbf{k})$$

$$= 3\left(\frac{1}{\sqrt{2}}\mathbf{i} - \frac{1}{2}\mathbf{j} + \frac{\sqrt{3}}{2}\mathbf{k}\right)$$

$$= \frac{3}{\sqrt{2}}\mathbf{i} - \frac{3}{2}\mathbf{j} + \frac{3\sqrt{3}}{2}\mathbf{k}. \quad \square$$

Exercises

For the first four exercises we set

$$\mathbf{a} = 2\mathbf{i} + \mathbf{j}, \quad \mathbf{b} = 3\mathbf{i} - \mathbf{j} + 2\mathbf{k}, \quad \mathbf{c} = 4\mathbf{i} + 3\mathbf{k}.$$

1.* Compute the three dot products, $\mathbf{a}\cdot\mathbf{b}$, $\mathbf{a}\cdot\mathbf{c}$, $\mathbf{b}\cdot\mathbf{c}$.
2. Compute the cosines of the angles between these vectors.
3.* Compute the components of $\mathbf{a}$ in the direction of $\mathbf{b}$ and $\mathbf{c}$.
4. Compute the components of $\mathbf{b}$ in the direction of $\mathbf{a}$ and $\mathbf{c}$.
5.* What can you conclude about $\mathbf{a}$ and $\mathbf{b}$ given that
   (a) $\|\mathbf{a}\|^2 + \|\mathbf{b}\|^2 = \|\mathbf{a} + \mathbf{b}\|^2$?
   (b) $\|\mathbf{a}\|^2 + \|\mathbf{b}\|^2 = \|\mathbf{a} - \mathbf{b}\|^2$?
   [HINT: Draw figures.]
6. Verify the equation

$$\|\mathbf{a} + \mathbf{b}\|^2 + \|\mathbf{a} - \mathbf{b}\|^2 = 2\|\mathbf{a}\|^2 + 2\|\mathbf{b}\|^2.$$

   What does this say about parallelograms?
7.* (*Important*) Show that $\mathbf{a}\cdot\mathbf{b} = \mathbf{a}\cdot\mathbf{c}$ does not necessarily imply that $\mathbf{b} = \mathbf{c}$. Draw a figure illustrating this fact for nonzero vectors.
8. Verify.

$$4(\mathbf{a}\cdot\mathbf{b}) = \|\mathbf{a} + \mathbf{b}\|^2 - \|\mathbf{a} - \mathbf{b}\|^2.$$

9. Show that

$$\mathbf{a} \perp \mathbf{b} \quad \text{iff} \quad \|\mathbf{a} + \mathbf{b}\| = \|\mathbf{a} - \mathbf{b}\|.$$

10. Derive Schwarz's inequality

$$|\mathbf{a}\cdot\mathbf{b}| \leq \|\mathbf{a}\| \, \|\mathbf{b}\|$$

   from the observation that the quadratic polynomial

$$f(x) = (a_1 x + b_1)^2 + (a_2 x + b_2)^2 + (a_3 x + b_3)^2$$

   is nonnegative.

[HINT: Rewrite the quadratic as

$$Ax^2 + Bx + C$$

and observe that its discriminant

$$B^2 - 4AC$$

cannot be positive.]

11.   Under what conditions does

$$|\mathbf{a} \cdot \mathbf{b}| = \|\mathbf{a}\| \, \|\mathbf{b}\|?$$

If a force $\mathbf{F}$ is applied throughout a displacement $\mathbf{r}$ then the work done is defined by

$$W = (\mathrm{comp}_{\mathbf{r}} \mathbf{F}) \|\mathbf{r}\|.$$

12.* Express the work W as a dot product.

13.   What is the work done if $\mathbf{F} \perp \mathbf{r}$?

14.   Two forces of the same magnitude $\mathbf{F}_1$ and $\mathbf{F}_2$ are applied throughout a displacement $\mathbf{r}$ at angles θ_1 and θ_2 respectively. Compare the work done by $\mathbf{F}_1$ to that done by $\mathbf{F}_2$ if
(a)* $\theta_1 = -\theta_2$.
(b) $\theta_1 = \pi - \theta_2$.
(c)* $\theta_1 = \pi/3, \quad \theta_2 = \pi/6$.

15.   What is the work done by $\mathbf{F}$ if the object moves completely around a triangle? Justify your answer.

16.   Find the numbers x for which
(a)* $\mathbf{a} = x\mathbf{i} + 11\mathbf{j} - 3\mathbf{k}$ and $\mathbf{b} = 2x\mathbf{i} - x\mathbf{j} - 5\mathbf{k}$ are perpendicular.
(b) the angle between

$$\mathbf{c} = x\mathbf{i} + \mathbf{j} + \mathbf{k} \quad \text{and} \quad \mathbf{d} = \mathbf{i} + x\mathbf{j} + \mathbf{k} \quad \text{is} \quad \pi/3.$$

17.   Find the angle between the diagonal of a cube and
(a)* one of its edges.
(b) the diagonal of one of its faces.

18.   (*Important*)   Show that the direction cosines of a nonzero vector satisfy

$$\cos^2 \alpha + \cos^2 \beta + \cos^2 \gamma = 1.$$

19.   Let $\mathbf{b}$ be a nonzero vector. Express the vector $\mathbf{a}$ as the sum of a vector parallel to $\mathbf{b}$ and a vector perpendicular to $\mathbf{b}$.
[HINT: Set $\mathbf{a} = s\mathbf{b} + (\mathbf{a} - s\mathbf{b})$ and choose s so that $\mathbf{a} - s\mathbf{b} \perp \mathbf{b}$.]

12.5 Lines

Vectors to us are simply ordered triples of real numbers and, as you have seen, they can be given many interpretations. When vectors are used to indicate position in three-dimensional space, they are called *position vectors*. In general we picture position vectors as emanating from the origin. In this section we will use position vectors to characterize lines.

We begin with the idea that two distinct points determine a line. In Figure 12.5.1 we have marked two points and the line *l* that they determine. To obtain a vector characterization of *l*, we choose the vectors **a** and **b** as in Figure 12.5.2. (Since we began with two distinct points, the vector **b** is nonzero. Keep this in mind.) In Figure 12.5.3 we have drawn an additional vector **c**. What we want is a necessary and sufficient condition on the vector **c** for the tip of **c** to fall on the line *l*. This is not hard to find:

FIGURE 12.5.1

FIGURE 12.5.2

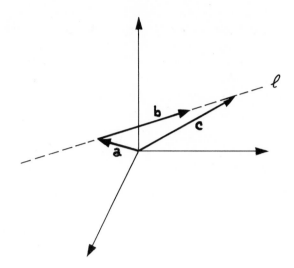

FIGURE 12.5.3

The tip of **c** will fall on *l* iff

$$\mathbf{c} - \mathbf{a} \quad \text{and} \quad \mathbf{b} \quad \text{are parallel;}$$

this in turn will happen iff

$$\mathbf{c} - \mathbf{a} = t\mathbf{b} \qquad \text{for some real } t$$

or, equivalently, iff

$$\mathbf{c} = \mathbf{a} + t\mathbf{b} \qquad \text{for some real } t.$$

In view of this we call the equation

$$\boxed{\mathbf{r}(t) = \mathbf{a} + t\mathbf{b}, \qquad t \text{ real}}$$

a *vector parametrization* for the line *l*. By varying *t*, we vary the vector $\mathbf{r}(t)$, but its tip remains on the line *l*. As *t* ranges over the set of real numbers, the tip of $\mathbf{r}(t)$ traces out the line *l*.

The role of **a** and **b** in this matter deserves further attention. The vector $\mathbf{a} = (a_1, a_2, a_3)$ places the point $P(a_1, a_2, a_3)$ on the line. The vector **b**, which as we remarked is nonzero, gives the direction of the line. It is called a *direction vector* for *l*.

Problem. Find a vector parametrization for the line that passes through the point $P(1, -1, 2)$ and is parallel to the vector $2\mathbf{i} - 3\mathbf{j} + \mathbf{k}$.

SOLUTION. Here we can take

$$\mathbf{a} = (1, -1, 2) = \mathbf{i} - \mathbf{j} + 2\mathbf{k} \qquad \text{and} \qquad \mathbf{b} = 2\mathbf{i} - 3\mathbf{j} + \mathbf{k}.$$

As a vector parametrization for the line we have

$$\mathbf{r}(t) = (\mathbf{i} - \mathbf{j} + 2\mathbf{k}) + t(2\mathbf{i} - 3\mathbf{j} + \mathbf{k}),$$

which we can rewrite as

$$\mathbf{r}(t) = (1 + 2t)\mathbf{i} - (1 + 3t)\mathbf{j} + (2 + t)\mathbf{k}. \quad \square$$

Problem. Given that the line

$$\mathbf{r}(t) = \mathbf{a} + t\mathbf{b}$$

passes through the origin, what can we conclude about $\mathbf{a}$ and $\mathbf{b}$?

SOLUTION. At first glance it may appear that $\mathbf{a}$ has to be $\mathbf{0}$ but this is not true. From the fact that the line passes through the origin we cannot conclude that $\mathbf{a}$ is $\mathbf{0}$ but only that there exists a real number t_0 such that

$$\mathbf{a} + t_0\mathbf{b} = \mathbf{0}.$$

This tells us that

$$\mathbf{a} = -t_0\mathbf{b}$$

and thus $\mathbf{a}$ is a scalar multiple of $\mathbf{b}$. $\square$

It is not hard to see that two distinct lines

$$l_1: \quad \mathbf{r}_1(t) = \mathbf{a} + t\mathbf{b}$$
$$l_2: \quad \mathbf{r}_2(t) = \mathbf{c} + t\mathbf{d}$$

will intersect iff there are numbers t_1 and t_2 such that

$$\mathbf{r}_1(t_1) = \mathbf{r}_2(t_2).$$

Problem. Find the point at which the lines

$$l_1: \quad \mathbf{r}_1(t) = (\mathbf{i} - 6\mathbf{j} + 2\mathbf{k}) + t(\mathbf{i} + 2\mathbf{j} + \mathbf{k})$$
$$l_2: \quad \mathbf{r}_2(t) = (4\mathbf{j} + \mathbf{k}) + t(2\mathbf{i} + \mathbf{j} + 2\mathbf{k})$$

intersect.

SOLUTION. We set

$$\mathbf{r}_1(t_1) = \mathbf{r}_2(t_2)$$

and solve for t_1 and t_2:

$$(\mathbf{i} - 6\mathbf{j} + 2\mathbf{k}) + t_1(\mathbf{i} + 2\mathbf{j} + \mathbf{k}) = (4\mathbf{j} + \mathbf{k}) + t_2(2\mathbf{i} + \mathbf{j} + 2\mathbf{k})$$
$$\mathbf{i} - 6\mathbf{j} + 2\mathbf{k} + t_1\mathbf{i} + 2t_1\mathbf{j} + t_1\mathbf{k} = 4\mathbf{j} + \mathbf{k} + 2t_2\mathbf{i} + t_2\mathbf{j} + 2t_2\mathbf{k}$$
$$(1 + t_1 - 2t_2)\mathbf{i} + (-10 + 2t_1 - t_2)\mathbf{j} + (1 + t_1 - 2t_2)\mathbf{k} = \mathbf{0}.$$

This tells us that

$$1 + \ t_1 - 2t_2 = 0$$
$$-10 + 2t_1 - \ t_2 = 0$$
$$1 + \ t_1 - 2t_2 = 0.$$

Note that the first and third equations are the same. Solving the first two equations simultaneously, we obtain

$$t_1 = 7, \qquad t_2 = 4.$$

As you can verify,

$$\mathbf{r}_1(7) = 8\mathbf{i} + 8\mathbf{j} + 9\mathbf{k} = \mathbf{r}_2(4).$$

The two lines intersect at the tip of this vector, which is the point $P(8, 8, 9)$. $\square$

In the setting of plane geometry we can think of two lines as parallel iff they do not intersect. This point of view is not satisfactory in three-dimensional space where there are many lines which fail to intersect which yet we would hesitate to call parallel. See Figure 12.5.4. We can get around this difficulty by using direction vectors; namely, we will call two lines *parallel* iff their direction vectors are parallel.

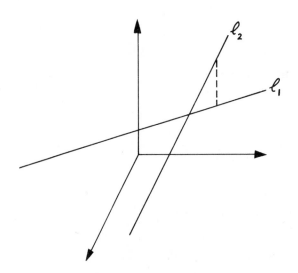

FIGURE 12.5.4

If two lines intersect, we can compute the angle between them by finding the angle between their direction vectors. Depending upon our choice of direction vectors (**b** or $-\mathbf{b}$, for example) there are two such angles, θ and $\pi - \theta$. We choose the smaller of the two, the one with nonnegative cosine.

Problem. Find the angle between

$$l_1 : \mathbf{r}_1(t) = (\mathbf{i} - 6\mathbf{j} + 2\mathbf{k}) + t(\mathbf{i} + 2\mathbf{j} + \mathbf{k}) \quad \text{and} \quad l_2 : \mathbf{r}_2(t) = (4\mathbf{j} + \mathbf{k}) + t(2\mathbf{i} + \mathbf{j} + 2\mathbf{k}).$$

SOLUTION.   As direction vectors we have

$$\mathbf{b}_1 = \mathbf{i} + 2\mathbf{j} + \mathbf{k} \qquad \text{and} \qquad \mathbf{b}_2 = 2\mathbf{i} + \mathbf{j} + 2\mathbf{k}.$$

As you can check,

$$\cos \theta = \frac{\mathbf{b}_1 \cdot \mathbf{b}_2}{\|\mathbf{b}_1\| \|\mathbf{b}_2\|} = \frac{6}{\sqrt{6}(3)} = \frac{\sqrt{2}}{\sqrt{3}}$$

so that

$$\theta = \text{arc} \cos \left(\frac{\sqrt{2}}{\sqrt{3}} \right). \quad \square$$

If two parallel vectors are both depicted by arrows emanating from the origin, then the two arrows will both fall on the same line. Because of this, parallel vectors are often called *collinear vectors*.

Exercises

1.* Given that

$$l: \quad \mathbf{r}(t) = (\mathbf{i} + 2\mathbf{j}) + t(6\mathbf{i} + \mathbf{j} - 5\mathbf{k}),$$

determine which of the following points lie on l:

$$P(1, 2, 0), \quad Q(-5, 1, 5), \quad R(-4, 2, 5).$$

2.* Determine which of the following lines are parallel:

$$l_1: \quad \mathbf{r}_1(t) = (\mathbf{i} + 2\mathbf{k}) + t(\mathbf{i} - 2\mathbf{j} + 3\mathbf{k})$$
$$l_2: \quad \mathbf{r}_2(t) = (\mathbf{i} + 2\mathbf{k}) + t(\mathbf{i} + 2\mathbf{j} - 3\mathbf{k})$$
$$l_3: \quad \mathbf{r}_3(t) = (6\mathbf{i} - \mathbf{j}) - t(2\mathbf{i} - 4\mathbf{j} + 6\mathbf{k})$$
$$l_4: \quad \mathbf{r}_4(t) = (\tfrac{1}{2} + \tfrac{1}{2}t)\mathbf{i} - t\mathbf{j} + (1 + \tfrac{3}{2}t)\mathbf{k}.$$

3.* The vector $\mathbf{b}$ serves as a direction vector for the line

$$l: \quad \mathbf{r}(t) = \mathbf{a} + t\mathbf{b}.$$

What other vectors could be used as direction vectors for this same line?

For each of the following pairs of lines, find the point at which they intersect. Then find the angle between the lines.

4. $l_1: \quad \mathbf{r}_1(t) = \mathbf{i} + t\mathbf{j}$
   $l_2: \quad \mathbf{r}_2(t) = \mathbf{j} + t(\mathbf{i} + \mathbf{j}).$
5.* $l_1: \quad \mathbf{r}_1(t) = (\mathbf{i} - 4\sqrt{3}\mathbf{j}) + t(\mathbf{i} + \sqrt{3}\mathbf{j})$
   $l_2: \quad \mathbf{r}_2(t) = (4\mathbf{i} + 3\sqrt{3}\mathbf{j}) + t(\mathbf{i} - \sqrt{3}\mathbf{j}).$
6. $l_1: \quad \mathbf{r}_1(t) = -6\mathbf{k} + t(\mathbf{i} - \mathbf{j} + 2\mathbf{k})$
   $l_2: \quad \mathbf{r}_2(t) = \mathbf{i} + \mathbf{j} - t(\mathbf{i} - 3\mathbf{j} - 2\mathbf{k}).$
7.* $l_1: \quad \mathbf{r}_1(t) = (3\mathbf{i} + \mathbf{j} + 5\mathbf{k}) + t(\mathbf{i} - \mathbf{j} + 2\mathbf{k}).$
   $l_2: \quad \mathbf{r}_2(t) = (\mathbf{i} + 4\mathbf{j} + 2\mathbf{k}) + t(\mathbf{j} + \mathbf{k}).$

8. Find a vector parametrization for the line that passes through
   (a)* $P(3, 1, 0)$ and is parallel to $l: \quad \mathbf{r}(t) = (\mathbf{i} - \mathbf{j}) + t\mathbf{k}.$
   (b) $P(1, -1, 2)$ and is parallel to $l: \quad \mathbf{r}(t) = t(3\mathbf{i} - \mathbf{j} + \mathbf{k}).$
   (c) the origin and $Q(b_1, b_2, b_3)$.
   (d)* $P(a_1, a_2, a_3)$ and $Q(b_1, b_2, b_3)$.

9.* Given the line

$$l: \quad \mathbf{r}(t) = \mathbf{a} + t\mathbf{b},$$

(a) find the scalar t_0 for which the vector $\mathbf{r}(t_0)$ is perpendicular to l.
(b) find the parametrizations

$$\mathbf{R}(t) = \mathbf{A} + t\mathbf{B} \quad \text{for } l$$

in which $\mathbf{A} \perp l$ and $\|\mathbf{B}\| = 1$.

10.* Find the distance between the line

$$l: \quad \mathbf{r}(t) = \mathbf{a} + t\mathbf{b} \quad \text{and} \quad \text{the origin}$$

given that

(a) $\mathbf{a} = \mathbf{j}$ and $\mathbf{b} = \mathbf{i} - \mathbf{j}$.
(b) $\mathbf{a} = \sqrt{3}\mathbf{i}$ and $\mathbf{b} = \dfrac{1}{\sqrt{3}}(\mathbf{i} + \mathbf{j} + \mathbf{k}).$

12.6 Planes

We derived an equation for a line by using a point from it and a nonzero vector parallel to it. We will now derive an equation for a plane by using a point from it and a nonzero vector *perpendicular* to it.

Let's assume that the plane passes through the point $P(x_0, y_0, z_0)$ and is perpendicular to the nonzero vector

$$\mathbf{N} = A\mathbf{i} + B\mathbf{j} + C\mathbf{k}.$$

For convenience we depict this vector $\mathbf{N}$ as an arrow emanating from the point $P(x_0, y_0, z_0)$ and ending at $R(x_0 + A, y_0 + B, z_0 + C)$. See Figure 12.6.1.

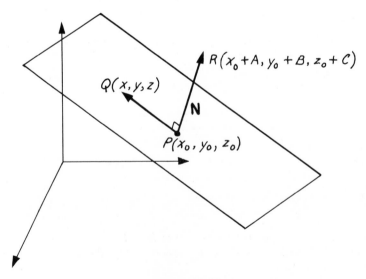

FIGURE 12.6.1

A point $Q(x, y, z)$ $[Q \neq P]$ will lie on the given plane iff the arrows $\overrightarrow{PR}$ and $\overrightarrow{PQ}$ meet at right angles; in vector terms iff

$$[A\mathbf{i} + B\mathbf{j} + C\mathbf{k}] \cdot [(x - x_0)\mathbf{i} + (y - y_0)\mathbf{j} + (z - z_0)\mathbf{k}] = 0$$

and thus, iff

(12.6.1) $$\boxed{A(x - x_0) + B(y - y_0) + C(z - z_0) = 0.}$$

This equation is the usual xyz-equation for the plane which passes through the point $P(x_0, y_0, z_0)$ and is perpendicular to the vector $\mathbf{N} = A\mathbf{i} + B\mathbf{j} + C\mathbf{k}$.

We can write this equation in more compact form by using vector notation. With

$$\mathbf{N} = A\mathbf{i} + B\mathbf{j} + C\mathbf{k}$$

and using the position vectors

$$\mathbf{r}_0 = x_0\mathbf{i} + y_0\mathbf{j} + z_0\mathbf{k}$$
$$\mathbf{r} = x\mathbf{i} + y\mathbf{j} + z\mathbf{k},$$

we can rewrite (12.6.1) as

$$\boxed{\mathbf{N} \cdot (\mathbf{r} - \mathbf{r}_0) = 0.}$$

See Figure 12.6.2.

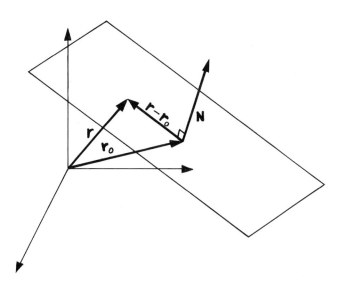

FIGURE 12.6.2

Problem. Find an equation in Cartesian coordinates for the plane that passes through the point $P(1, 0, 2)$ and is perpendicular to the vector $3\mathbf{i} - 2\mathbf{j} + \mathbf{k}$.

SOLUTION.   Here

$$P(x_0, y_0, z_0) = P(1, 0, 2) \qquad \text{and} \qquad \mathbf{N} = A\mathbf{i} + B\mathbf{j} + C\mathbf{k} = 3\mathbf{i} - 2\mathbf{j} + \mathbf{k}.$$

The general equation

$$A(x - x_0) + B(y - y_0) + C(z - z_0) = 0$$

becomes in this instance

$$3(x - 1) - 2y + (z - 2) = 0,$$

which, if you prefer, you can rewrite as

$$3x - 2y + z = 5. \quad \square$$

Problem.   Find a vector equation for the plane that passes through the point $P(1, 3, -2)$ and is perpendicular to the vector $\mathbf{i} - \mathbf{j}$. Then write the equation in terms of Cartesian coordinates.

SOLUTION.   Here we can take

$$\mathbf{r}_0 = \mathbf{i} + 3\mathbf{j} - 2\mathbf{k} \qquad \text{and} \qquad \mathbf{N} = \mathbf{i} - \mathbf{j}.$$

The vector equation

$$\mathbf{N} \cdot (\mathbf{r} - \mathbf{r}_0) = 0$$

becomes in this instance

$$[\mathbf{i} - \mathbf{j}] \cdot [\mathbf{r} - (\mathbf{i} + 3\mathbf{j} - 2\mathbf{k})] = 0.$$

To translate this equation into Cartesian coordinates, we set

$$\mathbf{r} = x\mathbf{i} + y\mathbf{j} + z\mathbf{k}.$$

This gives

$$[\mathbf{i} - \mathbf{j}] \cdot [(x - 1)\mathbf{i} + (y - 3)\mathbf{j} + (z + 2)\mathbf{k}] = 0$$
$$(x - 1) - (y - 3) = 0$$

and thus

$$x - y + 2 = 0.$$

This last equation looks very much like the equation of a line. If our domain of discourse were the xy-plane, then certainly

$$x - y + 2 = 0$$

should be interpreted as the equation of a line l. In this case, however, our domain of discourse is three-space. Here the equation

$$x - y + 2 = 0$$

represents the set of all points $Q(x, y, z)$, where $x - y + 2 = 0$ and z is unrestricted. This set forms a plane. The plane is vertical and intersects the xy-plane in the line l. $\square$

Problem. Find an equation in Cartesian coordinates for the plane determined by the three noncollinear points $P_0(-3, 2, 1)$, $P_1(1, -5, -5)$, $P_2(-4, 3, 2)$.

SOLUTION. Since $P_0(-3, 2, 1)$ lies on the plane, the equation can be written in the form

$$A(x - (-3)) + B(y - 2) + C(z - 1) = 0 \qquad \text{with } A, B, C \text{ not all 0.}$$

Since $P_1(1, -5, -5)$ and $P_2(-4, 3, 2)$ also lie on the plane,

$$A(1 - (-3)) + B(-5 - 2) + C(-5 - 1) = 0$$

and

$$A(-4 - (-3)) + B(3 - 2) + C(2 - 1) = 0.$$

These equations simplify to

$$4A - 7B - 6C = 0 \qquad \text{and} \qquad -A + B + C = 0.$$

Solving these equations simultaneously, we get

$$A = \tfrac{1}{3}C \qquad \text{and} \qquad B = -\tfrac{2}{3}C.$$

We can now assign any nonzero value to one of the constants.† The other two will then be determined. Setting $C = 3$, we get $A = 1$ and $B = -2$. The equation thus becomes

$$(x + 3) - 2(y - 2) + 3(z - 1) = 0,$$

which we can simplify to

$$x - 2y + 3z + 4 = 0. \quad \square$$

A nonzero vector $\mathbf{N}$ which is perpendicular to a plane p is said to be *normal* to p. If $\mathbf{N}$ is normal to p, then all the other normals are parallel to $\mathbf{N}$ and hence are scalar multiples of $\mathbf{N}$. In particular, there are only two normals of length 1:

$$\frac{\mathbf{N}}{\|\mathbf{N}\|} \qquad \text{and} \qquad -\frac{\mathbf{N}}{\|\mathbf{N}\|}.$$

These are called the *unit normals.*

Problem. Find the unit normals for the plane

$$3x - 2y + 5z = 2.$$

SOLUTION. The equation

$$A(x - x_0) + B(y - y_0) + C(z - z_0) = 0$$

can be rewritten in the form

$$Ax + By + Cz = Ax_0 + By_0 + Cz_0$$

---

† If we set one of the constants equal to 0, then the other two must also be 0 and no equation is determined.

and thus in the form

$$Ax + By + Cz = D.$$

The components for a normal can therefore be read off as the coefficients of x, y, z. Since in this case we are beginning with the equation

$$3x - 2y + 5z = 2,$$

we can take as a normal the vector

$$\mathbf{N} = 3\mathbf{i} - 2\mathbf{j} + 5\mathbf{k}.$$

With

$$\|\mathbf{N}\| = \sqrt{9 + 4 + 25} = \sqrt{38},$$

the unit normals are

$$\pm \frac{1}{\sqrt{38}} (3\mathbf{i} - 2\mathbf{j} + 5\mathbf{k}). \quad \square$$

Two planes are called *parallel* iff their normals are parallel. If two planes intersect, we compute the angle between them by finding the angle between their normals. Depending on our choice of normals ($\mathbf{N}$ or $-\mathbf{N}$, for example) there are two such angles, θ and $\pi - \theta$. We will choose the smaller of the two, the one with nonnegative cosine. See Figure 12.6.3.

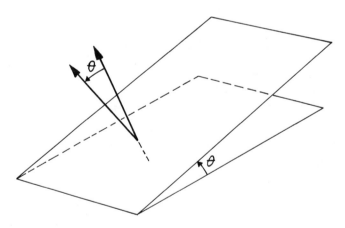

FIGURE 12.6.3

Problem. Let

$$
\begin{aligned}
p_1: &\quad 2(x - 1) - 3y + 5(z - 2) = 0 \\
p_2: &\quad -4x + 6y + 10z + 24 = 0 \\
p_3: &\quad 4x - 6y - 10z + 1 = 0 \\
p_4: &\quad 2x - 3y + 5z - 12 = 0.
\end{aligned}
$$

(a) Indicate which planes are identical.

(b) Indicate which planes are distinct and parallel.

(c) Find the angle between p_1 and p_2.

SOLUTION

(a) p_1 and p_4 are identical, as you can verify by simplifying the equation of p_1.

(b) p_2 and p_3 are distinct and parallel. The planes are distinct since $P(0, 0, \frac{1}{10})$ lies on p_3 but not on p_2. They are parallel since the normals $-4\mathbf{i} + 6\mathbf{j} + 10\mathbf{k}$ and $4\mathbf{i} - 6\mathbf{j} - 10\mathbf{k}$ are parallel.

(c) As normals we can take

$$\mathbf{N}_1 = 2\mathbf{i} - 3\mathbf{j} + 5\mathbf{k} \qquad \text{and} \qquad \mathbf{N}_2 = -4\mathbf{i} + 6\mathbf{j} + 10\mathbf{k}.$$

$$\cos \theta = \frac{\mathbf{N}_1 \cdot \mathbf{N}_2}{\|\mathbf{N}_1\| \, \|\mathbf{N}_2\|} = \frac{-8 - 18 + 50}{\sqrt{4 + 9 + 25}\sqrt{16 + 36 + 100}} = \frac{24}{\sqrt{38}\sqrt{152}} = \frac{24}{76} = \frac{6}{19}.$$

The angle between the planes is arc cos $(\frac{6}{19})$. $\square$

Problem.   Show that, if there are scalars α, β, γ not all zero such that

$$\alpha\mathbf{a} + \beta\mathbf{b} + \gamma\mathbf{c} = \mathbf{0},$$

then the points

$$P(a_1, a_2, a_3), \quad Q(b_1, b_2, b_3), \quad R(c_1, c_2, c_3)$$

all lie on the same plane through the origin.

SOLUTION.   Suppose that

$$\alpha\mathbf{a} + \beta\mathbf{b} + \gamma\mathbf{c} = \mathbf{0} \qquad \text{with } \alpha, \beta, \gamma \text{ not all } 0.$$

If $\alpha \neq 0$, then we can write

$$\mathbf{a} = -\frac{\beta}{\alpha}\mathbf{b} - \frac{\gamma}{\alpha}\mathbf{c}.$$

The plane through the origin that passes through Q and R has a vector equation of the form

$$\mathbf{N} \cdot \mathbf{r} = 0. \qquad\qquad \text{(We can take } \mathbf{r}_0 = \mathbf{0}.)$$

Here $\mathbf{N}$ is a normal vector and $\mathbf{r}$ is the position vector of any point of the plane. Since Q and R lie on the plane

$$\mathbf{N} \cdot \mathbf{b} = 0 \qquad \text{and} \qquad \mathbf{N} \cdot \mathbf{c} = 0.$$

Consequently

$$\mathbf{N} \cdot \mathbf{a} = \mathbf{N} \cdot \left(-\frac{\beta}{\alpha} \mathbf{b} - \frac{\gamma}{\alpha} \mathbf{c} \right)$$

$$= -\frac{\beta}{\alpha} \mathbf{N} \cdot \mathbf{b} - \frac{\gamma}{\alpha} \mathbf{N} \cdot \mathbf{c}$$

$$= 0.$$

This means that $P(a_1, a_2, a_3)$ lies on this same plane. The cases $\beta \neq 0$ and $\gamma \neq 0$ can be handled in a similar manner. $\square$

Because of this last result (and because the converse is also true) we call three vectors *coplanar* iff there are scalars α, β, γ not all zero such that

$$\alpha \mathbf{a} + \beta \mathbf{b} + \gamma \mathbf{c} = \mathbf{0}.$$

Exercises

1.* Given the plane

$$p: \quad 3(x - 1) + 4y - 5(z + 2) = 0,$$

determine which of the following points lie on p:

$$P(3, 2, 1), \quad Q(2, 3, 1), \quad R(1, 4, 1).$$

2.* Given the plane

$$p: \quad \mathbf{N} \cdot (\mathbf{r} - \mathbf{r}_0) = 0$$

with

$$\mathbf{N} = \mathbf{i} - 3\mathbf{j} + \mathbf{k} \qquad \text{and} \quad \mathbf{r}_0 = 4\mathbf{i} + \mathbf{j} - \mathbf{k},$$

determine which of the following points lie on p:

$$P(2, 1, -2), \quad Q(2, 0, 0), \quad R(4, 1, -1), \quad S(0, -1, -3).$$

Find the angle between the following pairs of planes:

3.* $5(x - 1) - 3(y + 2) + 2z = 0$
   $x + 3(y - 1) + 2(z + 4) = 0.$

4. $2x - y + 3z = 5$
   $5x + 5y - z = 1.$

5.* $x - y + z - 1 = 0$
   $2x + y + 3z + 5 = 0.$

6. $A_1(x - x_1) + B_1(y - y_1) + C_1(z - z_1) = 0$
   $A_2(x - x_2) + B_2(y - y_2) + C_2(z - z_2) = 0.$

Find the unit normals for the following planes:

7.* the xy-plane.

8. $2x - 3y + 7z - 3 = 0.$

9.* $\frac{1}{2}(x - 1) + 2(y - \frac{3}{2}) + 3(z - 2) = 0.$

10.* $A(x - x_0) + B(y - y_0) + C(z - z_0) = 0.$

Find the points at which the following planes meet the coordinate axes:

11.* $x + 2y - \sqrt{5}z = 5.$

12. $3x - y + 4z - 1 = 0.$

13.* $x - 3y - 3z = 0.$

14. $x - 3y - 3z = 1.$

Given that A, B and C are all different from zero, find the points at which the following planes meet the coordinate axes:

15.* $Ax + By + Cz = 0.$

16. $Ax + By + Cz = 1.$

17.* $x/A + y/B + z/C = 1.$

18. $A(x - x_0) + B(y - y_0) + C(z - z_0) = 0.$

19.   Find an equation for the plane with x-intercept a, y-intercept b, and z-intercept c.

Determine whether or not the following sets of vectors are coplanar.

20. $\mathbf{i}, \mathbf{i} - 2\mathbf{j}, 3\mathbf{j} + \mathbf{k}.$

21.* $4\mathbf{j} - \mathbf{k}, 3\mathbf{i} + \mathbf{j} + 2\mathbf{k}, \mathbf{0}.$

22. $\mathbf{j} - \mathbf{k}, 3\mathbf{i} - \mathbf{j} + 2\mathbf{k}, 3\mathbf{i} - 2\mathbf{j} + 3\mathbf{k}.$

23.* $\mathbf{i} + \mathbf{j} + \mathbf{k}, 2\mathbf{i} - \mathbf{j}, 3\mathbf{i} - \mathbf{j} - \mathbf{k}.$

24.   Show that two nonparallel lines

$$\mathbf{r}(t) = \mathbf{a} + t\mathbf{b}$$

and

$$\mathbf{R}(t) = \mathbf{A} + t\mathbf{B}$$

intersect iff the vectors $\mathbf{a} - \mathbf{A}$, $\mathbf{b}$, and $\mathbf{B}$ are coplanar.

25.   Let $\mathbf{a}$ and $\mathbf{b}$ be two noncollinear position vectors. Sketch a figure depicting all those position vectors $\mathbf{c}$ which satisfy $\mathbf{a} \cdot \mathbf{c} = \mathbf{a} \cdot \mathbf{b}$.

26.   (a) Show that the distance between the plane

$$A(x - x_0) + B(y - y_0) + C(z - z_0) = 0$$

and the origin is

$$\frac{|Ax_0 + By_0 + Cz_0|}{\sqrt{A^2 + B^2 + C^2}}.$$

[HINT: The point of the plane closest to the origin must be of the form $P(At, Bt, Ct)$.]

(b) Express this distance in terms of

$$\mathbf{N} = A\mathbf{i} + B\mathbf{j} + C\mathbf{k} \qquad \text{and} \qquad \mathbf{r}_0 = x_0\mathbf{i} + y_0\mathbf{j} + z_0\mathbf{k}$$

and sketch a figure illustrating the result.

12.7   The cross product

Here we explore a notion that should be of special value to those of you who have an interest in physics, particularly in mechanics and in electromagnetism. In mechanics cross products come up in connection with angular momentum, torque, and other phenomena of turning. In electromagnetism cross products play an important role. In particular they give us a convenient formulation of the law of forces between moving charges.

For vectors

$$\mathbf{a} = a_1\mathbf{i} + a_2\mathbf{j} + a_3\mathbf{k} \qquad \text{and} \qquad \mathbf{b} = b_1\mathbf{i} + b_2\mathbf{j} + b_3\mathbf{k},$$

we define the *cross product* $\mathbf{a} \times \mathbf{b}$ by

$$\mathbf{a} \times \mathbf{b} = (a_2b_3 - a_3b_2)\mathbf{i} + (a_3b_1 - a_1b_3)\mathbf{j} + (a_1b_2 - a_2b_1)\mathbf{k}.$$

While the dot product $\mathbf{a} \cdot \mathbf{b}$ is a scalar and is often called the scalar product of $\mathbf{a}$ and $\mathbf{b}$, the cross product $\mathbf{a} \times \mathbf{b}$ is a vector and it is often called the *vector product* of $\mathbf{a}$ and $\mathbf{b}$.

Examples. For

$$\mathbf{a} = \mathbf{i} - 2\mathbf{j} + 3\mathbf{k} \qquad \text{and} \qquad \mathbf{b} = 2\mathbf{i} + \mathbf{j} - \mathbf{k}$$

we have

$$\begin{aligned}
\mathbf{a} \times \mathbf{b} &= (a_2b_3 - a_3b_2)\mathbf{i} + (a_3b_1 - a_1b_3)\mathbf{j} + (a_1b_2 - a_2b_1)\mathbf{k} \\
&= \left[(-2)(-1) - (3)(1)\right]\mathbf{i} + \left[(3)(2) - (1)(-1)\right]\mathbf{j} + \left[(1)(1) - (-2)(2)\right]\mathbf{k} \\
&= -\mathbf{i} + 7\mathbf{j} + 5\mathbf{k}. \quad \square
\end{aligned}$$

For

$$\mathbf{a} = \mathbf{i} - \mathbf{j} \qquad \text{and} \qquad \mathbf{b} = \mathbf{i} + \mathbf{k},$$

we have

$$\begin{aligned}
\mathbf{a} \times \mathbf{b} &= (a_2b_3 - a_3b_2)\mathbf{i} + (a_3b_1 - a_1b_3)\mathbf{j} + (a_1b_2 - a_2b_1)\mathbf{k} \\
&= \left[(-1)(1) - (0)(0)\right]\mathbf{i} + \left[(0)(1) - (1)(1)\right]\mathbf{j} + \left[(1)(0) - (-1)(1)\right]\mathbf{k} \\
&= -\mathbf{i} - \mathbf{j} + \mathbf{k}. \quad \square
\end{aligned}$$

If you are familiar with determinants, you will find it easy to remember the defining formula by noting that

$$\mathbf{a} \times \mathbf{b} = \begin{vmatrix} \mathbf{i} & \mathbf{j} & \mathbf{k} \\ a_1 & a_2 & a_3 \\ b_1 & b_2 & b_3 \end{vmatrix} = \begin{vmatrix} a_2 & a_3 \\ b_2 & b_3 \end{vmatrix}\mathbf{i} - \begin{vmatrix} a_1 & a_3 \\ b_1 & b_3 \end{vmatrix}\mathbf{j} + \begin{vmatrix} a_1 & a_2 \\ b_1 & b_2 \end{vmatrix}\mathbf{k}.$$

Straightforward calculations that you can carry out yourself show that the cross product has the following properties:

$$\boxed{\mathbf{b} \times \mathbf{a} = -(\mathbf{a} \times \mathbf{b})}$$ (anticommutative)

$$\boxed{\mathbf{a} \times \mathbf{a} = \mathbf{0}}$$

$$\boxed{\alpha\mathbf{a} \times \beta\mathbf{b} = \alpha\beta(\mathbf{a} \times \mathbf{b})}$$ (scalars can be factored out)

$$\boxed{\mathbf{a} \times (\mathbf{b} + \mathbf{c}) = (\mathbf{a} \times \mathbf{b}) + (\mathbf{a} \times \mathbf{c})}$$ ($\times$ distributes over $+$)

$$\boxed{\mathbf{a} \times \mathbf{b} \perp \mathbf{a}, \quad \mathbf{a} \times \mathbf{b} \perp \mathbf{b}}$$

$$\boxed{\|\mathbf{a} \times \mathbf{b}\|^2 = \|\mathbf{a}\|^2\|\mathbf{b}\|^2 - (\mathbf{a}\cdot\mathbf{b})^2.}$$

We focus on the last two properties. The first of these tells us that $\mathbf{a} \times \mathbf{b}$ is perpendicular both to $\mathbf{a}$ and to $\mathbf{b}$. The second one gives us the length of $\mathbf{a} \times \mathbf{b}$. From it we see that if $\mathbf{a} = \mathbf{0}$ or $\mathbf{b} = \mathbf{0}$, then $\mathbf{a} \times \mathbf{b} = \mathbf{0}$. If, on the other hand, neither $\mathbf{a}$ nor $\mathbf{b}$ is $\mathbf{0}$, then we have

$$\mathbf{a}\cdot\mathbf{b} = \|\mathbf{a}\| \, \|\mathbf{b}\| \cos\theta,$$

so that

$$\begin{aligned}
\|\mathbf{a} \times \mathbf{b}\|^2 &= \|\mathbf{a}\|^2\|\mathbf{b}\|^2 - (\mathbf{a}\cdot\mathbf{b})^2 \\
&= \|\mathbf{a}\|^2\|\mathbf{b}\|^2 - \|\mathbf{a}\|^2\|\mathbf{b}\|^2 \cos^2\theta \\
&= \|\mathbf{a}\|^2\|\mathbf{b}\|^2(1 - \cos^2\theta) \\
&= \|\mathbf{a}\|^2\|\mathbf{b}\|^2 \sin^2\theta,
\end{aligned}$$

and

$$\|\mathbf{a} \times \mathbf{b}\| = \|\mathbf{a}\| \, \|\mathbf{b}\| \sin\theta.$$

This means (see Figure 12.7.1) that the length of $\mathbf{a} \times \mathbf{b}$ is simply the area of the parallelogram generated by $\mathbf{a}$ and $\mathbf{b}$.

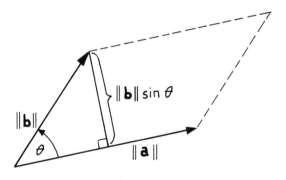

$$\text{Area} = \|\mathbf{a}\| \, \|\mathbf{b}\| \sin\theta = \|\mathbf{a} \times \mathbf{b}\|$$

FIGURE 12.7.1

From the formula

$$\|\mathbf{a} \times \mathbf{b}\| = \|\mathbf{a}\| \, \|\mathbf{b}\| \sin \theta,$$

it follows that

$$\mathbf{a} \times \mathbf{b} = 0 \quad \text{iff} \quad \mathbf{a} \text{ and } \mathbf{b} \text{ are parallel.}$$

We know that the cross product of $\mathbf{a}$ and $\mathbf{b}$ is perpendicular to $\mathbf{b}$, perpendicular to $\mathbf{b}$, and that it has length $\|\mathbf{a}\| \, \|\mathbf{b}\| \sin \theta$. Does this determine it completely? The answer is no. In general there are two such vectors, each the negative of the other. It can be argued that the vector we want, $\mathbf{a} \times \mathbf{b}$, is the one which makes

$$\mathbf{a}, \mathbf{b}, \mathbf{a} \times \mathbf{b}$$

a right-handed system. (See Figure 12.7.2.) In particular, as you can verify, we have

$$\mathbf{i} \times \mathbf{j} = \mathbf{k}, \quad \mathbf{j} \times \mathbf{k} = \mathbf{i}, \quad \mathbf{k} \times \mathbf{i} = \mathbf{j}. \quad \text{(See Figure 12.7.3.)}$$

An easy way to remember these products is to arrange $\mathbf{i}, \mathbf{j}, \mathbf{k}$ in cyclic order,

FIGURE 12.7.2

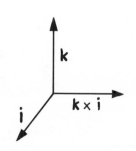

FIGURE 12.7.3

and note that

[each of the unit vectors] $\times$ [the next one] = [the third one].

From this observation and properties

$$\mathbf{b} \times \mathbf{a} = -(\mathbf{a} \times \mathbf{b})$$
$$\mathbf{a} \times \mathbf{a} = \mathbf{0}$$
$$\alpha\mathbf{a} \times \beta\mathbf{b} = \alpha\beta(\mathbf{a} \times \mathbf{b})$$
$$\mathbf{a} \times (\mathbf{b} + \mathbf{c}) = (\mathbf{a} \times \mathbf{b}) + (\mathbf{a} \times \mathbf{c}),$$

we can compute cross products without having to appeal to the somewhat complicated defining formula.

Examples

$$\mathbf{j} \times \mathbf{i} = -(\mathbf{i} \times \mathbf{j}) = -\mathbf{k}, \quad \mathbf{k} \times \mathbf{j} = -(\mathbf{j} \times \mathbf{k}) = -\mathbf{i},$$
$$\mathbf{i} \times \mathbf{k} = -(\mathbf{k} \times \mathbf{i}) = -\mathbf{j}.$$

$$\mathbf{i} \times \mathbf{i} = \mathbf{j} \times \mathbf{j} = \mathbf{k} \times \mathbf{k} = \mathbf{0}.$$

$$2\mathbf{i} \times 3\mathbf{k} = 6(\mathbf{i} \times \mathbf{k}) = -6(\mathbf{k} \times \mathbf{i}) = -6\mathbf{j}.$$

$$\mathbf{k} \times (-3\mathbf{j} + 2\mathbf{k}) = -3(\mathbf{k} \times \mathbf{j}) + 2(\mathbf{k} \times \mathbf{k}) = 3(\mathbf{j} \times \mathbf{k}) + \mathbf{0} = 3\mathbf{i}.$$

$$\begin{aligned}
(\mathbf{i} + \mathbf{j}) \times (-2\mathbf{j} + \mathbf{k}) &= [(\mathbf{i} + \mathbf{j}) \times (-2\mathbf{j})] + [(\mathbf{i} + \mathbf{j}) \times \mathbf{k}] \\
&= [2\mathbf{j} \times (\mathbf{i} + \mathbf{j})] - [\mathbf{k} \times (\mathbf{i} + \mathbf{j})] \\
&= 2(\mathbf{j} \times \mathbf{i}) + 2(\mathbf{j} \times \mathbf{j}) - (\mathbf{k} \times \mathbf{i}) - (\mathbf{k} \times \mathbf{j}) \\
&= -2(\mathbf{i} \times \mathbf{j}) + \mathbf{0} - \mathbf{j} + (\mathbf{j} \times \mathbf{k}) \\
&= -2\mathbf{k} - \mathbf{j} + \mathbf{i}. \quad \square
\end{aligned}$$

Problem.   Show that

$$(\mathbf{a} + \mathbf{b}) \times \mathbf{c} = (\mathbf{a} \times \mathbf{c}) + (\mathbf{b} \times \mathbf{c}).$$

SOLUTION

$$\begin{aligned}
(\mathbf{a} + \mathbf{b}) \times \mathbf{c} &= -[\mathbf{c} \times (\mathbf{a} + \mathbf{b})] \\
&= -[(\mathbf{c} \times \mathbf{a}) + (\mathbf{c} \times \mathbf{b})] \\
&= -(\mathbf{c} \times \mathbf{a}) - (\mathbf{c} \times \mathbf{b}) \\
&= (\mathbf{a} \times \mathbf{c}) + (\mathbf{b} \times \mathbf{c}). \quad \square
\end{aligned}$$

We use this last result in the next problem.

Problem.   Compute $\mathbf{a} \times \mathbf{b}$ given that

$$\mathbf{a} = 2\mathbf{i} - \mathbf{k}, \quad \mathbf{b} = \mathbf{i} - 3\mathbf{j} + 2\mathbf{k}.$$

SOLUTION

$$\begin{aligned}
\mathbf{a} \times \mathbf{b} &= (2\mathbf{i} - \mathbf{k}) \times (\mathbf{i} - 3\mathbf{j} + 2\mathbf{k}) \\
&= [2\mathbf{i} \times (\mathbf{i} - 3\mathbf{j} + 2\mathbf{k})] - [\mathbf{k} \times (\mathbf{i} - 3\mathbf{j} + 2\mathbf{k})] \\
&= 2(\mathbf{i} \times \mathbf{i}) - 6(\mathbf{i} \times \mathbf{j}) + 4(\mathbf{i} \times \mathbf{k}) - (\mathbf{k} \times \mathbf{i}) + 3(\mathbf{k} \times \mathbf{j}) - 2(\mathbf{k} \times \mathbf{k}) \\
&= 0 - 6\mathbf{k} - 4\mathbf{j} - \mathbf{j} - 3\mathbf{i} - 0 \\
&= -3\mathbf{i} - 5\mathbf{j} - 6\mathbf{k}. \quad \square
\end{aligned}$$

Problem. Find the volume of the parallelepiped with edges **a**, **b**, **c**. (See Figure 12.7.4.)

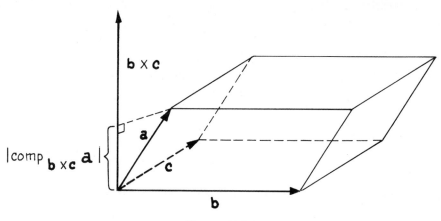

FIGURE 12.7.4

SOLUTION. As a base we take the parallelogram with edges **b** and **c**. The area of the base is $\|\mathbf{b} \times \mathbf{c}\|$. Since $\mathbf{b} \times \mathbf{c}$ is perpendicular to the base, the height is

$$|\text{comp}_{\mathbf{b} \times \mathbf{c}} \, \mathbf{a}| = \frac{|\mathbf{a} \cdot (\mathbf{b} \times \mathbf{c})|}{\|\mathbf{b} \times \mathbf{c}\|}.$$

Consequently

$$V = (\text{area of base}) (\text{height}) = |\mathbf{a} \cdot (\mathbf{b} \times \mathbf{c})|. \quad \square$$

The number $\mathbf{a} \cdot (\mathbf{b} \times \mathbf{c})$ that arises in the last problem is called the *triple scalar product* of the vectors **a**, **b**, **c**. In terms of coordinates we have

$$\mathbf{a} \cdot (\mathbf{b} \times \mathbf{c}) = \mathbf{a} \cdot [(b_2 c_3 - b_3 c_2)\mathbf{i} + (b_3 c_1 - b_1 c_3)\mathbf{j} + (b_1 c_2 - b_2 c_1)\mathbf{k}]$$

and thus

$$(12.7.1) \quad \boxed{\mathbf{a} \cdot (\mathbf{b} \times \mathbf{c}) = a_1(b_2 c_3 - b_3 c_2) + a_2(b_3 c_1 - b_1 c_3) + a_3(b_1 c_2 - b_2 c_1).}$$

If you are familiar with determinants, you have probably recognized that we have

$$\boxed{\mathbf{a} \cdot (\mathbf{b} \times \mathbf{c}) = \begin{vmatrix} a_1 & a_2 & a_3 \\ b_1 & b_2 & b_3 \\ c_1 & c_2 & c_3 \end{vmatrix}.}$$

Problem.   Given that

$$\mathbf{a} \cdot (\mathbf{b} \times \mathbf{c}) = 0$$

what can you conclude about **a**, **b**, and **c**?

SOLUTION.   If $\mathbf{a} \cdot (\mathbf{b} \times \mathbf{c}) = 0$, then the parallelepiped with edges **a**, **b**, **c** has volume 0. This can only happen if **a**, **b**, and **c** are coplanar.   □

From the last problem you know that

(12.7.2) $\boxed{\mathbf{a} \cdot (\mathbf{b} \times \mathbf{c}) = 0 \quad \text{iff} \quad \mathbf{a}, \mathbf{b}, \mathbf{c} \text{ are coplanar.}}$

We can use this to find a convenient equation for the plane that passes through three noncollinear points P_1, P_2, P_3. A point P will lie on this plane iff the arrows

$$\overrightarrow{P_1P}, \ \overrightarrow{P_1P_2}, \ \overrightarrow{P_1P_3}$$

are coplanar. By 12.7.2 this will happen only if

(12.7.3) $\boxed{\overrightarrow{P_1P} \cdot (\overrightarrow{P_1P_2} \times \overrightarrow{P_1P_3}) = 0.}$

Problem.   Find an equation in x, y, z for the plane that passes through $P_1(0, 1, 1)$, $P_2(1, 0, 1)$, $P_3(1, 1, 0)$.

SOLUTION.   The point $P = P(x, y, z)$ will lie on this plane only if

$$\overrightarrow{P_1P} \cdot (\overrightarrow{P_1P_2} \times \overrightarrow{P_1P_3}) = 0.$$

Here

$$\overrightarrow{P_1P} = x\mathbf{i} + (y - 1)\mathbf{j} + (z - 1)\mathbf{k}, \qquad \overrightarrow{P_1P_2} = \mathbf{i} - \mathbf{j}, \qquad \overrightarrow{P_1P_3} = \mathbf{i} - \mathbf{k}.$$

A calculation that you can carry out using (12.7.1) shows that

$$x + y + z - 2 = 0.   □$$

Exercises

Compute.

1.* $(\mathbf{i} + \mathbf{j}) \times (\mathbf{i} - \mathbf{j})$.
2. $(\mathbf{i} - \mathbf{j}) \times (\mathbf{j} - \mathbf{i})$.
3.* $(\mathbf{i} - \mathbf{j}) \times (\mathbf{j} - \mathbf{k})$.
4. $\mathbf{j} \times (2\mathbf{i} - \mathbf{k})$.
5.* $(2\mathbf{j} - \mathbf{k}) \times (\mathbf{i} - 3\mathbf{j})$.

6. $\mathbf{i} \cdot (\mathbf{j} \times \mathbf{k})$.
7.* $\mathbf{j} \cdot (\mathbf{i} \times \mathbf{k})$.
8. $(\mathbf{j} \times \mathbf{i}) \cdot (\mathbf{i} \times \mathbf{k})$.
9.* $(\mathbf{i} \times \mathbf{j}) \times \mathbf{k}$.
10. $(\mathbf{j} \times \mathbf{k}) \times \mathbf{i}$.

Compute.

11.* $(\mathbf{i} + \mathbf{j} + \mathbf{k}) \times (2\mathbf{i} + \mathbf{k})$.
12. $(2\mathbf{i} - \mathbf{k}) \times (\mathbf{i} - 2\mathbf{j} + 2\mathbf{k})$.
13.* $(2\mathbf{i} + \mathbf{j}) \cdot [(\mathbf{i} - 3\mathbf{j} + \mathbf{k}) \times (4\mathbf{i} + \mathbf{k})]$.

14. $[(-2\mathbf{i} + \mathbf{j} - 3\mathbf{k}) \times \mathbf{i}] \times (\mathbf{i} + \mathbf{j})$.

15.* $[(\mathbf{i} - \mathbf{j}) \times (\mathbf{j} - \mathbf{k})] \times [\mathbf{i} + 5\mathbf{k}]$.

16. $(\mathbf{i} - \mathbf{j}) \times [(\mathbf{j} - \mathbf{k}) \times (\mathbf{j} + 5\mathbf{k})]$.

17. Show that

$$\mathbf{b} \times \mathbf{a} = -(\mathbf{a} \times \mathbf{b})$$

and deduce from it that

$$\mathbf{a} \times \mathbf{a} = 0.$$

18. Show that

$$\mathbf{a} \times (\mathbf{b} + \mathbf{c}) = (\mathbf{a} \times \mathbf{b}) + (\mathbf{a} \times \mathbf{c}).$$

19. Show that

$$\mathbf{a} \times \mathbf{b} \perp \mathbf{a} \qquad \text{and} \qquad \mathbf{a} \times \mathbf{b} \perp \mathbf{b}.$$

20. Show that

$$\|\mathbf{a} \times \mathbf{b}\|^2 = \|\mathbf{a}\|^2\|\mathbf{b}\|^2 - (\mathbf{a} \cdot \mathbf{b})^2.$$

21. Is $\times$ associative? Namely, is it always true that

$$\mathbf{a} \times (\mathbf{b} \times \mathbf{c}) = (\mathbf{a} \times \mathbf{b}) \times \mathbf{c}?$$

22.* Find the area of the triangle with vertices
   (a) $P(0, 1, 0)$, $Q(-1, 1, 2)$, $R(2, 1, -1)$.
   (b) $P(1, 2, 3)$, $Q(-1, 3, 2)$, $R(3, -1, 2)$.

23.* Find the volume of the parallelepiped with edges
   (a) $\mathbf{i} + \mathbf{j}$, $2\mathbf{i} - \mathbf{k}$, $3\mathbf{j} + \mathbf{k}$.
   (b) $\mathbf{i} - 3\mathbf{j} + \mathbf{k}$, $2\mathbf{j} - \mathbf{k}$, $\mathbf{i} + \mathbf{j} - 2\mathbf{k}$.

24. Express

$$(\mathbf{a} + \mathbf{b}) \times (\mathbf{a} - \mathbf{b})$$

as a scalar multiple of $\mathbf{a} \times \mathbf{b}$.

25.* Find an equation in x, y, z for the plane that passes through the points
   (a) $P_1(1, 0, 1)$, $P_2(2, 1, 0)$, $P_3(1, 1, 1)$.
   (b) $P_1(1, 1, 1)$, $P_2(2, -2, -1)$, $P_3(0, 2, 1)$.

26. Let $\mathbf{a}$, $\mathbf{b}$, $\mathbf{c}$ be distinct nonzero vectors.
   Show that

$$\mathbf{a} \times \mathbf{b} = \mathbf{a} \times \mathbf{c} \qquad \text{iff} \qquad \mathbf{a} \text{ and } \mathbf{b} - \mathbf{c} \text{ are parallel.}$$

27. Sketch a figure depicting all those vectors $\mathbf{c}$ that satisfy

$$\mathbf{a} \times \mathbf{b} = \mathbf{a} \times \mathbf{c}.$$

28. Use cross products to derive the law of sines for triangles; that is, show that if a triangle has sides $\mathbf{a}$, $\mathbf{b}$, $\mathbf{c}$ and opposite angles A, B, C, then

$$\frac{\sin A}{\|\mathbf{a}\|} = \frac{\sin B}{\|\mathbf{b}\|} = \frac{\sin C}{\|\mathbf{c}\|}.$$

[HINT: Since

$$\mathbf{a} + \mathbf{b} + \mathbf{c} = \mathbf{0},$$

we have

$$\mathbf{a} \times [\mathbf{a} + \mathbf{b} + \mathbf{c}] = \mathbf{0},$$

from which you will find that

$$\mathbf{a} \times \mathbf{b} = \mathbf{c} \times \mathbf{a}.]$$

29. Show that if two distinct planes have a point in common, then they have a line in common.

[HINT: If the point $P(a_1, a_2, a_3)$ lies on both planes

$$\mathbf{n} \cdot (\mathbf{r} - \mathbf{r}_0) = 0 \quad \text{and} \quad \mathbf{N} \cdot (\mathbf{R} - \mathbf{R}_0) = 0,$$

then the vector

$$\mathbf{a} = a_1 \mathbf{i} + a_2 \mathbf{j} + a_3 \mathbf{k}$$

satisfies

$$\mathbf{n} \cdot (\mathbf{a} - \mathbf{r}_0) = 0 \quad \text{and} \quad \mathbf{N} \cdot (\mathbf{a} - \mathbf{R}_0) = 0.$$

Consider the line

$$\mathbf{r}(t) = \mathbf{a} + t(\mathbf{n} \times \mathbf{N}), \quad t \in \mathbf{R}.]$$

13

VECTOR CALCULUS

13.1 Vector functions

If f_1, f_2, f_3 are real-valued functions defined on some interval I, then for each $t \in I$ we can form the vector

$$\mathbf{f}(t) = f_1(t)\mathbf{i} + f_2(t)\mathbf{j} + f_3(t)\mathbf{k}$$

and thereby create a *vector-valued function* $\mathbf{f}$. For short we will call such a function a *vector function*.

Example. Taking for each real t

$$f_1(t) = a_1 + b_1 t, \qquad f_2(t) = a_2 + b_2 t, \qquad f_3(t) = a_3 + b_3 t$$

we can form the vector function

$$\mathbf{f}(t) = (a_1 + b_1 t)\mathbf{i} + (a_2 + b_2 t)\mathbf{j} + (a_3 + b_3 t)\mathbf{k}$$

$$= (a_1 + t b_1)\mathbf{i} + (a_2 + t b_2)\mathbf{j} + (a_3 + t b_3)\mathbf{k}.$$

If we now set

$$\mathbf{a} = a_1\mathbf{i} + a_2\mathbf{j} + a_3\mathbf{k}, \qquad \mathbf{b} = b_1\mathbf{i} + b_2\mathbf{j} + b_3\mathbf{k}$$

then we have

$$\mathbf{f}(t) = \mathbf{a} + t\mathbf{b}, \qquad t \in R.$$

(See Figure 13.1.1.) For $\mathbf{b} \neq \mathbf{0}$, this gives us the line through $P(a_1, a_2, a_3)$ parallel to the vector $\mathbf{b}$. If $\mathbf{b} = \mathbf{0}$, then we have simply the *constant* vector function

$$\mathbf{f}(t) = \mathbf{a}. \quad \square$$

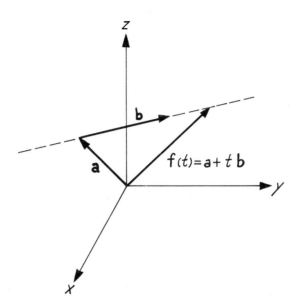

FIGURE 13.1.1

Example. Taking for real t

$$f_1(t) = \cos t, \qquad f_2(t) = \sin t, \qquad f_3(t) = 0$$

we obtain

$$\mathbf{f}(t) = \cos t\,\mathbf{i} + \sin t\,\mathbf{j}.$$

For each $t \in [0, 2\pi]$

$$\|\mathbf{f}(t)\| = \sqrt{\cos^2 t + \sin^2 t} = 1.$$

As t ranges over $[0, 2\pi]$, the position vector $\mathbf{f}(t)$ remains in the xy-plane and traces out the unit circle centered at the origin. (See Figure 13.1.2.) $\square$

The ideas of limit, continuity, derivative, and integral are easily extended to vector functions. Suppose that

$$\mathbf{f}(t) = f_1(t)\mathbf{i} + f_2(t)\mathbf{j} + f_3(t)\mathbf{k}, \qquad t \in I.$$

We say that $\mathbf{f}$ has a *limit* at t_0 provided that each of the component functions f_1, f_2, f_3 has a limit at t_0; namely, for $\mathbf{L} = l_1\mathbf{i} + l_2\mathbf{j} + l_3\mathbf{k}$, we set

$$\boxed{\lim_{t \to t_0} \mathbf{f}(t) = \mathbf{L} \qquad \text{iff} \qquad \lim_{t \to t_0} f_1(t) = l_1, \quad \lim_{t \to t_0} f_2(t) = l_2, \quad \lim_{t \to t_0} f_3(t) = l_3.}$$

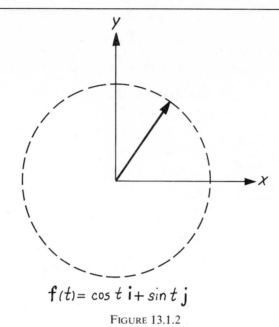

$$\mathbf{f}(t) = \cos t \, \mathbf{i} + \sin t \, \mathbf{j}$$

FIGURE 13.1.2

We say that $\mathbf{f}$ is *continuous* at t_0 provided that each of the component functions is continuous at t_0; that is, provided that

$$\lim_{t \to t_0} f_1(t) = f_1(t_0), \quad \lim_{t \to t_0} f_2(t) = f_2(t_0), \quad \lim_{t \to t_0} f_3(t) = f_3(t_0).$$

More briefly

$$\mathbf{f} \text{ is } \textit{continuous} \text{ at } t_0 \text{ provided that } \lim_{t \to t_0} \mathbf{f}(t) = \mathbf{f}(t_0).$$

Problem.   Find

$$\lim_{t \to 0} \mathbf{f}(t)$$

if

$$\mathbf{f}(t) = \cos(t + \pi)\mathbf{i} + 2\frac{\sin t}{t}\mathbf{j} + e^{-t^2}\mathbf{k}.$$

SOLUTION

$$\lim_{t \to 0} \mathbf{f}(t) = \lim_{t \to 0}\left[\cos(t + \pi)\mathbf{i} + 2\frac{\sin t}{t}\mathbf{j} + e^{-t^2}\mathbf{k}\right]$$

$$= \left[\lim_{t \to 0}\cos(t + \pi)\right]\mathbf{i} + \left[\lim_{t \to 0} 2\frac{\sin t}{t}\right]\mathbf{j} + \left[\lim_{t \to 0} e^{-t^2}\right]\mathbf{k}$$

$$= -\mathbf{i} + 2\mathbf{j} + \mathbf{k}. \quad \square$$

We say that $\mathbf{f}$ is *differentiable* at t provided that each of the component functions is differentiable at t. If this happens, then we write

$$\mathbf{f}'(t) = f_1'(t)\mathbf{i} + f_2'(t)\mathbf{j} + f_3'(t)\mathbf{k}$$

and call $\mathbf{f}'(t)$ the *derivative* of $\mathbf{f}$ at t. The derivative $\mathbf{f}'(t)$ can also be written as the limit of a *vector difference quotient*:

$$\mathbf{f}'(t) = \lim_{h \to 0} \frac{1}{h}[\mathbf{f}(t + h) - \mathbf{f}(t)].$$

Here is a proof:

$$\mathbf{f}'(t) = f_1'(t)\mathbf{i} + f_2'(t)\mathbf{j} + f_3'(t)\mathbf{k}$$

$$= \left[\lim_{h \to 0} \frac{f_1(t + h) - f_1(t)}{h}\right]\mathbf{i} + \left[\lim_{h \to 0} \frac{f_2(t + h) - f_2(t)}{h}\right]\mathbf{j} + \left[\lim_{h \to 0} \frac{f_3(t + h) - f_3(t)}{h}\right]\mathbf{k}$$

$$= \lim_{h \to 0} \left[\frac{f_1(t + h) - f_1(t)}{h}\mathbf{i} + \frac{f_2(t + h) - f_2(t)}{h}\mathbf{j} + \frac{f_3(t + h) - f_3(t)}{h}\mathbf{k}\right]$$

$$= \lim_{h \to 0} \frac{1}{h}[\mathbf{f}(t + h) - \mathbf{f}(t)]. \quad \square$$

Interpretations of the vector derivative and applications of vector differentiation are postponed until Sections 13.3 and 13.4. Here we content ourselves with simple computations.

Problem.   For

$$\mathbf{f}(t) = t\mathbf{i} + \sqrt{t + 1}\,\mathbf{j} - e^t\mathbf{k}$$

find:

(1) the domain of $\mathbf{f}$.
(2) $\mathbf{f}(0)$.
(3) $\mathbf{f}'(t)$.
(4) $\mathbf{f}'(0)$.
(5) $\|\mathbf{f}(t)\|$.
(6) $\mathbf{f}(t) \cdot \mathbf{f}'(t)$.

SOLUTION

(1) For a number to be in the domain of $\mathbf{f}$ it is necessary only that it be in the domain of each of its components. The domain of $\mathbf{f}$ is thus $[-1, \infty)$.
(2) $\mathbf{f}(0) = 0\mathbf{i} + \sqrt{0 + 1}\,\mathbf{j} - e^0\mathbf{k}$
    $= \mathbf{j} - \mathbf{k}$.
(3) $\mathbf{f}(t) = t\mathbf{i} + \sqrt{t + 1}\,\mathbf{j} - e^t\mathbf{k}$

$$\mathbf{f}'(t) = \mathbf{i} + \frac{1}{2\sqrt{t + 1}}\mathbf{j} - e^t\mathbf{k}.$$

(4) $\mathbf{f}'(0) = \mathbf{i} + \dfrac{1}{2\sqrt{0+1}}\mathbf{j} - e^0\mathbf{k} = \mathbf{i} + \dfrac{1}{2}\mathbf{j} - \mathbf{k}.$

(5) $\|\mathbf{f}(t)\| = \sqrt{t^2 + (\sqrt{t+1})^2 + (e^t)^2} = \sqrt{t^2 + t + 1 + e^{2t}}.$

(6) $\mathbf{f}(t)\cdot\mathbf{f}'(t) = (t\mathbf{i} + \sqrt{t+1}\mathbf{j} - e^t\mathbf{k})\cdot(\mathbf{i} + \dfrac{1}{2\sqrt{t+1}}\mathbf{j} - e^t\mathbf{k})$

$$= (t)(1) + (\sqrt{t+1})\left(\dfrac{1}{2\sqrt{t+1}}\right) + (-e^t)(-e^t)$$

$$= t + \dfrac{1}{2} + e^{2t}. \quad \square$$

In differentiating vector functions we need not stop with the first derivative. If $\mathbf{f}'$ is itself differentiable, we can form the second derivative $\mathbf{f}''$ and so on.

Problem. Given that

$$\mathbf{g}(t) = \dfrac{\sin t}{t}\mathbf{i} + e^{-t}\mathbf{j} + t\mathbf{k},$$

find

$$\mathbf{g}''(t).$$

SOLUTION

$$\mathbf{g}'(t) = \dfrac{t\cos t - \sin t}{t^2}\mathbf{i} - e^{-t}\mathbf{j} + \mathbf{k}$$

$$\mathbf{g}''(t) = \dfrac{t^2\dfrac{d}{dt}[t\cos t - \sin t] - (t\cos t - \sin t)\dfrac{d}{dt}[t^2]}{t^4}\mathbf{i} + e^{-t}\mathbf{j}$$

$$= \dfrac{t^2(-t\sin t + \cos t - \cos t) - (t\cos t - \sin t)2t}{t^4}\mathbf{i} + e^{-t}\mathbf{j}$$

$$= \dfrac{2\sin t - 2t\cos t - t^2\sin t}{t^3}\mathbf{i} + e^{-t}\mathbf{j}. \quad \square$$

Integration can also be handled componentwise; namely we set

$$\boxed{\int_a^b \mathbf{f}(t)\,dt = \left(\int_a^b f_1(t)\,dt\right)\mathbf{i} + \left(\int_a^b f_2(t)\,dt\right)\mathbf{j} + \left(\int_a^b f_3(t)\,dt\right)\mathbf{k}.}$$

Problem. Find

$$\int_0^1 \mathbf{f}(t)\,dt$$

for

$$\mathbf{f}(t) = t\mathbf{i} + \sqrt{t+1}\mathbf{j} - e^t\mathbf{k}.$$

SOLUTION

$$\int_0^1 f(t)\,dt = \left(\int_0^1 t\,dt\right)\mathbf{i} + \left(\int_0^1 \sqrt{t+1}\,dt\right)\mathbf{j} + \left(\int_0^1 (-e^t)\,dt\right)\mathbf{k}$$

$$= \left[\frac{t^2}{2}\right]_0^1 \mathbf{i} + \frac{2}{3}\left[(t+1)^{3/2}\right]_0^1 \mathbf{j} + \left[-e^t\right]_0^1 \mathbf{k}$$

$$= \frac{1}{2}\mathbf{i} + \frac{2}{3}(2\sqrt{2} - 1)\mathbf{j} + (1 - e)\mathbf{k}. \quad \square$$

Problem. Find $\mathbf{f}(t)$ given that

$$\mathbf{f}'(t) = 2\cos t\,\mathbf{i} - t\sin t^2\,\mathbf{j} + 2t\,\mathbf{k} \quad\text{and}\quad \mathbf{f}(0) = \mathbf{i} + 3\mathbf{k}.$$

SOLUTION.   By integrating $\mathbf{f}'(t)$ we get

$$\mathbf{f}(t) = (2\sin t + c_1)\mathbf{i} + (\tfrac{1}{2}\cos t^2 + c_2)\mathbf{j} + (t^2 + c_3)\mathbf{k},$$

where $c_1,\,c_2,\,c_3$ are constants to be determined. Since

$$\mathbf{i} + 3\mathbf{k} = \mathbf{f}(0) = c_1\mathbf{i} + (\tfrac{1}{2} + c_2)\mathbf{j} + c_3\mathbf{k},$$

we see that

$$c_1 = 1, \qquad c_2 = -\tfrac{1}{2}, \qquad c_3 = 3.$$

Thus

$$\mathbf{f}(t) = (2\sin t + 1)\mathbf{i} + (\tfrac{1}{2}\cos t^2 - \tfrac{1}{2})\mathbf{j} + (t^2 + 3)\mathbf{k}. \quad \square$$

In passing, we point out that

$$\boxed{\int_a^b [\mathbf{f}(t) + \mathbf{g}(t)]\,dt = \int_a^b \mathbf{f}(t)\,dt + \int_a^b \mathbf{g}(t)\,dt}$$

and

$$\boxed{\int_a^b [\alpha\mathbf{f}(t)]\,dt = \alpha\int_a^b \mathbf{f}(t)\,dt \qquad \text{for every scalar } \alpha.}$$

Not so obvious perhaps is that

(1)
$$\boxed{\int_a^b [\mathbf{c}\cdot\mathbf{f}(t)]\,dt = \mathbf{c}\cdot\int_a^b \mathbf{f}(t)\,dt \qquad \text{for every vector } \mathbf{c}}$$

and

(2)
$$\boxed{\left\|\int_a^b \mathbf{f}(t)\,dt\right\| \leq \int_a^b \|\mathbf{f}(t)\|\,dt.}$$

The proof of (1) we leave as an exercise. Here is a proof of (2): Set

$$\mathbf{c} = \int_a^b \mathbf{f}(t)\,dt.$$

Note that

$$||\mathbf{c}||^2 = \mathbf{c} \cdot \mathbf{c} = \mathbf{c} \cdot \int_a^b \mathbf{f}(t)\, dt = \int_a^b [\mathbf{c} \cdot \mathbf{f}(t)]\, dt \le \int_a^b ||\mathbf{c}||\, ||\mathbf{f}(t)||\, dt = ||\mathbf{c}|| \int_a^b ||\mathbf{f}(t)||\, dt.$$

by property (1) ——／   └── by Schwarz's inequality

If $\mathbf{c} \ne \mathbf{0}$, then we can divide by $||\mathbf{c}||$ and thereby get

$$||\mathbf{c}|| \le \int_a^b ||\mathbf{f}(t)||\, dt.$$

If $\mathbf{c} = \mathbf{0}$, the result is obvious in the first place. $\square$

Exercises

Differentiate.

1.* $\mathbf{f}(t) = (1 + 2t)\mathbf{i} + (3 - t)\mathbf{j} + (2 + 3t)\mathbf{k}.$
2. $\mathbf{f}(t) = 2\mathbf{i} - \cos t\,\mathbf{k}.$

3.* $\mathbf{f}(t) = \sqrt{1 - t}\,\mathbf{i} + \sqrt{1 + t}\,\mathbf{j} + \dfrac{1 - t}{1 + t}\,\mathbf{k}.$

4. $\mathbf{f}(t) = \dfrac{1 - t^2}{1 + t^2}\,\mathbf{i} + \dfrac{2t}{1 + t^2}\,\mathbf{j}.$

5.* $\mathbf{f}(t) = \sin t\,\mathbf{i} + \cos t\,\mathbf{j} + \tan t\,\mathbf{k}.$
6. $\mathbf{f}(t) = e^t\mathbf{i} + \log t\,\mathbf{j} + \arctan t\,\mathbf{k}.$
7.* $\mathbf{f}(t) = \arcsin t\,\mathbf{i} + \log(1 + 2t)\mathbf{j} + t^2\,\mathbf{k}.$
8. $\mathbf{f}(t) = \cosh t\,\mathbf{i} + \sinh t\,\mathbf{j}.$

Compute.

9.* $\displaystyle\int_1^2 \mathbf{f}(t)\, dt$ for $\mathbf{f}(t) = \mathbf{i} + 2t\mathbf{j}.$

10. $\displaystyle\int_1^2 \mathbf{f}(t)\, dt$ for $\mathbf{f}(t) = \mathbf{i} + \left(\dfrac{2}{t}\right)^{1/2}\mathbf{j} + \dfrac{1}{t}\mathbf{k}.$

11.* $\displaystyle\int_0^\pi \mathbf{r}(t)\, dt$ for $\mathbf{r}(t) = \sin t\,\mathbf{i} + \cos t\,\mathbf{j} + t\,\mathbf{k}.$

12. $\displaystyle\int_0^1 \mathbf{g}(t)\, dt$ for $\mathbf{g}(t) = e^t\mathbf{i} + \sqrt{2}\mathbf{j} + e^{-t}\mathbf{k}.$

13.* $\displaystyle\int_0^1 \mathbf{h}(t)\, dt$ for $\mathbf{h}(t) = e^{-t}[t^2\,\mathbf{i} + \sqrt{2}t\mathbf{j} + \mathbf{k}].$

14. Show that if $\mathbf{f}'(t) = \mathbf{0}$ for all t in some interval I, then $\mathbf{f}$ is constant on I. [That is, there exists a vector $\mathbf{c}$ such that $\mathbf{f}(t) = \mathbf{c}$ for all $t \in I.$]
15. Show that if $\mathbf{f}'(t) = \mathbf{g}'(t)$ for all t in some interval I, then $\mathbf{f}$ and $\mathbf{g}$ differ by a constant on I.

Find $\mathbf{f}(t)$ given that

16. $\mathbf{f}'(t) = \mathbf{i} + t^2\mathbf{j}$ and $\mathbf{f}(0) = \mathbf{j} - \mathbf{k}.$
17.* $\mathbf{f}'(t) = \cosh t\,\mathbf{i} + \sinh t\,\mathbf{j} + \mathbf{k}$ and $\mathbf{f}(0) = \mathbf{i} + \tfrac{1}{2}\mathbf{j} + \mathbf{k}.$

18. $\mathbf{f}'(t) = t\mathbf{i} + \dfrac{t}{\sqrt{1 + t^2}}\mathbf{j} + te^t\mathbf{k}$ and $\mathbf{f}(0) = \mathbf{i} + 2\mathbf{j} + 3\mathbf{k}.$

19.* $\mathbf{f}'(t) = 2\mathbf{f}(t)$ and $\mathbf{f}(0) = \mathbf{i} - \mathbf{k}$.

20. (*Important*) Show that

$$\lim_{t \to t_0} \mathbf{f}(t) = \mathbf{L} \quad \text{iff} \quad \lim_{t \to t_0} \|\mathbf{f}(t) - \mathbf{L}\| = 0.$$

21. Show that

$$\int_a^b [\mathbf{c} \cdot \mathbf{f}(t)] \, dt = \mathbf{c} \cdot \int_a^b \mathbf{f}(t) \, dt \qquad \text{for every vector } \mathbf{c}.$$

13.2 Differentiation formulas

Vector functions with a common domain can be combined in many ways to form new functions. From $\mathbf{f}$ and $\mathbf{g}$ we can form the sum $\mathbf{f} + \mathbf{g}$:

$$(\mathbf{f} + \mathbf{g})(t) = \mathbf{f}(t) + \mathbf{g}(t).$$

We can form scalar multiples $\alpha\mathbf{f}$ and thus linear combinations $\alpha\mathbf{f} + \beta\mathbf{g}$:

$$(\alpha\mathbf{f})(t) = \alpha\mathbf{f}(t), \qquad (\alpha\mathbf{f} + \beta\mathbf{g})(t) = \alpha\mathbf{f}(t) + \beta\mathbf{g}(t).$$

We can form the dot product $\mathbf{f} \cdot \mathbf{g}$:

$$(\mathbf{f} \cdot \mathbf{g})(t) = \mathbf{f}(t) \cdot \mathbf{g}(t).$$

We can also form the cross product $\mathbf{f} \times \mathbf{g}$:

$$(\mathbf{f} \times \mathbf{g})(t) = \mathbf{f}(t) \times \mathbf{g}(t).$$

There are two ways to bring scalar functions (real-valued functions) into play. If the scalar function u has the same domain as $\mathbf{f}$, we can form the product $u\mathbf{f}$:

$$(u\mathbf{f})(t) = u(t)\mathbf{f}(t).$$

If for each t in some interval, $u(t)$ is in the domain of $\mathbf{f}$, then we can form the composition $\mathbf{f} \circ u$:

$$(\mathbf{f} \circ u)(t) = \mathbf{f}(u(t)).$$

It is not hard to show that if the original functions are continuous, then so are the newly constructed ones. More interestingly, if the original functions are differentiable, then so are the new ones. The derivatives can be computed using the following rules:

(1)	$(\mathbf{f} + \mathbf{g})'(t) = \mathbf{f}'(t) + \mathbf{g}'(t)$.
(2)	$(\alpha\mathbf{f})'(t) = \alpha\mathbf{f}'(t)$.
(3)	$(u\mathbf{f})'(t) = u(t)\mathbf{f}'(t) + u'(t)\mathbf{f}(t)$.
(4)	$(\mathbf{f} \cdot \mathbf{g})'(t) = [\mathbf{f}(t) \cdot \mathbf{g}'(t)] + [\mathbf{f}'(t) \cdot \mathbf{g}(t)]$.
(5)	$(\mathbf{f} \times \mathbf{g})'(t) = [\mathbf{f}(t) \times \mathbf{g}'(t)] + [\mathbf{f}'(t) \times \mathbf{g}(t)]$.
(6)	$(\mathbf{f} \circ u)'(t) = \mathbf{f}'(u(t))u'(t) = u'(t)\mathbf{f}'(u(t))$. [chain rule]

The validity of these rules we show later. First a few comments. Rules (1) and (2) look exactly like those we used for differentiating ordinary functions. Rule (2) is just a special case of Rule (3): set $u(t) = \alpha$ for all t. Rules (3), (4), and (5) are all "product" rules and should remind you of the rule for differentiating the product of ordinary functions. Keep in mind that $\times$ is not commutative and therefore the order in Rule (5) is important. In Rule (6) we first wrote the scalar part $u'(t)$ on the right so that the formula would look like the chain rule for ordinary functions. In general $\mathbf{a}\alpha$ means the same as $\alpha\mathbf{a}$.

Problem. For

$$\mathbf{f}(t) = \cos t\,\mathbf{i} + \sin t\,\mathbf{j}$$
$$\mathbf{g}(t) = \mathbf{i} + \arctan t\,\mathbf{j} - t^2\,\mathbf{k}$$
$$u(t) = \log(t+1)$$

find

(A) $(\mathbf{f} + \mathbf{g})'(t)$.   (C) $(\mathbf{f}\cdot\mathbf{g})'(t)$.

(B) $(u\mathbf{f})'(t)$.   (D) $(\mathbf{f} \times \mathbf{g})'(t)$.

(E) $(\mathbf{f} \circ u)'(t)$.

SOLUTION

(A) $(\mathbf{f} + \mathbf{g})'(t) = \mathbf{f}'(t) + \mathbf{g}'(t)$

$$= (-\sin t\,\mathbf{i} + \cos t\,\mathbf{j}) + \left(\frac{1}{1+t^2}\mathbf{j} - 2t\,\mathbf{k}\right)$$

$$= -\sin t\,\mathbf{i} + \left(\cos t + \frac{1}{1+t^2}\right)\mathbf{j} - 2t\,\mathbf{k}.$$

We can achieve the same result by adding first and then differentiating:

$$(\mathbf{f} + \mathbf{g})(t) = \mathbf{f}(t) + \mathbf{g}(t)$$
$$= (\cos t\,\mathbf{i} + \sin t\,\mathbf{j}) + (\mathbf{i} + \arctan t\,\mathbf{j} - t^2\,\mathbf{k})$$
$$= (1 + \cos t)\mathbf{i} + (\sin t + \arctan t)\mathbf{j} - t^2\,\mathbf{k}.$$

Thus

$$(\mathbf{f} + \mathbf{g})'(t) = -\sin t\,\mathbf{i} + \left(\cos t + \frac{1}{1+t^2}\right)\mathbf{j} - 2t\,\mathbf{k}.$$

(B) $(u\mathbf{f})'(t) = u(t)\mathbf{f}'(t) + u'(t)\mathbf{f}(t)$

$$= \log(t+1)\,[-\sin t\,\mathbf{i} + \cos t\,\mathbf{j}] + \frac{1}{t+1}\,[\cos t\,\mathbf{i} + \sin t\,\mathbf{j}]$$

$$= \left[\frac{\cos t}{t+1} - \log(t+1)\sin t\right]\mathbf{i} + \left[\log(t+1)\cos t + \frac{\sin t}{t+1}\right]\mathbf{j}.$$

Another method:

$$(u\mathbf{f})(t) = u(t)\mathbf{f}(t)$$
$$= \log(t+1)[\cos t\,\mathbf{i} + \sin t\,\mathbf{j}]$$
$$= \log(t+1)\cos t\,\mathbf{i} + \log(t+1)\sin t\,\mathbf{j}$$
$$(u\mathbf{f})'(t) = \left[\log(t+1)(-\sin t) + \frac{\cos t}{t+1}\right]\mathbf{i} + \left[\log(t+1)\cos t + \frac{\sin t}{t+1}\right]\mathbf{j}$$
$$= \left[\frac{\cos t}{t+1} - \log(t+1)\sin t\right]\mathbf{i} + \left[\log(t+1)\cos t + \frac{\sin t}{t+1}\right]\mathbf{j}.$$

(C) $(\mathbf{f}\cdot\mathbf{g})'(t) = \mathbf{f}(t)\cdot\mathbf{g}'(t) + \mathbf{f}'(t)\cdot\mathbf{g}(t)$

$$= (\cos t\,\mathbf{i} + \sin t\,\mathbf{j})\cdot\left(\frac{1}{1+t^2}\mathbf{j} - 2t\,\mathbf{k}\right)$$
$$+ (-\sin t\,\mathbf{i} + \cos t\,\mathbf{j})\cdot(\mathbf{i} + \arctan t\,\mathbf{j} - t^2\,\mathbf{k})$$
$$= \frac{\sin t}{1+t^2} - \sin t + \cos t\,\arctan t.$$

Another method:

$$(\mathbf{f}\cdot\mathbf{g})(t) = \mathbf{f}(t)\cdot\mathbf{g}(t)$$
$$= (\cos t\,\mathbf{i} + \sin t\,\mathbf{j})\cdot(\mathbf{i} + \arctan t\,\mathbf{j} - t^2\mathbf{k})$$
$$= \cos t + \sin t\,\arctan t$$
$$(\mathbf{f}\cdot\mathbf{g})'(t) = -\sin t + \frac{\sin t}{1+t^2} + \cos t\,\arctan t.$$

(D) $(\mathbf{f}\times\mathbf{g})'(t) = [\mathbf{f}(t)\times\mathbf{g}'(t)] + [\mathbf{f}'(t)\times\mathbf{g}(t)]$

$$= (\cos t\,\mathbf{i} + \sin t\,\mathbf{j})\times\left(\frac{1}{1+t^2}\mathbf{j} - 2t\,\mathbf{k}\right)$$
$$+ (-\sin t\,\mathbf{i} + \cos t\,\mathbf{j})\times(\mathbf{i} + \arctan t\,\mathbf{j} - t^2\,\mathbf{k})$$
$$= (\sin t)(-2t)\mathbf{i} - (\cos t)(-2t)\mathbf{j} + \frac{\cos t}{1+t^2}\mathbf{k}$$
$$+ (\cos t)(-t^2)\mathbf{i} - (-\sin t)(-t^2)\mathbf{j} + (-\sin t\,\arctan t - \cos t)\mathbf{k}$$
$$= [(-t)(2\sin t + t\cos t)]\mathbf{i} + [t(2\cos t - t\sin t)]\mathbf{j}$$
$$+ \left[\frac{\cos t}{1+t^2} - \sin t\,\arctan t - \cos t\right]\mathbf{k}.$$

Another method:

$$(\mathbf{f}\times\mathbf{g})(t) = \mathbf{f}(t)\times\mathbf{g}(t)$$
$$= (\cos t\,\mathbf{i} + \sin t\,\mathbf{j})\times(\mathbf{i} + \arctan t\,\mathbf{j} - t^2\,\mathbf{k})$$
$$= (\sin t)(-t^2)\mathbf{i} - (\cos t)(-t^2)\mathbf{j} + (\cos t\,\arctan t - \sin t)\mathbf{k}$$
$$(\mathbf{f}\times\mathbf{g})'(t) = (-t^2\cos t - 2t\sin t)\mathbf{i} + [t^2(-\sin t) + 2t\cos t]\mathbf{j}$$
$$+ \left[\frac{\cos t}{1+t^2} - \sin t\,\arctan t - \cos t\right]\mathbf{k}$$

$$= [(-t)(t \cos t + 2 \sin t)]\mathbf{i} + [t(2 \cos t - t \sin t)]\mathbf{j}$$

$$+ \left[\frac{\cos t}{1 + t^2} - \sin t \arctan t - \cos t \right] \mathbf{k}.$$

(E) $(\mathbf{f} \circ u)'(t) = \mathbf{f}'(u(t))u'(t)$

$$= \left[-\sin \left(\log (t + 1) \right) \mathbf{i} + \cos \left(\log (t + 1) \right) \mathbf{j} \right] \frac{1}{t + 1}.$$

Another method:

$$(\mathbf{f} \circ u)(t) = \mathbf{f}(u(t))$$

$$= \left[\cos \left(\log (t + 1) \right) \right] \mathbf{i} + \left[\sin \left(\log (t + 1) \right) \right] \mathbf{j}$$

$$(\mathbf{f} \circ u)'(t) = -\sin \left(\log (t + 1) \right) \frac{1}{t + 1} \mathbf{i} + \cos \left(\log (t + 1) \right) \frac{1}{t + 1} \mathbf{j}. \quad \square$$

Proofs for the differentiation formulas (1)–(6) can be derived by componentwise differentiation. As an example we verify Formula (3):

$$(u\mathbf{f})'(t) = u(t)\mathbf{f}'(t) + u'(t)\mathbf{f}(t).$$

Setting

$$\mathbf{f}(t) = f_1(t)\mathbf{i} + f_2(t)\mathbf{j} + f_3(t)\mathbf{k},$$

we have

$$(u\mathbf{f})(t) = u(t)\mathbf{f}(t) = u(t)f_1(t)\mathbf{i} + u(t)f_2(t)\mathbf{j} + u(t)f_3(t)\mathbf{k}$$
$$(u\mathbf{f})'(t) = [u(t)f_1'(t) + u'(t)f_1(t)]\mathbf{i} + [u(t)f_2'(t) + u'(t)f_2(t)]\mathbf{j} + [u(t)f_3'(t) + u'(t)f_3(t)]\mathbf{k}$$
$$= u(t)[f_1'(t)\mathbf{i} + f_2'(t)\mathbf{j} + f_3'(t)\mathbf{k}] + u'(t)[f_1(t)\mathbf{i} + f_2(t)\mathbf{j} + f_3(t)\mathbf{k}]$$
$$= u(t)\mathbf{f}'(t) + u'(t)\mathbf{f}(t). \quad \square$$

Componentwise verification of the other formulas we leave as exercises.

Let's take another look at Formula (3), this time from a different point of view. Instead of casting everything in terms of components, we will work with the vectors directly.

To evaluate $(u\mathbf{f})'(t)$ is to compute the limit of the difference quotient

$$\frac{1}{h} [u(t + h)\mathbf{f}(t + h) - u(t)\mathbf{f}(t)]$$

as h tends to 0. By subtracting and adding $u(t + h)\mathbf{f}(t)$ inside the brackets and then factoring, we can rewrite the difference quotient as

$$u(t + h) \frac{1}{h} [\mathbf{f}(t + h) - \mathbf{f}(t)] + \frac{1}{h} [u(t + h) - u(t)]\mathbf{f}(t).$$

It is clear that

$$u(t + h) \qquad \text{tends to} \qquad u(t),$$

$$\frac{1}{h}[\mathbf{f}(t + h) - \mathbf{f}(t)] \qquad \text{tends to} \qquad \mathbf{f}'(t),$$

$$\frac{1}{h}[u(t + h) - u(t)] \qquad \text{tends to} \qquad u'(t).$$

It can now be argued that the difference quotient tends to

$$u(t)\mathbf{f}'(t) + u'(t)\mathbf{f}(t). \quad \square$$

It is instructive to apply the same point of view to Formula (4):

$$(\mathbf{f} \cdot \mathbf{g})'(t) = [\mathbf{f}(t) \cdot \mathbf{g}'(t)] + [\mathbf{f}'(t) \cdot \mathbf{g}(t)].$$

On the left we have the limit of the difference quotient

$$\frac{1}{h}[\mathbf{f}(t + h) \cdot \mathbf{g}(t + h) - \mathbf{f}(t) \cdot \mathbf{g}(t)],$$

as h tends to 0. Subtracting and adding $\mathbf{f}(t + h) \cdot \mathbf{g}(t)$ inside the brackets and rearranging, we obtain

$$\mathbf{f}(t + h) \cdot \frac{1}{h}[\mathbf{g}(t + h) - \mathbf{g}(t)] + \frac{1}{h}[\mathbf{f}(t + h) - \mathbf{f}(t)] \cdot \mathbf{g}(t).$$

It probably seems obvious now that the limit is

$$[\mathbf{f}(t) \cdot \mathbf{g}'(t)] + [\mathbf{f}'(t) \cdot \mathbf{g}(t)]. \quad \square$$

In passing, we remark that all of these differentiation formulas can be derived in a component-free manner.

In Leibniz's notation the formulas become

$$(1) \quad \frac{d}{dt}[\mathbf{f}(t) + \mathbf{g}(t)] = \frac{d}{dt}[\mathbf{f}(t)] + \frac{d}{dt}[\mathbf{g}(t)].$$

$$(2) \quad \frac{d}{dt}[\alpha\mathbf{f}(t)] = \alpha\frac{d}{dt}[\mathbf{f}(t)].$$

$$(3) \quad \frac{d}{dt}[u(t)\mathbf{f}(t)] = u(t)\frac{d}{dt}[\mathbf{f}(t)] + \frac{d}{dt}[u(t)]\mathbf{f}(t).$$

$$(4) \quad \frac{d}{dt}[\mathbf{f}(t) \cdot \mathbf{g}(t)] = \left(\mathbf{f}(t) \cdot \frac{d}{dt}[\mathbf{g}(t)]\right) + \left(\frac{d}{dt}[\mathbf{f}(t)] \cdot \mathbf{g}(t)\right).$$

$$(5) \quad \frac{d}{dt}[\mathbf{f}(t) \times \mathbf{g}(t)] = \left(\mathbf{f}(t) \times \frac{d}{dt}[\mathbf{g}(t)]\right) + \left(\frac{d}{dt}[\mathbf{f}(t)] \times \mathbf{g}(t)\right).$$

$$(6) \quad \frac{d}{dt}[\mathbf{f}(u(t))] = \mathbf{f}'(u(t))u'(t).$$

Exercises

Compute $\mathbf{f}'(t)$ and $\mathbf{f}''(t)$ for each of the following functions.

1.* $\mathbf{f}(t) = \mathbf{a} + t\mathbf{b}.$

2. $\mathbf{f}(t) = \mathbf{a} + t\mathbf{b} + t^2\mathbf{c}.$

3.* $\mathbf{f}(t) = e^{2t}\mathbf{i} - \sin t\,\mathbf{j}.$

4. $\mathbf{f}(t) = [(t^2\mathbf{i} - \mathbf{j})\cdot(\mathbf{i} - t^2\mathbf{j})]\mathbf{i}.$

5.* $\mathbf{f}(t) = \mathbf{g}(t^2).$

6. $\mathbf{f}(t) = t\mathbf{g}(t^2).$

7.* $\mathbf{f}(t) = t\mathbf{g}(\sqrt{t}).$

8. $\mathbf{f}(t) = (\cos t\,\mathbf{i} - \mathbf{j}) \times (t\,\mathbf{j} + \sin t\,\mathbf{k}).$

Find.

9.* $\dfrac{d}{dt}[e^{\cos t}\mathbf{i} + e^{\sin t}\mathbf{j}].$

10. $\dfrac{d^2}{dt^2}[e^t \cos t\,\mathbf{i} + e^t \sin t\,\mathbf{j}].$

11.* $\dfrac{d}{dt}[\cosh t\,\mathbf{i} + \sinh t\,\mathbf{j}].$

12. $\dfrac{d}{dt}[(\mathbf{a} + t\mathbf{b}) \times (\mathbf{c} + t\mathbf{d})].$

13.* $\dfrac{d^2}{dt^2}[(\mathbf{a} + t\mathbf{b}) \times (\mathbf{c} + t\mathbf{d})].$

14. $\dfrac{d}{dt}[(\mathbf{a} + t\mathbf{b})\cdot(\mathbf{a} + t\mathbf{b} + t^2\mathbf{c})].$

15. Show that

$$\frac{d}{dt}[u_1(t)\mathbf{r}_1(t) \times u_2(t)\mathbf{r}_2(t)] = u_1(t)u_2(t)\frac{d}{dt}[\mathbf{r}_1(t) \times \mathbf{r}_2(t)] + \frac{d}{dt}[u_1(t)u_2(t)][\mathbf{r}_1(t) \times \mathbf{r}_2(t)].$$

Find $\mathbf{f}(t)$ given that:

16. $\mathbf{f}'(t) = \mathbf{b}$ for all real t, $\mathbf{f}(0) = \mathbf{a}.$

17.* $\mathbf{f}''(t) = \mathbf{c}$ for all real t, $\mathbf{f}'(0) = \mathbf{b}$, $\mathbf{f}(0) = \mathbf{a}.$

18. $\mathbf{f}''(t) = \mathbf{a} + t\mathbf{b}$ for all real t, $\mathbf{f}'(0) = \mathbf{c}$, $\mathbf{f}(0) = \mathbf{d}.$

19. Show that, if $\mathbf{f}$ is differentiable at t, then $\mathbf{f}$ is continuous at t.

20. Show that

$$\frac{d}{dt}[\mathbf{f}(t) \times \mathbf{f}'(t)] = \mathbf{f}(t) \times \mathbf{f}''(t).$$

21. Given that

$$\mathbf{f}(t) = \cos t\,\mathbf{i} + \sin t\,\mathbf{j},$$

show that

$$\mathbf{f}(t)\cdot\mathbf{f}'(t) = 0.$$

22. Given that $\mathbf{f}$ is differentiable, show that

$$\|\mathbf{f}(t)\| \text{ is constant} \quad \text{iff} \quad \mathbf{f}(t)\cdot\mathbf{f}'(t) = 0 \quad \text{identically.}$$

23. Given that

$$g(t) = e^{kt}\mathbf{i} + e^{-kt}\mathbf{j},$$

show that $g(t)$ and $g''(t)$ have the same direction.

24. Give an informal derivation of the formula

$$(\mathbf{f} \times \mathbf{g})'(t) = [\mathbf{f}(t) \times \mathbf{g}'(t)] + [\mathbf{f}'(t) \times \mathbf{g}(t)]$$

without appealing to components.

25. Give a detailed proof of the chain rule for vector functions:

$$(\mathbf{f} \circ u)'(t) = \mathbf{f}(u(t))u'(t).$$

13.3 Curves and tangents

A linear vector function

$$\mathbf{r}(t) = \mathbf{a} + t\mathbf{b}$$

serves as a parametrization for a line l in the sense that, as t ranges over the set of real numbers, the tip of the position vector $\mathbf{r}(t)$ traces out the line l. (See Figure 13.1.1.) The vector function

$$\mathbf{r}(t) = \cos t\,\mathbf{i} + \sin t\,\mathbf{j}, \qquad t \in [0, 2\pi]$$

serves as a parametrization for the unit circle in the xy-plane in the sense that as t ranges over $[0, 2\pi]$ the tip of the vector $\mathbf{r}(t)$ traces out the unit circle in the xy-plane. (See Figure 13.1.2.)

In general a vector function

$$\mathbf{r}(t) = x(t)\mathbf{i} + y(t)\mathbf{j} + z(t)\mathbf{k}$$

differentiable on some interval I serves as a *parametrization for a curve C* in the sense that as t ranges over I the tip of the vector $\mathbf{r}(t)$ traces out the curve C. (See Figure 13.3.1.)

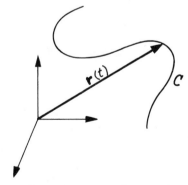

$$C: \mathbf{r}(t) = x(t)\mathbf{i} + y(t)\mathbf{j} + z(t)\mathbf{k}, t \in I$$

FIGURE 13.3.1

It is time we gave a geometric interpretation to the derivative

$$\mathbf{r}'(t) = x'(t)\mathbf{i} + y'(t)\mathbf{j} + z'(t)\mathbf{k}.$$

> The vector $\mathbf{r}'(t)$, if not $\mathbf{0}$, is said to be *tangent* to the curve C at the point
> $P(x(t), y(t), z(t))$.

To see why, recall that we have

$$\mathbf{r}'(t) = \lim_{h \to 0} \frac{\mathbf{r}(t + h) - \mathbf{r}(t)}{h}.$$

With $\mathbf{r}'(t) \neq \mathbf{0}$, we can be sure that for $t + h$ close enough to t, the vector

$$\mathbf{r}(t + h) - \mathbf{r}(t)$$

will not be $\mathbf{0}$. Consequently, we can think of the vector $\mathbf{r}(t + h) - \mathbf{r}(t)$ as pictured in Figure 13.3.2.

Let's agree that the line marked l in the figure corresponds to our intuitive notion of tangent. We know that l passes through the tip of $\mathbf{r}(t)$. To determine l, we need only find a direction vector for l. As h tends to zero, the vector

$$\mathbf{r}(t + h) - \mathbf{r}(t)$$

comes increasingly closer to serving as a direction vector for l. It may be tempting therefore to take the limiting case

$$\lim_{h \to 0} [\mathbf{r}(t + h) - \mathbf{r}(t)]$$

and call that a direction vector for l. The trouble here is that this limit vector is $\mathbf{0}$ and $\mathbf{0}$ has no direction. We can circumvent this difficulty by looking instead at the vector

$$\frac{1}{h}[\mathbf{r}(t + h) - \mathbf{r}(t)].$$

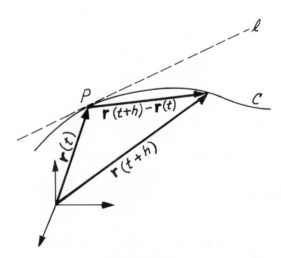

FIGURE 13.3.2

For each value of h, this vector is parallel to

$$\mathbf{r}(t + h) - \mathbf{r}(t)$$

and therefore its limit

$$\mathbf{r}'(t) = \lim_{h \to 0} \frac{1}{h}[\mathbf{r}(t + h) - \mathbf{r}(t)],$$

which by assumption is not $\mathbf{0}$, can be taken as a direction vector for l. This in a nutshell is why we call the vector $\mathbf{r}'(t)$ tangent to the curve C at the point $P(x(t), y(t), z(t))$. □

The *tangent line*, by definition, is the line through $P(x(t), y(t), z(t))$ with direction vector $\mathbf{r}'(t)$.

Problem.   Show that in the case of the circle

$$C: \quad \mathbf{r}(t) = \rho \cos t \, \mathbf{i} + \rho \sin t \, \mathbf{j}, \quad t \in [0, 2\pi]$$

the tangent vector is perpendicular to the radius vector.

SOLUTION.   As tangent vector we can take

$$\mathbf{r}'(t) = -\rho \sin t \, \mathbf{i} + \rho \cos t \, \mathbf{j}.$$

Since

$$\begin{aligned}
\mathbf{r}(t) \cdot \mathbf{r}'(t) &= (\rho \cos t \, \mathbf{i} + \rho \sin t \, \mathbf{j}) \cdot (-\rho \sin t \, \mathbf{i} + \rho \cos t \, \mathbf{j}) \\
&= -\rho^2 \cos t \sin t + \rho^2 \cos t \sin t = 0,
\end{aligned}$$

we have

$$\mathbf{r}(t) \perp \mathbf{r}'(t). \quad \square$$

Problem.   The curve

$$\mathbf{r}(t) = t\mathbf{i} + t^2\mathbf{j} + t^3\mathbf{k},$$

is called the "twisted" cubic. Find a vector tangent to the twisted cubic at the point $P(2, 4, 8)$ and find the tangent line.

SOLUTION

$$\mathbf{r}'(t) = \mathbf{i} + 2t\mathbf{j} + 3t^2\mathbf{k}.$$

Since $P(2, 4, 8)$ is the tip of $\mathbf{r}(2)$, a suitable tangent vector is

$$\mathbf{r}'(2) = \mathbf{i} + 4\mathbf{j} + 12\mathbf{k}.$$

As tangent line we have

$$l: \mathbf{R}(t) = (2\mathbf{i} + 4\mathbf{j} + 8\mathbf{k}) + t(\mathbf{i} + 4\mathbf{j} + 12\mathbf{k}). \quad \square$$

Problem. Find the point of the curve

$$\mathbf{r}(t) = (1 - 2t)\mathbf{i} + t^2\mathbf{j} + 2e^{2(t-1)}\mathbf{k}$$

that has the property that the tangent line at P passes through the origin.

SOLUTION. At each point $P(1 - 2t, t^2, 2e^{2(t-1)})$ we can use the tangent vector

$$\mathbf{r}'(t) = -2\mathbf{i} + 2t\mathbf{j} + 4e^{2(t-1)}\mathbf{k}.$$

As tangent line we have

$$\mathbf{R}(u) = [(1 - 2t)\mathbf{i} + t^2\mathbf{j} + 2e^{2(t-1)}\mathbf{k}] + u[-2\mathbf{i} + 2t\mathbf{j} + 4e^{2(t-1)}\mathbf{k}].$$

For the tangent line to pass through the origin, there must exist a real number u_0 such that

$$\mathbf{R}(u_0) = \mathbf{0}.$$

Consequently we must have

$$1 - 2t - 2u_0 = 0$$
$$t^2 + 2tu_0 = 0$$
$$2e^{2(t-1)} + 4e^{2(t-1)}u_0 = 0.$$

The last equation tells us that

$$u_0 = -\tfrac{1}{2}.$$

This in turn tells us that $t = 1$ and the point in question is $P(-1, 1, 2)$.   □

Two curves

$$C_1: \quad \mathbf{r}_1(t) = x_1(t)\mathbf{i} + y_1(t)\mathbf{j} + z_1(t)\mathbf{k}$$
$$C_2: \quad \mathbf{r}_2(t) = x_2(t)\mathbf{i} + y_2(t)\mathbf{j} + z_2(t)\mathbf{k}$$

will intersect iff there are numbers t_1 and t_2 such that

$$\mathbf{r}_1(t_1) = \mathbf{r}_2(t_2).$$

If two curves intersect, the angle between them is simply the angle between their tangent vectors.

Problem. Show that the circles

$$C_1: \quad \mathbf{r}_1(t) = \cos t\,\mathbf{i} + \sin t\,\mathbf{j}$$
$$C_2: \quad \mathbf{r}_2(t) = \cos t\,\mathbf{j} + \sin t\,\mathbf{k}$$

meet at right angles at the points $P(0, 1, 0)$ and $Q(0, -1, 0)$.

SOLUTION. Since

$$\mathbf{r}_1\left(\frac{\pi}{2}\right) = \mathbf{j} = \mathbf{r}_2(0),$$

the curves meet at the tip of $\mathbf{j}$, which is $P(0, 1, 0)$. Since

$$\mathbf{r}_1\left(\frac{3\pi}{2}\right) = -\mathbf{j} = \mathbf{r}_2(\pi),$$

the curves meet at the tip of $-\mathbf{j}$, which is $P(0, -1, 0)$. Obviously

$$\mathbf{r}_1'(t) = -\sin t\,\mathbf{i} + \cos t\,\mathbf{j} \quad \text{and} \quad \mathbf{r}_2'(t) = -\sin t\,\mathbf{j} + \cos t\,\mathbf{k}.$$

Since

$$\mathbf{r}_1'\left(\frac{\pi}{2}\right) = -\mathbf{i} \quad \text{and} \quad \mathbf{r}_2'(0) = \mathbf{k},$$

we have

$$\mathbf{r}_1'\left(\frac{\pi}{2}\right) \cdot \mathbf{r}_2'(0) = 0.$$

This tells us the curves are perpendicular at $P(0, 1, 0)$. Since

$$\mathbf{r}_1'\left(\frac{3\pi}{2}\right) = \mathbf{i} \quad \text{and} \quad \mathbf{r}_2'(\pi) = -\mathbf{k},$$

we have

$$\mathbf{r}_1'\left(\frac{3\pi}{2}\right) \cdot \mathbf{r}_2'(\pi) = 0.$$

This tells us the curves are perpendicular at $P(0, -1, 0)$. □

Exercises

1. Find a parametrization for the line tangent to the curve
    (a)* $\mathbf{r}(t) = \cos \pi t\,\mathbf{i} + \sin \pi t\,\mathbf{j} + t\,\mathbf{k}$ at $t = 2$.
    (b) $\mathbf{r}(t) = e^t\mathbf{i} + e^{-t}\mathbf{j} - \log t\,\mathbf{k}$ at $t = 1$.
    (c)* $\mathbf{r}(t) = \mathbf{a} + t\mathbf{b}$ at $t = t_0$.
    (d) $\mathbf{r}(t) = (t + 1)\mathbf{i} + (t^2 + 1)\mathbf{j} + (t^3 + 1)\mathbf{k}$ at $P(1, 1, 1)$.
    (e)* $\mathbf{r}(t) = 2t^2\mathbf{i} + (1 + t)\mathbf{j} + (3 + 2t^2)\mathbf{k}$ at $P(2, 0, 5)$.
2. Identify the curve and find an equation for it in x and y.
    (a)* $\mathbf{r}(t) = a \cos wt\,\mathbf{i} + b \sin wt\,\mathbf{j}$.
    (b) $\mathbf{r}(t) = a \cosh wt\,\mathbf{i} + a \sinh wt\,\mathbf{j}$.
    (c)* $\mathbf{r}(t) = at\mathbf{i} + bt^2\mathbf{j}$.
3.* Find the curve given that

$$\mathbf{r}'(t) = \alpha\mathbf{r}(t) \quad \text{for all real } t$$

and

$$\mathbf{r}(0) = \mathbf{i} + 2\mathbf{j} + 3\mathbf{k}.$$

4. The curves

$$\mathbf{r}_1(t) = (1 - e^t)\mathbf{i} + 2 \sin t\,\mathbf{j} + \log (t + 1)\mathbf{k}$$
$$\mathbf{r}_2(t) = (t + 1)\mathbf{i} + (t^2 - 1)\mathbf{j} + (t^3 + 1)\mathbf{k}$$

intersect at the origin. Find the angle of intersection.

5.* Find the point at which the curves

$$\mathbf{r}_1(t) = e^t\mathbf{i} + 2\sin\left(t + \frac{\pi}{2}\right)\mathbf{j} + (t^2 - 2)\mathbf{k}$$

$$\mathbf{r}_2(t) = t\mathbf{i} + 2\mathbf{j} + (t^2 - 3)\mathbf{k}$$

intersect and then find the angle of intersection.

6. Let $a > 0$. The curve

$$\mathbf{r}(t) = a\cos t\,\mathbf{i} + a\sin t\,\mathbf{j} + t\,\mathbf{k},$$

is called a *circular helix*.

(a) Show that the helix lies on the cylinder

$$x^2 + y^2 = a^2, \qquad z \text{ unrestricted.}$$

(b) Show that it intersects lines parallel to the z-axis at a constant angle.

(c) Sketch a figure of the curve.

13.4   Velocity and acceleration

A curve

$$C: \quad \mathbf{r}(t) = x(t)\mathbf{i} + y(t)\mathbf{j} + z(t)\mathbf{k}, \qquad t \in I$$

can be thought of as the path traced out by a moving object. We can interpret I as a time interval and use $\mathbf{r}(t)$ to indicate the position of the object at time t. Let's assume that $\mathbf{r}$ is twice differentiable. In this context the derivatives, $\mathbf{r}'(t)$ and $\mathbf{r}''(t)$, have special names and special significance.

Definition

The vector $\mathbf{r}'(t)$ is called the *velocity* of the object at time t and $\mathbf{r}''(t)$ is called the *acceleration*.

In symbols we have

$$\boxed{\mathbf{r}'(t) = \mathbf{v}(t) \qquad \text{and} \qquad \mathbf{r}''(t) = \mathbf{v}'(t) = \mathbf{a}(t).}$$

There should be nothing surprising about this. As before we have velocity as the rate of change of position and acceleration as the rate of change of velocity. Since

$$\mathbf{v}(t) = \mathbf{r}'(t),$$

we know from the last section that the velocity vector, when not $\mathbf{0}$, is tangent to the path of the motion. The direction of the velocity vector gives us the direction of the motion. (Figure 13.4.1)

The magnitude of the velocity vector tells us how fast the object is moving. The details will be made clear in the next section. At this point consider it true by definition; namely, for an object moving with velocity $\mathbf{v}(t)$ we define

$$\boxed{\|\mathbf{v}(t)\| = \text{speed at time } t.}$$

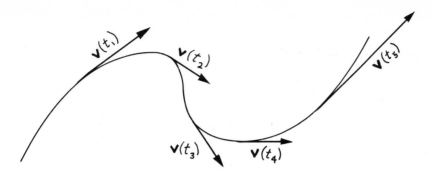

FIGURE 13.4.1

Problem. A particle moves along a circular helix

$$\mathbf{r}(t) = a \cos \omega t\, \mathbf{i} + a \sin \omega t\, \mathbf{j} + bt\, \mathbf{k}. \qquad [a > 0,\, b > 0]$$

For each time t, find
(a) the velocity.
(b) the speed.
(c) the acceleration.
(d) the magnitude of the acceleration vector.
(e) the angle between the velocity vector and the acceleration vector.

SOLUTION

(a) $\mathbf{v}(t) = \mathbf{r}'(t) = -a\omega \sin \omega t\, \mathbf{i} + a\omega \cos \omega t\, \mathbf{j} + b\, \mathbf{k}.$

(b) speed at time $t = \|\mathbf{v}(t)\|$

$$= \sqrt{a^2\omega^2 \sin^2 \omega t + a^2\omega^2 \cos^2 \omega t + b^2}$$

$$= \sqrt{a^2\omega^2 + b^2}.$$

The speed is thus constant.

Circular helix

FIGURE 13.4.2

(c) $\mathbf{a}(t) = \mathbf{v}'(t) = -a\omega^2 \cos \omega t \, \mathbf{i} - a\omega^2 \sin \omega t \, \mathbf{j}$
$$= -a\omega^2(\cos \omega t \, \mathbf{i} + \sin \omega t \, \mathbf{j}).\dagger$$

(d) magnitude of acceleration vector $= \|\mathbf{a}(t)\| = a\omega^2$.

(e) $\cos \theta = \dfrac{\mathbf{v}(t) \cdot \mathbf{a}(t)}{\|\mathbf{v}(t)\| \, \|\mathbf{a}(t)\|}$

$$= \frac{[-a\omega \sin \omega t \, \mathbf{i} + a\omega \cos \omega t \, \mathbf{j} + b \, \mathbf{k}] \cdot [-a\omega^2(\cos \omega t \, \mathbf{i} + \sin \omega t \, \mathbf{j})]}{\sqrt{a^2\omega^2 + b^2} \cdot a\omega^2}$$

$$= 0.$$

The angle is therefore $\pi/2$. $\square$

In classical mechanics the *momentum* $\mathbf{p}$ of an object is defined by the equation

$$\mathbf{p} = m\mathbf{v},$$

where m is the mass of the object and $\mathbf{v}$ is its velocity. To indicate the time dependence, we write

$$\mathbf{p}(t) = m\mathbf{v}(t).$$

The acceleration of an object is related to the *force* acting on it by Newton's Second Law of Motion:

$$\mathbf{F}(t) = m\mathbf{a}(t)$$

Force = [mass] times [acceleration].

Differentiating the momentum equation, we find that

$$\mathbf{p}'(t) = m\mathbf{v}'(t) = m\mathbf{a}(t).$$

Obviously then

$$\mathbf{F}(t) = \mathbf{p}'(t).$$

In other words, force is simply the rate of change of momentum.

Problem.   An object of mass m follows an elliptical path in such a manner that at each time t the object has position

$$\mathbf{r}(t) = a \cos \omega t \, \mathbf{i} + b \sin \omega t \, \mathbf{j}.$$

Find the force acting on the object.

SOLUTION

$$\mathbf{v}(t) = \mathbf{r}'(t) = -a\omega \sin \omega t \, \mathbf{i} + b\omega \cos \omega t \, \mathbf{j}.$$
$$\mathbf{a}(t) = \mathbf{v}'(t) = \mathbf{r}''(t) = -a\omega^2 \cos \omega t \, \mathbf{i} - b\omega^2 \sin \omega t \, \mathbf{j} = -\omega^2\mathbf{r}(t).$$
$$\mathbf{F}(t) = -m\omega^2\mathbf{r}(t). \quad \square$$

---

† Since the speed is constant, the acceleration comes from the change in direction of the velocity vector.

This force is called a *central* force because it acts along the line of the radius vector. It is called an *attractive* force because its direction is opposite to that of the radius vector. In magnitude this force is proportional to the distance of the object from the origin. We illustrate all this in Figure 13.4.3.

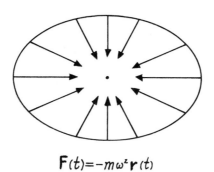

$$\mathbf{F}(t) = -m\omega^2 \mathbf{r}(t)$$

FIGURE 13.4.3

Problem. A force of magnitude α directed upward from the xy-plane is continually applied to an object of mass m. Given that the object starts at $P(0, y_0, z_0)$ with initial velocity $2\mathbf{j}$ find:

(a) the velocity of the object t seconds later.
(b) the speed of the object t seconds later.
(c) the momentum of the object t seconds later.
(d) the path followed by the object, both in vector form and in Cartesian coordinates.

SOLUTION.   We begin with

$$\mathbf{F}(t) = \alpha \mathbf{k}.$$

From

$$\mathbf{F}(t) = m\mathbf{a}(t),$$

we have

$$\mathbf{a}(t) = \frac{\alpha}{m} \mathbf{k}$$

and thus

$$\mathbf{v}(t) = c_1 \mathbf{i} + c_2 \mathbf{j} + \left(\frac{\alpha}{m} t + c_3 \right) \mathbf{k}.$$

Since

$$\mathbf{v}(0) = 2\mathbf{j},$$

we see that

$$c_1 = 0, \qquad c_2 = 2, \qquad c_3 = 0$$

and consequently

$$\mathbf{v}(t) = 2\mathbf{j} + \frac{\alpha}{m} t\mathbf{k}.$$

This gives

$$\mathbf{r}(t) = D_1\mathbf{i} + (2t + D_2)\mathbf{j} + \left(\frac{\alpha}{2m} t^2 + D_3\right)\mathbf{k}.$$

From

$$\mathbf{r}(0) = y_0\mathbf{j} + z_0\mathbf{k}$$

we find

$$D_1 = 0, \qquad D_2 = y_0, \qquad D_3 = z_0$$

and thus

$$\mathbf{r}(t) = (2t + y_0)\mathbf{j} + \left(\frac{\alpha}{2m} t^2 + z_0\right)\mathbf{k}, \quad t \geq 0.$$

This path is a parabolic arc in the yz-plane. (See Figure 13.4.4.) To get an equation for this arc in cartesian coordinates, we note that

$$x(t) = 0, \qquad y(t) = 2t + y_0, \qquad z(t) = \frac{\alpha}{2m} t^2 + z_0.$$

From the second equation we have

$$t = \frac{y(t) - y_0}{2}.$$

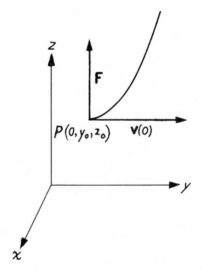

FIGURE 13.4.4

Substituting this into the last equation, we get

$$z(t) = \frac{\alpha}{2m}\left(\frac{y(t) - y_0}{2}\right)^2 + z_0.$$

Dispensing with t, we get

$$z = \frac{\alpha}{2m}\left(\frac{y - y_0}{2}\right) + z_0.$$

Of course we must bear in mind the extra condition $x = 0$. Answers to the problem:

(a) $\mathbf{v}(t) = 2\mathbf{j} + \dfrac{\alpha}{m}t\mathbf{k}.$ (velocity)

(b) $\|\mathbf{v}(t)\| = \dfrac{1}{m}\sqrt{4m^2 + \alpha^2 t^2}.$ (speed)

(c) $m\mathbf{v}(t) = 2m\mathbf{j} + \alpha t\mathbf{k}.$ (momentum)

(d) $\mathbf{r}(t) = (2t + y_0)\mathbf{j} + \left(\dfrac{\alpha}{2m}t^2 + z_0\right)\mathbf{k}, \qquad t \geq 0.$

$$z = \frac{\alpha}{2m}\left(\frac{y - y_0}{2}\right)^2 + z_0, \qquad x = 0. \quad \square$$

The scalar product

$$\mathbf{F}(t) \cdot \mathbf{v}(t)$$

is called the *power* (which is given to the object by the force). The *kinetic energy* of an object is defined as

$$\frac{1}{2}m\|\mathbf{v}(t)\|^2.$$

In Exercise 5 you are asked to show that power is the rate of change of kinetic energy:

$$\frac{d}{dt}\left(\frac{1}{2}m\|\mathbf{v}(t)\|^2\right) = \mathbf{F}(t) \cdot \mathbf{v}(t).$$

We will return to these notions later. Now let's talk briefly about the dynamics of rotations. The central notions here are *torque*, usually denoted by τ [the Greek letter "tau"], and *angular momentum*, usually denoted by **L**. Torque, from the Latin word for "twist", is defined by the equation

(13.4.1) $\boldsymbol{\tau}(t) = \mathbf{r}(t) \times \mathbf{F}(t).$

More precisely (13.4.1) gives the torque produced by the force $\mathbf{F}(t)$ about the origin. Angular momentum is defined by setting

$$\mathbf{L}(t) = \mathbf{r}(t) \times m\mathbf{v}(t).$$

Just as force is the rate of change of momentum, torque is the rate of change of angular momentum:

$$\begin{aligned}
\mathbf{L}'(t) &= [\mathbf{r}(t) \times m\mathbf{v}'(t)] + [\mathbf{r}'(t) \times m\mathbf{v}(t)] \\
&= [\mathbf{r}(t) \times m\mathbf{a}(t)] + [\mathbf{v}(t) \times m\mathbf{v}(t)] \\
&= [\mathbf{r}(t) \times m\mathbf{a}(t)] + \mathbf{0} \\
&= \boldsymbol{\tau}(t). \quad \square
\end{aligned}$$

Central forces, forces which act along the line of the radius vector, produce no torque. To verify this note that every central force has the form

$$\mathbf{F}(t) = u(t)\mathbf{r}(t).$$

Obviously then

$$\boldsymbol{\tau}(t) = \mathbf{r}(t) \times \mathbf{F}(t) = \mathbf{r}(t) \times u(t)\mathbf{r}(t) = 0. \quad \square$$

Using these ideas, we can demonstrate Kepler's marvelous equal-time equal-area law for planetary motion.

Kepler's Second Law

As a planet moves around the sun, the radius vector sweeps out equal areas in equal times.

For convenience we picture the sun at the origin of our coordinate system. (See Figure 13.4.5.)

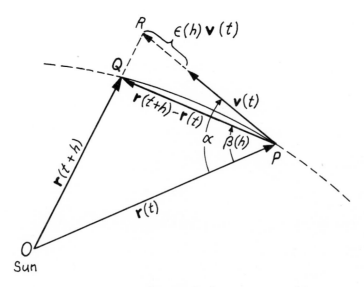

FIGURE 13.4.5

The force involved is the gravitational attraction of the sun. Since this is a central force, we know that the torque is zero and thus the angular momentum of the planet

$$\mathbf{L}(t) = \mathbf{r}(t) \times m\mathbf{v}(t)$$

is constant. In particular, its norm is constant and thus

$$||\mathbf{r}(t)|| \, ||\mathbf{v}(t)|| \, |\sin \alpha|$$

is constant.

We will use $A(t)$ to indicate the area swept out by the radius vector from some fixed time up to time t. Our task is to show that $A'(t)$ is constant. This we will do by showing that

$$A'(t) = \frac{1}{2} ||\mathbf{r}(t)|| \, ||\mathbf{v}(t)|| \, |\sin \alpha|.$$

The area swept out during the time interval $[t, t + h]$ is simply

$$A(t + h) - A(t).$$

From obvious geometric considerations,

$$\text{area of } \triangle OPQ \leq A(t + h) - A(t) \leq \text{area of } \triangle OPQ + \text{area of } \triangle PQR\dagger$$

and thus

$$(13.4.2) \quad \frac{\text{area of } \triangle OPQ}{h} \leq \frac{A(t + h) - A(t)}{h} \leq \frac{\text{area of } \triangle OPQ}{h} + \frac{\text{area of } \triangle PQR}{h}.$$

Since

$$\frac{\text{area of } \triangle OPQ}{h} = \frac{1}{2} ||\mathbf{r}(t)|| \, \left\| \frac{\mathbf{r}(t + h) - \mathbf{r}(t)}{h} \right\| \, |\sin \beta(h)|,$$

we see that

$$\lim_{h \downarrow 0} \frac{\text{area of } \triangle OPQ}{h} = \frac{1}{2} ||\mathbf{r}(t)|| \, ||\mathbf{v}(t)|| \, |\sin \alpha|.$$

We turn our attention now to the other triangle

$$\frac{\text{area of } \triangle PQR}{h} = \frac{1}{2} \left\| \frac{\mathbf{r}(t + h) - \mathbf{r}(t)}{h} \right\| \, ||\mathbf{v}(t) + t(h)\mathbf{v}(t)|| \, |\sin [\alpha - \beta(h)]|.$$

As h decreases to zero, $\beta(h)$ tends to α and thus $|\sin [\alpha - \beta(h)]|$ tends to zero. Since

$$\left\| \frac{\mathbf{r}(t + h) - \mathbf{r}(t)}{h} \right\| \quad \text{tends to} \quad ||\mathbf{v}(t)||,$$

and $||\mathbf{v}(t) + t(h)\mathbf{v}(t)||$ certainly remains bounded, we see that

$$\lim_{h \downarrow 0} \frac{\text{area of } \triangle PQR}{h} = 0.$$

---

† Here we are assuming that the path curves toward the sun and not away from it. This is physically obvious: gravitational force is an attracting force, not a repelling force.

From (13.4.2)

$$\lim_{h \downarrow 0} \frac{A(t+h) - A(t)}{h} = \frac{1}{2} \|\mathbf{r}(t)\| \|\mathbf{v}(t)\| |\sin \alpha|,$$

which assures us that

$$A'(t) = \frac{1}{2} \|\mathbf{r}(t)\| \|\mathbf{v}(t)\| |\sin \alpha|$$

as asserted.   □

Exercises

1.* An object of mass m moves along the hyperbolic path $\mathbf{r}(t) = a \cosh \omega t \, \mathbf{i} + b \sinh \omega t \, \mathbf{j}$ for each time $t \geq 0$. For each time t, find:
   (a) the velocity.
   (b) the speed.
   (c) the acceleration.
   (d) the momentum.
   (e) the force.
   (f) the power.
   (g) the kinetic energy.
   (h) the angular momentum.
   (i) the torque.

2.* Find the force required to propel a particle of mass m along a parabolic arc with

$$\mathbf{r}(t) = t\mathbf{j} + t^2\mathbf{k}, \qquad \text{for each time } t \geq 0.$$

3. At each point $P(x(t), y(t), z(t))$ of its motion an object of mass m is subject to a force

$$\mathbf{F}(t) = m[a \cos t \, \mathbf{i} + b \sin t \, \mathbf{j}]; \quad a > 0, b > 0.$$

   Given that

$$\mathbf{v}(0) = -b\mathbf{j} + \mathbf{k} \qquad \text{and} \qquad \mathbf{r}(0) = b\mathbf{i}$$

   find:
   (a) the velocity.
   (b) the speed.
   (c) the acceleration.
   (d) the momentum.
   (e) the power.
   (f) the kinetic energy.
   (g) the angular momentum.
   (h) the torque.
   (i) the path followed by the object.

4. Show that a particle subject to no outside forces is either stationary or moves with constant speed along a straight line.

5. Show that power is the rate of change of kinetic energy.

13.5 Arc length, speed, and curvature

Arc Length

In Figure 13.5.1 we have sketched a curve C and a polygonal approximation to it. The length of C is by definition the least upper bound of the lengths of such polygonal approximations.

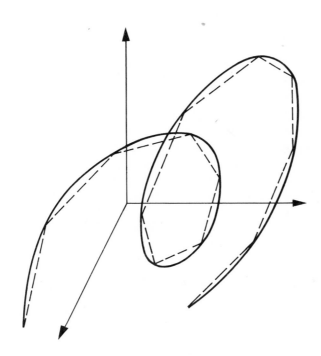

A space curve and a polygonal approximation

FIGURE 13.5.1

Earlier we considered plane curves and used the arc length formula

$$l(C) = \int_a^b \sqrt{[x'(t)]^2 + [y'(t)]^2}\, dt.$$

For space curves the formula becomes

$$l(C) = \int_a^b \sqrt{[x'(t)]^2 + [y'(t)]^2 + [z'(t)]^2}\, dt.$$

Both of these results can be cast in the form

$$l(C) = \int_a^b \|\mathbf{r}'(t)\|\, dt.$$

For plane curves,

$$\|\mathbf{r}'(t)\| = \|x'(t)\mathbf{i} + y'(t)\mathbf{j}\| = \sqrt{[x'(t)]^2 + [y'(t)]^2}$$

and for space curves,

$$\|\mathbf{r}'(t)\| = \|x'(t)\mathbf{i} + y'(t)\mathbf{j} + z'(t)\mathbf{k}\| = \sqrt{[x'(t)]^2 + [y'(t)]^2 + [z'(t)]^2}.$$

Theorem

The length of a continuously differentiable curve

$$C: \quad \mathbf{r}(t), \quad t \in [a, b]$$

is given by the formula

$$l(C) = \int_a^b \|\mathbf{r}'(t)\| \, dt.$$

PROOF.   First we show that

$$l(C) \leq \int_a^b \|\mathbf{r}'(t)\| \, dt.$$

To do this, we begin with an arbitrary partition P of $[a, b]$

$$P = \{a = t_0, \cdots, t_{i-1}, t_i, \cdots, t_n = b\}.$$

Such a partition gives rise to a finite number of points of C

$$\mathbf{r}(a) = \mathbf{r}(t_0), \cdots, \mathbf{r}(t_{i-1}), \mathbf{r}(t_i), \cdots, \mathbf{r}(t_n) = \mathbf{r}(b)$$

and thus to a polygonal path of total length

$$l_P = \sum_{i=1}^{n} \|\mathbf{r}(t_i) - \mathbf{r}(t_{i-1})\|. \qquad \text{(Figure 13.5.2)}$$

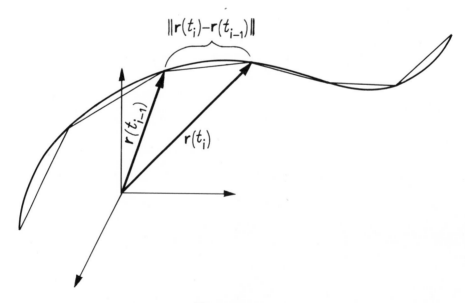

FIGURE 13.5.2

For each i,

$$\mathbf{r}(t_i) - \mathbf{r}(t_{i-1}) = \int_{t_{i-1}}^{t_i} \mathbf{r}'(t)\, dt.$$

This gives

$$\|\mathbf{r}(t_i) - \mathbf{r}(t_{i-1})\| = \left\| \int_{t_{i-1}}^{t_i} \mathbf{r}'(t)\, dt \right\| \leq \int_{t_{i-1}}^{t_i} \|\mathbf{r}'(t)\|\, dt$$

and thus

$$l_P = \sum_{i=1}^{n} \|\mathbf{r}(t_i) - \mathbf{r}(t_{i-1})\| \leq \sum_{i=1}^{n} \int_{t_{i-1}}^{t_i} \|\mathbf{r}'(t)\|\, dt = \int_{a}^{b} \|\mathbf{r}'(t)\|\, dt.$$

From the arbitrariness of P, we know that the inequality

$$l_P \leq \int_{a}^{b} \|\mathbf{r}'(t)\|\, dt$$

must hold for all the l_P. This makes the integral on the right an upper bound for all the l_P. Since $l(C)$ is the *least* upper bound of all the l_P, we can conclude right now that

$$l(C) \leq \int_{a}^{b} \|\mathbf{r}'(t)\|\, dt.$$

To show equality we need to know that arc length is additive; we need to know (see Figure 13.5.3) that the length of the curve from P to Q, plus the length of the curve from

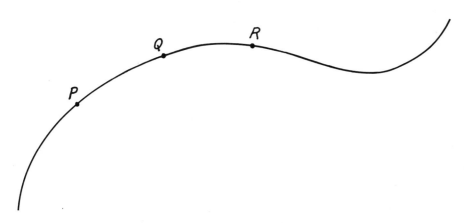

$$\ell(\overset{\frown}{PQ}) + \ell(\overset{\frown}{QR}) = \ell(\overset{\frown}{PR})$$

Figure 13.5.3

Q to R, is exactly equal to the length of the curve from P to R.† A proof of this is given in the supplement to this section.

---

† It is obvious that arc length should have this property. What we have to verify is that arc length, *as we have defined it*, has this property.

Let's go on. In Figure 13.5.4 we display a vector $\mathbf{r}(t)$ and a nearby vector $\mathbf{r}(t + h)$. We now set

$$s(t) = \text{length of the curve from } \mathbf{r}(a) \text{ to } \mathbf{r}(t)$$

and

$$s(t + h) = \text{length of the curve from } \mathbf{r}(a) \text{ to } \mathbf{r}(t + h).$$

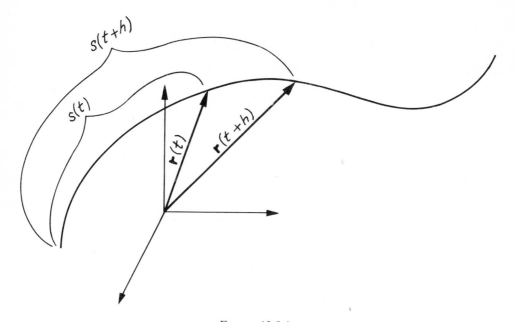

FIGURE 13.5.4

Assuming the additivity of arc length, we get

$$s(t + h) - s(t) = \text{length of the curve from } \mathbf{r}(t) \text{ to } \mathbf{r}(t + h).$$

From what we have shown already, we know that

$$\|\mathbf{r}(t + h) - \mathbf{r}(t)\| \leq s(t + h) - s(t) \leq \int_t^{t+h} \|\mathbf{r}'(u)\| \, du.$$

Dividing this inequality by h (which we are taking as positive), we get

$$\left\| \frac{\mathbf{r}(t + h) - \mathbf{r}(t)}{h} \right\| \leq \frac{s(t + h) - s(t)}{h} \leq \frac{1}{h} \int_t^{t+h} \|\mathbf{r}'(u)\| \, du.$$

As $h \downarrow 0$, both extremes of the inequality tend to $\|\mathbf{r}'(t)\|$ and consequently so does the middle term.† In short,

$$\lim_{h \downarrow 0} \frac{s(t + h) - s(t)}{h} = \|\mathbf{r}'(t)\|.$$

----

† One way to show that the right hand extreme of the inequality tends to $r'(t)$ is to use the First mean-value theorem for Integrals. (Section 9.1)

By taking $h < 0$ and proceeding in a similar manner, one can show that

$$\lim_{h \uparrow 0} \frac{s(t + h) - s(t)}{h} = \|\mathbf{r}'(t)\|.$$

It follows that

$$s'(t) = \lim_{h \to 0} \frac{s(t + h) - s(t)}{h} = \|\mathbf{r}'(t)\|.$$

Recall now that

$$s(t) = \text{length of the curve from } \mathbf{r}(a) \text{ to } \mathbf{r}(t).$$

Obviously then $s(a) = 0$. This condition, together with the fact that

$$s'(t) = \|\mathbf{r}'(t)\|,$$

implies that

$$s(t) = \text{length of the curve from } \mathbf{r}(a) \text{ to } \mathbf{r}(t) = \int_a^t \|\mathbf{r}'(u)\| \, du.$$

The total length of C is therefore

$$s(b) = \int_a^b \|\mathbf{r}'(t)\| \, dt. \quad \square$$

Problem. Find the length of the curve

$$C: \mathbf{r}(t) = 2 \cos t \, \mathbf{i} + 2 \sin t \, \mathbf{j} + t^2 \, \mathbf{k}$$

from $t = 0$ to $t = 1$.

SOLUTION

$$\mathbf{r}'(t) = -2 \sin t \, \mathbf{i} + 2 \cos t \, \mathbf{j} + 2t \, \mathbf{k}.$$
$$\|\mathbf{r}'(t)\| = \sqrt{4 \sin^2 t + 4 \cos^2 t + 4t^2}$$
$$= 2\sqrt{\sin^2 t + \cos^2 t + t^2}$$
$$= 2\sqrt{1 + t^2}.$$
$$l(C) = \int_0^1 \|\mathbf{r}'(t)\| \, dt$$
$$= 2 \int_0^1 \sqrt{1 + t^2} \, dt$$
$$= 2 \left[\frac{t}{2} \sqrt{1 + t^2} + \frac{1}{2} \log (t + \sqrt{1 + t^2}) \right]_0^1$$
$$= \sqrt{2} + \log(1 + \sqrt{2}). \quad \square$$

Speed

In the last section we considered motions parametrized by time and, somewhat arbitrarily, called $\|\mathbf{r}'(t)\|$ the speed of the motion. We are now in a position to justify this. Imagine that an object moves so that at time t it has position

$$\mathbf{r}(t) = x(t)\mathbf{i} + y(t)\mathbf{j} + z(t)\mathbf{k}.$$

During a time interval $[0, t]$, the object moves along its path from $\mathbf{r}(0)$ to $\mathbf{r}(t)$ for a total distance which is equal to the length of the curve from $\mathbf{r}(0)$ to $\mathbf{r}(t)$. If, as before, we denote this distance by $s(t)$, then we have

$$s(t) = \int_0^t \|\mathbf{r}'(u)\| \, du$$

and

$$s'(t) = \|\mathbf{r}'(t)\|.$$

In other words, $\|\mathbf{r}'(t)\|$ is the *rate of change of distance with respect to time.* That is why we call it the *speed.*

In this setting, speed is commonly abbreviated by the letter v. In symbols, we have

$$\boxed{s'(t) = v(t)}$$

or, in the Leibniz notation,

$$\boxed{\frac{ds}{dt} = v.}$$

While integration of the velocity vector gives the position vector

$$\mathbf{r}(t) = \mathbf{r}(0) + \int_0^t \mathbf{v}(u) \, du,$$

integration of the speed gives the distance traveled

$$s(t) = s(0) + \int_0^t v(u) \, du.$$

Curvature

For insight into the geometry of curves it is sometimes useful to use arc length as the parameter. Suppose that we have a curve

$$C: \mathbf{r}(s) = x(s)\mathbf{i} + y(s)\mathbf{j} + z(s)\mathbf{k}, \qquad s \in [0, l].$$

We shall say that C is *parametrized by arc length* iff for each $s \in [0, l]$, $\mathbf{r}(s)$ is that point of C which is at an arc distance s from the initial point $\mathbf{r}(0)$. The idea is illustrated in Figure 13.5.5.

There is a simple way to determine whether or not a given curve is being parametrized by arc length. In general

$$\int_0^s \|\mathbf{r}'(u)\| \, du = \text{the arc distance from } \mathbf{r}(0) \text{ to } \mathbf{r}(s).$$

The parametrization is with respect to arc length iff

$$\int_0^s \|\mathbf{r}'(u)\| \, du = s \qquad \text{for each value of the parameter } s.$$

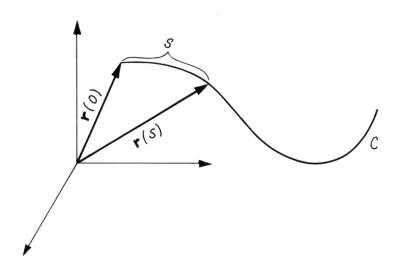

Curve parametrized by arc length

FIGURE 13.5.5

Example. The simplest and probably the most important example of a curve parametrized by arc length is the unit circle

$$\mathbf{r}(s) = \cos s\,\mathbf{i} + \sin s\,\mathbf{j}, \qquad s \in [0, 2\pi].$$

A slightly more general example is the circle of radius ρ

$$\mathbf{r}(s) = \rho \left[\cos \frac{s}{\rho}\,\mathbf{i} + \sin \frac{s}{\rho}\,\mathbf{j} \right].$$

To verify that this parametrization is with respect to arc length, note that

$$\mathbf{r}'(s) = -\sin \frac{s}{\rho}\,\mathbf{i} + \cos \frac{s}{\rho}\,\mathbf{j}.$$

It follows then that

$$\int_0^s \|\mathbf{r}'(u)\|\,du = \int_0^s \sqrt{\sin^2 \frac{u}{\rho} + \cos^2 \frac{u}{\rho}}\,du = \int_0^s 1\,du = s. \quad \square$$

If we have a curve parametrized by arc length, then

$$\int_0^s \|\mathbf{r}'(u)\|\,du = s.$$

Differentiation with respect to s, gives

$$\|\mathbf{r}'(s)\| = 1.$$

Geometrically, this means that, *in the case of a curve parametrized by arc length, the tangent vector $\mathbf{r}'(s)$ has constant length 1.*

Although the length of the tangent remains constantly 1, its direction can change as s changes. The vector $\mathbf{r}''(s)$ signals this change of direction and is called the *curvature vector*. Its magnitude

(13.5.1)
$$k(s) = \|\mathbf{r}''(s)\|$$

is called the *curvature*. It gives the magnitude of this change in direction per unit arc length.

Example.   In a circle of radius ρ the curvature is constantly $\dfrac{1}{\rho}$.

PROOF.   For convenience we place the circle in the xy-plane and center it at the origin. In terms of arc length we have

$$C\colon \mathbf{r}(s) = \rho\left[\cos\frac{s}{\rho}\,\mathbf{i} + \sin\frac{s}{\rho}\,\mathbf{j}\right].$$

This gives

$$\mathbf{r}'(s) = -\sin\frac{s}{\rho}\,\mathbf{i} + \cos\frac{s}{\rho}\,\mathbf{j}$$

and

$$\mathbf{r}''(s) = -\frac{1}{\rho}\left[\cos\frac{s}{\rho}\,\mathbf{i} + \sin\frac{s}{\rho}\,\mathbf{j}\right].$$

It follows then that

$$k(s) = \|\mathbf{r}''(s)\| = \frac{1}{\rho}$$

as asserted.   □

That the curvature of a circle of radius ρ should be $1/\rho$ is intuitively obvious. It is geometrically and physically evident that in a circular path the change in direction takes place at a constant rate. Since a complete revolution entails a change in direction of 2π radians and this change is carried out on a path of length $2\pi\rho$, the change in direction per unit arc length must be $1/\rho$.

Returning now to

$$\|\mathbf{r}'(s)\| = 1,$$

we see that

$$\mathbf{r}'(s)\cdot\mathbf{r}'(s) = 1$$
$$\mathbf{r}'(s)\cdot\mathbf{r}''(s) + \mathbf{r}''(s)\cdot\mathbf{r}'(s) = 0$$
$$2(\mathbf{r}'(s)\cdot\mathbf{r}''(s)) = 0$$

and therefore

$$\mathbf{r}'(s) \perp \mathbf{r}''(s).$$

This tells us that the *curvature vector is always perpendicular to the tangent vector.*

Curves other than the circle are seldom parametrized by arc length. It is therefore useful to know how to compute curvature in terms of an arbitrary parameter t, which for convenience we interpret as time.

Theorem

Let

$$C: \mathbf{r}(t) = x(t)\mathbf{i} + y(t)\mathbf{j} + z(t)\mathbf{k}, \qquad t \in [a, b]$$

be a twice differentiable curve. If $\mathbf{r}'(t) \neq \mathbf{0}$, the curvature is given by the formula

$$k(t) = \left\| \frac{\mathbf{T}'(t)}{s'(t)} \right\|$$

where $\mathbf{T}$ is the unit tangent

$$\mathbf{T}(t) = \frac{\mathbf{r}'(t)}{\|\mathbf{r}'(t)\|}.$$

PROOF.   We begin by assuming that $\mathbf{r}'(t) \neq \mathbf{0}$. By $s(t)$ we mean the length of the curve from $\mathbf{r}(a)$ to $\mathbf{r}(t)$. As t ranges from a to b, $s(t)$ ranges from 0 to l, the total length of the curve. For each number $s(t) \in [0, l]$, we define

$$\mathbf{g}(s(t)) = \mathbf{r}(t). \qquad \text{(See Figure 13.5.6)}$$

Since

$$\mathbf{g}'(s(t))s'(t) = \mathbf{r}'(t) \qquad \text{and} \qquad \mathbf{r}'(t) \neq \mathbf{0},$$

we see that

$$s'(t) \neq 0.$$

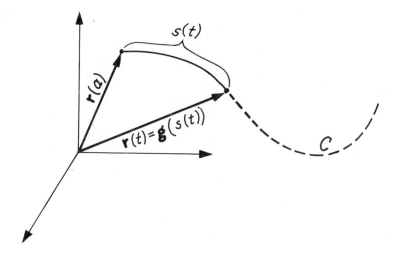

FIGURE 13.5.6

We defined the function **g** so that **g**(s) would give us an arc length parametrization for C. Consequently, we have as the unit tangent

$$\mathbf{T}(t) = \mathbf{g}'(s(t)).$$

Differentiating again, we get

$$\mathbf{T}'(t) = \mathbf{g}''(s(t))s'(t)$$

and thus

$$k(t) = \|\mathbf{g}''(s(t))\| = \left\|\frac{\mathbf{T}'(t)}{s'(t)}\right\| . \quad \square$$

This last result is often written

$$k = \frac{1}{v}\left\|\frac{d\mathbf{T}}{dt}\right\| .$$

Problem.   Find the curvature of the curve

$$\mathbf{r}(t) = t\mathbf{i} + t^2\mathbf{j} + \frac{2}{3}t^3\mathbf{k} \qquad \text{at } P\left(-1, 1, -\frac{2}{3}\right).$$

SOLUTION

$$\mathbf{r}'(t) = \mathbf{i} + 2t\mathbf{j} + 2t^2\mathbf{k}$$
$$s'(t) = \|\mathbf{r}'(t)\| = \sqrt{1 + 4t^2 + 4t^4} = 1 + 2t^2$$
$$\mathbf{T}(t) = \frac{\mathbf{r}'(t)}{\|\mathbf{r}'(t)\|} = \frac{1}{1 + 2t^2}[\mathbf{i} + 2t\mathbf{j} + 2t^2\mathbf{k}]$$
$$\mathbf{T}'(t) = \frac{(1 + 2t^2)[2\mathbf{j} + 4t\mathbf{k}] - 4t[\mathbf{i} + 2t\mathbf{j} + 2t^2\mathbf{k}]}{(1 + 2t^2)^2}$$
$$= \frac{-4t\mathbf{i} + (2 - 4t^2)\mathbf{j} + 4t\mathbf{k}}{(1 + 2t^2)^2} .$$

The point $P(-1, 1, -2/3)$ corresponds to the parameter value $t = -1$.

$$\mathbf{T}'(-1) = \frac{4\mathbf{i} - 2\mathbf{j} - 4\mathbf{k}}{9} , \qquad s'(-1) = 3$$

$$\|\mathbf{T}'(-1)\| = \frac{\sqrt{16 + 4 + 16}}{9} = \frac{\sqrt{36}}{9} = \frac{2}{3}$$

$$\left\|\frac{\mathbf{T}'(-1)}{s'(-1)}\right\| = \frac{2}{9} . \quad \square$$

Exercises

Find the lengths of the following curves.

1.* $\mathbf{r}(t) = a\cos t\,\mathbf{i} + a\sin t\,\mathbf{j} + bt\,\mathbf{k}$ from $t = 0$ to $t = 2\pi$.

2. $\mathbf{r}(t) = t\mathbf{i} + \frac{2\sqrt{2}}{3}t^{3/2}\mathbf{j} + \frac{t^2}{2}\mathbf{k}$ from $t = 0$ to $t = 2$.

3.* $r(t) = t\mathbf{i} + \log(\sec t)\mathbf{j} + 3\mathbf{k}$ from $t = 0$ to $t = \dfrac{\pi}{4}$.

4. $r(t) = t^3\mathbf{i} + t^2\mathbf{j}$ from $t = 0$ to $t = 1$.

5.* $r(t) = t\mathbf{i} + \mathbf{j} + \left(\dfrac{t^3}{6} + \dfrac{1}{2t}\right)\mathbf{k}$ from $t = 1$ to $t = 3$.

6. $r(t) = e^t[\cos t\,\mathbf{i} + \sin t\,\mathbf{j}]$ from $t = 0$ to $t = \pi$.

7.* $r(t) = 3t\cos t\,\mathbf{i} + 3t\sin t\,\mathbf{j} + 4t\,\mathbf{k}$ from $t = 0$ to $t = 4$.

8. $r(t) = 2t\mathbf{i} + (t^2 - 2)\mathbf{j} + (1 - t^2)\mathbf{k}$ from $t = 0$ to $t = 2$.

9.* Parametrize the ray

$$l: r(t) = \mathbf{a} + t\mathbf{b}, \qquad t \geq 0$$

by arc length.

10.   Show that straight lines have constant curvature 0.

Find the curvature of each of the following curves.

11.* $r(t) = 2t\mathbf{i} + (t^2 - 1)\mathbf{j}$.

12. $r(t) = t^2\mathbf{i} + (t^4 - t^5)\mathbf{j}$.

13.* $r(t) = a\cos^3 t\,\mathbf{i} + a\sin^3 t\,\mathbf{j}$.

14. $r(t) = 2abt\,\mathbf{i} + a^2\log t\,\mathbf{j} + b^2t^2\,\mathbf{k}$.

15.* $r(t) = (t - \sin t)\mathbf{i} + (1 - \cos t)\mathbf{j} + 4\sin\left(\tfrac{1}{2}t\right)\mathbf{k}$.

16. $r(t) = e^t\mathbf{i} + e^{-t}\mathbf{j} + \sqrt{2}t\mathbf{k}$.

17.* $r(t) = \cosh t\cos t\,\mathbf{i} + \cosh t\sin t\,\mathbf{j} + t\,\mathbf{k}$.

18.   Show that the curvature of a plane curve

$$r(t) = x(t)\mathbf{i} + y(t)\mathbf{j}$$

can be written

$$k(t) = \frac{|x'(t)y''(t) - y'(t)x''(t)|}{([x'(t)]^2 + [y'(t)]^2)^{3/2}}.$$

19.* Using exercise 18, find a formula for the curvature of a curve $y = f(x)$.

Find the curvature of the following plane curves.

20.* $y = \cosh x$.   22.* $x^{2/3} + y^{2/3} = 1$ at $(\sqrt{2}/4, \sqrt{2}/4)$.

21. $y = e^x$.   23. $y = \log(\sec x)$.

24.* Find the maximal and minimal curvature attained by the sine curve $y = \sin x$.

25.* Find the points of maximal curvature on the ellipse $x(t) = a\cos t$, $y(t) = b\sin t$, $a > b > 0$.

26.   Find the points of maximal curvature on the curves
   (a) $y = \log x$.   (b) $y = e^x$.

27.* Find a formula for the curvature of a curve given by a polar equation

$$r = f(\theta).$$

28.   Find the curvature of the logarithmic spiral

$$r = e^{a\theta}.$$

29.* Find the curvature of the spiral of Archimedes

$$r = a\theta.$$

30.   Show that the curvature of the cardioid

$$r = a(1 - \cos\theta)$$

is given by the formula

$$k = \frac{3}{2\sqrt{2ar}}.$$

SUPPLEMENT

The Additivity of Arc Length

With P, Q, and R as in Figure 13.5.3 we wish to show that

$$l(\widehat{PQ}) + l(\widehat{QR}) = l(\widehat{PR}).$$

If L_1 is a polygonal path inscribed in $\widehat{PQ}$ and L_2 is a polygonal path inscribed in $\widehat{QR}$, then

$$L_1 \cup L_2 \quad \text{is inscribed in} \quad \widehat{PR}.$$

Since

$$l(L_1) + l(L_2) = l(L_1 \cup L_2) \quad \text{and} \quad l(L_1 \cup L_2) \le l(\widehat{PR}),$$

we see that

$$l(L_1) + l(L_2) \le l(\widehat{PR}) \quad \text{and thus} \quad l(L_1) \le l(\widehat{PR}) - l(L_2).$$

Since L_1 is an arbitrary polygonal path inscribed in $\widehat{PQ}$, we conclude that

$$l(\widehat{PQ}) \le l(\widehat{PR}) - l(L_2).$$

This last inequality we can rewrite as

$$l(L_2) \le l(\widehat{PR}) - l(\widehat{PQ}).$$

From the arbitrariness of L_2 we conclude that

$$l(\widehat{QR}) \le l(\widehat{PR}) - l(\widehat{PQ}),$$

which we rewrite as

$$l(\widehat{PQ}) + l(\widehat{QR}) \le l(\widehat{PR}).$$

We now set out to prove that

$$l(\widehat{PR}) \le l(\widehat{PQ}) + l(\widehat{QR}).$$

To do this, we need only take

$$L = \overline{T_0 T_1} \cup \cdots \cup \overline{T_{n-1} T_n}$$

as an arbitrary polygonal path inscribed in $\overparen{PR}$ and show that

$$l(L) \leq l(\overparen{PQ}) + l(\overparen{QR}).$$

If Q is one of the T_i, say $Q = T_k$, then

$$L_1 = \overline{T_0 T_1} \cup \cdots \cup \overline{T_{k-1} T_k} \qquad \text{is inscribed in} \qquad \overparen{PQ}$$

and

$$L_2 = \overline{T_k T_{k+1}} \cup \cdots \cup \overline{T_{n-1} T_n} \qquad \text{is inscribed in} \qquad \overparen{QR}.$$

Moreover, $l(L) = l(L_1) + l(L_2)$, so that

$$l(L) \leq l(\overparen{PQ}) + l(\overparen{QR}).$$

If Q is none of the T_i, then for some k

$$Q \text{ lies between } T_k \text{ and } T_{k+1}.$$

Since

$$d(T_k, T_{k+1}) \leq d(T_k, Q) + d(Q, T_{k+1}),$$

it follows that the polygonal path

$$L' = \overline{T_0 T_1} \cup \cdots \cup \overline{T_k Q} \cup \overline{Q T_{k+1}} \cup \cdots \cup \overline{T_{n-1} T_n}$$

satisfies

$$l(L) \leq l(L').$$

Proceeding as before, we see that

$$l(L') \leq l(\overparen{PQ}) + l(\overparen{QR}),$$

and thus again we have

$$l(L) \leq l(\overparen{PQ}) + l(\overparen{QR}). \quad \square$$

FUNCTIONS OF SEVERAL VARIABLES

14.1 What are they?

First we talk about functions of two variables. To create such a function we pick out a portion of the xy-plane and call it D. To each point (x, y) in D we assign a real number $f(x, y)$. The set of all these assignments is called a *function of two variables*. We call the function f and the set D its *domain*.

Example. Take D as the closed unit disc:

$$D = \{(x, y): x^2 + y^2 \leq 1\}.$$

To each point (x, y) in D assign the number

$$f(x, y) = \sqrt{1 - (x^2 + y^2)}. \quad \square$$

Example. Take D as the entire xy-plane and to each pair (x, y) assign the number

$$g(x, y) = xy. \quad \square$$

Example. Take D as the set of all points off the x-axis and to each such point (x, y) assign the number

$$h(x, y) = \text{arc tan}\left(\frac{x}{y}\right). \quad \square$$

Functions of three variables are just as easy to come by. To create such a function we pick out a portion of space and call it D. To each point (x, y, z) in D we assign a real number $f(x, y, z)$. The set of all these assignments is called a *function of three variables*. We call the function f and D its *domain*.

Example. Take D as the closed unit ball:

$$D = \{(x, y, z): x^2 + y^2 + z^2 \le 1\}.$$

To each point (x, y, z) in D assign the number

$$f(x, y, z) = \sqrt{1 - (x^2 + y^2 + z^2)}. \quad \square$$

Example. Take D as all of three space and to each triple (x, y, z) assign the number

$$g(x, y, z) = xyz. \quad \square$$

Example. Take D as the set of all (x, y, z) such that $z \ne x + y$ and to each such triple assign the number

$$h(x, y, z) = \arctan\left(\frac{1}{x + y - z}\right). \quad \square$$

Functions of several variables arise naturally in very elementary settings. Here are some simple instances:

$$f(x, y) = xy, \qquad x > 0, y > 0$$

gives the area of a rectangle of width x and length y;

$$f(x, y, z) = xyz, \qquad x > 0, y > 0, z > 0$$

gives the volume of a rectangular solid of dimensions x, y, z;

$$f(x, y) = \pi x^2 y, \qquad x > 0, y > 0$$

gives the volume of a cylinder with base radius x and height y, while

$$f(x, y) = 2\pi x(x + y)$$

gives the total surface area;

$$f(x, y) = \sqrt{x^2 + y^2}$$

gives the norm of the vector $(x, y) = x\mathbf{i} + y\mathbf{j}$ and

$$f(x, y, z) = \sqrt{x^2 + y^2 + z^2}$$

gives the norm of the vector $(x, y, z) = x\mathbf{i} + y\mathbf{j} + z\mathbf{k}. \quad \square$

If the domain of a function of several variables is not explicitly given, it is to be understood that the domain is the maximal set for which the definition makes sense. Thus in the case of

$$f(x, y) = \frac{1}{x - y}$$

the domain is understood to be all the pairs (x, y) with $y \neq x$. That is, all points of the plane off the line $y = x$. In the case of

$$g(x, y, z) = \text{arc sin } (xyz)$$

the domain is understood to be all the triples (x, y, z) such that

$$-1 \leq xyz \leq 1. \quad \square$$

The *range* of a function of several variables is simply the set of values that it takes. To say that a function of several variables is *bounded* is simply to say that its range is bounded. For example, the functions

$$f(x, y) = \frac{1}{x - y} \qquad \text{and} \qquad g(x, y, z) = \text{arc sin } xyz$$

have ranges

$$(-\infty, 0) \cup (0, \infty) \qquad \text{and} \qquad \left[\frac{-\pi}{2}, \frac{\pi}{2} \right]$$

respectively. The second function is bounded but the first one is not. $\quad \square$

Exercises

Find the domain and range of each of the following functions.

1.* $f(x, y) = \dfrac{1}{x + y}.$

2. $f(x, y) = \sqrt{xy}.$

3.* $f(x, y) = \sqrt{1 - xy}.$

4. $f(x, y) = \dfrac{1}{x^2 + y^2}.$

5.* $f(x, y) = \dfrac{e^x - e^y}{e^x + e^y}.$

6. $f(x, y) = \dfrac{x^2}{x^2 + y^2}.$

7.* $f(x, y) = \dfrac{1}{x} - \dfrac{1}{y}.$

8. $f(x, y) = \dfrac{y}{x} + \dfrac{x}{y}.$

9.* $f(x, y, z) = \sqrt{x^2 + y^2 + z^2}.$

10. $f(x, y, z) = \dfrac{1}{\sqrt{x^2 + y^2 + z^2}}.$

11.* $f(x, y) = \dfrac{1}{\sqrt{x^2 - y^2}}.$

12. $f(x, y, z) = \cos x + \cos y + \cos z.$

13.* $f(x, y, z) = \dfrac{z^2}{x^2 - y^2}.$

14. $f(x, y, z) = \dfrac{z}{x - y}.$

14.2   Level curves and level surfaces

Here we take up the problem of representing functions of several variables by pictures. We begin with a function f of two variables defined on a subset D of the xy-plane. By the *graph of f* we mean the graph of the equation

$$z = f(x, y), \qquad (x, y) \in D.$$

Some Examples

In the case of

$$f(x, y) = x^2 + y^2$$

the domain is the entire plane. The graph of f is the paraboloid of revolution

$$z = x^2 + y^2.$$

For a sketch see Figure 14.2.1.   □

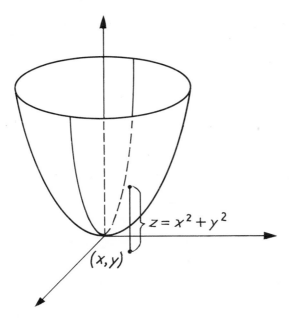

FIGURE 14.2.1

In the case of

$$g(x, y) = ax + by + c$$

the domain is again the entire xy-plane. The graph of g is the plane

$$z = ax + by + c.   \square \qquad\qquad \text{(See Figure 14.2.2.)}$$

Another function with a simple graph is

$$f(x, y) = \sqrt{r^2 - (x^2 + y^2)}.$$

The domain here is the disc of radius r centered at the origin:

$$\{(x, y) : x^2 + y^2 \le r^2\}.$$

The graph has equation

$$z = \sqrt{r^2 - (x^2 + y^2)}$$

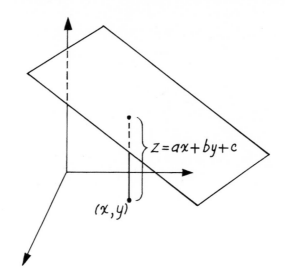

FIGURE 14.2.2

or equivalently

$$r^2 = x^2 + y^2 + z^2, \qquad z \geq 0.$$

It is the hemispherical surface depicted in Figure 14.2.3. □

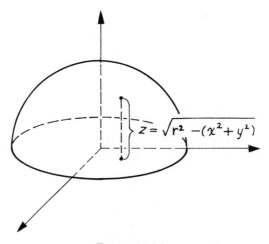

FIGURE 14.2.3

Our next example

$$f(x, y) = xy$$

is more interesting. The function is simple enough, but its graph

$$z = xy$$

is quite difficult to draw. It is the "saddle shaped" surface of Figure 14.2.4. □

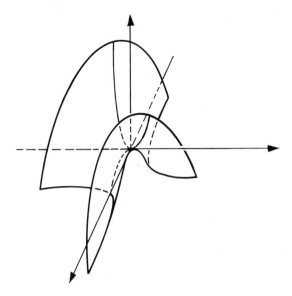

FIGURE 14.2.4

Level Curves

In practice the graph of a function of two variables is usually too difficult to draw. More-over, if drawn, it is often difficult to interpret. Fortunately there is an easier way to convey the same information.

We take our cue from the art of the map maker. In mapping mountainous terrain it is a common practice to sketch curves joining points of constant elevation. A collection of such curves, properly labelled, gives a good idea of the altitude variations in a region. (See Figure 14.2.5.)

FIGURE 14.2.5

We can do the same thing to portray functions of two variables. Suppose that f is defined on some portion of the xy-plane. For a given value c that f takes on, we can sketch the curve

$$f(x, y) = c.$$

Such a curve is called a *level curve* for f. It lies in the domain of f and on it f is constantly c. A collection of such curves, properly drawn and labeled, can give a good idea of the behavior of f. Below we give some examples.

We begin with the function

$$f(x, y) = x^2 + y^2.$$

The level curves (see Figure 14.2.6) are circles centered at the origin:

$$x^2 + y^2 = c, \qquad c > 0.$$

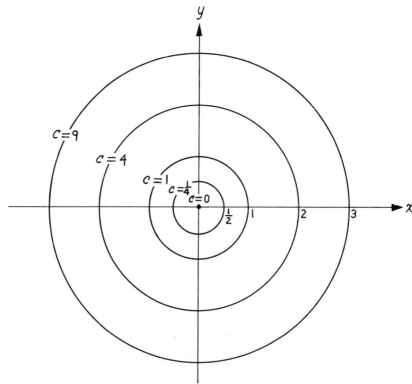

Level curves: $f(x, y) = x^2 + y^2$

FIGURE 14.2.6

The function takes on the value c on the circle of radius $\sqrt{c}$. At the origin the function is zero. □

In the case of

$$g(x, y) = x + y + 1 \qquad\qquad\qquad \text{(Figure 14.2.7)}$$

the level curves are parallel lines

$$x + y + 1 = c. \quad \square$$

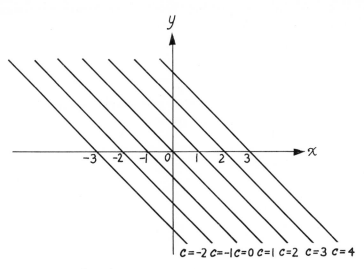

Level curves: $g(x,y) = x + y + 1$

FIGURE 14.2.7

As our next example we take the function

$$h(x, y) = \begin{cases} \sqrt{x^2 + y^2}, & x \geq 0 \\ |y|, & x < 0 \end{cases}.$$

For $x \geq 0$, $h(x, y)$ is the distance from (x, y) to the origin. For $x < 0$, $h(x, y)$ is the distance from (x, y) to the x-axis. The level curves are pictured in Figure 14.2.8. The

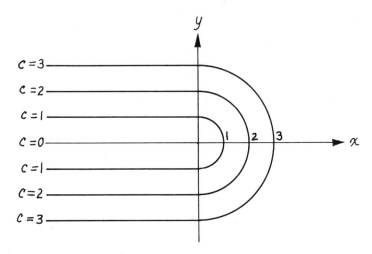

FIGURE 14.2.8

zero level curve is the nonpositive x-axis. The other level curves are horseshoe shaped: pairs of horizontal rays capped on the right by semicircles.   ☐

We go back now to the function

$$f(x, y) = xy.$$

The graph of f is the saddle shaped surface of Figure 14.2.4. This surface is readily understood in terms of its level curves. The 0-level curve consists of the two coordinate axes. The other level curves are simply hyperbolas

$$xy = c.$$

Some are displayed in Figure 14.2.9.   ☐

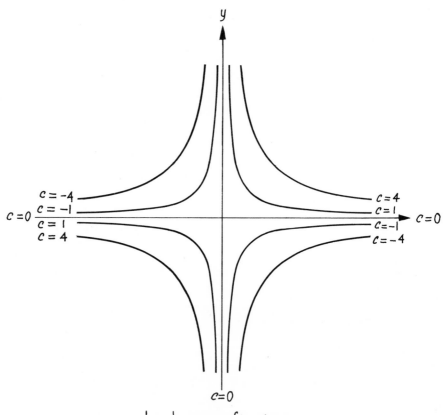

Level curves: $f(x,y) = xy$

FIGURE 14.2.9

Level Surfaces

Drawing graphs for functions of two variables is usually very difficult. Drawing graphs for functions of three variables is actually impossible. To draw such things, we would need four dimensions at our disposal. One way to try to visualize the behavior of a function of three variables is to examine its *level surfaces*. These are the sets with equations of the form

$$f(x, y, z) = c.$$

They are the counterparts of the level curves in the two variable case. Unlike level curves, level surfaces 'are usually hard to draw. Nevertheless a knowledge of what they are is usually helpful. We shall restrict ourselves to a few very simple examples. In the case of

$$f(x, y, z) = a_1x + a_2y + a_3z$$

the level surfaces are parallel planes

$$a_1x + a_2y + a_3z = c.$$

As the planes recede from the origin, $f(x, y, z)$ increases in absolute value. □

For

$$g(x, y, z) = \sqrt{x^2 + y^2 + z^2}$$

the level surfaces are concentric spheres

$$x^2 + y^2 + z^2 = c^2. \quad □$$

As our final example we take the function

$$f(x, y, z) = \frac{|z|}{x^2 + y^2}$$

which we extend to the origin by defining it there to be zero. At other points of the z-axis we leave f undefined. In the first place we note that f takes on only nonnegative values. Since it is zero only when $z = 0$, we see that the 0-level surface is the xy-plane. To get the other surfaces, we take $c > 0$ and set

$$f(x, y, z) = c.$$

This gives

$$\frac{|z|}{x^2 + y^2} = c$$

and thus

$$|z| = c(x^2 + y^2).$$

Each of these surfaces is a double-paraboloid (see Figure 14.2.10). The steeper the surface the greater the value of the function. □

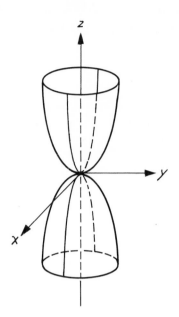

FIGURE 14.2.10

Exercises

Represent the following functions by level curves.

1. $f(x, y) = x - y$.

2. $f(x, y) = x^2 - y$.

3. $f(x, y) = 2x - y$.

4. $f(x, y) = \dfrac{x}{x + y}$.

5. $f(x, y) = \dfrac{y}{x^2}$.

6. $f(x, y) = x(y - 1)$.

7. $f(x, y) = x^3 - y$.

8. $f(x, y) = e^{xy}$.

9. $f(x, y) = x^2 - y^2$.

10. $f(x, y) = \dfrac{x^2}{x^2 + y^2}$.

11. $f(x, y) = x^2$.

12. $f(x, y) = \sin(xy)$.

Sketch the c-level surface.

13. $f(x, y, z) = x + 2y + 3z, \ c = 0$.

14. $f(x, y, z) = \dfrac{z}{\sqrt{x^2 + y^2}}, \ c = 1$.

15. $f(x, y, z) = x^2 + y^2, \ c = 4$.

16. $f(x, y, z) = \dfrac{x^2}{a^2} + \dfrac{y^2}{b^2} + \dfrac{z^2}{d^2}, \ c = 1$.

14.3   Partial derivatives

Two Variables

The idea of partial differentiation is a very simple one. Let's start with a function f of two variables, say

$$f(x, y) = 3x^2 y - 5x \cos \pi y.$$

The *partial derivative of f with respect to x* is the function f'_x obtained by differentiating f with respect to x, treating y as a constant; in this case

$$f'_x(x, y) = 6xy - 5 \cos \pi y.$$

The *partial derivative of f with respect to y* is the function f'_y obtained by differentiating f with respect to y, treating x as a constant; in this case

$$f'_y(x, y) = 3x^2 + 5\pi x \sin \pi y.$$

The limit definitions of these partial derivatives are as follows:

$$f'_x(x, y) = \lim_{h \to 0} \frac{f(x + h, y) - f(x, y)}{h}$$

$$f'_y(x, y) = \lim_{k \to 0} \frac{f(x, y + k) - f(x, y)}{k}.$$

Another Example

For

$$g(x, y) = x \text{ arc tan } xy$$

we have

$$g'_x(x, y) = x\,\frac{y}{1 + (xy)^2} + \text{arc tan } xy = \frac{xy}{1 + x^2 y^2} + \text{arc tan } xy$$

and

$$g'_y(x, y) = x\,\frac{x}{1 + (xy)^2} = \frac{x^2}{1 + x^2 y^2}. \quad \square$$

In the one variable case the derivative gives the rate of change of the function. In the two variable case, f'_x *gives the rate of change of f with respect to x* and f'_y *gives the rate of change of f with respect to y.*

Example. In the case of

$$f(x, y) = x \tan y - y \tan x$$

the rate of change of f with respect to x is

$$f'_x(x, y) = \tan y - y \sec^2 x$$

and the rate of change of f with respect to y is

$$f'_y(x, y) = x \sec^2 y - \tan x.$$

At the point $(0, \pi/4)$ we have

$$f'_x\left(0, \frac{\pi}{4}\right) = \tan\left(\frac{\pi}{4}\right) - \frac{\pi}{4}\sec^2 0 = 1 - \frac{\pi}{4}$$

and

$$f'_y\left(0, \frac{\pi}{4}\right) = 0 \sec^2\left(\frac{\pi}{4}\right) - \tan 0 = 0. \quad \square$$

Geometric Interpretation

For a geometric interpretation of $f'_x(x, y)$ and $f'_y(x, y)$ we refer to Figures 14.3.1 and 14.3.2. In Figure 14.3.1 we have marked the line l_1 parallel to the x-axis. On this line y is constant and thus $f(x, y)$ is a function of x alone; say

$$f(x, y) = g(x).$$

Now

$$f'_x(x, y) = g'(x) = \text{slope of the graph of } g.$$

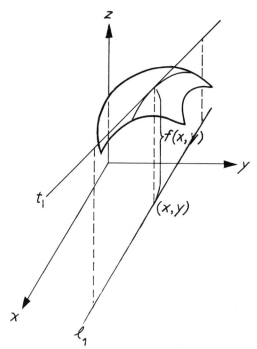

FIGURE 14.3.1

In other words, $f'_x(x, y)$ is the slope of the cross-sectional tangent line marked t_1 in the figure. In a similar manner you can convince yourself that $f'_y(x, y)$ is the slope of the cross-sectional tangent line marked t_2 in Figure 14.3.2.

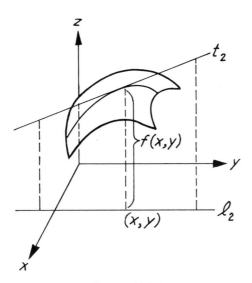

FIGURE 14.3.2

Three Variables

In the case of a function of three variables we can look for three partial derivatives: the partial with respect to x, the partial with respect to y, and also the partial with respect to z. These partials

$$f'_x(x, y, z), \qquad f'_y(x, y, z), \qquad f'_z(x, y, z)$$

are obtained by differentiating with respect to the subscript variable keeping the other two variables constant. The function f'_x *gives the rate of change with respect to* x, f'_y *gives the rate of change with respect to* y, *and* f'_z *gives the rate of change with respect to* z.

Example. For

$$f(x, y, z) = xy^2z^3$$

the rates of change are

$$f'_x(x, y, z) = y^2z^3, \qquad f'_y(x, y, z) = 2xyz^3, \qquad f'_z(x, y, z) = 3xy^2z^2.$$

In particular

$$f'_x(1, -2, -1) = -4, \qquad f'_y(1, -2, -1) = 4, \qquad f'_z(1, -2, -1) = 12. \quad \square$$

Example. For

$$g(x, y, z) = x^2e^{y/z}$$

we have

$$g'_x(x, y, z) = 2xe^{y/z}, \qquad g'_y(x, y, z) = \frac{x^2}{z}e^{y/z}, \qquad g'_z(x, y, z) = -\frac{x^2y}{z^2}e^{y/z}. \quad \square$$

Example.   If $T(x, y, z)$ gives the temperature at the point (x, y, z), then T'_x gives the rate of change of T with respect to x, T'_y the rate of change of T with respect to y, and T'_z the rate of change of T with respect to z. $\square$

Example.   For a function of the form

$$f(x, y, z) = F(x, y)G(y, z)$$

the partial derivatives are

$$f'_x(x, y, z) = F'_x(x, y)G(y, z)$$
$$f'_y(x, y, z) = F(x, y)G'_y(y, z) + F'_y(x, y)G(y, z)$$
$$f'_z(x, y, z) = F(x, y)G'_z(y, z).   \square$$

The geometric significance that we attached to the partials of a function of two variables has no analogue in the case of three variables. Figures 14.3.1 and 14.3.2 do not generalize to three variables.

Other Notations

The idea of partial derivative is not tied to the letters x, y, and z. In some cases it is more convenient to use other letters.

Problem.   Find the rate of change of the volume of a cylinder first with respect to its radius and then with respect to its height.

SOLUTION.   We could use the letter x for radius and the letter y for height, but it seems more natural to use r for radius and h for height. The volume then becomes

$$V(r, h) = \pi r^2 h.$$

The rate of change of V with respect to r is

$$V'_r(r, h) = 2\pi r h.$$

The rate of change of V with respect to h is

$$V'_h(r, h) = \pi r^2.   \square$$

Problem.   Let V be the volume of the frustrum of a cone of lower base radius R, upper base radius r, and height h. See Figure 14.3.3. Find the rate of change of V with respect to each of these variables.

SOLUTION.   The volume is given by the formula

$$V = \tfrac{1}{3}\pi h(R^2 + Rr + r^2).$$

To emphasize the dependence of V on R, r, and h we write

$$V(R, r, h) = \tfrac{1}{3}\pi h(R^2 + Rr + r^2).$$

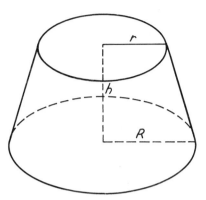

Frustrum of a cone

FIGURE 14.3.3

The rates of change we get by partial differentiation:

$$V'_R(R, r, h) = \tfrac{1}{3}\pi h(2R + r)$$
$$V'_r(R, r, h) = \tfrac{1}{3}\pi h(R + 2r)$$
$$V'_h(R, r, h) = \tfrac{1}{3}\pi(R^2 + Rr + r^2). \quad \square$$

The prime notation is not the only one used for partial differentiation. On the contrary, a variant of Leibniz's double-d notation is very common. In that notation the partials

$$f'_x, \qquad f'_y, \qquad f'_z$$

are denoted by

$$\frac{\partial f}{\partial x}, \qquad \frac{\partial f}{\partial y}, \qquad \frac{\partial f}{\partial z}.$$

Thus for

$$f(x, y, z) = x^3y^2z + \sin xy$$

we have

$$\frac{\partial f}{\partial x}(x, y, z) = 3x^2y^2z + y \cos xy$$

$$\frac{\partial f}{\partial y}(x, y, z) = 2x^3yz + x \cos xy$$

$$\frac{\partial f}{\partial z}(x, y, z) = x^3y^2$$

or more simply,

$$\frac{\partial f}{\partial x} = 3x^2y^2z + y \cos xy$$

$$\frac{\partial f}{\partial y} = 2x^3yz + x \cos xy$$

$$\frac{\partial f}{\partial z} = x^3y^2.$$

We can also write

$$\frac{\partial}{\partial x} (x^3y^2z + \sin xy) = 3x^2y^2z + y \cos xy$$

$$\frac{\partial}{\partial y} (x^3y^2z + \sin xy) = 2x^3yz + x \cos xy$$

$$\frac{\partial}{\partial z} (x^3y^2z + \sin xy) = x^3y^2.$$

Finally we remark that the "double decker" notation is not restricted to the letters x, y, z. For instance,

$$\frac{\partial}{\partial r} (r^2 \cos \theta + e^{\theta r}) = 2r \cos \theta + \theta e^{\theta r}$$

and

$$\frac{\partial}{\partial \theta} (r^2 \cos \theta + e^{\theta r}) = -r^2 \sin \theta + re^{\theta r}.$$

For

$$\rho = \sin 2\theta \cos 3\phi$$

we have

$$\frac{\partial \rho}{\partial \theta} = 2 \cos 2\theta \cos 3\phi \quad \text{and} \quad \frac{\partial \rho}{\partial \phi} = -3 \sin 2\theta \sin 3\phi. \quad \square$$

Exercises

Find the partial derivatives.

1.* $f(x, y) = 3x^2 - xy + y$.

2. $g(x, y) = x^2e^{-y}$.

3.* $z = Ax^2 + Bxy + Cy^2 + Dx + Ey + F$.

4. $\rho = \sin^2 (\theta - \phi)$.

5.* $f(x, y) = e^{x-y} - x^2y$.

6. $z = \sqrt{x^2 - 3y}$.

7.* $g(x, y) = \dfrac{Ax + By}{Cx + Dy}$.

8. $u = xy + yz + zx$.

9.* $u = xy^2e^{-z}$.

10. $f(x, y, z) = z \sin (x - y)$.

11.* $\rho = \left(\theta - \dfrac{\pi}{2}\right) \sin \left(\phi - \dfrac{\pi}{2}\right).$

12. $g(u, v, w) = \log (u^2 + vw - w^2)$.

13.* $\rho = e^{\theta + \phi} \cos (\theta - \phi)$.

14. $f(x, y) = (x + y) \sin (x - y)$.

15.* For $f(x, y) = e^z \log y$,   find $f'_z(0, e)$ and $f'_y(0, e)$.

16. For $f(x, y) = \dfrac{x}{x + y}$,   find $f'_z(1, 2)$ and $f'_y(1, 2)$.

17.* For $g(x, y) = e^{-z} \sin (x + 2y)$,   find $g'_z\left(0, \dfrac{\pi}{4}\right)$ and $g'_y\left(0, \dfrac{\pi}{4}\right)$.

18. Show that

$$u = Ax^4 + 2Bx^2y^2 + Cy^4 \quad \text{satisfies the equation} \quad x\frac{\partial u}{\partial x} + y\frac{\partial u}{\partial y} = 4u.$$

19. Show that

$$u = \frac{x^2y^2}{x + y} \quad \text{satisfies the equation} \quad x\frac{\partial u}{\partial x} + y\frac{\partial u}{\partial y} = 3u.$$

20. Show that

$$u = x^2y + y^2z + z^2x \quad \text{satisfies the equation} \quad \frac{\partial u}{\partial x} + \frac{\partial u}{\partial y} + \frac{\partial u}{\partial z} = (x + y + z)^2.$$

21.* The area of a triangle is given by the formula

$$K = \tfrac{1}{2}bc \sin A.$$

Suppose that $b = 10$ in., $c = 20$ in., and $A = \dfrac{\pi}{3}$ radians.

(a) Find the area of the triangle.

(b) Find the rate of change of the area with respect to the side b if c and A remain constant.

(c) Find the rate of change of the area with respect to the angle A if b and c remain constant.

(d) Using the rate found in (c), calculate (by differentials) the approximate change in area if the angle is increased by one degree.

(e) Find the rate of change of c with respect to b if the area and the angle remain constant.

22. The law of cosines for a triangle reads

$$a^2 = b^2 + c^2 - 2bc \cos A.$$

Suppose that $b = 10$ in., $c = 15$ in., and $A = \dfrac{\pi}{3}$ radians.

(a) Find a.

(b) Find the rate of change of a with respect to b if c and A remain constant.

(c) Using the rate found in (b), calculate (by differentials) the approximate change in a if b is decreased by 1 in.

(d) Find the rate of change of a with respect to A if b and c remain constant.

(e) Find the rate of change of c with respect to A if a and b remain constant.

14.4   Open sets and closed sets

The domain of a function of several variables can be thought of as a set of points or vectors **x**. In the two variable case the points are points of the plane:

$$\mathbf{x} = (x, y).$$

In the three variable case the points are in space:

$$\mathbf{x} = (x, y, z).$$

In this section we study some ways of describing such sets of points.

There are five simple notions that we wish to establish here:

(1) neighborhood of a point.
(2) interior of a set.
(3) boundary of a set.
(4) open set.
(5) closed set.

The fundamental notion here is the notion of neighborhood. The other four notions can be derived from it.

Definition of Neighborhood

A *neighborhood* of a point or vector $\mathbf{x}_0$ is a set of the form

$$\{\mathbf{x} : \|\mathbf{x} - \mathbf{x}_0\| < \delta\}.$$

In the plane a neighborhood of $\mathbf{x}_0 = (x_0, y_0)$ is the interior of a disc centered at (x_0, y_0). In three-space a neighborhood of $\mathbf{x}_0 = (x_0, y_0, z_0)$ is the interior of a ball centered at (x_0, y_0, z_0). See Figure 14.4.1.

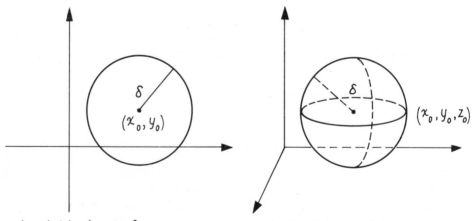

A neighborhood of $\mathbf{x}_0 = (x_0, y_0)$ A neighborhood of $\mathbf{x}_0 = (x_0, y_0, z_0)$

FIGURE 14.4.1

Definition of Interior

A point x_0 is said to be in the *interior* of the set S iff S contains some neighborhood of x_0.

Example. The points marked x_1 and x_2 in Figure 14.4.2 are interior points of the indicated set, but x_3 and x_4 are not. □

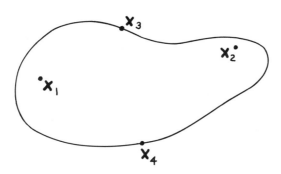

FIGURE 14.4.2

Definition of Boundary

A point x_0 is said to be on the *boundary* of the set S iff every neighborhood of x_0 contains points which are in S and points which are not in S.

Example. The points marked x_3 and x_4 in Figure 14.4.2 are boundary points. Each neighborhood of x_3 and of x_4 contains points in the set and points not in the set. □

It is now easy to phrase what we mean by open and closed.

Definition of Open Set

A set S is said to be *open* iff it contains a neighborhood of each of its points (iff each of its points is an interior point) (iff it contains no boundary points).

Definition of a Closed Set

A set S is said to be *closed* iff it contains its boundary.

Here are some examples of sets which are open, sets which are closed, and sets which are neither open nor closed:

Two-Dimensional Examples

The sets

$$S_1 = \{(x, y) : 1 < x < 2, \ 1 < y < 2\}$$
$$S_2 = \{(x, y) : 3 \leq x \leq 4, \ 1 \leq y \leq 2\}$$
$$S_3 = \{(x, y) : 5 \leq x \leq 6, \ 1 < y < 2\}$$

are displayed in Figure 14.4.3. S_1 is the inside of the square with the dotted boundary. S_1 is open because it contains a neighborhood of each of its points. S_2 is the inside of the indicated square together with its boundary. S_2 is closed because it contains its entire boundary. S_3 is the inside of the square together with that part of the boundary which is indicated by a solid line. S_3 is not open because it contains part of its boundary and it is not closed because it does not contain all of its boundary.

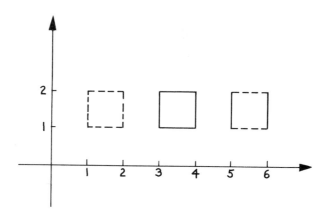

FIGURE 14.4.3

Three-Dimensional Examples

We now examine

$$S_1 = \{(x, y, z) : z > x^2 + y^2\},$$
$$S_2 = \{(x, y, z) : z \geq x^2 + y^2\},$$
$$S_3 = \left\{(x, y, z) : 1 \geq \frac{x^2 + y^2}{z}\right\}.$$

Each of these sets has as its boundary the surface

$$z = x^2 + y^2. \qquad \text{(Figure 14.2.1)}$$

The first set consists of all points above this surface. This is an open set because if a point is above that surface then all points sufficiently close to it will also be above that surface. The second set is closed because it contains all of its boundary. The third set is neither open nor closed. It is not open because it contains some boundary points; for example, it contains the point $(\frac{1}{2}, \frac{1}{2}, \frac{1}{2})$. It is not closed because it fails to contain the boundary point $(0, 0, 0)$.

Exercises

Specify the interior and the boundary of the set. State whether the set is open, closed, or neither. Sketch the set.

1.* $\{(x, y) : 2 \leq x \leq 4, 1 \leq y \leq 3\}$.
2. $\{(x, y) : 2 < x < 4, 1 < y < 3\}$.

3.* $\{(x, y) : 1 < x^2 + y^2 < 4\}$.

4. $\{(x, y) : 1 \le x^2 \le 4\}$.

5.* $\{(x, y) : 1 < x^2 \le 4\}$.

6. $\{(x, y) : y < x^2\}$.

7.* $\{(x, y) : y \le x^2\}$.

8. $\{(x, y, z) : 1 \le x \le 2, 1 \le y \le 2, 1 \le z \le 2\}$.

9.* $\{(x, y, z) : (x - 1)^2 + (y - 1)^2 + (z - 1)^2 < \frac{1}{4}\}$.

10. $\{(x, y, z) : x^2 + y^2 \le 1, 0 \le z \le 4\}$.

14.5 Limits and continuity; equality of mixed partials

The Notions

The limit process used in taking partial derivatives involved nothing new because in each instance all but one of the variables was held fixed. In this section we take up limits of the form

$$\lim_{(x,y) \to (x_0,y_0)} f(x, y) \quad \text{and} \quad \lim_{(x,y,z) \to (x_0,y_0,z_0)} f(x, y, z).$$

To avoid having to treat the two and three variable cases separately, we will write instead

$$\lim_{\mathbf{x} \to \mathbf{x}_0} f(\mathbf{x}).$$

This gives us both the two variable case [set $\mathbf{x} = (x, y)$ and $\mathbf{x}_0 = (x_0, y_0)$] and the three variable case [set $\mathbf{x} = (x, y, z)$ and $\mathbf{x}_0 = (x_0, y_0, z_0)$].

The essential idea of

$$\lim_{\mathbf{x} \to \mathbf{x}_0} f(\mathbf{x}) = l$$

is a simple one: as $\mathbf{x}$ gets close to $\mathbf{x}_0$ (as $\|\mathbf{x} - \mathbf{x}_0\|$ gets small), $f(\mathbf{x})$ gets close to l ($|f(\mathbf{x}) - l|$ gets small). For this idea to make sense we do not need that f be defined at $\mathbf{x}_0$ but we do need that f be defined at some points which are close to $\mathbf{x}_0$. To insure this, we shall assume that each neighborhood of $\mathbf{x}_0$ contains at least some points of the domain of f other than $\mathbf{x}_0$. We can now give the ϵ, δ definition of limit.

Definition of Limit

$$\lim_{\mathbf{x} \to \mathbf{x}_0} f(\mathbf{x}) = l \quad \text{iff} \quad \begin{cases} \text{for each } \epsilon > 0 \text{ there exists } \delta > 0 \text{ such that} \\ \text{if } 0 < \|\mathbf{x} - \mathbf{x}_0\| < \delta \quad \text{and} \quad \mathbf{x} \in \text{dom}(f) \\ \text{then} \qquad \qquad |f(\mathbf{x}) - l| < \epsilon. \end{cases}$$

As in the one variable case, a limit (if it exists) is unique. Moreover, if f and g are two functions with a common domain satisfying

$$\lim_{\mathbf{x} \to \mathbf{x}_0} f(\mathbf{x}) = l \quad \text{and} \quad \lim_{\mathbf{x} \to \mathbf{x}_0} g(\mathbf{x}) = m$$

then

$$\lim_{x \to x_0} [f(x) + g(x)] = l + m,$$

$$\lim_{x \to x_0} [\alpha f(x)] = \alpha l,$$

$$\lim_{x \to x_0} [f(x)g(x)] = lm,$$

$$\lim_{x \to x_0} [f(x)/g(x)] = l/m \qquad \text{provided } m \neq 0.$$

These results are not hard to derive. You can do it simply by imitating the comparable arguments in the one variable case.

The idea of continuity is the same as it is in other settings; namely, to say that f is *continuous* at x_0, is to say that

$$\boxed{\lim_{x \to x_0} f(x) = f(x_0)} \quad \text{or equivalently that} \quad \boxed{\lim_{h \to 0} f(x_0 + h) = f(x_0).}$$

In two variables we can write

$$\lim_{(x,y) \to (x_0,y_0)} f(x, y) = f(x_0, y_0)$$

and in three variables

$$\lim_{(x,y,z) \to (x_0,y_0,z_0)} f(x, y, z) = f(x_0, y_0, z_0).$$

To say that f is *continuous on the set S* is to say that f is continuous at all points of S.

Some Examples of Continuous Functions

Probably the simplest functions which are everywhere continuous are the polynomials. These are simply finite linear combinations of finite products of x, y, and z: for example,

$$P(x, y) = x^2y + 3x^3y^4 - x + 2y$$
$$Q(x, y, z) = 6x^3z - z^3y + 2xyz.$$

Rational functions, quotients of polynomials, are continuous everywhere except where the denominator takes on the value zero. Thus

$$f(x, y) = \frac{2x - y}{x^2 + y^2}$$

is continuous at each point of the xy-plane except at the origin $(0, 0)$;

$$g(x, y) = \frac{x^4}{x - y}$$

is continuous except on the line $y = x$;

$$h(x, y) = \frac{1}{x^2 - y}$$

is continuous except on the parabola $y = x^2$;

$$F(x, y, z) = \frac{2x}{x^2 + y^2 + z^2}$$

is continuous at each point of space except the origin $(0, 0, 0)$;

$$G(x, y, z) = \frac{x^5 - y}{ax + by + cz}$$

is continuous except on the plane $ax + by + cz = 0$. □

A simple way to construct more complicated continuous functions is to form composites:

$$\text{arc tan} \left(\frac{xz^2}{x + y} \right), \qquad \sqrt{x^2 + y^4 + z^6}, \qquad \sin(xyz).$$

The first function is continuous except at those points where $x = -y$. The last two functions are continuous at each point of space. The continuity of these composites follows from a simple theorem which we state and prove below.

Theorem (Continuity of Composites)

If g is continuous at $\mathbf{x}_0$ and f is continuous at $g(\mathbf{x}_0)$, then the composition $f \circ g$ is continuous at $\mathbf{x}_0$.

PROOF. We begin with $\epsilon > 0$. We must show that there exists $\delta > 0$ such that

$$\text{if} \quad \left\{ \begin{array}{c} \|\mathbf{x} - \mathbf{x}_0\| < \delta \\ \text{and} \\ \mathbf{x} \in \text{dom}(f \circ g) \end{array} \right\} \quad \text{then} \quad |f(g(\mathbf{x})) - f(g(\mathbf{x}_0))| < \epsilon.$$

From the continuity of f at $g(\mathbf{x}_0)$, we know that there exists $\delta_1 > 0$ such that

$$\text{if} \quad \left\{ \begin{array}{c} |y - g(\mathbf{x}_0)| < \delta_1 \\ \text{and} \\ y \in \text{dom}(f) \end{array} \right\} \quad \text{then} \quad |f(y) - f(g(\mathbf{x}_0))| < \epsilon.$$

From the continuity of g at $\mathbf{x}_0$, we know that there exists $\delta > 0$ such that

$$\text{if} \quad \left\{ \begin{array}{c} \|\mathbf{x} - \mathbf{x}_0\| < \delta \\ \text{and} \\ \mathbf{x} \in \text{dom}(g) \end{array} \right\} \quad \text{then} \quad |g(\mathbf{x}) - g(\mathbf{x}_0)| < \delta_1.$$

This last δ obviously works — for if

$$\|\mathbf{x} - \mathbf{x}_0\| < \delta \quad \text{and} \quad \mathbf{x} \in \text{dom}(f \circ g),$$

then

$$|g(\mathbf{x}) - g(\mathbf{x}_0)| < \delta_1 \quad \text{and} \quad g(\mathbf{x}) \in \text{dom}(f),$$

so that

$$|f(g(\mathbf{x})) - f(g(\mathbf{x}_0))| < \epsilon$$

as asserted.   □

Continuity In Each Variable Separately

A continuous function of several variables is continuous in each of its variables separately. In the two variable case this means that if

$$\lim_{(x,y)\to(x_0,y_0)} f(x, y) = f(x_0, y_0)$$

then

$$\lim_{x\to x_0} f(x, y_0) = f(x_0, y_0) \qquad \text{and} \qquad \lim_{y\to y_0} f(x_0, y) = f(x_0, y_0).$$

(This is not hard to prove.) The converse is false. It is possible for a function to be continuous in each variable separately and yet fail to be continuous as a function of several variables. You can see this kind of behavior in the next example.

Example

$$f(x, y) = \begin{cases} \dfrac{2xy}{x^2 + y^2}, & (x, y) \neq (0, 0) \\[2mm] 0, & (x, y) = (0, 0) \end{cases}.$$

Since

$$f(x, 0) = 0 \text{ for all } x \qquad \text{and} \qquad f(0, y) = 0 \text{ for all } y,$$

you can see that

$$\lim_{x\to 0} f(x, 0) = f(0, 0) \qquad \text{and} \qquad \lim_{y\to 0} f(0, y) = f(0, 0).$$

Namely, at the point $(0, 0)$, f is continuous in x and continuous in y. However, as a function of two variables, f is not continuous at $(0, 0)$. An easy way to see this is to note that we can approach $(0, 0)$ as closely as we want by points of the form (t, t) with $t \neq 0$. At such points f takes on the value 1:

$$f(t, t) = \frac{2tt}{t^2 + t^2} = 1.$$

Hence f cannot tend to $f(0, 0) = 0$ as required.   □

Continuity and Partial Differentiability

The existence of partial derivatives also fails to guarantee continuity. To show this, we can use the same example:

$$f(x, y) = \begin{cases} \dfrac{2xy}{x^2 + y^2}, & (x, y) \neq (0, 0) \\[2mm] 0, & (x, y) = (0, 0) \end{cases}.$$

Since both $f(x, 0)$ and $f(0, y)$ are constantly zero, both partials exist (and are zero) at $(0, 0)$ and yet, as you saw, the function is discontinuous at $(0, 0)$. $\square$

It is not hard to understand why a function can have partial derivatives and yet fail to be continuous. The existence of

$$\frac{\partial f}{\partial x}(x_0, y_0)$$

depends on the behavior of f only at points of the form

$$(x_0 + h, y_0).$$

Similarly, the existence of

$$\frac{\partial f}{\partial y}(x_0, y_0)$$

depends on the behavior of f only at points of the form

$$(x_0, y_0 + k).$$

On the other hand, continuity at (x_0, y_0) depends on the behavior of f at points of the more general form

$$(x_0 + h, y_0 + k).$$

More briefly, we can put it this way: *The existence of a partial derivative depends on the behavior of the function along one linear path but continuity depends on the behavior of the function in all directions.*

Equality of Mixed Partials

There is nevertheless an interesting tie-in between partial differentiation and continuity. To describe it, we begin with a function f of x and y having two partial derivatives

$$\frac{\partial f}{\partial x} \quad \text{and} \quad \frac{\partial f}{\partial y}.$$

These are again functions of x and y and may themselves possess partial derivatives:

$$\frac{\partial}{\partial x}\left(\frac{\partial f}{\partial x}\right) = \frac{\partial^2 f}{\partial x^2}, \quad \frac{\partial}{\partial y}\left(\frac{\partial f}{\partial x}\right) = \frac{\partial^2 f}{\partial y \partial x}$$

$$\frac{\partial}{\partial x}\left(\frac{\partial f}{\partial y}\right) = \frac{\partial^2 f}{\partial x \partial y}, \quad \frac{\partial}{\partial y}\left(\frac{\partial f}{\partial y}\right) = \frac{\partial^2 f}{\partial y^2}.$$

These last functions are called the *second order partials*. Note that there are two "mixed" partials

$$\frac{\partial^2 f}{\partial y \partial x} \quad \text{and} \quad \frac{\partial^2 f}{\partial x \partial y}.$$

The first of these is obtained by differentiating first with respect to x and then with respect to y. The second is obtained by differentiating first with respect to y and then with respect to x.

Example. For

$$f(x, y) = \sin (x^2 y)$$

we have

$$\frac{\partial f}{\partial x} = 2xy \cos (x^2 y) \quad \text{and} \quad \frac{\partial f}{\partial y} = x^2 \cos (x^2 y).$$

The second order partials are

$$\frac{\partial^2 f}{\partial x^2} = -4x^2 y^2 \sin (x^2 y) + 2y \cos (x^2 y),$$

$$\frac{\partial^2 f}{\partial y \partial x} = -2x^3 y \sin (x^2 y) + 2x \cos (x^2 y),$$

$$\frac{\partial^2 f}{\partial x \partial y} = -2x^3 y \sin (x^2 y) + 2x \cos (x^2 y),$$

$$\frac{\partial^2 f}{\partial y^2} = -x^4 \sin (x^2 y). \quad \square$$

Example. For

$$f(x, y) = \log (x^2 + y^3)$$

we have

$$\frac{\partial f}{\partial x} = \frac{2x}{x^2 + y^3} \quad \text{and} \quad \frac{\partial f}{\partial y} = \frac{3y^2}{x^2 + y^3}.$$

The second order partials are

$$\frac{\partial^2 f}{\partial x^2} = \frac{(x^2 + y^3)2 - 2x(2x)}{[x^2 + y^3]^2} = \frac{2(y^3 - x^2)}{[x^2 + y^3]^2},$$

$$\frac{\partial^2 f}{\partial y \partial x} = \frac{-2x(3y^2)}{[x^2 + y^3]^2} = -\frac{6xy^2}{[x^2 + y^3]^2},$$

$$\frac{\partial^2 f}{\partial x \partial y} = \frac{-3y^2(2x)}{[x^2 + y^3]^2} = -\frac{6xy^2}{[x^2 + y^3]^2},$$

$$\frac{\partial^2 f}{\partial y^2} = \frac{(x^2 + y^3)6y - 3y^2(3y^2)}{[x^2 + y^3]^2} = \frac{3y(2x^2 - y^3)}{[x^2 + y^3]^2}. \quad \square$$

You may have noticed that in both examples we had

$$\frac{\partial^2 f}{\partial y \partial x} = \frac{\partial^2 f}{\partial x \partial y}.$$

Since in neither case f is symmetric in x and y, this equality of the mixed partials cannot be due to symmetry. Actually it is due to continuity. Glossing over details, we can put the result this way:

$$\frac{\partial^2 f}{\partial y \partial x} = \frac{\partial^2 f}{\partial x \partial y}$$

in the case that

$$f, \frac{\partial f}{\partial x}, \frac{\partial f}{\partial y}, \frac{\partial^2 f}{\partial y \partial x}, \frac{\partial^2 f}{\partial x \partial y}$$

are all continuous functions.

In the case of a function of three variables you can look for three first partials

$$\frac{\partial f}{\partial x}, \frac{\partial f}{\partial y}, \frac{\partial f}{\partial z}$$

and nine second partials

$$\frac{\partial^2 f}{\partial x^2}, \frac{\partial^2 f}{\partial x \partial y}, \frac{\partial^2 f}{\partial x \partial z}$$

$$\frac{\partial^2 f}{\partial y \partial x}, \frac{\partial^2 f}{\partial y^2}, \frac{\partial^2 f}{\partial y \partial z}$$

$$\frac{\partial^2 f}{\partial z \partial x}, \frac{\partial^2 f}{\partial z \partial y}, \frac{\partial^2 f}{\partial z^2}.$$

Here again, there is equality of the mixed partials

$$\frac{\partial^2 f}{\partial y \partial x} = \frac{\partial^2 f}{\partial x \partial y}, \frac{\partial^2 f}{\partial z \partial x} = \frac{\partial^2 f}{\partial x \partial z}, \frac{\partial^2 f}{\partial y \partial z} = \frac{\partial^2 f}{\partial z \partial y}$$

provided that all the functions involved are continuous.

Example. For

$$f(x, y, z) = xe^y \sin \pi z$$

we have

$$\frac{\partial f}{\partial x} = e^y \sin \pi z, \qquad \frac{\partial f}{\partial y} = xe^y \sin \pi z, \qquad \frac{\partial f}{\partial z} = \pi xe^y \cos \pi z$$

$$\frac{\partial^2 f}{\partial x^2} = 0, \qquad \frac{\partial^2 f}{\partial y^2} = xe^y \sin \pi z, \qquad \frac{\partial^2 f}{\partial z^2} = -\pi^2 xe^y \sin \pi z$$

$$\frac{\partial^2 f}{\partial y \partial x} = e^y \sin \pi z = \frac{\partial^2 f}{\partial x \partial y}$$

$$\frac{\partial^2 f}{\partial z \partial x} = \pi e^y \cos \pi z = \frac{\partial^2 f}{\partial x \partial z}$$

$$\frac{\partial^2 f}{\partial y \partial z} = \pi xe^y \cos \pi z = \frac{\partial^2 f}{\partial z \partial y}. \qquad \square$$

Exercises

Find the second partials.

1.* $f(x, y) = Ax^2 + 2Bxy + Cy^2$.

2. $f(x, y) = Ax^3 + Bx^2y + Cxy^2 + Dy^3$.

3.* $f(x, y) = Ax + By + Ce^{xy}$.

4. $f(x, y) = \dfrac{Ax + By}{Cx + Dy}$.

5.* $f(x, y) = x^2 \cos y + y^2 \sin x$.

6. $f(x, y) = \sqrt{x + y^2}$.

7.* $f(x, y, z) = (x + y^2 + z^3)^2$.

8. $f(x, y) = \log\left(\dfrac{x}{x + y}\right)$.

9.* $f(x, y, z) = (x + y)(y + z)(z + x)$.

10. $f(x, y, z) = \arctan(xyz)$.

11. Show that

$$\text{if} \quad u = \frac{xy}{x + y} \quad \text{then} \quad x^2 \frac{\partial^2 u}{\partial x^2} + 2xy \frac{\partial^2 u}{\partial x \partial y} + y^2 \frac{\partial^2 u}{\partial y^2} = 0.$$

12. Show that

$$\text{if} \quad u = \log\sqrt{x^2 + y^2} \quad \text{then} \quad \frac{\partial^2 u}{\partial x^2} + \frac{\partial^2 u}{\partial y^2} = 0.$$

13. Show that

$$\text{if} \quad u = \frac{1}{\sqrt{x^2 + y^2 + z^2}} \quad \text{then} \quad \frac{\partial^2 u}{\partial x^2} + \frac{\partial^2 u}{\partial y^2} + \frac{\partial^2 u}{\partial z^2} = 0.$$

14.6   Differentiability and gradient

The Notion of Differentiability

Our object here is to generalize the notion of differentiability from functions of one variable to functions of several variables. Partial derivatives in themselves do not fulfill this role for they take into account only behavior along a particular line.

In the one variable case we formed the difference quotient

$$\frac{f(x + h) - f(x)}{h}$$

and called f differentiable at x provided that this quotient had a limit as h tended to zero. In the multivariable case we can still form the difference

$$f(\mathbf{x} + \mathbf{h}) - f(\mathbf{x})$$

but the "quotient"

$$\frac{f(\mathbf{x} + \mathbf{h}) - f(\mathbf{x})}{\mathbf{h}}$$

makes no sense because to divide by a vector makes no sense.

The notion of differentiability in the multivariable case is inspired not by difference quotients (we want to avoid **h**'s in the denominator) but rather by the characterization of $f'(x)$ as the unique number satisfying

$$f(x + h) - f(x) = f'(x)h + o(h).$$

By $o(h)$, you will recall, we mean any function $g(h)$ such that

$$\lim_{h \to 0} \frac{g(h)}{h} = 0, \quad \text{or equivalently,} \quad \lim_{h \to 0} \frac{g(h)}{|h|} = 0.$$

To set things up for the multivariable case, let us agree to call $o(\mathbf{h})$ any function $g(\mathbf{h})$ which satisfies

$$\lim_{\mathbf{h} \to 0} \frac{g(\mathbf{h})}{\|\mathbf{h}\|} = 0.$$

We now consider a function f of several variables defined at least in a neighborhood of **x**. In the three variable case, $\mathbf{x} = (x, y, z)$ and in the two variable case, $\mathbf{x} = (x, y)$.

Definition of Differentiability

The function f is said to be *differentiable* at **x** iff there exists a vector $\nabla f(\mathbf{x})$ such that

$$f(\mathbf{x} + \mathbf{h}) - f(\mathbf{x}) = \nabla f(\mathbf{x}) \cdot \mathbf{h} + o(\mathbf{h}).$$

The vector $\nabla f(\mathbf{x})$ is called the *gradient* of f at **x**.

The similarities between the one variable case,

$$f(x + h) - f(x) = f'(x)h + o(h),$$

and the multivariable case,

$$f(\mathbf{x} + \mathbf{h}) - f(\mathbf{x}) = \nabla f(\mathbf{x}) \cdot (\mathbf{h}) + o(\mathbf{h}),$$

are obvious. We point to the differences. There are essentially two of them:

(1) While the derivative $f'(x)$ is a number, the gradient $\nabla f(\mathbf{x})$ is a vector.
(2) While

$$f'(x)h$$

is the ordinary product of two real numbers,

$$\nabla f(\mathbf{x}) \cdot \mathbf{h}$$

is the dot product of two vectors.

Computing Gradients

First we compute some gradients by applying the definition directly. Then we bring in a theorem which makes such computations much easier. Finally we compute gradients by using the theorem. As for notation, in the two variable case we will write

$$\nabla f(\mathbf{x}) = \nabla f(x, y)$$

and in the three variable case

$$\nabla f(\mathbf{x}) = \nabla f(x, y, z).$$

Example. For

$$f(x, y, z) = ax + by + cz$$

we have

$$
\begin{aligned}
f(\mathbf{x} + \mathbf{h}) - f(\mathbf{x}) &= f(x + h_1, y + h_2, z + h_3) - f(x, y, z) \\
&= [a(x + h_1) + b(y + h_2) + c(z + h_3)] - [ax + by + cz] \\
&= ah_1 + bh_2 + ch_3 \\
&= [a\mathbf{i} + b\mathbf{j} + c\mathbf{k}] \cdot \mathbf{h}.
\end{aligned}
$$

The remainder $o(\mathbf{h})$ is here identically zero and

$$\nabla f(\mathbf{x}) = a\mathbf{i} + b\mathbf{j} + c\mathbf{k}. \quad \square$$

Example. For

$$f(x, y) = x^2 + y^2$$

we have

$$
\begin{aligned}
f(\mathbf{x} + \mathbf{h}) - f(\mathbf{x}) &= f(x + h_1, y + h_2) - f(x, y) \\
&= [(x + h_1)^2 + (y + h_2)^2] - [x^2 + y^2] \\
&= [2xh_1 + 2yh_2] + [h_1^2 + h_2^2] \\
&= [2x\mathbf{i} + 2y\mathbf{j}] \cdot \mathbf{h} + \|\mathbf{h}\|^2.
\end{aligned}
$$

As a remainder we have

$$o(\mathbf{h}) = \|\mathbf{h}\|^2$$

and as gradient

$$\nabla f(\mathbf{x}) = \nabla f(x, y) = 2x\mathbf{i} + 2y\mathbf{j}. \quad \square$$

Theorem

If f has continuous first partials in a neighborhood of $\mathbf{x}$, then f is differentiable at $\mathbf{x}$ and

$$\nabla f(\mathbf{x}) = \frac{\partial f}{\partial x}(\mathbf{x})\mathbf{i} + \frac{\partial f}{\partial y}(\mathbf{x})\mathbf{j} + \frac{\partial f}{\partial z}(\mathbf{x})\mathbf{k}.$$

In two variables,

$$\nabla f(\mathbf{x}) = \frac{\partial f}{\partial x}(\mathbf{x})\mathbf{i} + \frac{\partial f}{\partial y}(\mathbf{x})\mathbf{j}.$$

PROOF. We prove the theorem in the two variable case. The same ideas work for a proof in the three variable case but the details are more burdensome.

In the first place,

$$f(\mathbf{x} + \mathbf{h}) - f(\mathbf{x}) = f(x + h_1, y + h_2) - f(x, y).$$

We can rewrite this as

(1) $f(\mathbf{x} + \mathbf{h}) - f(\mathbf{x}) = [f(x + h_1, y + h_2) - f(x, y + h_2)] + [f(x, y + h_2) - f(x, y)].$

By the mean-value theorem for functions of one variable, we know that there are numbers

$$0 < \theta_1, \theta_2 < 1$$

such that

$$f(x + h_1, y + h_2) - f(x, y + h_2) = \frac{\partial f}{\partial x}(x + \theta_1 h_1, y + h_2)h_1$$

and

$$f(x, y + h_2) - f(x, y) = \frac{\partial f}{\partial y}(x, y + \theta_2 h_2)h_2.$$

By the continuity of $\partial f/\partial x$,

$$\frac{\partial f}{\partial x}(x + \theta_1 h_1, y + h_2) = \frac{\partial f}{\partial x}(x, y) + \epsilon_1(\mathbf{h}),$$

where

$$\epsilon_1(\mathbf{h}) \to 0 \quad \text{as} \quad \mathbf{h} \to 0.$$

By the continuity of $\partial f/\partial y$,

$$\frac{\partial f}{\partial y}(x, y + \theta_2 h_2) = \frac{\partial f}{\partial y}(x, y) + \epsilon_2(\mathbf{h}),$$

where

$$\epsilon_2(\mathbf{h}) \to 0 \quad \text{as} \quad \mathbf{h} \to 0.$$

Substituting these expressions in equation (1), we find that

$$f(\mathbf{x} + \mathbf{h}) - f(\mathbf{x}) = \left[\frac{\partial f}{\partial x}(x, y) + \epsilon_1(\mathbf{h})\right]h_1 + \left[\frac{\partial f}{\partial y}(x, y) + \epsilon_2(\mathbf{h})\right]h_2$$

and therefore

$$f(\mathbf{x} + \mathbf{h}) - f(\mathbf{x}) = \left[\frac{\partial f}{\partial x}(x, y)\mathbf{i} + \frac{\partial f}{\partial y}(x, y)\mathbf{j}\right] \cdot \mathbf{h} + \left[\epsilon_1(\mathbf{h})\mathbf{i} + \epsilon_2(\mathbf{h})\mathbf{j}\right] \cdot \mathbf{h}.$$

The proof will be complete once we show that

$$[\epsilon_1(\mathbf{h})\mathbf{i} + \epsilon_2(\mathbf{h})\mathbf{j}] \cdot \mathbf{h} = o(\mathbf{h}).$$

Using the Schwarz inequality

$$|\mathbf{a} \cdot \mathbf{b}| \le \|\mathbf{a}\|\|\mathbf{b}\|,$$

we see that

$$|[\epsilon_1(\mathbf{h})\mathbf{i} + \epsilon_2(\mathbf{h})\mathbf{j}] \cdot \mathbf{h}| \leq \|\epsilon_1(\mathbf{h})\mathbf{i} + \epsilon_2(\mathbf{h})\mathbf{j}\| \|\mathbf{h}\|$$

and thus

$$\frac{|[\epsilon_1(\mathbf{h})\mathbf{i} + \epsilon_2(\mathbf{h})\mathbf{j}] \cdot \mathbf{h}|}{\|\mathbf{h}\|} \leq \|\epsilon_1(\mathbf{h})\mathbf{i} + \epsilon_2(\mathbf{h})\mathbf{j}\| \leq \|\epsilon_1(\mathbf{h})\mathbf{i}\| + \|\epsilon_2(\mathbf{h})\mathbf{j}\|$$

$$= |\epsilon_1(\mathbf{h})| + |\epsilon_2(\mathbf{h})| \rightarrow 0,$$

since

$$\epsilon_1(\mathbf{h}) \rightarrow 0 \qquad \text{and} \qquad \epsilon_2(\mathbf{h}) \rightarrow 0. \quad \square$$

Example. For

$$f(x, y) = xe^y - ye^x$$

we have

$$\frac{\partial f}{\partial x}(x, y) = e^y - ye^x, \qquad \frac{\partial f}{\partial y}(x, y) = xe^y - e^x$$

and so

$$\nabla f(x, y) = (e^y - ye^x)\mathbf{i} + (xe^y - e^x)\mathbf{j}. \quad \square$$

Example. For

$$f(x, y, z) = \sin(xy^2z^3)$$

we have

$$\frac{\partial f}{\partial x}(x, y, z) = y^2z^3 \cos(xy^2z^3)$$

$$\frac{\partial f}{\partial y}(x, y, z) = 2xyz^3 \cos(xy^2z^3)$$

$$\frac{\partial f}{\partial z}(x, y, z) = 3xy^2z^2 \cos(xy^2z^3)$$

and

$$\nabla f(x, y, z) = \cos(xy^2z^3)[y^2z^3\mathbf{i} + 2xyz^3\mathbf{j} + 3xy^2z^2\mathbf{k}]. \quad \square$$

Example. As a numerical example, we take

$$f(x, y, z) = x \sin(\pi y) + y \cos(\pi z)$$

and evaluate ∇f at $(0, 1, 2)$.

Here

$$\frac{\partial f}{\partial x}(x, y, z) = \sin(\pi y)$$

$$\frac{\partial f}{\partial y}(x, y, z) = \pi x \cos(\pi y) + \cos(\pi z)$$

$$\frac{\partial f}{\partial z}(x, y, z) = -\pi y \sin(\pi z).$$

This gives

$$\frac{\partial f}{\partial x}(0, 1, 2) = 0, \qquad \frac{\partial f}{\partial y}(0, 1, 2) = 1, \qquad \frac{\partial f}{\partial z}(0, 1, 2) = 0$$

so that

$$\nabla f(0, 1, 2) = \mathbf{j}. \quad \square$$

Uniqueness

We defined the gradient at $\mathbf{x}$ as *the* vector $\nabla f(\mathbf{x})$ which satisfies

$$f(\mathbf{x} + \mathbf{h}) - f(\mathbf{x}) = \nabla f(\mathbf{x}) \cdot \mathbf{h} + o(\mathbf{h}).$$

To make sure that this definition makes sense, we must make sure that no two vectors can satisfy that condition; namely, we must make sure that if

$$f(\mathbf{x} + \mathbf{h}) - f(\mathbf{x}) = \mathbf{y} \cdot \mathbf{h} + o(\mathbf{h})$$

and

$$f(\mathbf{x} + \mathbf{h}) - f(\mathbf{x}) = \mathbf{z} \cdot \mathbf{h} + o(\mathbf{h}),$$

then

$$\mathbf{y} = \mathbf{z}.$$

You are asked to prove this in exercise 21.

Exercises

Find the gradient.

1.* $f(x, y) = xe^{xy}$.
2. $f(x, y) = x^2 + y^2$.
3.* $f(x, y) = 3x^2 - xy + y$.
4. $f(x, y) = Ax^2 + Bxy + Cy^2$.
5.* $f(x, y) = e^{x-y} - x^2y$.
6. $f(x, y) = \dfrac{Ax + By}{Cx + Dy}$.
7.* $f(x, y, z) = xy^2e^{-z}$.
8. $f(x, y, z) = z \sin(x - y)$.

9.* $f(x, y, z) = xy + yz + zx$.
10. $f(x, y, z) = \sqrt{x^2 + y^4 + z^6}$.
11.* $f(x, y) = (x + y)e^{x-y}$.
12. $f(x, y) = (x + y) \sin(x - y)$.
13.* $f(x, y) = e^x \log y$.
14. $f(x, y) = \dfrac{x^2}{y^2}$.
15.* $f(x, y, z) = x^2y + y^2z + z^2x$.
16. $f(x, y) = \dfrac{x - y}{x^2 + y^2}$.

17.* $f(x, y) = 2x^2 - 3xy + 4y^2$ at $(2, 3)$.

18. $f(x, y) = \dfrac{2x}{x - y}$ at $(3, 1)$.

19.* $f(x, y) = e^{-x} \sin(x + 2y)$ at $\left(0, \dfrac{\pi}{4}\right)$.

20. $f(x, y, z) = (x - y)\cos \pi z$ at $(1, 0, \frac{1}{2})$.

21. (Optional) Show that if

$$f(\mathbf{x} + \mathbf{h}) - f(\mathbf{x}) = \mathbf{y} \cdot \mathbf{h} + o(\mathbf{h})$$

and

$$f(\mathbf{x} + \mathbf{h}) - f(\mathbf{x}) = \mathbf{z} \cdot \mathbf{h} + o(\mathbf{h}),$$

then

$$\mathbf{y} = \mathbf{z}.$$

14.7   Some simple properties of gradients

Much of the calculus of functions of several variables is centered around gradients. Throughout the rest of this chapter we shall study them. In this section we begin.

Differentiability Implies Continuity

As in the one variable case, differentiability implies continuity; namely, *if f is differentiable at* $\mathbf{x}$, *then f is continuous at* $\mathbf{x}$. To see this, we need only write

$$f(\mathbf{x} + \mathbf{h}) - f(\mathbf{x}) = \nabla f(\mathbf{x}) \cdot \mathbf{h} + o(\mathbf{h}).$$

As $\mathbf{h} \to 0$,

$$o(\mathbf{h}) \to 0$$

and

$$|\nabla f(\mathbf{x}) \cdot \mathbf{h}| \leq \|\nabla f(\mathbf{x})\| \|\mathbf{h}\| \to 0.$$

It follows that

$$f(\mathbf{x} + \mathbf{h}) - f(\mathbf{x}) \to 0,$$

which means that

$$f(\mathbf{x} + \mathbf{h}) \to f(\mathbf{x}),$$

and thus f is continuous at $\mathbf{x}$.   □

Some Formulas

In many respects gradients behave just like derivatives do in the one variable case. In particular, if $\nabla f(\mathbf{x})$ and $\nabla g(\mathbf{x})$ exist, then so do

$$\nabla [f(\mathbf{x}) + g(\mathbf{x})], \qquad \nabla [\alpha f(\mathbf{x})] \qquad \text{and} \qquad \nabla [f(\mathbf{x})g(\mathbf{x})]$$

and

$$\nabla[f(\mathbf{x}) + g(\mathbf{x})] = \nabla f(\mathbf{x}) + \nabla g(\mathbf{x})$$

$$\nabla[\alpha f(\mathbf{x})] = \alpha \nabla f(\mathbf{x})$$

$$\nabla[f(\mathbf{x})g(\mathbf{x})] = f(\mathbf{x})\nabla g(\mathbf{x}) + g(\mathbf{x})\nabla f(\mathbf{x}).$$

The first two formulas are easy to derive. To derive the third formula, let's assume that $\nabla f(\mathbf{x})$ and $\nabla g(\mathbf{x})$ both exist. Our task is to show that

$$f(\mathbf{x} + \mathbf{h})g(\mathbf{x} + \mathbf{h}) - f(\mathbf{x})g(\mathbf{x}) = [f(\mathbf{x})\nabla g(\mathbf{x}) + g(\mathbf{x})\nabla f(\mathbf{x})] \cdot \mathbf{h} + o(\mathbf{h}).$$

A sketch of how this can be done is given below. See if you can justify each of the steps.

$$
\begin{aligned}
f(\mathbf{x} + \mathbf{h})g(\mathbf{x} + \mathbf{h}) - f(\mathbf{x})g(\mathbf{x}) &= [f(\mathbf{x} + \mathbf{h})g(\mathbf{x} + \mathbf{h}) - f(\mathbf{x})g(\mathbf{x} + \mathbf{h})] \\
&\quad + [f(\mathbf{x})g(\mathbf{x} + \mathbf{h}) - f(\mathbf{x})g(\mathbf{x})] \\
&= [f(\mathbf{x} + \mathbf{h}) - f(\mathbf{x})]g(\mathbf{x} + \mathbf{h}) + f(\mathbf{x})[g(\mathbf{x} + \mathbf{h}) - g(\mathbf{x})] \\
&= [\nabla f(\mathbf{x}) \cdot \mathbf{h} + o(\mathbf{h})]g(\mathbf{x} + \mathbf{h}) + f(\mathbf{x})[\nabla g(\mathbf{x}) \cdot \mathbf{h} + o(\mathbf{h})] \\
&= g(\mathbf{x} + \mathbf{h})\nabla f(\mathbf{x}) \cdot \mathbf{h} + f(\mathbf{x})\nabla g(\mathbf{x}) \cdot \mathbf{h} + o(\mathbf{h}) \\
&= g(\mathbf{x})\nabla f(\mathbf{x}) \cdot \mathbf{h} + f(\mathbf{x})\nabla g(\mathbf{x}) \cdot \mathbf{h} \\
&\quad + [g(\mathbf{x} + \mathbf{h}) - g(\mathbf{x})]\nabla f(\mathbf{x}) \cdot \mathbf{h} + o(\mathbf{h}) \\
&= [g(\mathbf{x})\nabla f(\mathbf{x}) + f(\mathbf{x})\nabla g(\mathbf{x})] \cdot \mathbf{h} + o(\mathbf{h}). \quad \square
\end{aligned}
$$

If you don't like this proof of the product rule for gradients, you can construct another one by setting

$$\nabla f(\mathbf{x}) = \frac{\partial f}{\partial x}(\mathbf{x})\mathbf{i} + \frac{\partial f}{\partial y}(\mathbf{x})\mathbf{j} + \frac{\partial f}{\partial z}(\mathbf{x})\mathbf{k},$$

etc. In that case you must make the added assumption that the partials are continuous.

Directional Derivatives

Here we take up an idea which generalizes the notion of partial derivative. Its connection to gradients will be made clear as we go on. The partial derivatives

$$\frac{\partial f}{\partial x}(x, y, z) = \lim_{h \to 0} \frac{f(x + h, y, z) - f(x, y, z)}{h}$$

$$\frac{\partial f}{\partial y}(x, y, z) = \lim_{h \to 0} \frac{f(x, y + h, z) - f(x, y, z)}{h}$$

$$\frac{\partial f}{\partial z}(x, y, z) = \lim_{h \to 0} \frac{f(x, y, z + h) - f(x, y, z)}{h}$$

can be expressed more elegantly in the form

$$\frac{\partial f}{\partial x}(\mathbf{x}) = \lim_{h \to 0} \frac{f(\mathbf{x} + h\mathbf{i}) - f(\mathbf{x})}{h}$$

$$\frac{\partial f}{\partial y}(\mathbf{x}) = \lim_{h \to 0} \frac{f(\mathbf{x} + h\mathbf{j}) - f(\mathbf{x})}{h}$$

$$\frac{\partial f}{\partial z}(\mathbf{x}) = \lim_{h \to 0} \frac{f(\mathbf{x} + h\mathbf{k}) - f(\mathbf{x})}{h}.$$

Each of the partials is therefore the limit of a quotient of the form

$$\frac{f(\mathbf{x} + h\mathbf{v}) - f(\mathbf{x})}{h},$$

where $\mathbf{v}$ is one of the unit coordinate vectors $\mathbf{i}, \mathbf{j}$, or $\mathbf{k}$. There is no reason to be so restrictive on $\mathbf{v}$. If f is defined in a neighborhood of $\mathbf{x}$, then, for small h, the difference quotient

$$\frac{f(\mathbf{x} + h\mathbf{v}) - f(\mathbf{x})}{h}$$

makes sense for each fixed unit vector $\mathbf{v}$.

Definition of Directional Derivative

For each *unit vector* $\mathbf{v}$, the limit

$$f_{\mathbf{v}}'(\mathbf{x}) = \lim_{h \to 0} \frac{f(\mathbf{x} + h\mathbf{v}) - f(\mathbf{x})}{h},$$

if it exists, is called the *directional derivative* of f at $\mathbf{x}$ in the direction $\mathbf{v}$.

The partials are of course themselves directional derivatives:

$$\frac{\partial f}{\partial x}(\mathbf{x}) = f_{\mathbf{i}}'(\mathbf{x}), \qquad \frac{\partial f}{\partial y}(\mathbf{x}) = f_{\mathbf{j}}'(\mathbf{x}), \qquad \frac{\partial f}{\partial z}(\mathbf{x}) = f_{\mathbf{k}}'(\mathbf{x}).$$

As you know, the partials of f give the rates of change of f in the $\mathbf{i}, \mathbf{j}, \mathbf{k}$ directions. The directional derivative $f_{\mathbf{v}}'$ gives *the rate of change of f in the direction $\mathbf{v}$*.

There is a simple link between the gradient at $\mathbf{x}$ and the directional derivatives at $\mathbf{x}$.

Theorem

If f is differentiable, then f has a directional derivative in every direction and

$$f_{\mathbf{v}}'(\mathbf{x}) = \nabla f(\mathbf{x}) \cdot \mathbf{v}.$$

PROOF.   We take $\mathbf{v}$ as a unit vector and assume that f is differentiable at $\mathbf{x}$. The differentiability at $\mathbf{x}$ tells us that $\nabla f(\mathbf{x})$ exists and

$$f(\mathbf{x} + h\mathbf{v}) - f(\mathbf{x}) = \nabla f(\mathbf{x}) \cdot h\mathbf{v} + o(h\mathbf{v}).$$

Division by h gives

$$\frac{f(\mathbf{x} + h\mathbf{v}) - f(\mathbf{x})}{h} = \nabla f(\mathbf{x}) \cdot \mathbf{v} + \frac{o(h\mathbf{v})}{h}.$$

It is not hard to see that the remainder term tends to zero with h and thus

$$\frac{f(\mathbf{x} + h\mathbf{v}) - f(\mathbf{x})}{h} \to \nabla f(\mathbf{x}) \cdot \mathbf{v},$$

which is what we were trying to show. $\square$

With $\mathbf{v}$ as a unit vector, we have

$$f_\mathbf{v}'(\mathbf{x}) = \nabla f(\mathbf{x}) \cdot \mathbf{v} = \frac{\nabla f(\mathbf{x}) \cdot \mathbf{v}}{\|\mathbf{v}\|} = \mathrm{comp}_\mathbf{v}\, \nabla f(\mathbf{x}).$$

Namely, the *directional derivative of a function is simply the component of its gradient vector in that direction.* We illustrate this in Figure 14.7.1.

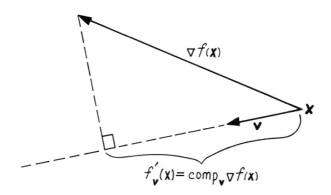

FIGURE 14.7.1

If the first partials of f are continuous, then

$$\nabla f(\mathbf{x}) = \frac{\partial f}{\partial x}(\mathbf{x})\mathbf{i} + \frac{\partial f}{\partial y}(\mathbf{x})\mathbf{j} + \frac{\partial f}{\partial z}(\mathbf{x})\mathbf{k},$$

and the relation,

$$f_\mathbf{v}'(\mathbf{x}) = \nabla f(\mathbf{x}) \cdot \mathbf{v}$$

gives

$$f_\mathbf{v}'(\mathbf{x}) = \frac{\partial f}{\partial x}(\mathbf{x})v_1 + \frac{\partial f}{\partial y}(\mathbf{x})v_2 + \frac{\partial f}{\partial z}(\mathbf{x})v_3.$$

Setting

$$\mathbf{x} = (x, y, z),$$

we have

$$f_{\mathbf{v}}'(x, y, z) = \frac{\partial f}{\partial x}(x, y, z)v_1 + \frac{\partial f}{\partial y}(x, y, z)v_2 + \frac{\partial f}{\partial z}(x, y, z)v_3.$$

In the two variable case, the z term drops out and we have

$$f_{\mathbf{v}}'(x, y) = \frac{\partial f}{\partial x}(x, y)v_1 + \frac{\partial f}{\partial y}(x, y)v_2.$$

Below we carry out some computations.

Problem. Find the directional derivative of

$$f(x, y) = x^2 + y^2$$

at $(1, 2)$ in the direction of $2\mathbf{i} - 3\mathbf{j}$.

SOLUTION. In the first place $2\mathbf{i} - 3\mathbf{j}$ is not a unit vector. Its norm is $\sqrt{13}$. The unit vector we want is

$$\mathbf{v} = \frac{1}{\sqrt{13}}(2\mathbf{i} - 3\mathbf{j}).$$

Since we are in the two variable case,

$$f_{\mathbf{v}}'(x, y) = \frac{\partial f}{\partial x}(x, y)v_1 + \frac{\partial f}{\partial y}(x, y)v_2.$$

From

$$\frac{\partial f}{\partial x}(x, y) = 2x \qquad \text{and} \qquad \frac{\partial f}{\partial y}(x, y) = 2y,$$

we get

$$\frac{\partial f}{\partial x}(1, 2) = 2 \qquad \text{and} \qquad \frac{\partial f}{\partial y}(1, 2) = 4.$$

Since

$$v_1 = \frac{2}{\sqrt{13}} \qquad \text{and} \qquad v_2 = -\frac{3}{\sqrt{13}},$$

we have

$$f_{\mathbf{v}}'(1, 2) = \frac{2(2)}{\sqrt{13}} + \frac{4(-3)}{\sqrt{13}} = -\frac{8}{\sqrt{13}}. \quad \square$$

Problem.　Find the directional derivative of

$$f(x, y, z) = x \cos y \sin z$$

at $(1, \pi, \pi/4)$ in the direction of $2\mathbf{i} - \mathbf{j} + 4\mathbf{k}$.

SOLUTION.　The unit vector we want is

$$\mathbf{v} = \frac{1}{\sqrt{21}} (2\mathbf{i} - \mathbf{j} + 4\mathbf{k}).$$

Here we are in the three variable case:

$$f_\mathbf{v}'(x, y, z) = \frac{\partial f}{\partial x}(x, y, z)v_1 + \frac{\partial f}{\partial y}(x, y, z)v_2 + \frac{\partial f}{\partial z}(x, y, z)v_3.$$

From

$$\frac{\partial f}{\partial x}(x, y, z) = \cos y \sin z, \qquad \frac{\partial f}{\partial y}(x, y, z) = -x \sin y \sin z, \qquad \frac{\partial f}{\partial z}(x, y, z) = x \cos y \cos z$$

we get

$$\frac{\partial f}{\partial x}\left(1, \pi, \frac{\pi}{4}\right) = \frac{-\sqrt{2}}{2}, \quad \frac{\partial f}{\partial y}\left(1, \pi, \frac{\pi}{4}\right) = 0, \quad \frac{\partial f}{\partial z}\left(1, \pi, \frac{\pi}{4}\right) = \frac{-\sqrt{2}}{2}.$$

Since

$$v_1 = \frac{2}{\sqrt{21}}, \qquad v_2 = \frac{-1}{\sqrt{21}}, \qquad v_3 = \frac{4}{\sqrt{21}},$$

it follows that

$$f_\mathbf{v}'\left(1, \pi, \frac{\pi}{4}\right) = \left(-\frac{\sqrt{2}}{2}\right)\frac{2}{\sqrt{21}} + 0\left(\frac{-1}{\sqrt{21}}\right) + \left(-\frac{\sqrt{2}}{2}\right)\frac{4}{\sqrt{21}} = -3\frac{\sqrt{2}}{\sqrt{21}}. \quad \square$$

Gradient As A Maximal Increase Vector

The relation

$$f_\mathbf{v}'(\mathbf{x}) = \nabla f(\mathbf{x}) \cdot \mathbf{v}$$

gives

$$f_\mathbf{v}'(\mathbf{x}) = \|\nabla f(\mathbf{x})\| \|\mathbf{v}\| \cos \theta$$

and thus

$$\boxed{f_\mathbf{v}'(\mathbf{x}) = \|\nabla f(\mathbf{x})\| \cos \theta,}$$

where θ is the angle between $\nabla f(\mathbf{x})$ and the unit vector $\mathbf{v}$. It follows that to maximize $f_\mathbf{v}'(\mathbf{x})$ we must choose $\mathbf{v}$ in the direction of $\nabla f(\mathbf{x})$. [$\theta = 0$] To minimize $f_\mathbf{v}'(\mathbf{x})$ we must choose $\mathbf{v}$ in the direction of $-\nabla f(\mathbf{x})$. [$\theta = \pi$] In other words, the *gradient vector points in the direction of maximal increase of the function and the negative of the gradient points in the direction of maximal decrease.* At each point **x** the extreme rates of change are respectively

$$\|\nabla f(\mathbf{x})\| \qquad \text{and} \qquad -\|\nabla f(\mathbf{x})\|.$$

Example. In the case of

$$f(x, y) = \sqrt{1 - (x^2 + y^2)}$$

the graph is the upper hemisphere of radius one centered at the origin. The gradient

$$\nabla f(x, y) = \frac{-x}{\sqrt{1 - (x^2 + y^2)}}\,\mathbf{i} + \frac{-y}{\sqrt{1 - (x^2 + y^2)}}\,\mathbf{j}$$

points from (x, y) through the origin. See Figure 14.7.2. The path of steepest ascent along the surface is the great circle route through the north pole. $\square$

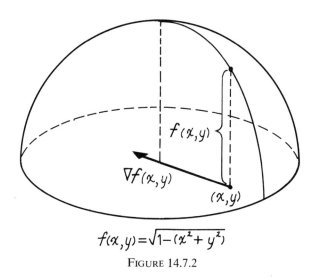

$$f(x,y)=\sqrt{1-(x^2+y^2)}$$

FIGURE 14.7.2

Problem. The temperature distribution on a metal plate is given by the function

$$T(x, y) = x^2 e^y + y^2 e^x.$$

(a) What is the direction of maximal temperature increase at the point $(1, 0)$? What is this rate of increase?

(b) What is the direction of maximal cooling?

SOLUTION

$$\nabla T(x, y) = \frac{\partial T}{\partial x}(x, y)\mathbf{i} + \frac{\partial T}{\partial y}(x, y)\mathbf{j}$$

$$= [2xe^y + y^2 e^x]\mathbf{i} + [x^2 e^y + 2ye^x]\mathbf{j}.$$

(a) The maximal temperature increase at $(1, 0)$ takes place in the direction of the gradient

$$\nabla T(1, 0) = 2\mathbf{i} + \mathbf{j}.$$

This rate of increase is

$$\|\nabla T(1, 0)\| = \|2\mathbf{i} + \mathbf{j}\| = \sqrt{5}.$$

(b) The direction of maximal cooling is given by

$$-\nabla T(1, 0) = -(2\mathbf{i} + \mathbf{j}). \quad \Box$$

Problem. The temperature distribution of a metal ball centered at the origin is given by the function

$$T(x, y, z) = ce^{-(x^2+y^2+z^2)}, \qquad c \text{ a positive constant.}$$

(a) What is the direction of maximal temperature increase at the point (x, y, z)? What is this rate of temperature increase?
(b) What is the direction of maximal cooling?
(c) What is the rate of temperature change at (x, y, z) in the directions of $\mathbf{i}, \mathbf{j}$, and $\mathbf{k}$?

SOLUTION. The gradient

$$\nabla T(x, y, z) = \frac{\partial T}{\partial x}(x, y, z)\mathbf{i} + \frac{\partial T}{\partial y}(x, y, z)\mathbf{j} + \frac{\partial T}{\partial z}(x, y, z)\mathbf{k}$$

$$= -2ce^{-(x^2+y^2+z^2)}[x\mathbf{i} + y\mathbf{j} + z\mathbf{k}]$$

$$= -2T(x, y, z)\mathbf{r}$$

points from (x, y, z) toward the origin.
(a) The direction of maximal temperature increase is toward the origin. The rate of increase is

$$\|\nabla T(x, y, z)\| = 2T(x, y, z)\|\mathbf{r}\|.$$

(b) The direction of maximal cooling is directly away from the origin.
(c) The rates of temperature change along the directions $\mathbf{i}, \mathbf{j}$, and $\mathbf{k}$ are given by the directional derivatives

$$T'_{\mathbf{i}}(x, y, z) = \nabla T(x, y, z)\cdot\mathbf{i} = -2xT(x, y, z)$$
$$T'_{\mathbf{j}}(x, y, z) = \nabla T(x, y, z)\cdot\mathbf{j} = -2yT(x, y, z)$$
$$T'_{\mathbf{k}}(x, y, z) = \nabla T(x, y, z)\cdot\mathbf{k} = -2zT(x, y, z). \quad \Box$$

Problem. The temperature distribution of a plate is given by the function

$$T(x, y) = A - 2x^2 - y^2.$$

(a) What is the hottest point? (b) Find the path followed by a heat-seeking particle which starts out at the point $(-2, 1)$.

SOLUTION: The hottest point is obviously the origin. The particle, starting out at $(-2, 1)$, will proceed at each point in the direction of the gradient. From

$$T(x, y) = A - 2x^2 - y^2$$

we have

$$\nabla T(x, y) = -4x\mathbf{i} - 2y\mathbf{j}.$$

We now want the curve

$$C:\ \mathbf{r}(t) = x(t)\mathbf{i} + y(t)\mathbf{j}$$

which begins at $(-2, 1)$ and has at each point the tangent vector ∇T. We can obtain the first condition by setting

$$x(0) = -2, \qquad y(0) = 1.$$

We can obtain the second condition by setting

$$x'(t) = -4x(t), \qquad y'(t) = -2y(t). \hspace{3cm} \text{(Explain)}$$

These differential equations, together with initial conditions at $t = 0$, imply that

$$x(t) = -2e^{-4t}, \qquad y(t) = e^{-2t}.$$

We can eliminate the parameter t by noting that

$$x(t) = -2e^{-4t} = -2[e^{-2t}]^2 = -2[y(t)]^2.$$

In terms of just x and y, the path becomes

$$x = -2y^2.$$

This is a parabolic path. The part that concerns us begins at $(-2, 1)$ and ends at the origin. □

Exercises

Find the directional derivative of each function at the given point in the indicated direction.

1.* $f(x, y) = x^2 + 3y^2$ at $(1, 1)$ in the direction of $\mathbf{i} - \mathbf{j}$.

2. $f(x, y) = x + \sin(x + y)$ at $(0, 0)$ in the direction of $2\mathbf{i} + \mathbf{j}$.

3.* $f(x, y) = xe^y - ye^x$ at $(1, 0)$ in the direction of $3\mathbf{i} + 4\mathbf{j}$.

4. $f(x, y) = \dfrac{2x}{x - y}$ at $(1, 0)$ in the direction of $\mathbf{i} - \sqrt{3}\mathbf{j}$.

5.* $f(x, y) = \dfrac{ax + by}{x + y}$ at $(1, 1)$ in the direction of $\mathbf{i} - \mathbf{j}$.

6. $f(x, y) = \dfrac{x + y}{cx + dy}$ at $(1, 1)$ in the direction of $c\mathbf{i} - d\mathbf{j}$.

7.* $f(x, y, z) = xy + yz + zx$ at $(1, -1, 1)$ in the direction of $\mathbf{i} + 2\mathbf{j} + \mathbf{k}$.

8. $f(x, y, z) = x^2y + y^2z + z^2x$ at $(1, 0, 1)$ in the direction of $3\mathbf{j} - \mathbf{k}$.

9.* $f(x, y, z) = (x + y^2 + z^3)^2$ at $(1, -1, 1)$ in the direction of $\mathbf{i} + \mathbf{j}$.

10. $f(x, y, z) = Ax^2 + Bxyz + Cy^2$ at $(1, 2, 1)$ in the direction of $A\mathbf{i} + B\mathbf{j} + C\mathbf{k}$.

11.* Find the directional derivative of
$$f(x, y) = \log \sqrt{x^2 + y^2}$$
in the direction toward the origin.

12. Find the directional derivative of
$$f(x,y) = (x - 1)y^2 e^{xy}$$
at $(0, 1)$ in the direction toward $(-1, 3)$.

13.* Find the directional derivative of
$$f(x, y) = Ax^2 + 2Bxy + Cy^2$$
at (a, b) in the direction toward (b, a)
(i) if $a > b$.   (ii) if $a < b$.

14. Find the directional derivative of
$$f(x, y, z) = xy^2 + y^2z^3 + z^3x$$
at $(2, -1, 1)$ in the direction of the maximal increase of f.

15.* Find the directional derivative of
$$f(x, y, z) = x\,e^{y^2-z^2}$$
at $(1, 2, -2)$ in the direction of the path
$$\mathbf{r}(t) = t\mathbf{i} + 2\cos(t - 1)\mathbf{j} - 2\,e^{t-1}\,\mathbf{k}.$$

16. Given the temperature distribution
$$T(x, y) = 48 - \frac{4}{3}x^2 - 3y^2$$
find the rate of temperature change
(a) at $(1, -1)$ in the direction of maximal cooling.
(b) at $(1, 2)$ in the direction $\mathbf{i}$.
(c) at $(2, 2)$ in the direction away from the origin.

17.* The temperature distribution of a metal plate is given by the function
$$T(x, y) = A - x^2 - 3y^2.$$
Find the path followed by a heat-seeking particle which starts out at the point $(1, 1)$.

18. Same as 17 except that the particle starts out at $(1, -2)$.

19.* The temperature distribution of a metal plate is given by the function
$$T(x, y) = 1 - a^2x^2 - b^2y^2.$$
Find the path followed by a heat-seeking particle which starts out at the point (a^2, b^2).

20. (Optional) A heat-fleeing particle starts out at the origin. Find the path followed if the temperature distribution is given by the function
$$T(x, y) = A + x + 2y - x^2 - 3y^2.$$

[HINT: The resulting differential equations can be solved by the methods of Section 5.5.]

14.8 Mean-value theorem and chain rule

You are already familiar with results bearing these names in the one variable case. Here we take up the multivariable case.

Mean-Value Theorem

If f is differentiable at each point of the line segment $\mathbf{ab}$, then there exists on that line segment a point $\mathbf{c}$ between $\mathbf{a}$ and $\mathbf{b}$ such that

$$f(\mathbf{b}) - f(\mathbf{a}) = \nabla f(\mathbf{c}) \cdot (\mathbf{b} - \mathbf{a}).$$

PROOF.   The idea of the proof is to apply the one variable mean-value theorem to the function

$$g(t) = f(\mathbf{a} + t(\mathbf{b} - \mathbf{a})), \qquad t \in [0, 1].$$

To get the differentiability of g, we take $t \in (0, 1)$ and form

$$
\begin{aligned}
g(t + h) - g(t) &= f(\mathbf{a} + (t + h)(\mathbf{b} - \mathbf{a})) - f(\mathbf{a} + t(\mathbf{b} - \mathbf{a})) \\
&= f(\mathbf{a} + t(\mathbf{b} - \mathbf{a}) + h(\mathbf{b} - \mathbf{a})) - f(\mathbf{a} + t(\mathbf{b} - \mathbf{a})) \\
&= \nabla f(\mathbf{a} + t(\mathbf{b} - \mathbf{a})) \cdot h(\mathbf{b} - \mathbf{a}) + o(h(\mathbf{b} - \mathbf{a})).
\end{aligned}
$$

Since

$$\nabla f(\mathbf{a} + t(\mathbf{b} - \mathbf{a})) \cdot h(\mathbf{b} - \mathbf{a}) = [\nabla f(\mathbf{a} + t(\mathbf{b} - \mathbf{a})) \cdot (\mathbf{b} - \mathbf{a})]h$$

and the $o(h(\mathbf{b} - \mathbf{a}))$ term is obviously $o(h)$, we can write

$$g(t + h) - g(t) = [\nabla f(\mathbf{a} + t(\mathbf{b} - \mathbf{a})) \cdot (\mathbf{b} - \mathbf{a})]h + o(h).$$

Dividing both sides by h, we see that g is differentiable and

$$g'(t) = \nabla f(\mathbf{a} + t(\mathbf{b} - \mathbf{a})) \cdot (\mathbf{b} - \mathbf{a}).$$

The function g is clearly continuous at 0 and at 1. Applying the one variable mean-value theorem to g, we can conclude that there exists a number t_0 between 0 and 1 such that

(1) $$g(1) - g(0) = g'(t_0)(1 - 0).$$

Since

$$g(1) = f(\mathbf{b}), \quad g(0) = f(\mathbf{a}) \quad \text{and} \quad g'(t_0) = \nabla f(\mathbf{a} + t_0(\mathbf{b} - \mathbf{a})) \cdot (\mathbf{b} - \mathbf{a}),$$

condition (1) gives us

$$f(\mathbf{b}) - f(\mathbf{a}) = \nabla f(\mathbf{a} + t_0(\mathbf{b} - \mathbf{a})) \cdot (\mathbf{b} - \mathbf{a}).$$

Setting

$$\mathbf{c} = \mathbf{a} + t_0(\mathbf{b} - \mathbf{a}),$$

we get

$$f(\mathbf{b}) - f(\mathbf{a}) = \nabla f(\mathbf{c}) \cdot (\mathbf{b} - \mathbf{a}). \quad \square$$

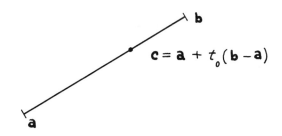

There exists **c** between **a** and **b** such that
$$f(\mathbf{b}) - f(\mathbf{a}) = \nabla f(\mathbf{c}) \cdot (\mathbf{b} - \mathbf{a})$$

FIGURE 14.8.1

Before stating the chain rule we go over some terminology.

1. To say that a function f of several variables is *continuously differentiable* on a set U is to say that f is differentiable on U and its gradient ∇f is continuous on U.
2. To say that U is *open* is to say that U contains a neighborhood of each of its points.
   (Section 14.4).
3. To say that **r** is a *differentiable curve* in U is to say that **r** is a differentiable vector function defined on an interval of real numbers and its range lies in U; namely,

$$\mathbf{r}'(t) \text{ exists} \quad \text{and} \quad \mathbf{r}(t) \in U.$$

Chain Rule

If f is continuously differentiable on an open set U and **r** is a differentiable curve in U, then the composition $f \circ \mathbf{r}$ is differentiable and

$$\frac{d}{dt}[f(\mathbf{r}(t))] = \nabla f(\mathbf{r}(t)) \cdot \mathbf{r}'(t).$$

PROOF.   We will show that

$$\lim_{h \to 0} \frac{f(\mathbf{r}(t+h)) - f(\mathbf{r}(t))}{h} = \nabla f(\mathbf{r}(t)) \cdot \mathbf{r}'(t).$$

For $h \neq 0$ and sufficiently small, the line segment joining $\mathbf{r}(t)$ to $\mathbf{r}(t+h)$ lies entirely in U. This we get because U is open and **r** is continuous. (See Figure 14.8.2.) For such h, the mean-value theorem just proved tells us that there exists a point $\mathbf{c}(h)$ between $\mathbf{r}(t)$ and $\mathbf{r}(t+h)$ such that

$$f(\mathbf{r}(t+h)) - f(\mathbf{r}(t)) = \nabla f(\mathbf{c}(h)) \cdot [\mathbf{r}(t+h) - \mathbf{r}(t)].$$

Dividing both sides by h, we get

$$\frac{f(\mathbf{r}(t+h)) - f(\mathbf{r}(t))}{h} = \nabla f(\mathbf{c}(h)) \cdot \left[\frac{\mathbf{r}(t+h) - \mathbf{r}(t)}{h}\right].$$

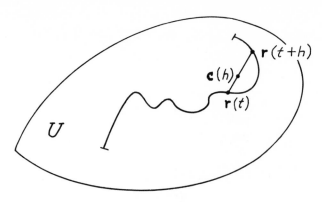

FIGURE 14.8.2

As h tends to zero, $\mathbf{c}(h)$ tends to $\mathbf{r}(t)$ and by the continuity of ∇f,

$$\nabla f(\mathbf{c}(h)) \to \nabla f(\mathbf{r}(t)).$$

Since

$$\frac{\mathbf{r}(t + h) - \mathbf{r}(t)}{h} \to \mathbf{r}'(t),$$

the result follows.   □

For

$$\mathbf{r}(t) = x(t)\mathbf{i} + y(t)\mathbf{j} + z(t)\mathbf{k}$$

the chain rule

$$\frac{d}{dt}[f(\mathbf{r}(t))] = \nabla f(\mathbf{r}(t)) \cdot \mathbf{r}'(t)$$

becomes

$$\frac{d}{dt}[f(x(t), y(t), z(t))] = \nabla f(x(t), y(t), z(t)) \cdot [x'(t)\mathbf{i} + y'(t)\mathbf{j} + z'(t)\mathbf{k}].$$

In the two variable case, we have

$$\frac{d}{dt}[f(x(t), y(t))] = \nabla f(x(t), y(t)) \cdot [x'(t)\mathbf{i} + y'(t)\mathbf{j}].$$

Problem.   Compute

$$\frac{d}{dt}[f(x(t), y(t), z(t))]$$

for

$$f(x, y, z) = x^2 y + z \cos x; \qquad x(t) = t, \ y(t) = t^2, \ z(t) = t^3.$$

SOLUTION

$$\nabla f(x, y, z) = (2xy - z \sin x)\mathbf{i} + x^2\mathbf{j} + \cos x \, \mathbf{k}$$

$$\nabla f(x(t), y(t), z(t)) = [2x(t)y(t) - z(t) \sin x(t)]\mathbf{i} + [x(t)]^2\mathbf{j} + \cos x(t)\mathbf{k}$$

$$= (2t^3 - t^3 \sin t)\mathbf{i} + t^2\mathbf{j} + \cos t \, \mathbf{k}.$$

$$x'(t)\mathbf{i} + y'(t)\mathbf{j} + z'(t)\mathbf{k} = \mathbf{i} + 2t\mathbf{j} + 3t^2\mathbf{k}.$$

Thus

$$\frac{d}{dt}[f(x(t), y(t), z(t))] = \nabla f(x(t), y(t), z(t)) \cdot [x'(t)\mathbf{i} + y'(t)\mathbf{j} + z'(t)\mathbf{k}]$$

$$= 2t^3 - t^3 \sin t + 2t^3 + 3t^2 \cos t$$

$$= 4t^3 - t^3 \sin t + 3t^2 \cos t.$$

This differentiation can also be carried out directly:

$$f(x(t), y(t), z(t)) = [x(t)]^2 y(t) + z(t) \cos x(t)$$

$$= t^4 + t^3 \cos t$$

$$\frac{d}{dt}[f(x(t), y(t), z(t))] = 4t^3 - t^3 \sin t + 3t^2 \cos t. \quad \square$$

Problem. Find

$$\frac{d}{dt}[f(t^2, 1 - t)]$$

for an arbitrary differentiable f.

SOLUTION

$$\frac{d}{dt}[f(t^2, 1 - t)] = \nabla f(t^2, 1 - t) \cdot [2t\mathbf{i} - \mathbf{j}]$$

$$= \left[\frac{\partial f}{\partial x}(t^2, 1 - t)\right](2t) + \left[\frac{\partial f}{\partial y}(t^2, 1 - t)\right](-1)$$

$$= 2t\frac{\partial f}{\partial x}(t^2, 1 - t) - \frac{\partial f}{\partial y}(t^2, 1 - t). \quad \square$$

Problem. Find

$$\frac{d}{dt}[f(t, \sin t, \cos t)]$$

for an arbitrary differentiable f.

SOLUTION

$$\frac{d}{dt}[f(t, \sin t, \cos t)] = \nabla f(t, \sin t, \cos t) \cdot [\mathbf{i} + \cos t \, \mathbf{j} - \sin t \, \mathbf{k}].$$

The right hand side expands to

$$\frac{\partial f}{\partial x}(t, \sin t, \cos t) + \cos t \frac{\partial f}{\partial y}(t, \sin t, \cos t) - \sin t \frac{\partial f}{\partial z}(t, \sin t, \cos t). \quad \square$$

There are other ways to write the chain rule. If we set

$$u(t) = f(\mathbf{r}(t)),$$

then the chain rule

$$\frac{d}{dt}[f(\mathbf{r}(t))] = \nabla f(\mathbf{r}(t)) \cdot \mathbf{r}'(t)$$

can be written

$$\frac{du}{dt} = \frac{\partial u}{\partial x}\frac{dx}{dt} + \frac{\partial u}{\partial y}\frac{dy}{dt} + \frac{\partial u}{\partial z}\frac{dz}{dt}.$$

In the two variable case we have

$$\frac{du}{dt} = \frac{\partial u}{\partial x}\frac{dx}{dt} + \frac{\partial u}{\partial y}\frac{dy}{dt}.$$

Problem.   Find $\dfrac{du}{dt}$ if

$$u = x^2 - y^2 \quad \text{and} \quad x = t^2 - 1, y = 3 \sin \pi t.$$

SOLUTION.   Here we are in the two variable case

$$\frac{du}{dt} = \frac{\partial u}{\partial x}\frac{dx}{dt} + \frac{\partial u}{\partial y}\frac{dy}{dt}.$$

Since

$$\frac{\partial u}{\partial x} = 2x, \qquad \frac{\partial u}{\partial y} = -2y, \qquad \frac{dx}{dt} = 2t, \qquad \frac{dy}{dt} = 3\pi \cos \pi t,$$

we have

$$\frac{du}{dt} = (2x)(2t) + (-2y)(3\pi \cos \pi t)$$

$$= 2(t^2 - 1)(2t) + (-2)(3 \sin \pi t)(3\pi \cos \pi t)$$

$$= 2[2t(t^2 - 1) - 9\pi \sin \pi t \cos \pi t]. \quad \square$$

Problem.   The upper radius of the frustrum of a cone is 10 in., the lower radius is 12 in., and the height is 18 in. At what rate is the volume changing if the upper radius decreases at the rate of 2 in. per minute, the lower radius increases at the rate of 3 in. per minute, and the height decreases at the rate of 4 in. per minute?

SOLUTION.   Let x = upper radius, y = lower radius, and z = height. Then

$$V = \frac{1}{3}\pi z(x^2 + xy + y^2)$$

so that

$$\frac{\partial V}{\partial x} = \frac{1}{3}\pi z(2x + y), \qquad \frac{\partial V}{\partial y} = \frac{1}{3}\pi z(x + 2y), \qquad \frac{\partial V}{\partial z} = \frac{1}{3}\pi(x^2 + xy + y^2).$$

From the chain rule

$$\frac{dV}{dt} = \frac{1}{3}\pi z(2x + y)\frac{dx}{dt} + \frac{1}{3}\pi z(x + 2y)\frac{dy}{dt} + \frac{1}{3}\pi(x^2 + xy + y^2)\frac{dz}{dt}.$$

Using

$$x = 10, \qquad y = 12, \qquad z = 18, \qquad \frac{dx}{dt} = -2, \qquad \frac{dy}{dt} = 3, \qquad \frac{dz}{dt} = -4,$$

you will find that

$$\frac{dV}{dt} = -\frac{772}{3}\pi.$$

The volume decreases at the rate of $(772/3)\pi$ cu. in. per minute.   □

A real valued function whose derivative is zero on an interval I is constant on I. We have a similar result for functions of several variables.

Theorem

Let U be an open set with the property that any two points of U can be joined by a differentiable curve which lies entirely in U. If $\nabla f(x) = \mathbf{0}$ for all $\mathbf{x}$ in U, then f is constant on U.

PROOF.   Let $\mathbf{a}$ and $\mathbf{b}$ be two points of U. We join these two points by a differentiable curve $\mathbf{r}(t)$ with $\mathbf{r}(a) = \mathbf{a}$ and $\mathbf{r}(b) = \mathbf{b}$. (See Figure 14.8.3.) Let f be the function in question. Since

$$\nabla f(\mathbf{r}(t)) = \mathbf{0} \qquad \text{for all } t \in [a, b],$$

we have

$$\int_a^b [\nabla f(\mathbf{r}(t))\cdot\mathbf{r}'(t)]\, dt = 0.$$

On the other hand

$$\int_a^b [\nabla f(\mathbf{r}(t))\cdot\mathbf{r}'(t)]\, dt = \int_a^b \frac{d}{dt}[f(\mathbf{r}(t))]\, dt$$

$$= f(\mathbf{r}(b)) - f(\mathbf{r}(a))$$

$$= f(\mathbf{b}) - f(\mathbf{a}).$$

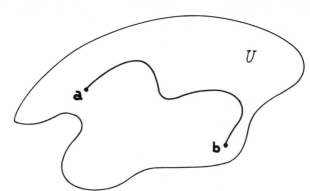

Any two points of U can be joined by a
differentiable curve which lies entirely in U

FIGURE 14.8.3

This tells us that

$$f(\mathbf{b}) = f(\mathbf{a}).$$

Since $\mathbf{a}$ and $\mathbf{b}$ are arbitrary points of U, f must be constant on U.   □

Corollary

If $\nabla f(\mathbf{x}) = \nabla g(\mathbf{x})$ for all $\mathbf{x}$ in U, then f and g differ by a constant on U.

PROOF.   If

$$\nabla f(\mathbf{x}) = \nabla g(\mathbf{x}) \qquad \text{for all } \mathbf{x} \text{ in } U,$$

then

$$\nabla [f(\mathbf{x}) - g(\mathbf{x})] = \nabla f(\mathbf{x}) - \nabla g(\mathbf{x}) = \mathbf{0} \qquad \text{for all } \mathbf{x} \text{ in } U$$

and by the theorem $f - g$ must be constant on U.   □

CAUTION: The last theorem and the corollary to it depend strongly on our being able to join any two points of U by a differentiable curve *which lies entirely in U*. If U is "disconnected," as in Figure 14.8.4, the results do not hold.

Exercises

Find $\dfrac{du}{dt}$ by the methods of this section.

1.* $u = x^2 - 3xy + 2y^2$; $x = \cos t$, $y = \sin t$.
2.* $u = x + 4\sqrt{xy} - 3y$; $x = t^3$, $y = t^{-1}$.

3.* $u = e^x \sin y + e^y \sin x$; $x = \dfrac{1}{2}t$, $y = 2t$.

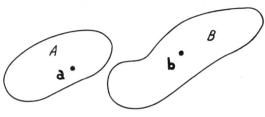

$$U = A \cup B$$

a and b cannot be joined by a curve lying
entirely in U

FIGURE 14.8.4

4. $u = 2x^2 - xy + y^2; \quad x = \cos 2t, \ y = \sin t.$

5. $u = xy + yz + zx; \quad x = t^{-1}, \ y = e^t, \ z = e^{-t}.$

6. $u = x \sin y - z \cos (x + y); \quad x = t^2, \ y = e^{2t}, \ z = \sqrt{t}.$

7.* Find

$$\frac{d}{dt} [f(x(t), y(t), z(t))]$$

if

$$f(x, y, z) = y^2 \sin (x + z), \qquad x(t) = 2t, \qquad y(t) = \cos t, \qquad z(t) = t^3.$$

8. Find

$$\frac{d}{dt} [f(\sqrt{t}, \log t, \text{arc tan } t)]$$

for an arbitrary differentiable f.

9.* Find

$$\frac{d}{dt} [f(g(x(t)), h(y(t)))].$$

10. The height of a cone is 20 in. and the radius is 14 in. At what rate is the volume changing if the height decreases at the rate of 2 in. per second and the radius increases at the rate of 3 in. per second?

11.* Find $\dfrac{\partial u}{\partial r}$ and $\dfrac{\partial u}{\partial s}$ if

$$u = f(x, y), \qquad x = \phi(r, s), \qquad y = \psi(r, s).$$

12.* Find f, given that

$$\nabla f(x, y, z) = a_1 \mathbf{i} + a_2 \mathbf{j} + a_3 \mathbf{k} \qquad \text{for all } (x, y, z).$$

13.   What can you conclude about f and g given that

$$\nabla f(x, y, z) - \nabla g(x, y, z) = a_1\mathbf{i} + a_2\mathbf{j} + a_3\mathbf{k} \qquad \text{for all } (x, y, z)?$$

14.* A point is moving on the curve of intersection of the sphere $x^2 + y^2 + z^2 = 49$ and the plane $y = 2$. When x is 6 and is increasing 4 units per second, find (a) the rate at which z is changing and (b) the speed with which the point is moving.

15.* A point is moving on the curve of intersection of the surface $x^2 + xy + y^2 - z^2 = 0$ and the plane $x - y + 2 = 0$. When x is 3 and is increasing 2 units per second, find (a) the rate at which y is changing, (b) the rate at which z is changing, (c) the speed with which the point is moving.

16.* The characteristic equation of a perfect gas is $R\theta = pv$, where θ is the temperature, p the pressure, v the volume, and R a constant. At a certain instant a given amount of gas has a volume of 15 cu. ft. and is under a pressure of 25 lb. per square inch. Assuming $R = 96$, find the temperature and the rate at which the temperature is changing if the volume is increasing at the rate of $\frac{1}{2}$ cu. ft. per second and the pressure is decreasing at the rate of $\frac{1}{10}$ lb. per square inch per second.

17.* A triangle ABC is being transformed so that the angle A changes at a uniform rate from $0°$ to $90°$ in 10 sec., while side AC decreases 1 in. per second and side AB increases 1 in. per second. If at the time of observation $A = 60°$, $AC = 16$ in., and $AB = 10$ in., (a) how fast is BC changing? (b) how fast is the area of ABC changing?

18.   Show that if

$$\| \nabla f(\mathbf{x}) \| \le M \quad \text{for all } \mathbf{x} \text{ with } \| \mathbf{x} \| \le K$$

then

$$|f(\mathbf{x}) - f(\mathbf{y})| \le M \| \mathbf{x} - \mathbf{y} \|$$

for all $\mathbf{x}$ and $\mathbf{y}$ such that

$$\| \mathbf{x} \| \le K, \qquad \| \mathbf{y} \| \le K.$$

14.9   Gradient as a normal; tangent lines and tangent planes

Functions of Two Variables

You have seen that the gradient of a function points in the direction of maximal increase of the function. Here we show that *the gradient is at each point perpendicular to the level curve which passes through that point.*

We begin with a function f and a point (x_0, y_0) in its domain. We suppose that $f(x_0, y_0) = c$ and parametrize the level curve $f(x, y) = c$ by

$$\mathbf{r}(t) = x(t)\mathbf{i} + y(t)\mathbf{j}, \quad t \in I.$$

We take t_0 so that

$$\mathbf{r}(t_0) = x_0\mathbf{i} + y_0\mathbf{j} = (x_0, y_0)$$

and assume that the tangent vector $\mathbf{r}'(t_0)$ exists and is not $\mathbf{0}$. Since on the level curve f is constantly c, we have

$$f(\mathbf{r}(t)) = c \qquad \text{for all } t \in I.$$

For such t

$$\frac{d}{dt}[f(\mathbf{r}(t))] = \nabla f(\mathbf{r}(t)) \cdot \mathbf{r}'(t) = 0.$$

In particular

$$\nabla f(\mathbf{r}(t_0)) \cdot \mathbf{r}'(t_0) = 0,$$

which means that

$$\nabla f(\mathbf{r}(t_0)) \perp \mathbf{r}'(t_0).$$

Since $\mathbf{r}'(t_0)$ is tangent to the level curve at (x_0, y_0), it follows that $\nabla f(\mathbf{r}(t_0)) = \nabla f(x_0, y_0)$ is perpendicular to the level curve at (x_0, y_0).   □

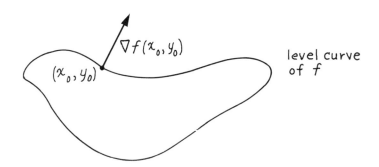

The gradient vector at (x_0, y_0) is perpendicular
to the level curve at (x_0, y_0).

FIGURE 14.9.1

Example.   For

$$f(x, y) = x^2 + y^2$$

the level curves are concentric circles

$$x^2 + y^2 = c.$$

At each point $(x, y) \neq (0, 0)$ the gradient

$$\nabla f(x, y) = 2x\mathbf{i} + 2y\mathbf{j}$$

points radially away from the origin and is thus perpendicular to the circle in question. At the origin the level curve is reduced to a point and the gradient is simply **0**.   □

Tangent Lines

We consider now a curve γ defined implicitly by an equation

$$f(x, y) = c.$$

We can think of this curve as the c-level curve of a function f. If f is differentiable, then the gradient $\nabla f(x_0, y_0)$ is perpendicular to the curve at (x_0, y_0). If $\nabla f(x_0, y_0) = 0$, there is not much more to say. Suppose therefore that $\nabla f(x_0, y_0) \neq 0$. In this case we can use $\nabla f(x_0, y_0)$ as a normal vector and from it derive an equation for the normal and tangent lines at $\mathbf{x}_0 = (x_0, y_0)$. Let's proceed. Using $\nabla f(x_0, y_0)$ as a direction vector, we can parametrize the normal line by setting

$$\mathbf{R}(t) = \mathbf{x}_0 + t\nabla f(\mathbf{x}_0) = \left[x_0 + t\frac{\partial f}{\partial x}(x_0, y_0) \right]\mathbf{i} + \left[y_0 + t\frac{\partial f}{\partial y}(x_0, y_0) \right]\mathbf{j}.$$

In terms of components, we have

$$x(t) = x_0 + t\frac{\partial f}{\partial x}(x_0, y_0) \qquad \text{and} \qquad y(t) = y_0 + t\frac{\partial f}{\partial y}(x_0, y_0).$$

This gives

$$(x(t) - x_0)\frac{\partial f}{\partial y}(x_0, y_0) = (y(t) - y_0)\frac{\partial f}{\partial x}(x_0, y_0). \qquad \text{(Explain)}$$

Eliminating the t altogether, we get

$$(x - x_0)\frac{\partial f}{\partial y}(x_0, y_0) = (y - y_0)\frac{\partial f}{\partial x}(x_0, y_0).$$

Usually the right side is transferred to the left so that the equation for the normal line becomes

$$\boxed{(x - x_0)\frac{\partial f}{\partial y}(x_0, y_0) - (y - y_0)\frac{\partial f}{\partial x}(x_0, y_0) = 0.}$$

The tangent line, being perpendicular to the normal, has equation

$$\boxed{(x - x_0)\frac{\partial f}{\partial x}(x_0, y_0) + (y - y_0)\frac{\partial f}{\partial y}(x_0, y_0) = 0.}$$

Problem. Find equations for the tangent and normal lines of the ellipse

$$b^2x^2 + a^2y^2 = a^2b^2$$

at the point (x_0, y_0).

SOLUTION. We can represent the ellipse by

$$f(x, y) = b^2x^2 + a^2y^2 - a^2b^2 = 0.$$

Note that

$$\frac{\partial f}{\partial x}(x, y) = 2b^2x, \quad \frac{\partial f}{\partial y}(x, y) = 2a^2y,$$

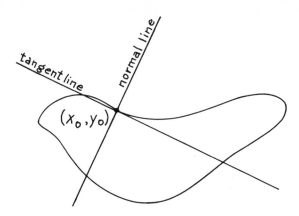

FIGURE 14.9.2

so that

$$\frac{\partial f}{\partial x}(x_0, y_0) = 2b^2x_0, \quad \frac{\partial f}{\partial y}(x_0, y_0) = 2a^2y_0.$$

For the normal, we have

$$(x - x_0)2a^2y_0 - (y - y_0)2b^2x_0 = 0,$$

which we can simplify to

$$a^2y_0(x - x_0) - b^2x_0(y - y_0) = 0.$$

For the tangent, we have

$$(x - x_0)2b^2x_0 + (y - y_0)2a^2y_0 = 0.$$

Using the fact that

$$b^2x_0{}^2 + a^2y_0{}^2 = a^2b^2, \qquad \text{(Explain)}$$

we can simplify the equation for the tangent to read

$$b^2x_0x + a^2y_0y = a^2b^2. \quad \square$$

Problem. Find an equation for the tangent to the leaf of Descartes

$$x^3 + y^3 - 3axy = 0$$

at the point (x_0, y_0).

SOLUTION. Here

$$\frac{\partial f}{\partial x}(x, y) = 3(x^2 - ay) \quad \text{and} \quad \frac{\partial f}{\partial y}(x, y) = 3(y^2 - ax).$$

The tangent at $(x_0, y_0) \neq (0, 0)$ is given by

$$3(x_0^2 - ay_0)(x - x_0) + 3(y_0^2 - ax_0)(y - y_0) = 0.$$

As you can verify, this simplifies to

$$(x_0^2 - ay_0)x + (y_0^2 - ax_0)y = ax_0y_0.$$

At the origin the gradient is zero and our analysis breaks down. A more detailed investigation would reveal that there are two branches through the origin (See Figure 14.9.3), one with a vertical tangent, the other with a horizontal tangent. Such refinements, however, are outside the scope of our treatment. □

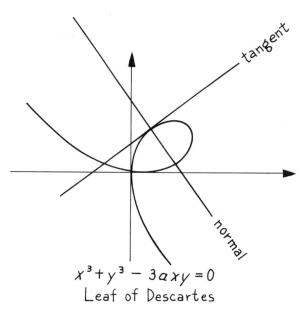

$$x^3 + y^3 - 3axy = 0$$
Leaf of Descartes

FIGURE 14.9.3

Functions of Three Variables

Here instead of level curves we have level surfaces, but the results are similar: *at each point the gradient is perpendicular to the level surface which passes through that point.*

To verify this, we take a differentiable function f, of three variables this time, and fix our attention on a point $x_0 = (x_0, y_0, z_0)$ of its domain. If $f(x_0, y_0, z_0) = c$, then the level surface through $x_0 = (x_0, y_0, z_0)$ has equation

$$f(x, y, z) = c.$$

We suppose now that

$$\mathbf{r}(t) = x(t)\mathbf{i} + y(t)\mathbf{j} + z(t)\mathbf{k}, \qquad t \in I$$

is a differentiable curve which lies on the given surface and passes through the point $x_0 = (x_0, y_0, z_0)$. Moreover, we suppose that

$$\mathbf{r}(t_0) = \mathbf{x}_0 = (x_0, y_0, z_0) \qquad \text{and} \qquad r'(t_0) \neq \mathbf{0}.$$

Since $\mathbf{r}(t)$ lies on the surface,

$$f(\mathbf{r}(t)) = c \qquad \text{for every } t.$$

Consequently,

$$\frac{d}{dt}[f(\mathbf{r}(t))] = \nabla f(\mathbf{r}(t)) \cdot \mathbf{r}'(t) = 0.$$

In particular,

$$\nabla f(\mathbf{r}(t_0)) \cdot \mathbf{r}'(t_0) = 0.$$

This tells us that the gradient

$$\nabla f(\mathbf{r}(t_0)) = \nabla f(\mathbf{x}_0) = \nabla f(x_0, y_0, z_0)$$

is perpendicular to the curve in question. This same argument applies to every differentiable curve which lies on the level surface and passes through the point $\mathbf{x}_0 = (x_0, y_0, z_0)$. Consequently we view $\nabla f(\mathbf{x}_0)$ as perpendicular to the surface itself.

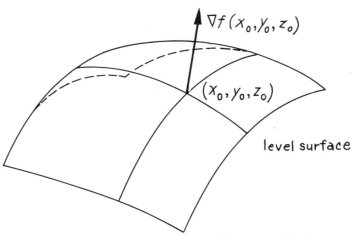

The gradient vector $\nabla f(x_0, y_0, z_0)$ is perpendicular to the level surface at (x_0, y_0, z_0)

FIGURE 14.9.4

Tangent Planes

You have seen that the gradient vector ∇f is perpendicular to the surface

$$f(x, y, z) = c.$$

If the gradient vector ∇f is not zero, we can use it as a normal vector. We can then define the *tangent plane at* $\mathbf{x}_0 = (x_0, y_0, z_0)$ *as the plane through* $\mathbf{x}_0$ *with normal* $\nabla f(\mathbf{x}_0)$. As a vector equation for this tangent plane, we have

$$\boxed{\nabla f(\mathbf{x}_0) \cdot (\mathbf{x} - \mathbf{x}_0) = 0.}$$

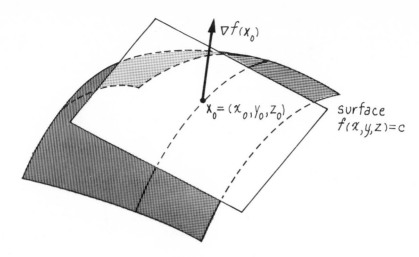

Tangent plane to a surface $f(x, y, z) = c$

FIGURE 14.9.5

In Cartesian coordinates, this equation becomes

$$(x - x_0)\frac{\partial f}{\partial x}(x_0, y_0, z_0) + (y - y_0)\frac{\partial f}{\partial y}(x_0, y_0, z_0) + (z - z_0)\frac{\partial f}{\partial z}(x_0, y_0, z_0) = 0.$$

Geometrically, the tangent plane at a point is the plane that locally best approximates the surface. We will come back to this idea later.

Problem. Find an equation for the plane tangent to the surface

$$xy + yz + zx = 11$$

at the point $(1, 2, 3)$.

SOLUTION. Here

$$f(x, y, z) = xy + yz + zx,$$

so that

$$\frac{\partial f}{\partial x}(x, y, z) = y + z, \qquad \frac{\partial f}{\partial y}(x, y, z) = x + z, \qquad \frac{\partial f}{\partial z}(x, y, z) = x + y$$

and

$$\frac{\partial f}{\partial x}(1, 2, 3) = 5, \qquad \frac{\partial f}{\partial y}(1, 2, 3) = 4, \qquad \frac{\partial f}{\partial z}(1, 2, 3) = 3.$$

For the tangent plane we have

$$5(x - 1) + 4(y - 2) + 3(z - 3) = 0,$$

which can also be written

$$5x + 4y + 3z - 22 = 0. \quad \square$$

If a surface has the property that no line parallel to the z-axis intersects it more than once, then it can be expressed by an equation of the form

$$z = g(x, y).$$

We can write this equation in the more general form by setting

$$f(x, y, z) = g(x, y) - z = 0.$$

If g is differentiable, then so is f. Moreover,

$$\frac{\partial f}{\partial x}(x, y, z) = \frac{\partial g}{\partial x}(x, y), \qquad \frac{\partial f}{\partial y}(x, y, z) = \frac{\partial g}{\partial y}(x, y), \qquad \frac{\partial f}{\partial z}(x, y, z) = -1.$$

The tangent plane at (x_0, y_0, z_0) has equation

$$(x - x_0)\frac{\partial g}{\partial x}(x_0, y_0) + (y - y_0)\frac{\partial g}{\partial y}(x_0, y_0) + (z - z_0)(-1) = 0,$$

which we can rewrite as

$$\boxed{(x - x_0)\frac{\partial g}{\partial x}(x_0, y_0) + (y - y_0)\frac{\partial g}{\partial y}(x_0, y_0) = z - z_0.}$$

If $\nabla g(x_0, y_0) = \mathbf{0}$, then both partials of g are zero at (x_0, y_0) and the equation reduces to

$$\boxed{z = z_0}$$

In this case the tangent plane is *horizontal*.

Problem.   Find an equation for the plane tangent to the surface

$$z = \frac{x^2}{2p} + \frac{y^2}{2q}$$

at the point (x_0, y_0).

SOLUTION.   We set

$$g(x, y) = \frac{x^2}{2p} + \frac{y^2}{2q}$$

and note that

$$\frac{\partial g}{\partial x}(x, y) = \frac{x}{p} \qquad \text{and} \qquad \frac{\partial g}{\partial y}(x, y) = \frac{y}{q}.$$

As an equation for the tangent plane we have

$$\frac{x_0}{p}(x - x_0) + \frac{y_0}{q}(y - y_0) = z - z_0. \quad \square$$

Problem.   At what points of the surface

$$z = 3xy - x^3 - y^3$$

is the tangent plane horizontal?

SOLUTION.   We set

$$g(x, y) = 3xy - x^3 - y^3$$

and seek the pairs (x, y) for which

$$\frac{\partial g}{\partial x}(x, y) = 0 = \frac{\partial g}{\partial y}(x, y).$$

Since

$$\frac{\partial g}{\partial x}(x, y) = 3y - 3x^2 \quad \text{and} \quad \frac{\partial g}{\partial y}(x, y) = 3x - 3y^2,$$

we must solve the equations

$$3y - 3x^2 = 0 \quad \text{and} \quad 3x - 3y^2 = 0$$

simultaneously. This gives

$$x = 0, \quad y = 0 \quad \text{and} \quad x = 1, \quad y = 1.$$

Each pair gives rise to a point at which the tangent plane is horizontal. These points are $(0, 0, 0)$ and $(1, 1, 1)$. $\square$

Exercises

Find equations for the tangent and normal lines at the point indicated.

1.* $x^2 + xy + y^2 = 3$ at $(-1, -1)$.
2. $(y - x)^2 = 2x$ at $(2, 4)$.
3.* $(x^2 + y^2)^2 = 9(x^2 - y^2)$ at $(\sqrt{2}, 1)$.
4. $x^3 + y^3 = 9$ at $(1, 2)$.
5.* $xy^2 - 2x^2 + y + 5x = 6$ at $(4, 2)$.
6. $x^5 + y^5 = 2x^3$ at $(1, 1)$.
7.* $2x^3 - x^2y^2 - 3x + y + 7 = 0$ at $(1, -2)$.

8. Find an equation for the tangent to the curve $x^3 + y^2 + 2x = 6$ at a point where $y = 3$.

9.* Find the slope of the tangent to the curve $x^2y = a^2(a - y)$ at the point $(0, a)$.

Find an equation for the tangent plane at the point indicated.

10. $z = (x^2 + y^2)^2$ at $(1, 1, 4)$.
11.* $x^3 + y^3 = 3xyz$ at $(1, 2, \frac{3}{2})$.
12. $xy^2 + 2z^2 = 12$ at $(1, 2, 2)$.
13.* $\sqrt{x} + \sqrt{y} + \sqrt{z} = 4$ at $(1, 4, 1)$.
14. $z = axy$ at $\left(1, \dfrac{1}{a}, 1\right)$.
15.* $z = \sin x + \sin y + \sin (x + y)$ at $(0, 0, 0)$.
16. $z = x^2 + xy + y^2 - 6x + 2$ at $(4, -2, -10)$.
17.* $b^2c^2x^2 - a^2c^2y^2 - a^2b^2z^2 = a^2b^2c^2$ at (x_0, y_0, z_0).

Find the point(s) of the surface at which the tangent plane is horizontal.

18. $z = 4x + 2y - x^2 + xy - y^2$.
19.* $z - 2x^2 - 2xy + y^2 + 5x - 3y + 2 = 0$.
20. $xy + \dfrac{a^3}{x} + \dfrac{b^3}{y} - z = 0$.
21.* $z = 3axy - x^3 - y^3$.
22. $x + y + z + xy - x^2 - y^2 = 0$.

23.* Given that the surfaces

$$F(x, y, z) = 0 \quad \text{and} \quad G(x, y, z) = 0$$

intersect at right angles in a curve γ, what condition must be satisfied by the partial derivatives of F and G on γ?

24.   Show that in the case of a surface of the form

$$z = xf\left(\frac{x}{y}\right) \quad \text{with} \quad f \text{ differentiable}$$

all the tangent planes share a point in common.

25.* Show that all the pyramids formed by the coordinate planes and a plane tangent to the surface $xyz = a^3$ have the same volume. What is this volume?

26.   Show that the sum of the intercepts on the coordinate axes of a plane tangent to the surface

$$\sqrt{x} + \sqrt{y} + \sqrt{z} = \sqrt{a}$$

is constant.

27.   Show that the surfaces

$$xy = az^2, \quad x^2 + y^2 + z^2 = b, \quad z^2 + 2x^2 = c(z^2 + 2y^2)$$

are mutually perpendicular.

14.10   Maximum and minimum values

In Chapter 3 we talked about the local extreme values of a function of one variable. Here we take up the subject for functions of several variables. The ideas are much the same.

Definition of Local Maximum and Local Minimum

A function f of several variables is said to have a *local maximum* at x_0 iff

$$f(x_0) \geq f(x) \qquad \text{for all } x \text{ in some neighborhood of } x_0.$$

It is said to have a *local minimum* at x_0 iff

$$f(x_0) \leq f(x) \qquad \text{for all } x \text{ in some neighborhood of } x_0.$$

As in the one variable case, the local maxima and local minima together comprise the *local extreme values.*

In the one variable case we know that if f is differentiable at x_0 and has a local extreme at x_0, then

$$f'(x_0) = 0.$$

We have a similar result for functions of several variables.

Theorem

If f is differentiable at x_0 and has a local extreme at x_0, then

$$\nabla f(x_0) = 0.$$

PROOF.   Let's take f as a function of two variables and assume that f is differentiable at $x_0 = (x_0, y_0)$. (The three variable case is similar.) If f has a local extreme at $x_0 = (x_0, y_0)$, then $g(x) = f(x, y_0)$ must have a local extreme at x_0 and, being differentiable there, must satisfy

$$g'(x_0) = \frac{\partial f}{\partial x}(x_0, y_0) = 0.$$

Similarly, $h(y) = f(x_0, y)$ must have a local extreme at y_0 and, being differentiable there, must satisfy

$$h'(y_0) = \frac{\partial f}{\partial y}(x_0, y_0) = 0.$$

The gradient is 0 since both partials are 0. $\square$

   Although the ideas introduced so far are completely general, their application to functions of more than two variables is generally laborious. From now on we restrict ourselves to functions of two variables. Not only are the computations less formidable but also we can make use of our geometric intuition.

Two Variables

A continuously differentiable function of two variables can be viewed geometrically as a surface

$$z = f(x, y).$$

Where f has a local maximum, the surface has a high point. Where f has a local minimum, the surface has a low point. Where f has either a local maximum or a local minimum, the gradient is $\mathbf{0}$ and therefore the tangent plane is horizontal. (See Figures 14.10.1 and 14.10.2.)

FIGURE 14.10.1

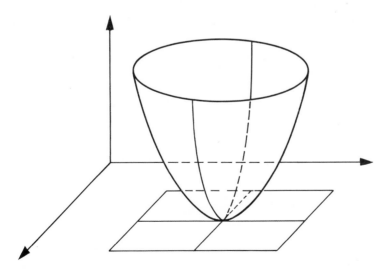

FIGURE 14.10.2

A zero gradient signals the possibility of an extreme value. It does not guarantee it. For example, in the case of the saddle shaped surface of Figure 14.10.3, there is a horizontal tangent plane at the origin and therefore the gradient is zero there, but the origin produces neither a local maximum nor a local minimum.

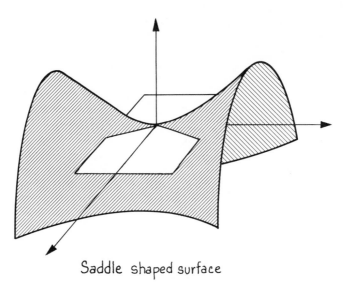

Saddle shaped surface

FIGURE 14.10.3

Points at which the gradient is zero are called *stationary points*. Those stationary points that give rise to extreme values are called *extreme points*. Those stationary points that do not give rise to extreme values are called *saddle points*.

Below we examine some differentiable functions for extreme values. In each case our first step is to seek out the stationary points.

Example. For

$$f(x, y) = 2x^2 - xy + y^2 - 7y,$$

we have

$$\nabla f(x, y) = (4x - y)\mathbf{i} + (2y - x - 7)\mathbf{j}.$$

To find the stationary points, we set

$$\nabla f(x, y) = \mathbf{0}.$$

This gives

$$4x - y = 0 \quad \text{and} \quad 2y - x - 7 = 0.$$

The only simultaneous solution to these equations is given by $x = 1$, $y = 4$. The point $(1, 4)$ is therefore the only stationary point. Now we compare the value of f at $(1, 4)$ with the values of f at nearby points $(1 + h, 4 + k)$:

$$f(1, 4) = 2 - 4 + 16 - 28 = -14$$
$$f(1 + h, 4 + k) = 2(1 + h)^2 - (1 + h)(4 + k) + (4 + k)^2 - 7(4 + k)$$
$$= 2 + 4h + 2h^2 - 4 - 4h - k - hk + 16 + 8k + k^2 - 28 - 7k$$
$$= 2h^2 + k^2 - hk - 14$$
$$f(1 + h, 4 + k) - f(1, 4) = 2h^2 + k^2 - hk = h^2 + (h^2 - hk + k^2).$$

The difference

$$f(1 + h, 4 + k) - f(1, 4) = h^2 + (h^2 - hk + k^2)$$

is positive for small h and k (in fact for all h and k different from 0). It follows that f has a minimum value at $(1, 4)$. This minimum value is -14. □

Example. In the case of

$$f(x, y) = y^2 - xy + 2x + y + 1$$

we have

$$\nabla f(x, y) = (2 - y)\mathbf{i} + (2y - x + 1)\mathbf{j}.$$

Setting

$$\nabla f(x, y) = \mathbf{0}$$

gives

$$2 - y = 0 \quad \text{and} \quad 2y - x + 1 = 0.$$

The only simultaneous solution to these equations is $x = 5$, $y = 2$. The point $(5, 2)$ is the only stationary point. To determine its nature, we compare $f(5, 2)$ with $f(5 + h, 2 + k)$ for small h and k:

$$f(5, 2) = 4 - 10 + 10 + 2 + 1 = 7.$$
$$f(5 + h, 2 + k) = (2 + k)^2 - (5 + h)(2 + k) + 2(5 + h) + (2 + k) + 1$$
$$= 4 + 4k + k^2 - 10 - 2h - 5k - hk + 10 + 2h + 2 + k + 1$$
$$= k^2 - hk + 7.$$
$$f(5 + h, 2 + k) - f(5, 2) = k^2 - hk = k(k - h).$$

This last expression does not keep a constant sign for small h and k. It follows that $(5, 2)$ is a saddle point. □

Example. For

$$f(x, y) = x^3 + y^3 - 3xy$$

we have

$$\nabla f(x, y) = (3x^2 - 3y)\mathbf{i} + (3y^2 - 3x)\mathbf{j}.$$

Setting

$$\nabla f(x, y) = \mathbf{0}$$

gives

$$x^2 - y = 0 \quad \text{and} \quad y^2 - x = 0.$$

The only simultaneous solutions to these equations are given by $x = 0$, $y = 0$ and $x = 1$, $y = 1$. The points $(0, 0)$ and $(1, 1)$ are the only stationary points. To investigate $(0, 0)$ we first note that $f(0, 0) = 0$. For small t,

$$f(t, t) = t^3 + t^3 - 3t^2 = 2t^3 - 3t^2 = t^2(2t - 3) < 0$$

and

$$f(t, -t) = t^3 - t^3 + 3t^2 = 3t^2 > 0.$$

It follows that $f(0, 0) = 0$ is neither a local maximum nor a local minimum. The origin $(0, 0)$ is therefore a saddle point.

Now we investigate the function at $(1, 1)$ and at nearby points $(1 + h, 1 + k)$:

$$f(1, 1) = 1 + 1 - 3 = -1.$$
$$f(1 + h, 1 + k) = (1 + h)^3 + (1 + k)^3 - 3(1 + h)(1 + k)$$
$$= 1 + 3h + 3h^2 + h^3 + 1 + 3k + 3k^2 + k^3 - 3 - 3h - 3k - 3hk$$
$$= -1 + 3h^2 + 3k^2 - 3hk + h^3 + k^3.$$

$$f(1 + h, 1 + k) - f(1, 1) = 3h^2 + 3k^2 - 3hk + h^3 + k^3.$$

The idea now is to play around with the right hand side until we can determine whether or not it keeps a constant sign for small h and k. Our problems are over once we realize that we can rewrite the equation to read

$$f(1 + h, 1 + k) - f(1, 1) = (h^2 + h^3) + (k^2 + k^3) + (h^2 + k^2 - hk) + (h^2 - 2hk + k^2)$$
$$= h^2(1 + h) + k^2(1 + k) + (h^2 + k^2 - hk) + (h^2 - 2hk + k^2).$$

For small h and k the first three terms on the right are positive and the last is non-negative. It follows that

$$f(1 + h, 1 + k) - f(1, 1) > 0.$$

We conclude that the point $(1, 1)$ gives rise to a local minimum. This minimum is -1. □

The next example is more complicated. The function there has an infinite number of stationary points.

Example. For

$$f(x, y) = \frac{x^2 + 2y^2}{(x + y)^2}, \quad (x, y) \neq (0, 0)$$

we have

$$\nabla f(x, y) = 2y \frac{x - 2y}{(x + y)^3} \mathbf{i} + 2x \frac{2y - x}{(x + y)^3} \mathbf{j}.$$

Setting

$$\nabla f(x, y) = \mathbf{0}$$

gives

$$2y \frac{x - 2y}{(x + y)^3} = 0 \quad \text{and} \quad 2x \frac{2y - x}{(x + y)^3} = 0.$$

Solving these two equations simultaneously, we get

$$x = 2y.$$

The stationary points are all the points of the line $x = 2y$, except of course for $(0, 0)$ which was originally excluded. At each stationary point (x_0, y_0) the function takes on the value $\frac{2}{3}$:

$$f(x_0, y_0) = f(2y_0, y_0) = \frac{(2y_0)^2 + 2y_0^2}{(2y_0 + y_0)^2} = \frac{6y_0^2}{9y_0^2} = \frac{2}{3}.$$

In a moment we will show that for all $(x, y) \neq (0, 0)$

$$f(x, y) = \frac{x^2 + 2y^2}{(x + y)^2} \geq \frac{2}{3}.$$

It will then follow that every stationary point is a minimum point and the number $\frac{2}{3}$ is a minimum value.

The inequality

$$\frac{x^2 + 2y^2}{(x + y)^2} \geq \frac{2}{3}$$

can be justified by the following sequence of equivalent inequalities, the last of which is obvious:

$$3(x^2 + 2y^2) \geq 2(x + y)^2$$
$$3x^2 + 6y^2 \geq 2x^2 + 4xy + 2y^2$$
$$x^2 - 4xy + 4y^2 \geq 0$$
$$(x - 2y)^2 \geq 0. \quad \square$$

So far we have considered only functions which have gradients on their entire domain. A local extreme value can also occur at a point where the gradient does not exist. As an example we can take the function

$$f(x, y) = \sqrt{x^2 + y^2}. \qquad \text{(Figure 14.10.4)}$$

Obviously f has a minimum at $(0, 0)$, but the gradient

$$\nabla f(x, y) = \frac{x}{\sqrt{x^2 + y^2}} \mathbf{i} + \frac{y}{\sqrt{x^2 + y^2}} \mathbf{j}$$

is not defined at $(0, 0)$. The surface comes to a sharp point at $(0, 0)$ and there is no tangent plane. $\square$

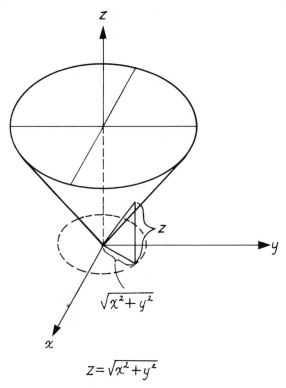

$$z = \sqrt{x^2 + y^2}$$

FIGURE 14.10.4

Exercises

Classify the stationary points and find the local extreme values.

1.* $f(x, y) = 2x - x^2 - y^2$.

2. $f(x, y) = x^2 + 2y^2 - 4y$.

3.* $f(x, y) = 2x + 2y - x^2 + y^2 + 5$.

4. $f(x, y) = x^2 - xy + y^2 + 1$.

5.* $f(x, y) = x^2 + xy + y^2 + 3x + 1$.

6. $f(x, y) = x^3 - y^2 + 2y$.

7.* $f(x, y) = x^3 - 3x + y$.

8. $f(x, y) = x^5 - 3x^2 - 2y$.

9.* $f(x, y) = x^2 + xy + y^2 - 3x - 3y$.

10. $f(x, y) = x^2 - xy + y^2 + 2x + 2y - 6$.

11.* $f(x, y) = |x| + |y|$.

12. $f(x, y) = 5xy - 7x^2 - y^2 + 3x - 6y$.

13.* $f(x, y) = x^2 + xy + 2x + 2y + 1$.

14. $f(x, y) = x \sin y, \qquad -\pi < y < \pi$.

15.* Find the point with the property that the sum of the squares of its distances from the vertices $P_1(x_1, y_1)$, $P_2(x_2, y_2)$, $P_3(x_3, y_3)$ of a given triangle is a minimum.

16.* Given that $0 < a < b$, find the two numbers x and y between a and b such that

$$\frac{xy}{(a + x)(x + y)(b + y)}$$

is a maximum.

14.11   Second-partials test

We start with a function g of one variable. Suppose now that $g'(x_0) = 0$. The second derivative test for extreme values can be phrased this way:

If $g''(x_0) > 0$, then g has a minimum at x_0.

If $g''(x_0) < 0$, then g has a maximum at x_0.

If $g''(x_0) = 0$, then anything can happen.

For functions of two variables we have a similar test. As you might expect, it is a little more complicated to state.

Second-Partials Test

Suppose that f has continuous second order partials in a neighborhood of (x_0, y_0) and suppose that $\nabla f(x_0, y_0) = \mathbf{0}$. Set

$$A = \frac{\partial^2 f}{\partial x^2}(x_0, y_0), \qquad B = \frac{\partial^2 f}{\partial y \partial x}(x_0, y_0), \qquad C = \frac{\partial^2 f}{\partial y^2}(x_0, y_0)$$

and form the discriminant

$$D = B^2 - AC.$$

---

1. If $D > 0$, (x_0, y_0) is a saddle point.
2. If $D < 0$, there is a maximum at (x_0, y_0) if $A < 0$ and a minimum if $A > 0$.
3. If $D = 0$, then anything can happen.

A detailed justification of this test would be extremely burdensome at this point. We will not attempt to give one. Instead we move on directly to some examples.

Example.   For

$$f(x, y) = x^3 - y^3 + 3xy$$

we have

$$\frac{\partial f}{\partial x}(x, y) = 3x^2 + 3y \qquad \text{and} \qquad \frac{\partial f}{\partial y}(x, y) = -3y^2 + 3x.$$

Setting both partials equal to zero, we get

$$x^2 + y = 0 \qquad \text{and} \qquad -y^2 + x = 0.$$

The only simultaneous solutions to these equations are given by $x = 0$, $y = 0$ and $x = 1$, $y = -1$. The points $(0, 0)$ and $(1, -1)$ are the only stationary points. The second partials are

$$\frac{\partial^2 f}{\partial x^2}(x, y) = 6x, \qquad \frac{\partial^2 f}{\partial y \partial x}(x, y) = 3, \qquad \frac{\partial^2 f}{\partial y^2}(x, y) = -6y.$$

At $(0, 0)$ we have

$$A = 0, \qquad B = 3, \qquad C = 0$$

and thus

$$D = B^2 - AC = 9 > 0.$$

The test tells us that $(0, 0)$ is a saddle point. At $(1-1)$ we have

$$A = 6, \qquad B = 3, \qquad C = 6$$

and thus

$$D = B^2 - AC = 9 - 36 = -27 < 0.$$

From $D < 0$ and $A > 0$ we can conclude that $(1, -1)$ gives rise to a local minimum. This minimum is

$$f(1, -1) = 1 + 1 - 3 = -1. \quad \square$$

Example. For

$$f(x, y) = x^2 + xy + y^2 - 3x - 3y$$

we have

$$\frac{\partial f}{\partial x}(x, y) = 2x + y - 3 \qquad \text{and} \qquad \frac{\partial f}{\partial y}(x, y) = x + 2y - 3.$$

Setting both of these partials equal to zero, we have

$$2x + y - 3 = 0 \qquad \text{and} \qquad x + 2y - 3 = 0.$$

The only simultaneous solution to these equations is $x = 1$, $y = 1$. The point $(1, 1)$ is the only stationary point. Since

$$\frac{\partial^2 f}{\partial x^2}(x, y) = 2, \qquad \frac{\partial^2 f}{\partial y \partial x}(x, y) = 1, \qquad \frac{\partial^2 f}{\partial y^2}(x, y) = 2,$$

we have

$$A = 2, \qquad B = 1, \qquad C = 2$$

and thus

$$D = B^2 - AC = 1 - 4 = -3 < 0.$$

With $D < 0$ and $A > 0$ we can conclude that $(1, 1)$ gives a local minimum. This minimum is

$$f(1, 1) = 1 + 1 + 1 - 3 - 3 = -3. \quad \square$$

Example.   For

$$f(x, y) = \sin x + \sin y + \sin (x + y), \quad \begin{matrix} 0 < x < \pi \\ 0 < y < \pi \end{matrix}$$

we have

$$\frac{\partial f}{\partial x}(x, y) = \cos x + \cos (x + y), \qquad \frac{\partial f}{\partial y}(x, y) = \cos y + \cos (x + y).$$

Setting both of these partials equal to zero, we have

$$\cos x + \cos (x + y) = 0, \qquad \cos y + \cos (x + y) = 0.$$

Together these equations imply that

$$\cos x = \cos y.$$

Since x and y must lie between 0 and π, we conclude that

$$x = y.$$

The condition

$$\cos x + \cos (x + y) = 0$$

now leads to

$$\cos x + \cos 2x = 0.$$

Into this last equation we substitute the identity

$$\cos 2x = 2 \cos^2 x - 1$$

and thereby obtain

$$2 \cos^2 x + \cos x - 1 = 0.$$

This is a quadratic in $\cos x$ with solutions

$$\cos x = \frac{-1 \pm \sqrt{1 + 8}}{4} = -1 \text{ or } \frac{1}{2}.$$

We throw out the solution -1 because x has to lie between 0 and π. The other possibility, $\cos x = \dfrac{1}{2}$, leads to $x = \dfrac{\pi}{3}$. Since $x = y$, we also have $y = \dfrac{\pi}{3}$. This shows that $\left(\dfrac{\pi}{3}, \dfrac{\pi}{3}\right)$ is the only stationary point. The second partials are given by

$$\frac{\partial^2 f}{\partial x^2}(x, y) = -\sin x - \sin (x + y)$$

$$\frac{\partial^2 f}{\partial y \partial x}(x, y) = -\sin (x + y)$$

$$\frac{\partial^2 f}{\partial y^2}(x, y) = -\sin y - \sin (x + y).$$

At $\left(\dfrac{\pi}{3}, \dfrac{\pi}{3}\right)$ we have

$$A = -\sin \frac{\pi}{3} - \sin \frac{2\pi}{3} = -\frac{\sqrt{3}}{2} - \frac{\sqrt{3}}{2} = -\sqrt{3}$$

$$B = -\sin \frac{2\pi}{3} = -\frac{\sqrt{3}}{2}$$

$$C = -\sin \frac{\pi}{3} - \sin \frac{2\pi}{3} = -\frac{\sqrt{3}}{2} - \frac{\sqrt{3}}{2} = -\sqrt{3}$$

and thus

$$D = B^2 - AC = \frac{3}{4} - 3 < 0.$$

From $D < 0$ and $A < 0$ we can conclude that $\left(\dfrac{\pi}{3}, \dfrac{\pi}{3}\right)$ gives a local maximum. This maximum is

$$f\left(\frac{\pi}{3}, \frac{\pi}{3}\right) = \sin \frac{\pi}{3} + \sin \frac{\pi}{3} + \sin \frac{2\pi}{3} = \frac{\sqrt{3}}{2} + \frac{\sqrt{3}}{2} + \frac{\sqrt{3}}{2} = \frac{3\sqrt{3}}{2}. \quad \square$$

That anything can happen when $D = 0$ is illustrated by the behavior of

$$f(x, y) = x^4 + y^4$$
$$g(x, y) = -(x^4 + y^4)$$
$$h(x, y) = 2x^2 - 3xy^2 + y^4.$$

As you can readily verify, for each of these functions $(0, 0)$ is a stationary point at which $D = 0$, and yet

(1) for f, $(0, 0)$ gives a minimum
(2) for g, $(0, 0)$ gives a maximum
(3) for h, $(0, 0)$ is a saddle point.

Statements (1) and (2) are obvious. To confirm (3), note that h can be written in the form

$$h(x, y) = (y^2 - x)(y^2 - 2x).$$

The parabolas

$$y^2 = x \qquad \text{and} \qquad y^2 = 2x$$

divide the plane in the manner depicted in Figure 14.11.1. The function is zero on the parabolas, negative between the parabolas and positive elsewhere. That the origin is a saddle point follows from the fact that, at the origin, the function is zero, but, in every neighborhood of the origin, the function takes on both positive and negative values. $\square$

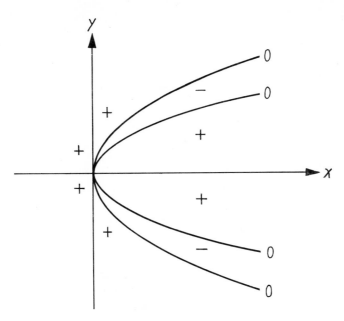

FIGURE 14.11.1

Exercises

Find the local maxima and minima of the following functions.

1.* $f(x, y) = x^2 + xy + y^2 - 6x + 2$.
2. $f(x, y) = x^2 + 2xy + 3y^2 + 2x + 10y + 1$.
3.* $f(x, y) = 4x + 2y - x^2 + xy - y^2$.
4. $f(x, y) = x^2 - xy + y^2 + 2x + 2y - 1$.
5.* $f(x, y) = x^3 - 6xy + y^3$.
6. $f(x, y) = 3x^2 + xy - y^2 + 5x - 5y + 4$.
7.* $f(x, y) = x^3 + y^2 - 6xy + 6x + 3y - 2$.
8. $f(x, y) = x^2 + xy + y^2 - 6y + 5$.
9.* $g(x, y) = e^x \cos y$.
10. $g(x, y) = x^2 - 2xy + 2y^2 - 3x + 5y$.
11.* $g(x, y) = x \sin y$.
12. $g(x, y) = y + x \sin y$.
13.* $h(x, y) = (x + y)(xy + 1)$.
14. $h(x, y) = \dfrac{x}{y} - \dfrac{y}{x}$.
15.* $F(x, y) = xy + \dfrac{1}{x} + \dfrac{8}{y}$.
16. $G(x, y) = x^3 y^2 (1 - x - y)$.

17.* $f(x, y) = (x^2 + 2y^2)e^{-(x^2+y^2)}$.

18. $g(x, y) = (x - y)(xy - 1)$.

19.* Find the volume of the largest rectangular solid that has three faces on the coordinate planes and one vertex on the plane $x + y + z = 1$.

20. Describe the behavior of the function

$$f(x, y) = 2 \cos (x + y) + e^{xy}$$

at the origin.

21.* Find the volume of the largest rectangular solid that can be inscribed in the ellipsoid

$$\frac{x^2}{a^2} + \frac{y^2}{b^2} + \frac{z^2}{c^2} = 1.$$

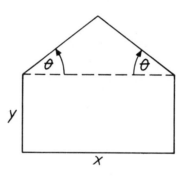

FIGURE 14.11.2

22.* A pentagon is composed of a rectangle surmounted by an isosceles triangle. Given that the perimeter of the pentagon has a fixed value P, find the dimensions for the maximum area.

23.* Find the maximum value of

$$f(x, y) = \frac{(ax + by + c)^2}{x^2 + y^2 + 1}.$$

14.12 Maxima and minima with side conditions

When we ask for the distance between a point $P(x_0, y_0)$ and a line $l: Ax + By + C = 0$, we are asking for the minimum value of

$$f(x, y) = \sqrt{(x - x_0)^2 + (y - y_0)^2}$$

with (x, y) subject to the side condition

$$Ax + By + C = 0.$$

When we ask for the distance between a point $P(x_0, y_0, z_0)$ and a plane $p\colon Ax + By + Cz + D = 0$, we are asking for the minimum value of

$$f(x, y, z) = \sqrt{(x - x_0)^2 + (y - y_0)^2 + (z - z_0)^2}$$

with (x, y, z) subject to the side condition

$$Ax + By + Cz + D = 0.$$

These particular problems we have already treated by special techniques. Our interest here is to present techniques for handling problems of this sort in general. In the two variable case, the problems will take the form of maximizing (or minimizing) some function $f(x, y)$ subject to a side condition $g(x, y) = 0$. In the three variable case, we will seek to maximize (or minimize) some function $f(x, y, z)$ subject to a side condition $g(x, y, z) = 0$. We begin with two simple examples.

Problem. Find the maximum value of xy subject to the side condition $x + y - 1 = 0$.

SOLUTION. The condition $x + y - 1 = 0$ gives us $y = 1 - x$. Our initial problem can therefore be solved simply by maximizing the product

$$h(x) = x(1 - x).$$

Obviously

$$h'(x) = 1 - 2x.$$

Setting

$$h'(x) = 0$$

gives

$$x = \tfrac{1}{2}.$$

Since

$$h''(x) = -2 < 0,$$

we know from the second derivative test that

$$h(\tfrac{1}{2}) = \tfrac{1}{2}(1 - \tfrac{1}{2}) = \tfrac{1}{4}$$

is the desired maximum. □

Problem. Find the maximum volume of a rectangular solid given that the sum of the lengths of its edges is $12a$.

SOLUTION. We denote the dimensions of the solid by x, y, z. The volume then becomes

$$V = xyz.$$

The stipulation on the edges of the solid requires that

$$4(x + y + z) = 12a.$$

Solving this last equation for z, we get

$$z = 3a - (x + y).$$

If we now substitute this expression for z in the volume formula, we get

$$V = xy[3a - (x + y)].$$

Our problem is now simply to maximize the function

$$V(x, y) = xy[3a - (x + y)].$$

The partials are

$$\frac{\partial V}{\partial x}(x, y) = xy(-1) + y[3a - (x + y)] = 3ay - 2xy - y^2,$$

$$\frac{\partial V}{\partial y}(x, y) = xy(-1) + x[3a - (x + y)] = 3ax - x^2 - 2xy.$$

Setting both partials equal to zero, we get

$$(3a - 2x - y)y = 0$$
$$(3a - x - 2y)x = 0.$$

The possibilities $x = 0$ and $y = 0$ do not interest us here. (Why?) We can therefore simplify the equations to read

$$3a - 2x - y = 0$$
$$3a - x - 2y = 0.$$

Solving these equations simultaneously, we find that

$$x = y = a.$$

The corresponding value of V is a^3. The conditions of the problem make it clear that this is a maximum.   □

The last two problems were extremely easy. They were easy in part because the side conditions were such that we could solve for one of the variables in terms of the other(s). In general this is not possible and a more sophisticated approach is required.

The Method of Lagrange

We begin with what looks like a detour. To avoid having to make separate statements for the two and three variable cases, we will use vector notation.

Throughout the discussion, f will be a function of two or three variables continuously differentiable on some open set U. We take

$$C: \quad \mathbf{r}(t), \quad t \in I$$

as a curve which lies entirely in U and has at each point a non-zero tangent vector $\mathbf{r}'(t)$. The basic result is this:

(14.12.1)

> If $\mathbf{x}_0$ maximizes (or minimizes) $f(\mathbf{x})$ on C, then $\nabla f(\mathbf{x}_0)$ is perpendicular to C at $\mathbf{x}_0$.

To show this, we suppose that

$$\mathbf{r}(t_0) = \mathbf{x}_0.$$

The composition

$$f(\mathbf{r}(t)), \qquad t \in I$$

has a maximum (or minimum) at t_0. Consequently its derivative,

$$\frac{d}{dt}[f(\mathbf{r}(t))] = \nabla f(\mathbf{r}(t)) \cdot \mathbf{r}'(t),$$

must be zero at t_0:

$$0 = \nabla f(\mathbf{r}(t_0)) \cdot \mathbf{r}'(t_0) = \nabla f(\mathbf{x}_0) \cdot \mathbf{r}'(t_0).$$

This shows that

$$\nabla f(\mathbf{x}_0) \perp \mathbf{r}'(t_0).$$

Since $\mathbf{r}'(t_0)$ is tangent to C at $\mathbf{x}_0$, we have $\nabla f(\mathbf{x}_0)$ perpendicular to C at $\mathbf{x}_0$.   □

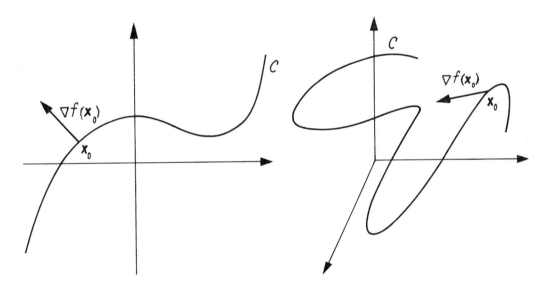

Two variables   Three variables

If $\mathbf{x}_0$ maximizes $f(\mathbf{x})$ on C, then $\nabla f(\mathbf{x}_0) \perp C$

FIGURE 14.12.1

We are now ready for the side condition problems. Suppose that g is a continuously differentiable function of two or three variables defined on a subset of the domain of f. Suppose furthermore that the gradient ∇g is never $\mathbf{0}$. Lagrange made the following observation:

(14.12.2)

> If x_0 maximizes (or minimizes) $f(x)$ subject to the side condition $g(x) = 0$, then $\nabla f(x_0)$ and $\nabla g(x_0)$ are collinear. Consequently there exists a scalar λ such that
>
> $$\nabla f(x_0) = \lambda \nabla g(x_0).$$

Such a scalar λ is now called a *Lagrange multiplier*.

A Geometric Argument for (14.12.2)

Suppose that x_0 maximizes (or minimizes) $f(x)$ subject to the side condition $g(x) = 0$. In the two variable case we have

$$x_0 = (x_0, y_0) \qquad \text{and} \qquad \text{the equation } g(x, y) = 0.$$

This equation defines a curve C, which, we assume, has everywhere a non-zero tangent. Since (x_0, y_0) maximizes (or minimizes) $f(x, y)$ on C, we know that $f(x_0, y_0)$ is perpendicular to C at (x_0, y_0). Since $\nabla g(x_0, y_0)$ is also perpendicular to C at (x_0, y_0) [Section 14.9], the two gradients must be collinear.

In the three variable case we have

$$x_0 = (x_0, y_0, z_0) \qquad \text{and} \qquad \text{the equation } g(x, y, z) = 0.$$

This equation defines a surface Γ that lies in the domain of f. Now let C be a curve which lies in Γ and passes through (x_0, y_0, z_0). As usual we assume that C has a non-zero tangent vector. We know that (x_0, y_0, z_0) maximizes (or minimizes) $f(x, y, z)$ on C. Consequently, $\nabla f(x_0, y_0, z_0)$ is perpendicular to C at (x_0, y_0, z_0). Since this is true for each such curve C, $\nabla f(x_0, y_0, z_0)$ must be perpendicular to Γ itself. But $\nabla g(x_0, y_0, z_0)$ is also perpendicular to Γ at (x_0, y_0, z_0). [Section 14.9] It follows that $\nabla f(x_0, y_0, z_0)$ and $\nabla g(x_0, y_0, z_0)$ are collinear. $\square$

It is time to apply Lagrange's idea to some problems.

Problem. Maximize and minimize

$$f(x, y) = xy$$

subject to the side condition

$$x^2 + y^2 = 1.$$

SOLUTION. Setting

$$g(x, y) = x^2 + y^2 - 1,$$

we can state the side condition as

$$g(x, y) = 0.$$

We are looking for those points (x, y) which satisfy a Lagrange condition

$$\nabla f(x, y) = \lambda \nabla g(x, y)$$

and, simultaneously, the side condition

$$g(x, y) = 0.$$

The gradients are

$$\nabla f(x, y) = y\mathbf{i} + x\mathbf{j}$$
$$\nabla g(x, y) = 2x\mathbf{i} + 2y\mathbf{j}.$$

Setting

$$\nabla f(x, y) = \lambda \nabla g(x, y)$$

we obtain

$$y = 2\lambda x, \qquad x = 2\lambda y.$$

Multiplying the first equation by y and the second equation by x, we find that

$$y^2 = 2\lambda xy, \qquad x^2 = 2\lambda xy$$

and thus

$$y^2 = x^2.$$

This equation together with the side condition

$$g(x, y) = x^2 + y^2 - 1 = 0$$

gives

$$2x^2 - 1 = 0$$
$$x^2 = \frac{1}{2}$$
$$x = \pm \frac{1}{\sqrt{2}}.$$

The points under consideration are therefore

$$\left(\frac{1}{\sqrt{2}}, \frac{1}{\sqrt{2}}\right), \left(\frac{1}{\sqrt{2}}, -\frac{1}{\sqrt{2}}\right), \left(-\frac{1}{\sqrt{2}}, \frac{1}{\sqrt{2}}\right), \left(-\frac{1}{\sqrt{2}}, -\frac{1}{\sqrt{2}}\right).$$

At the first and fourth points f takes on the value $1/2$. At the second and third points f takes on the value $-1/2$. The first is a maximum and the second a minimum.   □

Problem.   Find the minimum value taken on by the function

$$f(x, y) = x^2 + (y - 2)^2$$

on the hyperbola

$$x^2 - y^2 = 1.$$

SOLUTION.   We set

$$g(x, y) = x^2 - y^2 - 1.$$

Our problem is to minimize $f(x, y)$ subject to the side condition

$$g(x, y) = x^2 - y^2 - 1 = 0.$$

The points of interest must satisfy a Lagrange condition

$$\nabla f(x, y) = \lambda \nabla g(x, y)$$

together with

$$g(x, y) = 0.$$

Here

$$\nabla f(x, y) = 2x\mathbf{i} + 2(y - 2)\mathbf{j}, \qquad \nabla g(x, y) = 2x\mathbf{i} - 2y\mathbf{j}.$$

The condition

$$\nabla f(x, y) = \lambda \nabla g(x, y)$$

gives

$$2x = 2\lambda x, \qquad 2(y - 2) = -2\lambda y,$$

which we can simplify to

$$x = \lambda x, \qquad y - 2 = -\lambda y.$$

The points of interest must therefore satisfy the following three equations:

$$x = \lambda x, \qquad y - 2 = -\lambda y, \qquad x^2 - y^2 - 1 = 0.$$

The last equation shows that x cannot be zero. Dividing $x = \lambda x$ by x, we get $\lambda = 1$. This means that $y - 2 = -y$ and therefore $y = 1$. With $y = 1$, the last equation gives $x = \pm \sqrt{2}$. The points to be checked are therefore $(-\sqrt{2}, 1)$ and $(\sqrt{2}, 1)$. At each of these points f takes on the value 3. This is the desired minimum. □

Problem.   Maximize

$$f(x, y, z) = xyz$$

subject to the side condition

$$x^3 + y^3 + z^3 = 1.$$

SOLUTION.   We set

$$g(x, y, z) = x^3 + y^3 + z^3 - 1$$

so that the side condition becomes

$$g(x, y, z) = 0.$$

We seek those triples (x, y, z) which simultaneously satisfy a Lagrange condition

$$\nabla f(x, y, z) = \lambda \nabla g(x, y, z)$$

and the side condition

$$g(x, y, z) = 0.$$

The gradients are

$$\nabla f(x, y, z) = yz\mathbf{i} + xz\mathbf{j} + xy\mathbf{k}$$
$$\nabla g(x, y, z) = 3x^2\mathbf{i} + 3y^2\mathbf{j} + 3z^2\mathbf{k}.$$

Setting

$$\nabla f(x, y, z) = \lambda \nabla g(x, y, z),$$

we find that

$$yz = \lambda 3x^2, \qquad xz = \lambda 3y^2, \qquad xy = \lambda 3z^2.$$

Multiplying the first equation by x, the second by y, and the third by z, we get

$$xyz = \lambda 3x^3, \qquad xyz = \lambda 3y^3, \qquad xyz = \lambda 3z^3$$

and consequently

$$\lambda x^3 = \lambda y^3 = \lambda z^3.$$

We can exclude $\lambda = 0$ because if $\lambda = 0$ then at least one of the other variables would have to be zero. That would force xyz to be 0 and that is obviously not a maximum. Having excluded $\lambda = 0$, we can divide by λ, and get

$$x^3 = y^3 = z^3.$$

This gives

$$x = y = z.$$

The side condition

$$x^3 + y^3 + z^3 = 1$$

now gives

$$z = \left(\frac{1}{3}\right)^{1/3}, \qquad y = \left(\frac{1}{3}\right)^{1/3}, \qquad z = \left(\frac{1}{3}\right)^{1/3}.$$

The desired maximum is $1/3$. □

Problem. Show that of all the triangles inscribed in a fixed circle, the equilateral triangle has the largest perimeter.

SOLUTION. In Figure 14.12.2 we have marked the angles α, β, γ at the center of the circumscribed circle. The length of the side subtended by α is

$$2R \sin \tfrac{1}{2}\alpha.$$

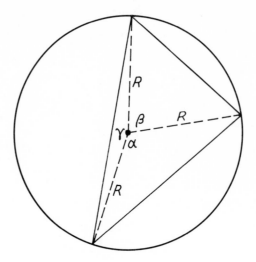

FIGURE 14.12.2

Hence the perimeter is given by

$$f(\alpha, \beta, \gamma) = 2R(\sin \tfrac{1}{2}\alpha + \sin \tfrac{1}{2}\beta + \sin \tfrac{1}{2}\gamma).$$

As a side condition we have

$$g(\alpha, \beta, \gamma) = \alpha + \beta + \gamma - 2\pi = 0.$$

To maximize the perimeter we form the gradients

$$\nabla f(\alpha, \beta, \gamma) = R(\cos \tfrac{1}{2}\alpha \, \mathbf{i} + \cos \tfrac{1}{2}\beta \, \mathbf{j} + \cos \tfrac{1}{2}\gamma \, \mathbf{k})$$
$$\nabla g(\alpha, \beta, \gamma) = \mathbf{i} + \mathbf{j} + \mathbf{k}.$$

The Lagrange condition

$$\nabla f(\alpha, \beta, \gamma) = \lambda \nabla g(\alpha, \beta, \gamma)$$

results in

$$\lambda = R \cos \tfrac{1}{2}\alpha, \qquad \lambda = R \cos \tfrac{1}{2}\beta, \qquad \lambda = R \cos \tfrac{1}{2}\gamma.$$

Under the special conditions of the problem this means that

$$\alpha = \beta = \gamma.$$

With the central angles equal, the sides are equal. The triangle is therefore equilateral. □

Exercises

1.* Minimize $x^2 + y^2$ subject to the condition $xy = 1$.

2. Maximize xy subject to the condition $\dfrac{x^2}{a^2} + \dfrac{y^2}{b^2} = 1$.

3.* Minimize xy subject to the condition $\dfrac{x^2}{a^2} + \dfrac{y^2}{b^2} = 1$.

4. Minimize xy^2 subject to the condition $x^2 + y^2 = 1$.

5.* Maximize xy^2 subject to the condition $\dfrac{x^2}{a^2} + \dfrac{y^2}{b^2} = 1$.

6. Maximize $x + y$ subject to the condition $x^4 + y^4 = 1$.

7.* Minimize xyz subject to the condition $x^2 + y^2 + z^2 = 1$.

8. Maximize xyz subject to the condition $\dfrac{x^2}{a^2} + \dfrac{y^2}{b^2} + \dfrac{z^2}{c^2} = 1$.

9.* Maximize xy^2z^3 subject to the condition $x + y + z = 1$.

10. Minimize $x + 2y + 4z$ subject to the condition $x^2 + y^2 + z^2 = 7$.

11.* Maximize $2x + 3y + 5z$ subject to the condition $x^2 + y^2 + z^2 = 19$.

12. Minimize $x^4 + y^4 + z^4$ subject to the side condition $x + y + z = 1$.

13.* Maximize the volume of a rectangular solid which has three faces on the coordinate planes and one vertex, the plane

$$\frac{x}{a} + \frac{y}{b} + \frac{z}{c} = 1. \qquad\qquad (a > 0,\, b > 0,\, c > 0)$$

14. Show that the square has the largest area of all the rectangles with a given perimeter.

15.* Find the distance between the point $(0, 1)$ and the parabola $x^2 = 4y$.

16. Find the distance between the point $(p, 4p)$ and the parabola $y^2 = 2px$.

17.* Find the largest volume of a rectangular solid which has the property that the sum of the areas of the six faces is $6a^2$.

18. Use the method of Lagrange multipliers to find the distance from the origin to the plane $Ax + By + Cz + D = 0$.

19.* Within a triangle, there is a point P such that the sum of the squares of its distances from the sides of the triangle is a minimum. Find this point.

20. Show that of all the triangles inscribed in a fixed circle the equilateral one has the largest
(a) product of the lengths of the sides.
(b) sum of the squares of the lengths of the sides.

21. A plane passes through the point (a, b, c). Find its intercepts with the coordinate axes if the volume of the solid bounded by the plane and the coordinate planes is a minimum.

22. Show that of all the triangles with a given perimeter the equilateral triangle has the largest area. (HINT): Use

$$\text{Area} = \sqrt{s(s - a)(s - b)(s - c)}$$

where s is the semiperimeter

$$s = \tfrac{1}{2}(a + b + c).$$

14.13   Differentials

We begin by reviewing the one-variable case. If f is differentiable at x, then

$$f(x + h) - f(x) = f'(x)h + o(h).$$

This tells us that for small h

$$f(x + h) - f(x) \quad \text{and} \quad f'(x)h$$

are approximately equal and consequently we can use the differential

$$df = f'(x)h$$

to approximate the increment

$$\triangle f = f(x + h) - f(x).$$

In symbols

$$\triangle f \cong df.$$

The differential of a function of several variables is defined in a similar manner and plays a similar approximating role. If f, now a function of several variables, is differentiable at $\mathbf{x}$, then

$$f(\mathbf{x} + \mathbf{h}) - f(\mathbf{x}) = \nabla f(\mathbf{x}) \cdot \mathbf{h} + o(\mathbf{h}).$$

This says that, for small $\mathbf{h}$,

$$f(\mathbf{x} + \mathbf{h}) - f(\mathbf{x}) \quad \text{and} \quad \nabla f(\mathbf{x}) \cdot \mathbf{h}$$

are approximately equal. In this setting, we call

$$\triangle f = f(\mathbf{x} + \mathbf{h}) - f(\mathbf{x})$$

the *increment* of f and

$$df = \nabla f(\mathbf{x}) \cdot \mathbf{h}$$

the *differential* (more formally, the *total differential*) at $\mathbf{x}$ with increment $\mathbf{h}$. The key point is that, as before,

$$\triangle f \cong df.$$

In the two variable case we set

$$\mathbf{x} = (x, y) \quad \text{and} \quad \mathbf{h} = (\triangle x, \triangle y).$$

The increment

$$\triangle f = f(\mathbf{x} + \mathbf{h}) - f(\mathbf{x})$$

then becomes

$$\triangle f = f(x + \triangle x, y + \triangle y) - f(x, y)$$

and the differential

$$df = \nabla f(\mathbf{x}) \cdot \mathbf{h}$$

becomes

$$df = \frac{\partial f}{\partial x}(x, y)\triangle x + \frac{\partial f}{\partial y}(x, y)\triangle y.$$

The approximation

$$\triangle f \cong df$$

is illustrated in Figure 14.13.1. There we have represented f as a surface $z = f(x, y)$. Through a point $(x_0, y_0, f(x_0, y_0))$ we have drawn the tangent plane. The difference

$$df - \triangle f$$

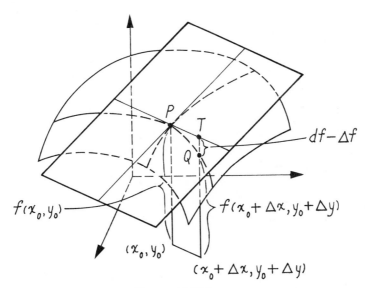

FIGURE 14.13.1

is simply the vertical separation between this tangent plane and the surface as measured above the point $(x_0 + \triangle x, y_0 + \triangle y)$. To verify this assertion, we set

$$P = \left(x_0, y_0, f(x_0, y_0)\right) \quad \text{and} \quad Q = \left(x_0 + \triangle x, y_0 + \triangle y, f(x_0 + \triangle x, y_0 + \triangle y)\right).$$

The plane tangent to the surface at P has equation

$$(x - x_0)\frac{\partial f}{\partial x}(x_0, y_0) + (y - y_0)\frac{\partial f}{\partial y}(x_0, y_0) = z - f(x_0, y_0).$$

As you can check, the point

$$T\left(x_0 + \triangle x, \ y_0 + \triangle y, \ f(x_0, y_0) + \frac{\partial f}{\partial x}(x_0, y_0)\triangle x + \frac{\partial f}{\partial y}(x_0, y_0)\triangle y\right)$$

lies on this plane. The difference

$$df - \triangle f = \left(\frac{\partial f}{\partial x}(x_0, y_0)\triangle x + \frac{\partial f}{\partial y}(x_0, y_0)\triangle y \right) - \left(f(x_0 + \triangle x, y_0 + \triangle y) - f(x_0, y_0) \right)$$

$$= \left(f(x_0, y_0) + \frac{\partial f}{\partial x}(x_0, y_0)\triangle x + \frac{\partial f}{\partial y}(x_0, y_0)\triangle y \right) - \left(f(x_0 + \triangle x, y_0 + \triangle y) \right)$$

is simply the vertical separation between T and Q. □

For the three variable case we set

$$\mathbf{x} = (x, y, z) \quad \text{and} \quad \mathbf{h} = (\triangle x, \triangle y, \triangle z).$$

The increment then becomes

$$\triangle f = f(x + \triangle x, y + \triangle y, z + \triangle z) - f(x, y, z)$$

and the approximating differential

$$df = \frac{\partial f}{\partial x}(x, y, z)\triangle x + \frac{\partial f}{\partial y}(x, y, z)\triangle y + \frac{\partial f}{\partial z}(x, y, z)\triangle z.$$

Problem. Use differentials to find the approximate value of

$$\sqrt{27}\sqrt[3]{1021}.$$

SOLUTION. Here we take

$$f(x, y) = \sqrt{x}\sqrt[3]{y} = x^{1/2}y^{1/3}.$$

The approximation formula

$$\triangle f \cong df,$$

can be written

$$f(x + \triangle x, y + \triangle y) - f(x, y) \cong \frac{\partial f}{\partial x}(x, y)\triangle x + \frac{\partial f}{\partial y}(x, y)\triangle y.$$

In this instance,

$$(x + \triangle x)^{1/2}(y + \triangle y)^{1/3} - x^{1/2}y^{1/3} \cong \tfrac{1}{2}x^{-1/2}y^{1/3}\triangle x + \tfrac{1}{3}x^{1/2}y^{-2/3}\triangle y.$$

Taking $x = 25$ (we know the square root of 25), taking $y = 1000$ (we know the cube root of 1000), and setting $\triangle x = 2$, $\triangle y = 21$, we have

$$27^{1/2}1021^{1/3} - 25^{1/2}1000^{1/3} \cong \tfrac{1}{2}(25^{-1/2})(1000^{1/3})(2) + \tfrac{1}{3}(25^{1/2})(1000^{-2/3})(21) = 2.35$$

and consequently

$$27^{1/2}1021^{1/3} \cong 25^{1/2}1000^{1/3} + 2.35 = 50 + 2.35 = 52.35. □$$

Problem. The legs of a right triangle are 3.5 in. and 4.3 in. respectively. Use differentials to estimate the length of the hypotenuse.

SOLUTION. The length of the hypotenuse is given by the function

$$f(x, y) = \sqrt{x^2 + y^2}$$

where x and y are the lengths of the legs. The approximation

$$\triangle f \cong df$$

once again takes the form

$$f(x + \triangle x, y + \triangle y) - f(x, y) \cong \frac{\partial f}{\partial x}(x, y)\triangle x + \frac{\partial f}{\partial y}(x, y)\triangle y.$$

In this instance,

$$\sqrt{(x + \triangle x)^2 + (y + \triangle y)^2} - \sqrt{x^2 + y^2} \cong \frac{x}{\sqrt{x^2 + y^2}}\triangle x + \frac{y}{\sqrt{x^2 + y^2}}\triangle y.$$

Taking $x = 3$, $y = 4$, $\triangle x = 0.5$, and $\triangle y = 0.3$, we get

$$\sqrt{(3.5)^2 + (4.3)^2} - \sqrt{3^2 + 4^2} \cong \frac{3}{\sqrt{3^2 + 4^2}}(0.5) + \frac{4}{\sqrt{3^2 + 4^2}}(0.3)$$

$$\sqrt{(3.5)^2 + (4.3)^2} - 5 \cong .54$$

and consequently

$$\sqrt{(3.5)^2 + (4.3)^2} \cong 5.54.$$

The hypotenuse is approximately 5.54 inches long. □

Problem. The frustrum of a cone of height 6 in., upper radius 3 in., and base radius 8 in. is incorrectly measured to have upper radius 2.7 in., base radius 8.1 in., and height 6.3 in. Estimate the resulting (a) error in volume, (b) relative error in volume, (c) percentage error in volume.

SOLUTION. The volume is given by the formula

$$V(r, R, h) = \frac{1}{3}\pi h(R^2 + Rr + r^2).$$

Here

$$\frac{\partial V}{\partial r}(r, R, h) = \frac{1}{3}\pi h(R + 2r), \qquad \frac{\partial V}{\partial R}(r, R, h) = \frac{1}{3}\pi h(2R + r),$$

$$\frac{\partial V}{\partial h}(r, R, h) = \frac{1}{3}\pi(R^2 + Rr + r^2).$$

Setting $r = 3$, $R = 8$, $h = 6$, $\triangle r = -0.3$, $\triangle R = 0.1$, and $\triangle h = 0.3$, we have

$$\text{error} = \triangle V = V(3 - .3, 8 + .1, 6 + .3) - V(3, 8, 6)$$

estimated error $= dV$

$$= \left[\frac{\partial V}{\partial r}(3, 8, 6)\right](-0.3) + \left[\frac{\partial V}{\partial R}(3, 8, 6)\right](0.1) + \left[\frac{\partial V}{\partial h}(3, 8, 6)\right](0.3)$$

$$= (28\pi)(-0.3) + (38\pi)(0.1) + \left(\frac{97\pi}{3}\right)(0.3)$$

$$= 5.1\pi \text{ cu. in.}$$

relative error $= \dfrac{\Delta V}{V} \cong \dfrac{dV}{V} = \dfrac{5.1\pi}{194\pi} = \dfrac{51}{1940}$

percentage error $= 100\dfrac{\Delta V}{V}\% \cong 100\dfrac{dV}{V}\% = \dfrac{510}{194}\% \cong 3\%.$ $\square$

Exercises

Find the total differential du.

1.* $u = x^3y - x^2y^2$.

2. $u = xy + yz + xz$.

3.* $u = x\cos y - y\cos x$.

4. $u = x^2ye^{2z}$.

5.* $u = x - y\tan z$.

6. $u = (x - y)\log(x + y)$.

7.* Compute Δu and du for $u = x^2 - 3xy + 2y^2$ at $x = 2$, $y = -3$, $\Delta x = -0.3$, $\Delta y = 0.2$.

8.* Compute du for $u = (x + y)\sqrt{x - y}$ at $x = 6$, $y = 2$, $\Delta x = \frac{1}{4}$, $\Delta y = -\frac{1}{2}$.

Use differentials to find the approximate value.

9.* $\sqrt{125}\sqrt[4]{17}$.

10. $(1 - \sqrt{10})(1 + \sqrt{24})$.

11.* $\sin\dfrac{6\pi}{7}\cos\dfrac{\pi}{5}$.

12. $\sqrt{8}\tan\left(\dfrac{5\pi}{16}\right)$.

13.* Given that

$$z = \frac{x - y}{x + y}$$

find the approximate change in z if x is increased from 4 to $4\frac{1}{10}$ and y is increased from 2 to $2\frac{1}{10}$.

14. The diameter and altitude of a right circular cylinder are found by measurement to be 12 in. and 8 in. respectively. Given that these measurements are each accurate within 0.2 in., estimate the greatest possible error in the computed volume.

15.* The specific gravity of a solid is given by the formula

$$s = \frac{P}{w}$$

where P is the weight in a vacuum and w is the weight of an equal volume of water.

How is the computed specific gravity affected by an error of ±0.1 in weighing P and ±0.05 in weighing w, assuming $P = 8$ and $w = 1$, (a) if both errors are positive? (b) if one error is negative? (c) Estimate the largest possible percentage error.

16.* The diameter and slant height of a right circular cone are found by measurement to be 10 in. and 20 in. respectively. Given that there is a possible error of 0.2 in. in each measurement, estimate the greatest possible error in the computed value of (a) the volume? (b) the lateral area?

17. The length l and the period P of a simple pendulum are connected by the equation $4\pi^2 l = P^2 g$. If l is calculated assuming $P = 1$ sec. and $g = 32$ ft. per second per second, what approximately is the error in l if the true values are $P = 1.02$ sec. and $g = 32.01$ ft. per second per second? What is the percentage error?

18. A solid is in the form of a cylinder capped at each end by a hemisphere of the same radius as the cylinder. Its measured dimensions are diameter $= 8$ in. and total length $= 20$ in. What approximately is the error in volume and surface area if the tape used in measuring has stretched uniformly $\frac{1}{2}\%$ beyond its proper length?

14.14　Reconstructing a function from its gradient

This section has essentially three parts. In the first part we show how to find $f(x, y)$, given its gradient

$$\nabla f(x, y) = \frac{\partial f}{\partial x}(x, y)\mathbf{i} + \frac{\partial f}{\partial y}(x, y)\mathbf{j}.$$

In the second part we show that, although all gradients $\nabla f(x, y)$ are of the form

$$P(x, y)\mathbf{i} + Q(x, y)\mathbf{j}$$

$$\left[\text{set } P = \frac{\partial f}{\partial x} \text{ and } Q = \frac{\partial f}{\partial y}\right], \text{ not all combinations of the form}$$

$$P(x, y)\mathbf{i} + Q(x, y)\mathbf{j}$$

are actually gradients. In the third part we tackle the problem of recognizing which combinations

$$P(x, y)\mathbf{i} + Q(x, y)\mathbf{j}$$

are gradients.

Problem. Find f given that

$$\nabla f(x, y) = y^2\mathbf{i} + (2xy - 1)\mathbf{j}.$$

SOLUTION.　Since

$$\nabla f(x, y) = \frac{\partial f}{\partial x}(x, y)\mathbf{i} + \frac{\partial f}{\partial y}(x, y)\mathbf{j}$$

we must have

$$\frac{\partial f}{\partial x}(x, y) = y^2 \quad \text{and} \quad \frac{\partial f}{\partial y}(x, y) = 2xy - 1.$$

Integrating the first relation with respect to x, we have

$$f(x, y) = y^2x + \phi(y)$$

where $\phi(y)$ is independent of x but may depend on y. Integrating the second relation with respect to y, we have

$$f(x, y) = xy^2 - y + \psi(x)$$

where $\psi(x)$ is independent of y but may depend on x. To reconcile

$$f(x, y) = xy^2 + \phi(y) \qquad \text{with} \qquad f(x, y) = xy^2 - y + \psi(x),$$

we set

$$xy^2 + \phi(y) = xy^2 - y + \psi(x).$$

This forces

$$\phi(y) = -y + \psi(x)$$

and thus

$$\phi(y) + y = \psi(x).$$

The left-hand side can depend at most on y and the right-hand side at most on x. This means that both sides are equal to some constant C. This gives

$$\phi(y) + y = C \qquad \text{and} \qquad \psi(x) = C.$$

The relation

$$f(x, y) = xy^2 + \phi(y)$$

now gives

$$f(x, y) = xy^2 - y + C.$$

The relation

$$f(x, y) = xy^2 - y + \psi(x)$$

also gives

$$f(x, y) = xy^2 - y + C. \qquad \square$$

REMARK.   Once we had derived

$$f(x, y) = xy^2 - y + C$$

from the relation

$$f(x, y) = xy^2 + \phi(y),$$

it was unnecessary to derive the same result from

$$f(x, y) = xy^2 - y + \psi(x).$$

We did it simply to check our computations. It is reassuring to get the same answer from both relations.

Problem. Find f given that

$$\nabla f(x, y) = (y^{1/2} - \tfrac{1}{2}yx^{-1/2} + 2x)\mathbf{i} + (\tfrac{1}{2}xy^{-1/2} - x^{1/2} + 1)\mathbf{j}.$$

SOLUTION.   We begin by observing that

$$\frac{\partial f}{\partial x}(x, y) = y^{1/2} - \frac{1}{2}yx^{-1/2} + 2x \quad\text{and}\quad \frac{\partial f}{\partial y}(x, y) = \frac{1}{2}xy^{-1/2} - x^{1/2} + 1.$$

Integration of the first relation with respect to x, gives

$$f(x, y) = y^{1/2}x - x^{1/2}y + x^2 + \phi(y)$$

with $\phi(y)$ independent of x. Integration of the second relation with respect to y, gives

$$f(x, y) = xy^{1/2} - x^{1/2}y + y + \psi(x).$$

with $\psi(x)$ independent of y. These two characterizations of $f(x, y)$ can be reconciled only by having

$$x^2 + \phi(y) = y + \psi(x).$$

This in turn gives

$$\phi(y) - y = \psi(x) - x^2.$$

The left-hand side can depend at most on y, and the right-hand side at most on x. Both sides must therefore be constant. The relations

$$\phi(y) - y = C \quad\text{and}\quad \psi(x) - x^2 = C$$

lead to

$$\phi(y) = y + C \quad\text{and}\quad \psi(x) = x^2 + C.$$

Each of these relations gives

$$f(x, y) = xy^{1/2} - x^{1/2}y + x^2 + y + C. \quad\square$$

The function

$$f(x, y) = xy^{1/2} - x^{1/2}y + x^2 + y + C$$

that we first found is in its most general form in the sense that it contains an arbitrary constant C. If we want f to take on a particular value z_0 at some particular point (x_0, y_0) we need only adjust the constant C accordingly. Let's suppose for example that we require

$$f(1, 4) = 5.$$

Note that

$$f(1, 4) = 1\sqrt{4} - \sqrt{1}\cdot 4 + 1^2 + 4 + C = 3 + C.$$

To get

$$f(1, 4) = 5$$

we must have

$$3 + C = 5$$

and thus

$$C = 2. \quad \square$$

The next problem shows that not all linear combinations

$$P(x, y)\mathbf{i} + Q(x, y)\mathbf{j}$$

are actually gradients.

Problem. Show that there is no function f such that

$$\nabla f(x, y) = y\mathbf{i} - x\mathbf{j}.$$

SOLUTION. Suppose on the contrary that there is such a function. Then of course we must have

$$\frac{\partial f}{\partial x}(x, y) = y \quad \text{and} \quad \frac{\partial f}{\partial y}(x, y) = -x.$$

Integrating the first equation with respect to x, we get

$$f(x, y) = xy + \phi(y)$$

where $\phi(y)$ is independent of x. Integrating the second equation with respect to y, we get

$$f(x, y) = -xy + \psi(x)$$

where $\psi(x)$ is independent of y. To reconcile these two characterizations of f, we must have

$$xy + \phi(y) = -xy + \psi(x)$$

and consequently,

$$\psi(x) = 2xy + \phi(y).$$

Differentiation of this equation with respect to y gives

$$\frac{\partial}{\partial y}[\psi(x)] = 2x + \phi'(y).$$

$$0 = 2x + \phi'(y)$$

$$-2x = \phi'(y).$$

Differentiation of this last equation with respect to x gives

$$-2 = 0.$$

The assumption that

$$y\mathbf{i} - x\mathbf{j}$$

was a gradient has led to an absurdity. $\quad \square$

We come now to the problem of recognizing which linear combinations

$$P(x, y)\mathbf{i} + Q(x, y)\mathbf{j}$$

are gradients.

Theorem 14.14.1

Let P and Q be functions of two variables each continuously differentiable in an open rectangle S, which we take to have sides parallel to the coordinate axes. The linear combination

$$P(x, y)\mathbf{i} + Q(x, y)\mathbf{j}$$

is a gradient in S iff

$$\frac{\partial P}{\partial y}(x, y) = \frac{\partial Q}{\partial x}(x, y) \qquad \text{for all } (x, y) \in S.$$

PROOF.   Suppose that

$$P(x, y)\mathbf{i} + Q(x, y)\mathbf{j}$$

is a gradient in S, say

$$\nabla f(x, y) = P(x, y)\mathbf{i} + Q(x, y)\mathbf{j}.$$

Since

$$\nabla f(x, y) = \frac{\partial f}{\partial x}(x, y)\mathbf{i} + \frac{\partial f}{\partial y}(x, y)\mathbf{j},$$

we have

$$P = \frac{\partial f}{\partial x} \qquad \text{and} \qquad Q = \frac{\partial f}{\partial y}.$$

Since P and Q have continuous first partials, f has continuous second partials. Consequently, its mixed partials are equal, and

$$\frac{\partial P}{\partial y} = \frac{\partial^2 f}{\partial y \partial x} = \frac{\partial^2 f}{\partial x \partial y} = \frac{\partial Q}{\partial x}.$$

Conversely, suppose that

$$\frac{\partial P}{\partial y}(x, y) = \frac{\partial Q}{\partial x}(x, y) \qquad \text{for all } (x, y) \in S.$$

We must show that

$$P(x, y)\mathbf{i} + Q(x, y)\mathbf{j}$$

is a gradient in S. To do this, we choose a point (x_0, y_0) and form the function

$$f(x, y) = C + \int_{x_0}^{x} P(u, y_0) \, du + \int_{y_0}^{y} Q(x, v) \, dv, \qquad (x, y) \in S.$$

[If you want to visualize f, you can refer to Figure 14.14.1. The function P is being integrated along the horizontal line segment joining (x_0, y_0) to (x, y_0) and Q is being integrated along the vertical line segment joining (x, y_0) to (x, y). Our assumptions on S guarantee that these line segments remain in S. C is simply an arbitrary constant.]

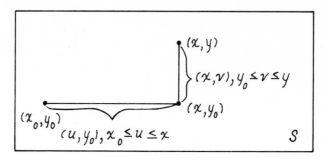

FIGURE 14.14.1

The first integral is independent of y. Hence

$$\frac{\partial f}{\partial y}(x, y) = \frac{\partial}{\partial y}\left(\int_{y_0}^{y} Q(x, v)\, dv\right) = Q(x, y).$$

The last equality holds because we are differentiating an integral with respect to its upper limit.† Differentiating f with respect to x is a little more complicated:

$$\frac{\partial f}{\partial x}(x, y) = \frac{\partial}{\partial x}\left(\int_{x_0}^{x} P(u, y_0)\, du\right) + \frac{\partial}{\partial x}\left(\int_{y_0}^{y} Q(x, v)\, dv\right).$$

In the first term the variable x appears as an upper limit. In the second term the variable x appears under the sign of integration. Differentiation under the sign of integration is justified in more advanced texts.‡ Anticipating this result, we get

$$\frac{\partial f}{\partial x}(x, y) = P(x, y_0) + \int_{y_0}^{y} \frac{\partial Q}{\partial x}(x, v)\, dv$$

$$= P(x, y_0) + \int_{y_0}^{y} \frac{\partial P}{\partial y}(x, v)\, dv$$

$$= P(x, y_0) + P(x, y) - P(x, y_0)$$

$$= P(x, y).$$

With

$$P(x, y) = \frac{\partial f}{\partial x}(x, y) \quad \text{and} \quad Q(x, y) = \frac{\partial f}{\partial y}(x, y),$$

---

† This is a fundamental notion. If you are fuzzy on it, see Theorem 4.3.2.
‡ See for example Einar Hille, *Analysis* (Waltham, Mass.: Blaisdell, 1966), Vol. 2.

we have

$$P(x, y)\mathbf{i} + Q(x, y)\mathbf{j}$$

as the gradient of f. □

The theorem we just proved for a rectangle can be extended to more general regions. The proof that we gave depended on our being able to join arbitrary points of S by a path consisting of a horizontal and a vertical line segment both of which remained in S. For more general regions a more complicated proof is required.

The test for gradients that is furnished by the theorem is easy to apply.

Examples

(1) To determine whether

$$xy\mathbf{i} + \tfrac{1}{2}(x + 1)^2y^2\mathbf{j}$$

is a gradient, we set

$$P(x, y) = xy \quad \text{and} \quad Q(x, y) = \tfrac{1}{2}(x + 1)^2y^2.$$

Since

$$\frac{\partial P}{\partial y}(x, y) = x \quad \text{and} \quad \frac{\partial Q}{\partial x}(x, y) = (x + 1)y^2,$$

we have

$$\frac{\partial P}{\partial y}(x, y) \neq \frac{\partial Q}{\partial x}(x, y).$$

It follows that

$$xy\mathbf{i} + \tfrac{1}{2}(x + 1)^2y^2\mathbf{j}$$

is not a gradient.

(2) In the case of

$$2x \sin y\,\mathbf{i} + x^2 \cos y\,\mathbf{j}$$

we have

$$P(x, y) = 2x \sin y, \qquad Q(x, y) = x^2 \cos y$$

$$\frac{\partial P}{\partial y}(x, y) = 2x \cos y, \qquad \frac{\partial Q}{\partial x}(x, y) = 2x \cos y.$$

Since the two partials are equal, the initial linear combination is a gradient. □

Exercises

Find the function with the given gradient.

1.* $xy^2\mathbf{i} + x^2y\mathbf{j}$.

2. $x\mathbf{i} + y\mathbf{j}$.

3.* $y\mathbf{i} + x\mathbf{j}$.

4. $(x^2 + y)\mathbf{i} + (y^3 + x)\mathbf{j}$.

5.* $(y^3 + x)\mathbf{i} + (x^2 + y)\mathbf{j}$.

6. $(y^2e^x - y)\mathbf{i} + (2ye^x - x)\mathbf{j}$.

7.* $(\cos x - y \sin x)\mathbf{i} + \cos x \mathbf{j}$.

8. $(1 + e^y)\mathbf{i} + (xe^y + y^2)\mathbf{j}$.

9.* $(\cosh x + \sinh y)\mathbf{i} + (x \cosh y)\mathbf{j}$.

10. $(\cosh x - x \sinh y)\mathbf{i} + (2y \cosh x)\mathbf{j}$.

11.* $ye^z(1 + x)\mathbf{i} + (xe^z - e^{-y})\mathbf{j}$.

12. $(x \tan y + \sec^2 x)\mathbf{i} + (\frac{1}{2}x^2 \sec^2 y + \pi y)\mathbf{j}$.

13.* $(x^2 \arcsin y)\mathbf{i} + \left(\dfrac{x^3}{3\sqrt{1 - y^2}} - \log y\right)\mathbf{j}$.

14. $\left(\dfrac{\arctan y}{\sqrt{1 - x^2}} + \dfrac{x}{y}\right)\mathbf{i} + \left(\dfrac{\arcsin x}{1 + y^2} - \dfrac{x^2}{2y^2} + 1\right)\mathbf{j}$.

14.15   Work and line integrals, part I

If an object moves along a straight line subject to a constant force $\mathbf{F}$, the work done is, by definition, the component of $\mathbf{F}$ in the direction of the displacement, multiplied by the length of the displacement:

$$W = (\text{comp}_\mathbf{d}\mathbf{F}) \cdot \|\mathbf{d}\|.$$

We can write this more briefly as a dot product.

$$\boxed{W = \mathbf{F} \cdot \mathbf{d}.}$$ (See Figure 14.15.1)

This elementary notion of work may be useful, but it is not sufficient. Take for example the case of an object which moves through a magnetic field or a gravitational field. In such a situation the path of the motion is generally not a straight line but a curve, and the force does not remain constant but instead varies from point to point. What we want is a notion of work that applies also to this more general situation.

Elementary Notion of Work

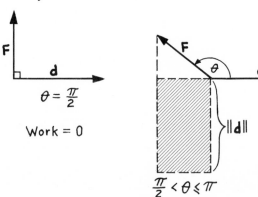

$W = \mathbf{F} \cdot \mathbf{d}$

FIGURE 14.15.1

Suppose that an object moves through a force field and that at each time t it has position $\mathbf{r}(t)$ and is subject to a force $\mathbf{F}(\mathbf{r}(t))$. As the object moves from time a to time b, it traces out a curve

$$C: \mathbf{r}(t) = x(t)\mathbf{i} + y(t)\mathbf{j} + z(t)\mathbf{k}, \qquad t \in [a, b]$$

which we assume is *smooth*. (That is, we assume $\mathbf{r}'$ exists and is continuous.) What we want to do is *define* the total work done by $\mathbf{F}$ along the curve C.

To decide how to do this, we begin by focusing our attention on what happens during a short time interval $[t, t + h]$. As an estimate for the work done during this short time interval, we use the dot product

$$\mathbf{F}(\mathbf{r}(t)) \cdot [\mathbf{r}(t + h) - \mathbf{r}(t)].$$

In making this estimate (see Figure 14.15.2), we are using the force vector at time t and we are replacing the curved path from $\mathbf{r}(t)$ to $\mathbf{r}(t + h)$ by the corresponding line segment.

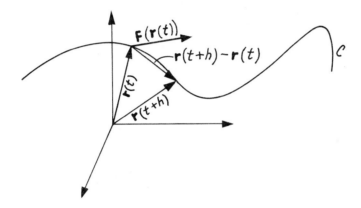

FIGURE 14.15.2

If we set

$$W(t) = \text{total work done up to time } t$$

and

$$W(t + h) = \text{total work done up to time } t + h,$$

then the work done from time t to time $t + h$ must be the difference

$$W(t + h) - W(t).$$

Bringing our estimate into play, we are led to the approximate equation

$$W(t + h) - W(t) \cong \mathbf{F}(\mathbf{r}(t)) \cdot [\mathbf{r}(t + h) - \mathbf{r}(t)],$$

which, upon division by h, becomes

$$\frac{W(t + h) - W(t)}{h} \cong \mathbf{F}(\mathbf{r}(t)) \cdot \frac{[\mathbf{r}(t + h) - \mathbf{r}(t)]}{h}.$$

The quotients here are average rates of change and the equation is only an approximate one, but, presumably, we want it to become increasingly accurate as h tends to zero. The definition of work is made by requiring that, as h tends to zero, both sides have exactly the same limit; in other words, by requiring that

$$W'(t) = \mathbf{F}(\mathbf{r}(t)) \cdot \mathbf{r}'(t).$$

The rest is now predetermined. Since by definition

$$W(a) = 0 \quad \text{and} \quad W(b) = \text{total work done,}$$

we have

$$\text{total work done} = W(b) - W(a) = \int_a^b W'(t)\,dt = \int_a^b [\mathbf{F}(\mathbf{r}(t)) \cdot \mathbf{r}'(t)]\,dt.$$

In short, we have arrived at the following definition of work:

$$\boxed{W = \int_a^b [\mathbf{F}(\mathbf{r}(t)) \cdot \mathbf{r}'(t)]\,dt.}$$

The integral on the right is called a *line integral*. More precisely, it is called the *line integral of F over C* and is commonly denoted by

$$\boxed{\int_C \mathbf{F}(\mathbf{r}) \cdot d\mathbf{r}.}$$

In symbols, we have

$$\boxed{W = \int_C \mathbf{F}(\mathbf{r}) \cdot d\mathbf{r} = \int_a^b [\mathbf{F}(\mathbf{r}(t)) \cdot \mathbf{r}'(t)]\,dt.}$$

Problem.   Find the total work done when an object traverses the parabolic arc

$$C: \mathbf{r}(t) = t\mathbf{i} + t^2\mathbf{j}, \qquad t \in [0, 1]$$

subject to a force

$$\mathbf{F}(x, y) = xy\mathbf{i} + y^2\mathbf{j}.$$

SOLUTION

$$\mathbf{F}(\mathbf{r}(t)) = \mathbf{F}(x(t), y(t)) = x(t)y(t)\mathbf{i} + [y(t)]^2\mathbf{j} = t^3\mathbf{i} + t^4\mathbf{j}$$

$$\mathbf{r}'(t) = \mathbf{i} + 2t\mathbf{j}$$

$$W = \int_C \mathbf{F}(\mathbf{r}) \cdot d\mathbf{r} = \int_0^1 [\mathbf{F}(\mathbf{r}(t)) \cdot \mathbf{r}'(t)]\,dt = \int_0^1 (t^3 + 2t^5)\,dt$$

$$= \left[\frac{t^4}{4} + \frac{t^6}{3}\right]_0^1 = \frac{1}{4} + \frac{1}{3} = \frac{7}{12}. \quad \Box$$

Problem. Find the total work done when an object traverses the twisted cubic

$$C: \mathbf{r}(t) = t\mathbf{i} + t^2\mathbf{j} + t^3\mathbf{k}, \qquad t \in [-1, 1]$$

subject to a force

$$\mathbf{F}(x, y, z) = xy\mathbf{i} + yz\mathbf{j} + xz\mathbf{k}.$$

SOLUTION

$$\mathbf{F}(\mathbf{r}(t)) = \mathbf{F}(x(t), y(t), z(t)) = x(t)y(t)\mathbf{i} + y(t)z(t)\mathbf{j} + x(t)z(t)\mathbf{k}$$
$$= t^3\mathbf{i} + t^5\mathbf{j} + t^4\mathbf{k}$$

$$\mathbf{r}'(t) = \mathbf{i} + 2t\mathbf{j} + 3t^2\mathbf{k}$$

$$W = \int_C \mathbf{F}(\mathbf{r}) \cdot d\mathbf{r} = \int_{-1}^{1} [\mathbf{F}(\mathbf{r}(t)) \cdot \mathbf{r}'(t)]\, dt$$

$$= \int_{-1}^{1} [t^3 + 2t^6 + 3t^6]\, dt$$

$$= \int_{-1}^{1} [t^3 + 5t^6]\, dt$$

$$= \left[\frac{t^4}{4} + \frac{5t^7}{7} \right]_{-1}^{1}$$

$$= \frac{10}{7}. \quad \square$$

If a curve C is not smooth but is made up of a finite number of smooth pieces $C_1, C_2, \ldots, C_n$, then we define the integral over C (and therefore the work done) as the sum of the integrals over the C_i:

$$\boxed{\int_C = \int_{C_1} + \int_{C_2} + \cdots + \int_{C_n}.}$$

A curve of this type is said to be *piece-wise smooth*. Some pictorial examples are given in Figure 14.15.3.

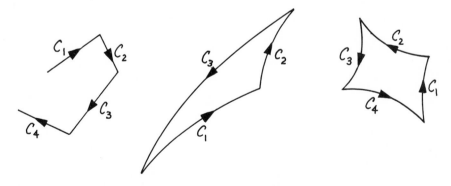

Three piece—wise smooth curves

FIGURE 14.15.3

Triangles are of course piece-wise smooth curves. In the next problem we integrate over a triangle. We do this by integrating over each of the sides and then adding up the results. Keep in mind that the directed line segment which begins at $\mathbf{a} = (a_1, a_2)$ and ends at $\mathbf{b} = (b_1, b_2)$ can be parametrized by setting

$$\mathbf{r}(t) = (1 - t)\mathbf{a} + t\mathbf{b}, \qquad t \in [0, 1].$$

Problem.   Evaluate the line integral

$$\int_C \mathbf{F}(\mathbf{r}) \cdot d\mathbf{r}$$

if

$$\mathbf{F}(x, y) = e^y \mathbf{i} - \sin \pi x \, \mathbf{j}$$

and C is the triangle with vertices $(1, 0)$, $(0, 1)$, $(-1, 0)$ traversed counterclockwise.

SOLUTION.   The path C (Figure 14.15.4) is made up of the three line segments

$C_1 \colon \mathbf{r}(t) = (1 - t)\mathbf{i} + t\mathbf{j}, \qquad t \in [0, 1]$
$C_2 \colon \mathbf{r}(t) = (1 - t)\mathbf{j} + t(-\mathbf{i}) = -t\mathbf{i} + (1 - t)\mathbf{j}, \qquad t \in [0, 1]$
$C_3 \colon \mathbf{r}(t) = (1 - t)(-\mathbf{i}) + t\mathbf{i} = (2t - 1)\mathbf{i}, \qquad t \in [0, 1].$

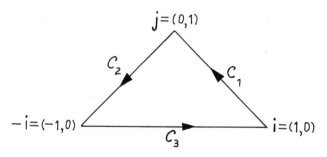

FIGURE 14.15.4

As you can verify,

$$\int_{C_1} \mathbf{F}(\mathbf{r}) \cdot d\mathbf{r} = \int_0^1 \left[e^{y(t)} x'(t) - \sin[\pi x(t)]\, y'(t) \right] dt$$

$$= \int_0^1 \left[[-e^t - \sin[\pi(1 - t)]] \right] dt$$

$$= \left[-e^t - \frac{1}{\pi} \cos[\pi(1 - t)] \right]_0^1$$

$$= 1 - e - \frac{2}{\pi}$$

$$\int_{C_2} \mathbf{F}(\mathbf{r}) \cdot d\mathbf{r} = \int_0^1 \left[e^{y(t)} x'(t) - \sin \left[\pi x(t) \right] y'(t) \right] dt$$

$$= \int_0^1 \left[-e^{1-t} + \sin(-\pi t) \right] dt$$

$$= \left[e^{1-t} + \frac{1}{\pi} \cos(-\pi t) \right]_0^1$$

$$= 1 - e - \frac{2}{\pi}$$

and

$$\int_{C_3} \mathbf{F}(\mathbf{r}) \cdot d\mathbf{r} = \int_0^1 \left[e^{y(t)} x'(t) - \sin \left[\pi x(t) \right] y'(t) \right] dt$$

$$= \int_0^1 2 \, dt$$

$$= 2.$$

As the integral over the entire triangle, we have

$$\int_C \mathbf{F}(\mathbf{r}) \cdot d\mathbf{r} = \left[1 - e - \frac{2}{\pi} \right] + \left[1 - e - \frac{2}{\pi} \right] + 2 = 4 - 2e - \frac{4}{\pi}. \quad \square$$

When we are integrating over a curve, we are integrating in a given direction. If we integrate in the opposite direction, our answer is altered by a factor of -1. To see how this comes about (and incidentally clarify this idea), let C be a piece-wise smooth curve and let $-C$ denote the same path traversed in the opposite direction. See Figure 14.15.5. It's not hard to see that if

$$C: \quad \mathbf{r}(t), \quad t \in [a, b]$$

then

$$-C: \quad \mathbf{R}(u) = \mathbf{r}(a + b - u), \quad u \in [a, b].$$

In a more formal treatment this is how $-C$ would be defined. Our assertion is that

$$\boxed{\int_{-C} \mathbf{F}(\mathbf{R}) \cdot d\mathbf{R} = - \int_C \mathbf{F}(\mathbf{r}) \cdot d\mathbf{r}}$$

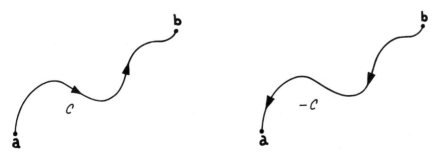

FIGURE 14.15.5

or more briefly that

$$\int_{-C} = - \int_{C}.$$

PROOF. We prove the result first in the case that C is smooth. Setting

$$t(u) = a + b - u,$$

we have

$$t(b) = a \quad \text{and} \quad t(a) = b.$$

Moreover,

$$\mathbf{R}(u) = \mathbf{r}(t(u)) \quad \text{and} \quad \mathbf{R}'(u) = \mathbf{r}'(t(u))t'(u).$$

The change of variables formula gives

$$\int_{a=t(b)}^{b=t(a)} f(t)\,dt = \int_{b}^{a} f(t(u))t'(u)\,du.$$

Applying this formula to

$$f(t) = \mathbf{F}(\mathbf{r}(t)) \cdot \mathbf{r}'(t),$$

we get

$$\int_{C} \mathbf{F}(\mathbf{r}) \cdot d\mathbf{r} = \int_{a=t(b)}^{b=t(a)} [\mathbf{F}(\mathbf{r}(t)) \cdot \mathbf{r}'(t)]\,dt$$

$$= \int_{b}^{a} [\mathbf{F}(\mathbf{r}(t(u))) \cdot \mathbf{r}'(t(u))]t'(u)\,du$$

$$= \int_{b}^{a} [\mathbf{F}(\mathbf{R}(u)) \cdot \mathbf{R}'(u)]\,du$$

$$= - \int_{a}^{b} [\mathbf{F}(\mathbf{R}(u)) \cdot \mathbf{R}'(u)]\,du$$

$$= - \int_{-C} \mathbf{F}(\mathbf{R}) \cdot d\mathbf{R}.$$

If C is only piece-wise smooth, the result still holds because it holds for each of the smooth pieces. $\square$

We will come back to these ideas in the next section.

Exercises

Compute the line integral of $\mathbf{F}$ on the indicated curve.

1.* $\mathbf{F}(x, y) = y\mathbf{i} + x\mathbf{j}$; $\mathbf{r}(t) = t\mathbf{i} + t^2\mathbf{j}$, $t \in [0, 1]$.
2. $\mathbf{F}(x, y) = (x^2 - y)\mathbf{i} + x\mathbf{j}$; $\mathbf{r}(t) = (t - 2)\mathbf{i}$, $t \in [0, 2]$.
3.* $\mathbf{F}(x, y) = y\mathbf{i} + x\mathbf{j}$; the unit circle traversed clockwise.
4. $\mathbf{F}(x, y) = y^2 x\mathbf{i} + 2\mathbf{j}$; $\mathbf{r}(t) = e^t\mathbf{i} + e^{-t}\mathbf{j}$, $t \in [0, 1]$.
5.* $\mathbf{F}(x, y) = (x - y)\mathbf{i} + xy\mathbf{j}$; the line segment from $(2, 3)$ to $(1, 2)$.
6. $\mathbf{F}(x, y) = (x - y)\mathbf{i} + xy\mathbf{j}$; the line segment from $(1, 2)$ to $(2, 3)$.

7.* $F(x, y) = (\cos x - y \sin x)\mathbf{i} + \cos x \mathbf{j}$;　the triangle with vertices $(0, 2)$, $(2, 3)$, $(1, 4)$ traversed counterclockwise.

8.　$F(x, y) = e^{x-y}\mathbf{i} + e^{x+y}\mathbf{j}$;　the line segment from $(-1, 1)$ to $(1, 2)$.

9.* $F(x, y) = \dfrac{1}{xy^2}\mathbf{i} + \dfrac{1}{x^2y}\mathbf{j}$;　$\mathbf{r}(t) = \sqrt{t}\mathbf{i} + \sqrt{1+t}\mathbf{j}$,　　$t \in [1, 4]$.

10.　$F(x, y) = \dfrac{1}{xy^2}\mathbf{i} + \dfrac{1}{x^2y}\mathbf{j}$;　the curve of exercise 9 traversed in the opposite sense.

11.* $F(x, y) = (x + y)\mathbf{i} + (y^2 - x)\mathbf{j}$;　the closed curve which begins at $(-1, 0)$, proceeds along the x-axis to $(1, 0)$, and returns to $(-1, 0)$ by the upper part of the unit circle.

12.　$F(x, y, z) = x\mathbf{i} + xy\mathbf{j} + xyz\mathbf{k}$;　the line segment from $(0, 1, 4)$ to $(1, 0, -4)$.

13.* $F(x, y, z) = yz\mathbf{i} + x^2\mathbf{j} + xz\mathbf{k}$;　$\mathbf{r}(t) = t\mathbf{i} + t^2\mathbf{j} + t^3\mathbf{k}$,　　$t \in [0, 1]$.

14.　$F(x, y, z) = e^{\sqrt{y}}\mathbf{i} + yz\mathbf{j} + e^{xy}\mathbf{k}$;　the curve of exercise 13.

15.* An object orbits an ellipse in standard position subject to a force

$$F(x, y) = -\tfrac{1}{2}[y\mathbf{i} - x\mathbf{j}].$$

Find a relation between the work done and the area of the ellipse.

16.　Show that if C is a smooth curve which begins and ends at the same point, then

$$\int_C \nabla f(\mathbf{r}) \cdot d\mathbf{r} = 0.$$

14.16　Work and line integrals, Part II

There are many kinds of energy that a physicist recognizes. Among the most important of these is *kinetic energy*, which is the energy possessed by an object because of its motion. The kinetic energy of an object depends on its mass m and its speed v:

$$\boxed{\text{K.E.} = \frac{1}{2}mv^2.}$$

There is an important relation between work and kinetic energy which we will now derive.
　　Suppose that an object of mass m moves along a curve

$$C: \quad \mathbf{r}(t), \quad t \in [a, b]$$

subject to a force $\mathbf{F}(\mathbf{r})$. The total work done on the object along the curve is given by the formula

$$W = \int_C \mathbf{F}(\mathbf{r}) \cdot d\mathbf{r} = \int_a^b [\mathbf{F}(\mathbf{r}(t)) \cdot \mathbf{r}'(t)]\, dt.$$

From Newton's Second Law of Motion, we know that at time t,

$$\mathbf{F}(\mathbf{r}(t)) = m\mathbf{a}(t) = m\mathbf{r}''(t).$$

It follows then that

$$\mathbf{F}(\mathbf{r}(t)) \cdot \mathbf{r}'(t) = m\mathbf{r}''(t) \cdot \mathbf{r}'(t)$$

$$= \frac{d}{dt}\left[\frac{1}{2}m(\mathbf{r}'(t) \cdot \mathbf{r}'(t))\right]$$

$$= \frac{d}{dt}\left[\frac{1}{2}m\|\mathbf{r}'(t)\|^2\right]$$

$$= \frac{d}{dt}\left[\frac{1}{2}m\,[v(t)]^2\right].$$

Substituting this last expression into the work integral, we find that

$$W = \int_a^b \frac{d}{dt}\left[\frac{1}{2}m\,[v(t)]^2\right]dt = \frac{1}{2}m\,[v(b)]^2 - \frac{1}{2}m\,[v(a)]^2.$$

This last equation says that the work done on an object along a curve C is exactly equal to the difference in the kinetic energy of the object as measured at the end points of C. In short, we have the following result:

$$\boxed{\text{work done} = \text{change in kinetic energy.}}$$

   In general, if an object moves from one point to another, the work done depends on the path of the motion. There is however an important exception. If the force field is a *gradient field*,

$$\mathbf{F} = \nabla f,$$

then the work done depends only on the end points of the path and not on the path itself. Returning to pure mathematics for a moment, we have the following theorem.

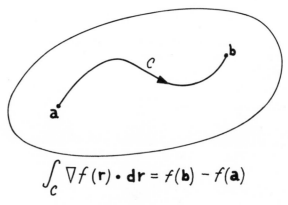

$$\int_C \nabla f(\mathbf{r}) \cdot d\mathbf{r} = f(\mathbf{b}) - f(\mathbf{a})$$

FIGURE 14.16.1

The Fundamental Theorem for Line Integrals

Let

$$C: \quad \mathbf{r}(t), \quad t \in [a, b]$$

be a piece-wise smooth curve which begins at $\mathbf{a}(\mathbf{r}(a) = \mathbf{a})$ and ends at $\mathbf{b}(\mathbf{r}(b) = \mathbf{b})$. If ∇f is continuous (has continuous components) on an open set which contains C, then

$$\int_C \nabla f(\mathbf{r}) \cdot d\mathbf{r} = f(\mathbf{b}) - f(\mathbf{a}).$$

PROOF.   If C is smooth, a one line proof is possible

$$\int_C \nabla f(\mathbf{r}) \cdot d\mathbf{r} = \int_a^b [\nabla f(\mathbf{r}(t)) \cdot \mathbf{r}'(t)] \, dt = \int_a^b \frac{d}{dt} [f(\mathbf{r}(t))] \, dt = f(\mathbf{r}(b)) - f(\mathbf{r}(a))$$

$$= f(\mathbf{b}) - f(\mathbf{a}).$$

If C is not actually smooth but only piece-wise smooth, then we break up C into smooth pieces

$$C = C_1 \cup C_2 \cup \cdots \cup C_n.$$

With obvious notation, we have

$$\int_C \nabla f(\mathbf{r}) \cdot d\mathbf{r} = \int_{C_1} \nabla f(\mathbf{r}) \cdot d\mathbf{r} + \int_{C_2} \nabla f(\mathbf{r}) \cdot d\mathbf{r} + \cdots + \int_{C_n} \nabla f(\mathbf{r}) \cdot d\mathbf{r}$$

$$= [f(\mathbf{a}_1) - f(\mathbf{a}_o)] + [f(\mathbf{a}_2) - f(\mathbf{a}_1)] + \cdots + [f(\mathbf{a}_n) - f(\mathbf{a}_{n-1})]$$

$$= f(\mathbf{a}_n) - f(\mathbf{a}_o)$$

$$= f(\mathbf{b}) - f(\mathbf{a}). \quad \square$$

If the curve C is closed [if $\mathbf{a} = \mathbf{b}$], then of course

$$f(\mathbf{b}) = f(\mathbf{a})$$

and thus

$$\int_C \nabla f(\mathbf{r}) \cdot d\mathbf{r} = 0.$$

If a force field is a gradient field, then the work done along any closed path is 0. *An object which starts at a point with a given kinetic energy returns to that same point with exactly the same kinetic energy.*

We can use these ideas in computations.

Problem.   Find the work done if an object traverses the helix

$$C: \mathbf{r}(t) = \cos t \, \mathbf{i} + \sin t \, \mathbf{j} + t \, \mathbf{k}, \qquad t \in [0, 2\pi],$$

subject to a force

$$\mathbf{F}(\mathbf{r}) = \frac{K}{\|\mathbf{r}\|^2} \mathbf{r}.$$

SOLUTION.   The first thing we do is try to determine whether **F** is a gradient. In terms of x, y, z we have

$$F(x, y, z) = \frac{K}{x^2 + y^2 + z^2} (x\mathbf{i} + y\mathbf{j} + z\mathbf{k}).$$

It is not hard to see that

$$F(x, y, z) = \nabla f(x, y, z) \quad \text{where} \quad f(x, y, z) = \frac{K}{2} \log (x^2 + y^2 + z^2).$$

In terms of **r**, we have

$$f(\mathbf{r}) = \frac{K}{2} \log \|\mathbf{r}\|^2 = K \log \|\mathbf{r}\|.$$

To compute the work integral we need only evaluate f at the end points of C. Since

$$\mathbf{r}(0) = \mathbf{i} \quad \text{and} \quad \mathbf{r}(2\pi) = \mathbf{i} + 2\pi\mathbf{k},$$

we have

$$\begin{aligned}
W &= \int_C \mathbf{F}(\mathbf{r}) \cdot d\mathbf{r} = f(\mathbf{i} + 2\pi\mathbf{k}) - f(\mathbf{i}) \\
&= K \log \|\mathbf{i} + 2\pi\mathbf{k}\| - K \log \|\mathbf{i}\| \\
&= K \log \sqrt{1 + 4\pi^2} - K \log 1 \\
&= \frac{K}{2} \log (1 + 4\pi^2). \quad \square
\end{aligned}$$

Problem.   Evaluate the line integral

$$\int_C \mathbf{F}(\mathbf{r}) \cdot d\mathbf{r}$$

where C is the circular arc

$$\mathbf{r}(t) = \cos t\, \mathbf{i} + \sin t\, \mathbf{j}, \quad t \in \left[0, \frac{\pi}{2}\right]$$

and

$$F(x, y) = y^2\mathbf{i} + (2xy - e^y)\mathbf{j}.$$

SOLUTION.   Here $F(x, y)$ has the form

$$P(x, y)\mathbf{i} + Q(x,y)\mathbf{j}$$

with

$$P(x, y) = y^2 \quad \text{and} \quad Q(x, y) = 2xy - e^y.$$

Since

$$\frac{\partial P}{\partial y}(x, y) = 2y = \frac{\partial Q}{\partial x}(x, y),$$

we know from Section 14.14 that $\mathbf{F}(x, y)$ is a gradient. Since the integral then depends only on the end points of C and not on C itself, we may as well simplify our computations and integrate over the line segment C' that joins the same end points. (Figure 14.16.2) With

$$C': \mathbf{r}(t) = (1 - t)\mathbf{i} + t\mathbf{j}, \qquad t \in [0, 1]$$

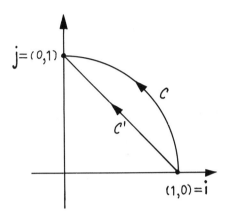

FIGURE 14.16.2

we have

$$\int_C \mathbf{F}(\mathbf{r}) \cdot d\mathbf{r} = \int_{C'} \mathbf{F}(\mathbf{r}) \cdot d\mathbf{r}$$

$$= \int_0^1 [\mathbf{F}(\mathbf{r}(t)) \cdot \mathbf{r}'(t)] \, dt$$

$$= \int_0^1 \left[[y(t)]^2 x'(t) + [2x(t)y(t) - e^{y(t)}]y'(t) \right] dt$$

$$= \int_0^1 [2t - 3t^2 - e^t] \, dt$$

$$= \left[t^2 - t^3 - e^t \right]_0^1$$

$$= 1 - e.$$

ALTERNATE SOLUTION.   Once we recognize

$$\mathbf{F}(x, y) = y^2 \mathbf{i} + (2xy - e^y)\mathbf{j}$$

as a gradient $\nabla f(x, y)$, we can apply the methods of Section 14.14 to find $f(x, y)$. With

$$\frac{\partial f}{\partial x}(x, y) = y^2 \qquad \text{and} \qquad \frac{\partial f}{\partial y}(x, y) = 2xy - e^y,$$

we have

$$f(x, y) = xy^2 + \phi(y) \qquad \text{and} \qquad f(x, y) = xy^2 - e^y + \psi(x).$$

Equating these two expressions for $f(x, y)$, we have

$$\phi(y) = -e^y + \psi(x)$$

and therefore

$$\phi(y) + e^y = \psi(x).$$

It is obvious then that $\psi(x)$ must be constant and therefore

$$f(x, y) = xy^2 - e^y + c.$$

Since the curve C begins at $(1, 0)$ and ends at $(0, 1)$, we have

$$\int_C \mathbf{F(r)} \cdot \mathbf{dr} = f(0, 1) - f(1, 0) = -e + 1 = 1 - e. \quad \square$$

Problem.   Evaluate the line integral

$$\int_C \mathbf{F(r)} \cdot \mathbf{dr}$$

where C is the unit circle

$$\mathbf{r}(t) = \cos t\,\mathbf{i} + \sin t\,\mathbf{j}, \qquad t \in [0, 2\pi]$$

and

$$\mathbf{F}(x, y, z) = (y^2 + y)\mathbf{i} + (2xy - e^y)\mathbf{j}.$$

SOLUTION.   Although

$$(y^2 + y)\mathbf{i} + (2xy - e^y)\mathbf{j}$$

is not a gradient, part of it

$$y^2\mathbf{i} + (2xy - e^y)\mathbf{j}$$

is a gradient. (See last problem.) Since we are integrating over a closed curve, the contribution of the gradient part is 0. All we need compute therefore is

$$\int_C \mathbf{G(r)} \cdot \mathbf{dr} \qquad \text{where} \qquad \mathbf{G}(x, y) = y\mathbf{i}.$$

This is easy to do:

$$\int_C \mathbf{G(r)} \cdot \mathbf{dr} = \int_C \mathbf{G}(\mathbf{r}(t)) \cdot \mathbf{r}'(t)\, dt$$

$$= \int_0^{2\pi} y(t)x'(t)\, dt$$

$$= \int_0^{2\pi} -\sin^2(t)\, dt$$

$$= \int_0^{2\pi} \frac{\cos 2t - 1}{2}\, dt$$

$$= -\pi. \quad \square$$

Exercises

Compute the line integral of $\mathbf{F}$ on the indicated curve.

1.* $\mathbf{F}(x, y) = x\mathbf{i} + y\mathbf{j}$; $\mathbf{r}(t) = a \cos t\,\mathbf{i} + b \sin t\,\mathbf{j}$, $t \in [0, 2\pi]$.

2. $\mathbf{F}(x, y) = (x + y)\mathbf{i} + y\mathbf{j}$;   the curve of exercise 1.

3.* $\mathbf{F}(x, y) = \cos(\pi y)\mathbf{i} - \pi x \sin(\pi y)\mathbf{j}$; $\mathbf{r}(t) = t^2\mathbf{i} - t^3\mathbf{j}$, $t \in [0, 1]$.

4. $\mathbf{F}(x, y) = [x^2 + \cos(\pi y)]\mathbf{i} + [x - \pi x \sin(\pi y)]\mathbf{j}$;   the curve of exercise 1.

5.* $\mathbf{F}(x, y) = [2x^2 y \sinh x^2 + y \cosh x^2]\mathbf{i} + [x \cosh x^2]\mathbf{j}$;   the curve of exercise 1.

6. $\mathbf{F}(x, y) = xy^2\mathbf{i} + x^2 y\mathbf{j}$; $\mathbf{r}(t) = t \sin(\pi t)\mathbf{i} + \cos(\pi t^2)\mathbf{j}$, $t \in [0, 1]$.

7.* $\mathbf{F}(x, y) = (1 + e^y)\mathbf{i} + (xe^y - x)\mathbf{j}$;   the square with vertices $(-1, -1)$, $(1, -1)$, $(1, 1)$, $(-1, 1)$ traversed counterclockwise.

8. $\mathbf{F}(x, y) = (1 + e^y)\mathbf{i} + (xe^y - 4)\mathbf{j}$; $\mathbf{r}(t) = \cos t\,\mathbf{i} + \sin t\,\mathbf{j}$, $t \in [0, \pi]$.

9.* $\mathbf{F}(x, y) = 2xy \sinh(x^2 y)\mathbf{i} + x^2 \sinh(x^2 y)\mathbf{j}$;   the curve of exercise 9.

10.* Show that every central force field

$$\mathbf{F}(\mathbf{r}) = \frac{K}{\|\mathbf{r}\|^n}\,\mathbf{r}, \qquad n \text{ a positive integer}$$

is a gradient field. Find a function f such that

$$\nabla f(\mathbf{r}) = \mathbf{F}(\mathbf{r})$$

(a) if $n = 2$,   (b) if $n \neq 2$.

15

MULTIPLE INTEGRALS

We began with ordinary integrals

$$\int_a^b f(x)\, dx.$$

Then we discussed line integrals

$$\int_C \mathbf{F}(\mathbf{r}) \cdot \mathbf{dr}.$$

Now we take up double integrals

$$\iint\limits_{\Omega} f(x, y)\, dxdy$$

and a little later triple integrals

$$\iiint\limits_{S} f(x, y, z)\, dxdydz.$$

15.1 The double integral over a rectangle

We start with a function f continuous on the rectangle

$$R = \{(x, y) : x \in [a, b],\ y \in [c, d]\}.$$

See Figure 15.1.1. Our object is to define the double integral

$$\iint\limits_{R} f(x, y)\, dxdy.$$

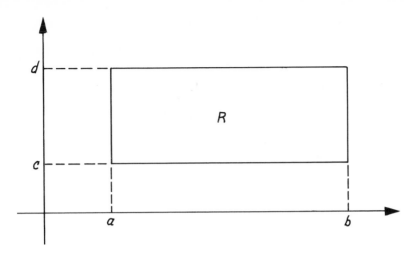

FIGURE 15.1.1

To define

$$\int_a^b f(x)\,dx$$

we first introduced some auxiliary notions: partition P, upper sum $U_f(P)$, and lower sum $L_f(P)$. We were then able to define

$$\int_a^b f(x)\,dx$$

as the unique number I which satisfies the inequality

$$L_f(P) \le I \le U_f(P) \qquad \text{for all partitions } P \text{ of } [a, b]. \qquad \text{(See Section 4.2.)}$$

We will follow exactly the same procedure to define the double integral

$$\iint_R f(x, y)\,dx\,dy.$$

First we explain what we mean by a partition of the rectangle R. To do this, we begin with a partition

$$P_1 = \{x_0, x_1, \ldots, x_m\} \qquad \text{of} \qquad [a, b]$$

and a partition

$$P_2 = \{y_0, y_1, \ldots, y_n\} \qquad \text{of} \qquad [c, d].$$

A set of the form

$$P = P_1 \times P_2 = \{(x_i, y_j) : x_i \in P_1, y_j \in P_2\}$$

is called a *partition of R*. The idea is illustrated in Figure 15.1.2. P consists of all the grid points (x_i, y_j).

FIGURE 15.1.2

The partition P breaks up R into $m \times n$ non-overlapping rectangles

$$R_{ij} = \{(x, y) : x \in [x_{i-1}, x_i], y \in [y_{j-1}, y_j]\}. \quad \text{(See Figure 15.1.3.)}$$

On each rectangle R_{ij}, f takes on a maximum value M_{ij} and a minimum value m_{ij}.†

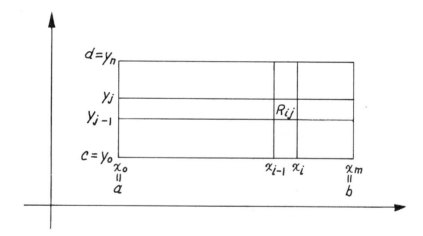

FIGURE 15.1.3

---

† It can be shown that every continuous function takes on both a maximum and a minimum on every closed bounded set. Since R_{ij} is closed and bounded, we can be sure that f takes on both a maximum and a minimum there.

The sum of all the products

$$M_{ij}(\text{area of } R_{ij}) = M_{ij}(x_i - x_{i-1})(y_j - y_{j-1})$$

is called the *upper sum* generated by the partition P:

$$U_f(P) = [M_{11}(\text{area of } R_{11}) + \cdots + M_{1n}(\text{area of } R_{1n})]$$
$$+ [M_{21}(\text{area of } R_{21}) + \cdots + M_{2n}(\text{area of } R_{2n})]$$
$$.$$
$$.$$
$$.$$
$$+ [M_{m1}(\text{area of } R_{m1}) + \cdots + M_{mn}(\text{area of } R_{mn})].$$

The sum of all the products

$$m_{ij}(\text{area of } R_{ij}) = m_{ij}(x_i - x_{i-1})(y_j - y_{j-1})$$

is called the *lower sum* generated by the partition P:

$$L_f(P) = [m_{11}(\text{area of } R_{11}) + \cdots + m_{1n}(\text{area of } R_{1n})]$$
$$+ [m_{21}(\text{area of } R_{21}) + \cdots + m_{2n}(\text{area of } R_{2n})]$$
$$.$$
$$.$$
$$.$$
$$+ [m_{m1}(\text{area of } R_{m1}) + \cdots + m_{mn}(\text{area of } R_{mn})].$$

Example.   Suppose that

$$R = \{(x, y) : x \in [0, 3], \ y \in [0, 2]\}$$

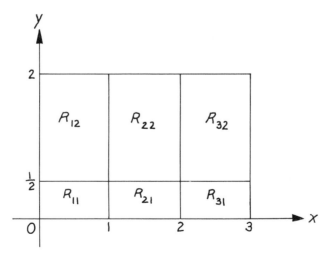

FIGURE 15.1.4

and that

$$f(x, y) = x + y.$$

As a partition of $[0, 3]$ we can take

$$P_1 = \{0, 1, 2, 3\}$$

and as a partition of $[0, 2]$ we can take

$$P_2 = \{0, \tfrac{1}{2}, 2\}.$$

The partition

$$P = P_1 \times P_2$$

then breaks up the initial rectangle into the six rectangles marked in Figure 15.1.4. On each rectangle R_{ij}, f takes on its maximum value M_{ij} at the corner furthest away from the origin, (x_i, y_j); namely,

$$M_{ij} = f(x_i, y_j).$$

Since

$$f(x, y) = x + y,$$

we have

$$M_{ij} = x_i + y_j.$$

The upper sum is given by

$$\begin{aligned}
U_f(P) &= M_{11}(\text{area of } R_{11}) + M_{12}(\text{area of } R_{12}) + M_{21}(\text{area of } R_{21}) \\
&\quad + M_{22}(\text{area of } R_{22}) + M_{31}(\text{area of } R_{31}) + M_{32}(\text{area of } R_{32}) \\
&= (1 + \tfrac{1}{2})\tfrac{1}{2} + (1 + 2)\tfrac{3}{2} + (2 + \tfrac{1}{2})\tfrac{1}{2} + (2 + 2)\tfrac{3}{2} + (3 + \tfrac{1}{2})\tfrac{1}{2} + (3 + 2)\tfrac{3}{2} \\
&= \tfrac{87}{4}.
\end{aligned}$$

On each rectangle R_{ij}, f takes on its minimum value m_{ij} at the corner closest to the origin, (x_{i-1}, y_{j-1}); namely,

$$m_{ij} = f(x_{i-1}, y_{j-1}) = x_{i-1} + y_{j-1}.$$

The lower sum is given by

$$\begin{aligned}
L_f(P) &= m_{11}(\text{area of } R_{11}) + m_{12}(\text{area of } R_{12}) + m_{21}(\text{area of } R_{21}) \\
&\quad + m_{22}(\text{area of } R_{22}) + m_{31}(\text{area of } R_{31}) + m_{32}(\text{area of } R_{32}) \\
&= (0 + 0)\tfrac{1}{2} + (0 + \tfrac{1}{2})\tfrac{3}{2} + (1 + 0)\tfrac{1}{2} + (1 + \tfrac{1}{2})\tfrac{3}{2} + (2 + 0)\tfrac{1}{2} + (2 + \tfrac{1}{2})\tfrac{3}{2} \\
&= \tfrac{33}{4}. \quad \square
\end{aligned}$$

We return now to the general situation. As in the one variable case, it can be shown that, if f is continuous, then there exists one and only one number I which satisfies the inequality

$$L_f(P) \leq I \leq U_f(P) \qquad \text{for all partitions } P \text{ of } R.$$

Definition of the Double Integral Over R

This unique number I is called the *double integral of f over R* and is denoted by

$$\iint_R f(x, y)\, dxdy.$$

The Double Integral As A Volume

If f is non-negative on the rectangle R, the equation

$$z = f(x, y)$$

represents a surface that lies above R. The double integral

$$\iint_R f(x, y)\, dxdy$$

then gives the volume of the solid S which is bounded below by R and above by the surface $z = f(x, y)$. See Figure 15.1.5.

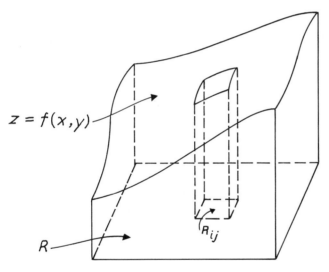

FIGURE 15.1.5

To see how this comes about, consider a partition P of R. P breaks up R into sub-rectangles R_{ij} and thus the entire solid S into parts S_{ij}. Since S_{ij} contains a rectangular solid with base R_{ij} and height m_{ij} (Figure 15.1.6), we must have

$$m_{ij}(\text{area of } R_{ij}) \leq \text{volume of } S_{ij}.$$

Since S_{ij} is contained in a rectangular solid with base R_{ij} and height M_{ij} (Figure 15.1.7), we must have

$$\text{volume of } S_{ij} \leq M_{ij}(\text{area of } R_{ij}).$$

FIGURE 15.1.6   FIGURE 15.1.7

In short, for each pair of indices i and j, we must have

$$m_{ij}(\text{area of } R_{ij}) \leq \text{volume of } S_{ij} \leq M_{ij}(\text{area of } R_{ij}).$$

Adding up these inequalities, we are forced to conclude that

$$L_f(P) \leq \text{volume of } S \leq U_f(P).$$

Since P is arbitrary, the volume of S must be the double integral:

$$\text{volume of } S = \iint\limits_R f(x, y)\, dxdy.$$

The integral

$$\iint\limits_R 1\, dxdy = \iint\limits_R dxdy$$

gives the volume of a solid of constant height 1 erected over R. This is simply the area of R:

$$\text{area of } R = \iint\limits_R dxdy.$$

Some Computations

Double integrals are generally computed by techniques that we will take up later. It is however possible to evaluate simple double integrals directly from the definition. Below we give some examples. In carrying out the calculations we will be using double sums,

$$\sum_{i=1}^{m}\sum_{j=1}^{n} a_{ij}.$$

Since you are already familiar with the sigma notation for ordinary sums

$$\sum_{j=1}^{n} b_j = b_1 + b_2 + \cdots + b_m, \qquad \text{(Chapter 10)}$$

you will probably find the double sigma notation easy to understand:

$$\sum_{i=1}^{m} \sum_{j=1}^{n} a_{ij} = \sum_{i=1}^{m} \left(\sum_{j=1}^{n} a_{ij} \right)$$

$$= \sum_{j=1}^{n} a_{1j} + \sum_{j=1}^{n} a_{2j} + \cdots + \sum_{j=1}^{n} a_{mj}$$

$$= [a_{11} + \cdots + a_{1n}] + [a_{21} + \cdots + a_{2n}] + \cdots + [a_{m1} + \cdots + a_{mn}].$$

Since constants α can be factored through single sums, they can also be factored through double sums:

$$\sum_{i=1}^{m} \sum_{j=1}^{n} \alpha a_{ij} = \alpha \sum_{i=1}^{m} \sum_{j=1}^{n} a_{ij}.$$

Obviously also

$$\sum_{i=1}^{m} \sum_{j=1}^{n} (a_{ij} + b_{ij}) = \sum_{i=1}^{m} \sum_{j=1}^{n} a_{ij} + \sum_{i=1}^{m} \sum_{j=1}^{n} b_{ij}.$$

Problem. Evaluate

$$\iint_R \alpha \, dx dy$$

where

$$R = \{(x, y) : x \in [a, b], \quad y \in [c, d]\}.$$

SOLUTION. Here

$$f(x, y) = \alpha \qquad \text{for all} \quad (x, y) \in R.$$

We begin with

$$P_1 = \{x_0, x_1, \ldots, x_m\}$$

as an arbitrary partition of $[a, b]$ and

$$P_2 = \{y_0, y_1, \ldots, y_n\}$$

as an arbitrary partition of $[c, d]$. This gives

$$P = P_1 \times P_2 = \{(x_i, y_j) : x_i \in P_1, y_j \in P_2\}$$

as an arbitrary partition of R. On each rectangle R_{ij}, f has constant value α. This gives $M_{ij} = \alpha$ and $m_{ij} = \alpha$ throughout. Thus

$$U_f(P) = \sum_{i=1}^{m} \sum_{j=1}^{n} \alpha(\text{area of } R_{ij}) = \alpha \sum_{i=1}^{m} \sum_{j=1}^{n} \text{area of } R_{ij}$$

$$= \alpha(\text{area of } R) = \alpha(b - a)(d - c)$$

and similarly

$$L_f(P) = \alpha(b - a)(d - c).$$

Since

$$L_f(P) \leq \alpha(b - a)(d - c) \leq U_f(P),$$

and P was chosen arbitrarily, the inequality must hold for all partitions P of R. This means that

$$\iint_R f(x, y) \, dxdy = \alpha(b - a)(d - c). \quad \square$$

REMARK.   If $\alpha > 0$,

$$\iint_R \alpha \, dxdy = \alpha(b - a)(d - c)$$

gives the volume of the rectangular solid of constant height α erected over the rectangle R.

Problem.   Evaluate

$$\iint_R (x + y) \, dxdy$$

where again R is the rectangle

$$\{(x, y) : x \in [a, b], \ y \in [c, d]\}.$$

SOLUTION.   We take

$$P_1 = \{x_0, x_1, \ldots, x_m\}$$

as an arbitrary partition of $[a, b]$ and

$$P_2 = \{y_0, y_1, \ldots, y_n\}$$

as an arbitrary partition of $[c, d]$. This gives

$$P = P_1 \times P_2 = \{(x_i, y_j) : x_i \in P_1, y_j \in P_2\}$$

as an arbitrary partition of R. On each rectangle

$$R_{ij} = \{(x, y) : x \in [x_{i-1}, x_i], \ y \in [y_{j-1}, y_j]\}$$

the function

$$f(x, y) = x + y$$

has a maximum

$$M_{ij} = x_i + y_j$$

and a minimum

$$m_{ij} = x_{i-1} + y_{j-1}.$$

Thus

$$U_f(P) = \sum_{i=1}^{m} \sum_{j=1}^{n} M_{ij}(\text{area of } R_{ij})$$

$$= \sum_{i=1}^{m} \sum_{j=1}^{n} (x_i + y_j)(x_i - x_{i-1})(y_j - y_{j-1})$$

and

$$L_f(P) = \sum_{i=1}^{m} \sum_{j=1}^{n} m_{ij}(\text{area of } R_{ij})$$

$$= \sum_{i=1}^{m} \sum_{j=1}^{n} (x_{i-1} + y_{j-1})(x_i - x_{i-1})(y_j - y_{j-1}).$$

For each pair of indices i and j,

$$x_{i-1} + y_{j-1} \le \tfrac{1}{2}(x_i + x_{i-1}) + \tfrac{1}{2}(y_j + y_{j-1}) \le x_i + y_j. \qquad \text{(Explain)}$$

Consequently,

$$L_f(P) \le \sum_{i=1}^{m} \sum_{j=1}^{n} [\tfrac{1}{2}(x_i + x_{i-1}) + \tfrac{1}{2}(y_j + y_{j-1})](x_i - x_{i-1})(y_j - y_{j-1}) \le U_f(P).$$

The middle term can be written as

$$\sum_{i=1}^{m} \sum_{j=1}^{n} \tfrac{1}{2}(x_i + x_{i-1})(x_i - x_{i-1})(y_j - y_{j-1}) + \sum_{i=1}^{m} \sum_{j=1}^{n} \tfrac{1}{2}(y_j + y_{j-1})(x_i - x_{i-1})(y_j - y_{j-1}).$$

The first double sum reduces to

$$\sum_{i=1}^{m} \tfrac{1}{2}(x_i^2 - x_{i-1}^2)\left(\sum_{j=1}^{n} (y_j - y_{j-1})\right) = \tfrac{1}{2}\sum_{i=1}^{m} (x_i^2 - x_{i-1}^2)(y_n - y_0)$$

$$= \tfrac{1}{2}\sum_{i=1}^{m} (x_i^2 - x_{i-1}^2)(d - c)$$

$$= \tfrac{1}{2}(d - c)\sum_{i=1}^{m} (x_i^2 - x_{i-1}^2)$$

$$= \tfrac{1}{2}(d - c)(x_m^2 - x_0^2)$$

$$= \tfrac{1}{2}(d - c)(b^2 - a^2).$$

In a similar manner, the second double sum reduces to

$$\tfrac{1}{2}(b - a)(d^2 - c^2).$$

The sum of these two numbers

$$I = \tfrac{1}{2}(d - c)(b^2 - a^2) + \tfrac{1}{2}(b - a)(d^2 - c^2) = \tfrac{1}{2}(a + b + c + d)(b - a)(d - c)$$

satisfies the inequality

$$L_f(P) \le I \le U_f(P).$$

Since P is arbitrary, we have

$$I = \tfrac{1}{2}(a + b + c + d)(b - a)(d - c)$$

as the desired integral:

$$\iint\limits_{R} (x + y)\, dxdy = \tfrac{1}{2}(a + b + c + d)(b - a)(d - c). \quad \square$$

REMARK.   If $x + y$ is positive on the rectangle

$$R = \{(x, y) : x \in [a, b], y \in [c, d]\},$$

then the double integral

$$\iint\limits_{R} (x + y)\, dxdy = \tfrac{1}{2}(a + b + c + d)(b - a)(d - c)$$

gives the volume of the prism bounded above by the plane $z = x + y$ and below by R.

Problem.   Evaluate

$$\iint\limits_{R} (y - 2x)\, dxdy$$

where

$$R = \{(x, y) : x \in [1, 2], y \in [3, 5]\}.$$

SOLUTION.   With

$$P_1 = \{x_0, x_1, \ldots, x_m\} \text{ as an arbitrary partition of } [1, 2]$$

and

$$P_2 = \{y_0, y_1, \ldots, y_n\} \text{ as an arbitrary partition of } [3, 5]$$

we have

$$P = P_1 \times P_2 = \{(x, y) : x \in P_1, y \in P_2\}$$

as an arbitrary partition of R.   On each rectangle

$$R_{ij} = \{(x, y) : x \in [x_{i-1}, x_i], y \in [y_{j-1}, y_j]\},$$

the function

$$f(x, y) = y - 2x$$

has a maximum

$$M_{ij} = y_j - 2x_{i-1} \quad [y \text{ is maximized and } x \text{ is minimized}]$$

and a minimum

$$m_{ij} = y_{j-1} - 2x_i. \quad [y \text{ is minimized and } x \text{ is maximized}]$$

Thus

$$U_f(P) = \sum_{i=1}^{m} \sum_{j=1}^{n} M_{ij}(\text{area of } R_{ij})$$

$$= \sum_{i=1}^{m} \sum_{j=1}^{n} (y_j - 2x_{i-1})(x_i - x_{i-1})(y_j - y_{j-1})$$

and

$$L_f(P) = \sum_{i=1}^{m} \sum_{j=1}^{n} m_{ij}(\text{area of } R_{ij})$$

$$= \sum_{i=1}^{m} \sum_{j=1}^{n} (y_{j-1} - 2x_i)(x_i - x_{i-1})(y_j - y_{j-1}).$$

For each pair of indices i and j,

$$y_{j-1} - 2x_i \leq \tfrac{1}{2}(y_j + y_{j-1}) - (x_i + x_{i-1}) \leq y_j - 2x_{i-1}.$$

This means that for arbitrary P we have

$$L_f(P) \leq \sum_{i=1}^{m} \sum_{j=1}^{n} [\tfrac{1}{2}(y_j + y_{j-1}) - (x_i + x_{i-1})](x_i - x_{i-1})(y_j - y_{j-1}) \leq U_f(P).$$

The middle term can be written as

$$\sum_{i=1}^{m} \sum_{j=1}^{n} \tfrac{1}{2}(y_j + y_{j-1})(x_i - x_{i-1})(y_j - y_{j-1}) + \sum_{i=1}^{m} \sum_{j=1}^{n} - (x_i + x_{i-1})(x_i - x_{i-1})(y_j - y_{j-1}).$$

The first double sum reduces to

$$\tfrac{1}{2}(x_m - x_0)(y_n^2 - y_0^2).$$

The second double sum reduces to

$$-(x_m^2 - x_0^2)(y_n - y_0).$$

With

$$x_0 = 1, \qquad x_m = 2, \qquad y_0 = 3, \qquad y_n = 5$$

we have

$$\tfrac{1}{2}(x_m - x_0)(y_n^2 - y_0^2) - (x_m^2 - x_0^2)(y_n - y_0) = 8 - 3(2) = 2.$$

Since

$$L_f(P) \leq 2 \leq U_f(P) \qquad \text{for arbitrary } P,$$

the integral is 2:

$$\iint_R (y - 2x)\,dx\,dy = 2. \quad \square$$

REMARK. This last integral should not be interpreted as a volume. The expression $y - 2x$ does not keep a constant sign on

$$R = \{(x, y) : x \in [1, 2], \ y \in [3, 5]\}.$$

Exercises

For exercises 1–9 take

$$f(x, y) = x + 2y \quad \text{on } R = \{(x, y) : x \in [0, 2], \quad y \in [0, 1]\}$$

and P as the partition $P = P_1 \times P_2$.

1.* Find $L_f(P)$ if $P_1 = \{0, 1, 2\}$ and $P_2 = \{0, 1\}$.
2.* Find $U_f(P)$ with P_1 and P_2 as in exercise 1.
3. Find $L_f(P)$ if $P_1 = \{0, 1, 2\}$ and $P_2 = \{0, \frac{1}{2}, 1\}$.
4. Find $U_f(P)$ with P_1 and P_2 as in exercise 3.
5.* Find $L_f(P)$ if $P_1 = \{0, 1, \frac{3}{2}, 2\}$ and $P_2 = \{0, \frac{1}{2}, 1\}$.
6.* Find $U_f(P)$ with P_1 and P_2 as in exercise 5.
7. Find $L_f(P)$ if $P_1 = \{x_0, x_1, \ldots, x_n\}$ is an arbitrary partition of $[0, 2]$ and $P_2 = \{y_0, y_1, \ldots, y_m\}$ is an arbitrary partition of $[0, 1]$.
8. Find $U_f(P)$ with P_1 and P_2 as in exercise 7.
9.* (*Optional*) Using exercises 7 and 8, evaluate the double integral

$$\iint_R (x + 2y)\, dx dy$$

and give a geometric interpretation to your answer.

For exercises 10–14 take

$$f(x, y) = x - y \quad \text{on } R = \{(x, y) : x \in [0, 1], \ y \in [0, 1]\}$$

and P as the partition $P = P_1 \times P_2$.

10.* Find $L_f(P)$ if $P_1 = \{0, \frac{1}{2}, \frac{3}{4}, 1\}$ and $P_2 = \{0, \frac{1}{2}, 1\}$.
11.* Find $U_f(P)$ with P_1 and P_2 as in exercise 10.
12. Find $L_f(P)$ if $P_1 = \{x_0, x_1, \ldots, x_m\}$ and $P_2 = \{y_0, y_1, \ldots, y_n\}$ are both arbitrary partitions of $[0, 1]$.
13. Find $U_f(P)$ with P_1 and P_2 as in exercise 12.
14.* (*Optional*) Using exercises 12 and 13, evaluate the double integral

$$\iint_R (x - y)\, dx dy.$$

15.* (*Optional*) Evaluate the double integral

$$\iint_R (x^2 + y)\, dx dy \quad \text{with } R = \{(x, y) : x \in [0, 1], \ y \in [0, 2]\}$$

by any method at your disposal. [HINT: Think in terms of volume. You can use the method of this section and/or the method of parallel cross sections.]

15.2   The double integral over more general regions

We start with a region Ω that we depict in Figure 15.2.1. We suppose that f is continuous on Ω. Our object is to define the double integral

$$\iint_{\Omega} f(x, y)\, dxdy.$$

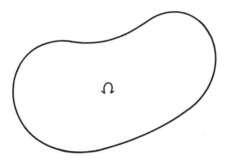

FIGURE 15.2.1

To do this, we surround Ω by a rectangle R in the manner of Figure 15.2.2. We now extend f to all of R by setting f equal to 0 outside of Ω. This extended function f is now continuous on all of R, except possibly at the boundary of Ω. If this boundary is not too wild, (the details here are outside the scope of this course) the double integral

$$\iint_{R} f(x, y)\, dxdy$$

will still exist. We can then define the double integral over Ω by setting

$$\boxed{\iint_{\Omega} f(x, y)\, dxdy = \iint_{R} f(x, y)\, dxdy.}$$

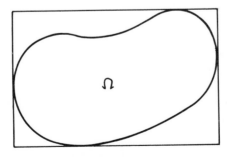

FIGURE 15.2.2

If f is nonnegative over Ω, the extended f is nonnegative on all of R. The double integral gives the volume of the solid trapped between the surface $z = f(x, y)$ and the rectangle R. But since the surface has height 0 outside of Ω, the volume outside of Ω is 0. It follows therefore that

$$\iint_\Omega f(x, y) \, dx dy$$

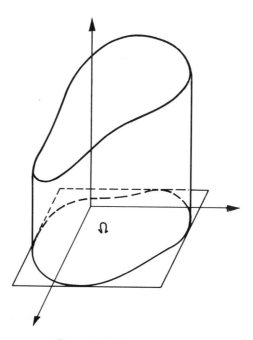

FIGURE 15.2.3

gives the volume of the solid bounded above by $z = f(x, y)$ and below by Ω. The double integral

$$\iint_\Omega 1 \, dx dy = \iint_\Omega dx dy$$

gives the volume of a solid of constant height 1 over Ω. This is of course just the area of Ω:

$$\text{area of } \Omega = \iint_\Omega dx dy.$$

15.3   The evaluation of double integrals by repeated integrals

The Reduction Formulas

We now discuss the problem of evaluating the double integral

$$\iint_{\Omega} f(x, y)\, dxdy.$$

For simplicity we restrict our attention to sets of the form depicted in Figure 15.3.1. In both cases we assume that the bounding functions ϕ_1 and ϕ_2 are continuous. The

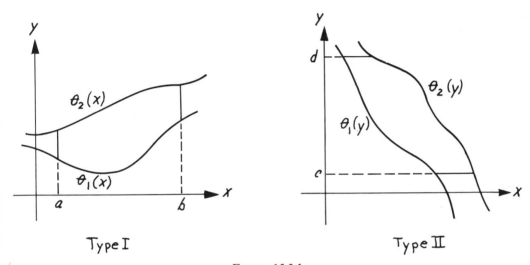

FIGURE 15.3.1

fundamental idea is that double integrals over sets of this form can be reduced to "repeated" ordinary integrals: If Ω is of type I,

$$\Omega = \{(x, y) : a \leq x \leq b, \quad \phi_1(x) \leq y \leq \phi_2(x)\},$$

then

$$\iint_{\Omega} f(x, y)\, dxdy = \int_a^b \left[\int_{\phi_1(x)}^{\phi_2(x)} f(x, y)\, dy \right] dx.$$

If Ω is of type II,

$$\Omega = \{(x, y) : c \leq y \leq d, \quad \phi_1(y) \leq x \leq \phi_2(y)\},$$

then

$$\iint_{\Omega} f(x, y)\, dxdy = \int_c^d \left[\int_{\phi_1(y)}^{\phi_2(y)} f(x, y)\, dx \right] dy.$$

These formulas, although difficult to prove, are easy to understand geometrically.

The Reduction Formulas Viewed Geometrically

Let's take f as non-negative and Ω of type I. The double integral over Ω gives the volume of the solid S which is trapped between Ω and the surface $z = f(x, y)$:

(1) $$\iint_\Omega f(x, y)\, dx dy = \text{volume of } S. \qquad \text{(Figure 15.3.2)}$$

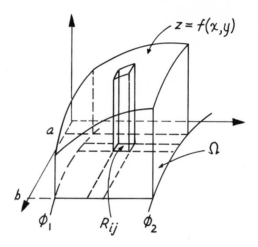

Volume by double integration
$$V = \iint_\Omega f(x, y)\, dx\, dy$$

FIGURE 15.3.2

We can also compute the volume of S by the method of parallel cross sections. Letting $A(x)$ be the area of that cross section of S which has first coordinate x, we can argue that

$$\int_a^b A(x)\, dx$$

also gives the volume of S. Recognizing that

$$A(x) = \int_{\phi_1(x)}^{\phi_2(x)} f(x, y)\, dy,$$

we are led to setting

(2) $$\int_a^b \left[\int_{\phi_1(x)}^{\phi_2(x)} f(x, y)\, dy \right] dx = \text{volume of } S. \qquad \text{(Figure 15.3.3)}$$

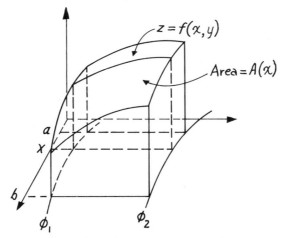

Volume by parallel cross-sections

$$V = \int_a^b A(x)\,dx = \int_a^b \left[\int_{\phi_1(x)}^{\phi_2(x)} f(x,y)\,dy \right] dx$$

FIGURE 15.3.3

Combining (1) with (2), we have the first reduction formula

$$\iint_\Omega f(x, y)\,dxdy = \int_a^b \left[\int_{\phi_1(x)}^{\phi_2(x)} f(x, y)\,dy \right] dx.$$

The other reduction formula can be obtained in a similar manner.

Our argument is of course a very loose one. How do we know for example that the "volume" obtained by double integration is the same as the "volume" obtained by the method of parallel cross sections? Intuitively it seems evident, but mathematically it is not clear. Certainly we have not proved it. We shall not pursue the matter further.

Computations

Problem. Evaluate

$$\iint_\Omega (x^2 - y)\,dxdy$$

with Ω as in Figure 15.3.4.

SOLUTION. Here

$$\Omega = \{(x, y) : -1 \leq x \leq 1,\ -x^2 \leq y \leq x^2\}$$

so that we are in case I.

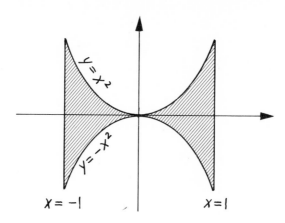

FIGURE 15.3.4

$$\iint\limits_{\Omega} (x^2 - y)\, dxdy = \int_{-1}^{1}\left[\int_{-x^2}^{x^2}(x^2 - y)\, dy\right] dx$$

$$= \int_{-1}^{1}\left[x^2y - \frac{y^2}{2}\right]_{-x^2}^{x^2} dx$$

$$= \int_{-1}^{1}\left[\left(x^4 - \frac{x^4}{2}\right) - \left(-x^4 - \frac{x^4}{2}\right)\right] dx$$

$$= \int_{-1}^{1} 2x^4\, dx = \left[\frac{2}{5}\, x^5\right]_{-1}^{1} = \frac{4}{5}. \quad \square$$

Problem.   Evaluate

$$\iint\limits_{\Omega}(xy - y^3)\, dxdy$$

with Ω as in Figure 15.3.5.

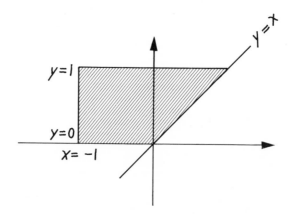

FIGURE 15.3.5

SOLUTION.   We can express Ω as

$$\{(x, y) : 0 \le y \le 1, \quad -1 \le x \le y\}.$$

This puts us in case II. Consequently,

$$\iint_{\Omega} (xy - y^3)\, dx\, dy = \int_0^1 \left[\int_{-1}^{y} (xy - y^3)\, dx \right] dy$$

$$= \int_0^1 \left[\frac{x^2 y}{2} - xy^3 \right]_{-1}^{y} dy$$

$$= \int_0^1 \left(-\frac{y}{2} - \frac{y^3}{2} - y^4 \right) dy$$

$$= \left[-\frac{y^2}{4} - \frac{y^4}{8} - \frac{y^5}{5} \right]_0^1 = -\frac{23}{40}. \quad \square$$

Problem.   Evaluate

$$\iint_{R} (y - 2x)\, dx\, dy$$

where R is the rectangle

$$\{(x, y) : 1 \le x \le 2,\ 3 \le y \le 5\}.$$

SOLUTION.   In Section 15.1 we evaluated this integral by considering upper and lower sums. It is of course much easier to use two repeated integrals. It makes no difference in which order we integrate. Setting

$$\phi_1(x) = 3 \quad \text{and} \quad \phi_2(x) = 5,$$

we can view the rectangle as being of type I:

$$\iint_{R} (y - 2x)\, dx\, dy = \int_1^2 \left[\int_3^5 (y - 2x)\, dy \right] dx$$

$$= \int_1^2 \left[\frac{y^2}{2} - 2xy \right]_3^5 dx$$

$$= \int_1^2 \left[\left(\frac{25}{2} - 10x \right) - \left(\frac{9}{2} - 6x \right) \right] dx$$

$$= \int_1^2 (8 - 4x)\, dx = \left[8x - 2x^2 \right]_1^2 = 2.$$

We can obtain the same result by setting

$$\phi_1(y) = 1, \quad \phi_2(y) = 2$$

and viewing the rectangle as being of type II:

$$
\iint_R (y - 2x)\, dx\, dy = \int_3^5 \left[\int_1^2 (y - 2x)\, dx \right] dy
$$

$$
= \int_3^5 \left[yx - x^2 \right]_1^2 dy
$$

$$
= \int_3^5 \left[(2y - 4) - (y - 1) \right] dy
$$

$$
= \int_3^5 (y - 3)\, dy
$$

$$
= \left[\frac{1}{2} y^2 - 3y \right]_3^5 = 2. \quad \square
$$

Problem.   Evaluate

$$
\iint_\Omega \frac{x}{1 + xy}\, dx\, dy
$$

where Ω is the unit square

$$
\{(x, y) : 0 \le x \le 1, \quad 0 \le y \le 1\}.
$$

SOLUTION.   Setting

$$
\phi_1(x) = 0 \quad \text{and} \quad \phi_2(x) = 1,
$$

we can view the unit square as being of type I. This gives

$$
\iint_\Omega \frac{x}{1 + xy}\, dx\, dy = \int_0^1 \left[\int_0^1 \frac{x}{1 + xy}\, dy \right] dx
$$

$$
= \int_0^1 \left[\log (1 + xy) \right]_0^1 dx
$$

$$
= \int_0^1 \log (1 + x)\, dx.
$$

This last integral can be computed by parts:

$$
\int_0^1 \log (1 + x)\, dx = \left[(1 + x) \log (1 + x) \right]_0^1 - \int_0^1 \frac{1 + x}{1 + x}\, dx
$$

$$
= 2 \log 2 - 1. \quad \square
$$

Problem.   Evaluate

$$
\iint_\Omega (x^{1/2} - y^2)\, dx\, dy
$$

where Ω is the bounded region in the first quadrant which lies between $y = x^2$ and $x = y^4$.

SOLUTION.   See Figure 15.3.6. The two curves intersect at the points $(0, 0)$ and $(1, 1)$. It is immaterial in which order we integrate. We can describe Ω as

$$
\{(x, y) : 0 \le x \le 1, \ x^2 \le y \le x^{1/4}\}
$$

or as

$$
\{(x, y) : 0 \le y \le 1, \ y^4 \le x \le y^{1/2}\}.
$$

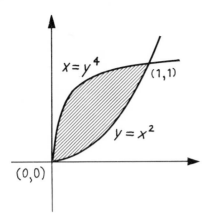

FIGURE 15.3.6

The first characterization of Ω leads to

$$\iint_{\Omega} (x^{1/2} - y^2)\, dx\, dy = \int_0^1 \left[\int_{x^2}^{x^{1/4}} (x^{1/2} - y^2)\, dy \right] dx$$

$$= \int_0^1 \left[x^{1/2} y - \frac{1}{3} y^3 \right]_{x^2}^{x^{1/4}} dx$$

$$= \int_0^1 \left(\frac{2}{3} x^{3/4} - x^{5/2} + \frac{1}{3} x^6 \right) dx$$

$$= \left[\frac{8}{21} x^{7/4} - \frac{2}{7} x^{7/2} + \frac{1}{21} x^7 \right]_0^1$$

$$= \frac{8}{21} - \frac{2}{7} + \frac{1}{21} = \frac{1}{7}.$$

The second characterization of Ω leads to the same result:

$$\iint_{\Omega} (x^{1/2} - y^2)\, dx\, dy = \int_0^1 \left[\int_{y^4}^{y^{1/2}} (x^{1/2} - y^2)\, dx \right] dy$$

$$= \int_0^1 \left[\frac{2}{3} x^{3/2} - y^2 x \right]_{y^4}^{y^{1/2}} dy$$

$$= \int_0^1 \left(\frac{2}{3} y^{3/4} - y^{5/2} + \frac{1}{3} y^6 \right) dy$$

$$= \left[\frac{8}{21} y^{7/4} - \frac{2}{7} y^{7/2} + \frac{1}{21} y^7 \right]_0^1$$

$$= \frac{8}{21} - \frac{2}{7} + \frac{1}{21} = \frac{1}{7}. \quad \square$$

Problem. Calculate by double integration the area of the region Ω which lies between $\sqrt{x} + \sqrt{y} = \sqrt{a}$ and $x + y = a$.

SOLUTION.   The region Ω is pictured in Figure 15.3.7. Its area is given by the double integral

$$\iint_{\Omega} dx dy.$$

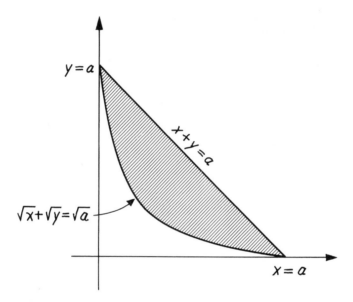

FIGURE 15.3.7

We can characterize Ω as

$$\{(x, y) : 0 \leq x \leq a, \ (\sqrt{a} - \sqrt{x})^2 \leq y \leq a - x\}.$$

This gives

$$\begin{aligned}
\iint_{\Omega} dx dy &= \int_0^a \left[\int_{(\sqrt{a} - \sqrt{x})^2}^{a-x} dy \right] dx \\
&= \int_0^a \left[(a - x) - (\sqrt{a} - \sqrt{x})^2 \right] dx \\
&= \int_0^a (-2x + 2\sqrt{a}\sqrt{x})\, dx \\
&= \left[-x^2 + \frac{4}{3} \sqrt{a}x\sqrt{x} \right]_0^a \\
&= -a^2 + \frac{4}{3} a^2 = \frac{1}{3} a^2.
\end{aligned}$$

We can also characterize Ω as

$$\{(x, y) : 0 \leq y \leq a, \ (\sqrt{a} - \sqrt{y})^2 \leq x \leq a - y\}.$$

This gives

$$\iint\limits_{\Omega} dx\, dy = \int_0^a \left[\int_{(\sqrt{a} - \sqrt{y})^2}^{a-y} dx \right] dy,$$

which is also $\dfrac{1}{3}a^2$. □

Problem. Calculate the volume of that part of the cylinder $x^2 + y^2 = b^2$ (z arbitrary) which lies between the planes $y + z = a^2$ and $z = 0$.

SOLUTION. See Figure 15.3.8. The solid in question is bounded below by the disc

$$\Omega = \{(x, y) : x^2 + y^2 \leq b^2\}$$

and above by the plane

$$z = a^2 - y.$$

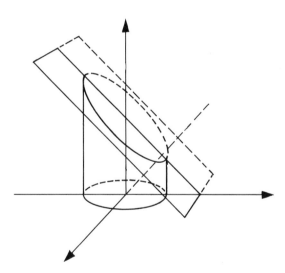

FIGURE 15.3.8

The volume is given by the double integral

$$\iint\limits_{\Omega} (a^2 - y)\, dx\, dy.$$

To compute this double integral we express Ω as

$$\{(x, y) : -b \leq x \leq b, \ -\sqrt{b^2 - x^2} \leq y \leq \sqrt{b^2 - x^2}\}.$$

This puts us in case I. Consequently,

$$V = \iint_{\Omega} (a^2 - y)\, dxdy = \int_{-b}^{b} \left[\int_{-\sqrt{b^2 - x^2}}^{\sqrt{b^2 - x^2}} (a^2 - y)\, dy \right] dx$$

$$= \int_{-b}^{b} \left[a^2 y - \frac{y^2}{2} \right]_{-\sqrt{b^2 - x^2}}^{\sqrt{b^2 - x^2}} dx$$

$$= \int_{-b}^{b} 2a^2 \sqrt{b^2 - x^2}\, dx$$

$$= \pi a^2 b^2. \quad \square$$

Problem.   Compute the volume of the ellipsoid

$$\frac{x^2}{a^2} + \frac{y^2}{b^2} + \frac{z^2}{c^2} = 1.$$

SOLUTION.   The upper half is the set bounded above by the surface

$$z = c \sqrt{1 - \frac{x^2}{a^2} - \frac{y^2}{b^2}} = \frac{c}{b} \sqrt{\frac{b^2}{a^2}(a^2 - x^2) - y^2}$$

and below by the elliptical region

$$\Omega = \left\{ (x, y) : \frac{x^2}{a^2} + \frac{y^2}{b^2} \le 1 \right\}.$$

The total volume is therefore

$$V = 2 \iint_{\Omega} \frac{c}{b} \sqrt{\frac{b^2}{a^2}(a^2 - x^2) - y^2}\, dxdy.$$

To transform this double integral into a pair of repeated integrals, we express Ω as

$$\left\{ (x, y) : -a \le x \le a, \quad -\frac{b}{a}\sqrt{a^2 - x^2} \le y \le \frac{b}{a}\sqrt{a^2 - x^2} \right\}.$$

This gives

$$V = 2 \int_{-a}^{a} \left[\int_{(-b/a)\sqrt{a^2 - x^2}}^{(b/a)\sqrt{a^2 - x^2}} \frac{c}{b} \sqrt{\frac{b^2}{a^2}(a^2 - x^2) - y^2}\, dy \right] dx$$

$$= \frac{8c}{b} \int_{0}^{a} \left[\int_{0}^{(b/a)\sqrt{a^2 - x^2}} \sqrt{\frac{b^2}{a^2}(a^2 - x^2) - y^2}\, dy \right] dx$$

$$= \frac{8c}{b} \int_{0}^{a} \left[\frac{y}{2} \sqrt{\frac{b^2}{a^2}(a^2 - x^2) - y^2} + \frac{b^2}{2a^2}(a^2 - x^2)\arcsin\frac{ay}{b\sqrt{a^2 - x^2}} \right]_{0}^{(b/a)\sqrt{a^2 - x^2}} dx$$

$$= \frac{8c}{b} \int_{0}^{a} \frac{\pi}{4} \frac{b^2}{a^2}(a^2 - x^2)\, dx$$

$$= \frac{2\pi bc}{a^2} \int_{0}^{a} (a^2 - x^2)\, dx$$

$$= \frac{2\pi bc}{a^2} \left[a^2 x - \frac{x^3}{3} \right]_{0}^{a}$$

$$= \frac{2\pi bc}{a^2} \left(\frac{2a^3}{3} \right) = \frac{4}{3}\pi abc. \quad \square$$

Exercises

Evaluate.

1.* $\iint\limits_{\Omega} x^2\,dx\,dy$ with $\Omega = \{(x, y) : -1 \le x \le 1, -1 \le y \le 1\}$.

2. $\iint\limits_{\Omega} e^{x+y}\,dx\,dy$ with Ω as in exercise 1.

3.* $\iint\limits_{\Omega} \cos\left(\tfrac{1}{2}\pi y\right)\,dx\,dy$ with Ω as in exercise 1.

4. $\iint\limits_{\Omega} x^3 y\,dx\,dy$ with $\Omega = \{(x, y) : 0 \le x \le 1, 0 \le y \le x\}$.

5.* $\iint\limits_{\Omega} (y + \sin \pi x^2)\,dx\,dy$ with Ω as in exercise 4.

6. $\iint\limits_{\Omega} \cos(x + y)\,dx\,dy$ with $\Omega = \left\{(x, y) : 0 \le x \le \frac{\pi}{2}, 0 \le y \le \frac{\pi}{2}\right\}$.

7.* $\iint\limits_{\Omega} \sin(x + y)\,dx\,dy$ with Ω as in exercise 6.

8. $\iint\limits_{\Omega} (x + y)\,dx\,dy$ with $\Omega = \{(x, y) : x^2 + y^2 \le 1\}$.

9.* $\iint\limits_{\Omega} (x^2 + 3y^2)\,dx\,dy$ with Ω as in exercise 8.

10. $\iint\limits_{\Omega} \sqrt{xy}\,dx\,dy$ with $\Omega = \{(x, y) : 0 \le y \le 1, y^2 \le x \le y\}$.

11.* $\iint\limits_{\Omega} y e^x\,dx\,dy$ with $\Omega = \{(x, y) : 0 \le y \le 1, 0 \le x \le y^2\}$.

12. $\iint\limits_{\Omega} (4 - y^2)\,dx\,dy$ with Ω the region between $y^2 = 2x$ and $y^2 = 8 - 2x$.

13.* $\iint\limits_{\Omega} e^{x^2}\,dx\,dy$ where Ω is the triangle formed by $2y = x$, $x = 2$, and the x-axis.

Calculate by double integration the area of the bounded region determined by the following pairs of curves.

14. $x^2 = 4y$, $2y - x - 4 = 0$.

15.* $y = x$, $x = 4y - y^2$.

16. $y = x$, $4y^3 = x^2$.

17.* $x + y = 4$, $x^{2/3} + y^{2/3} = 4^{2/3}$.

18.   Find the volume of the solid bounded above by $z = x + y$ and below by the triangle with vertices $(0, 0)$, $(0, 1)$, $(1, 0)$.

19.* Find the volume of the solid bounded by $\dfrac{x}{2} + \dfrac{y}{3} + \dfrac{z}{4} = 1$ and the coordinate planes.

20.   Find the volume of the solid bounded above by the plane $z = 2x + 3y$ and below by the unit square $\{(x, y) : 0 \leq x \leq 1, 0 \leq y \leq 1\}$.

21.* Find the volume of the solid bounded above by $z = x^3 y$ and below by the triangle with vertices $(0, 0)$, $(2, 0)$, $(0, 1)$.

22.   Find the volume of the solid bounded above by $z = 2x + 1$ and below by $\{(x, y) : (x - 1)^2 + y^2 \leq 1\}$.

23.* Find the volume of the solid which lies between the paraboloid $z = x^2 + y^2$ and the unit disc $\{(x, y) : x^2 + y^2 \leq 1\}$.

24.   Find the volume of the solid bounded above by $z = 4 - y^2 - \dfrac{x^2}{4}$ and below by the disc $\{(x, y) : (y - 1)^2 + x^2 \leq 1\}$.

25.   Show that if

$$R = \{(x, y) : a \leq x \leq b, c \leq y \leq d\},$$

then

$$\iint\limits_{R} f(x)g(y)\, dxdy = \left[\int_a^b f(x)\, dx \right] \cdot \left[\int_c^d g(y)\, dy \right].$$

15.4   Double integrals in polar coordinates

We start with a region R given in polar coordinates by a pair of inequalities

$$r^* \leq r \leq r^{**}, \quad \theta^* \leq \theta \leq \theta^{**}.(\dagger) \qquad \text{(See Figure 15.4.1)}$$

Such a set will be called a "polar rectangle." (It does not look like a rectangle but analytically it has the structure of a rectangle.) Over R we place a surface

$$z = f(r, \theta). \qquad \text{(Figure 15.4.2)}$$

The solid which lies between R and the surface $z = f(r, \theta)$ has volume

$$\boxed{V = \iint\limits_{R} f(r, \theta) r\, drd\theta.} \qquad \text{(Note the extra } r \text{ present.)}$$

To show how this comes about, we begin by partitioning the intervals $[r^*, r^{**}]$ and $[\theta^*, \theta^{**}]$:

$$r^* = r_0 < \cdots < r_{i-1} < r_i < \cdots < r_m = r^{**}$$
$$\theta^* = \theta_0 < \cdots < \theta_{j-1} < \theta_j < \cdots < \theta_n = \theta^{**}.$$

---

†Throughout this chapter we take $r \geq 0$. Here $r^* \geq 0$ and $\theta^* \leq \theta^{**} \leq \theta^* + 2\pi$.

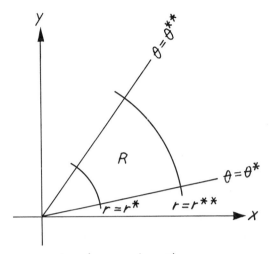

A polar rectangle

FIGURE 15.4.1

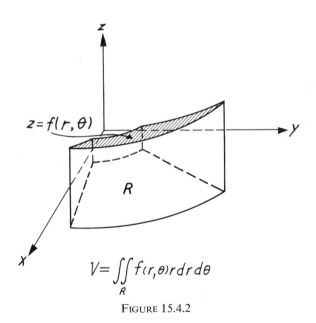

$$V = \iint_R f(r,\theta)\,r\,dr\,d\theta$$

FIGURE 15.4.2

These partitions break up R into $m \times n$ "polar rectangles"

$$R_{ij} : r_{i-1} \leq r \leq r_i, \ \theta_{j-1} \leq \theta \leq \theta_j. \qquad \text{(Figure 15.4.3)}$$

On each such "polar rectangle" f has a maximum value M_{ij} and a minimum value m_{ij}.

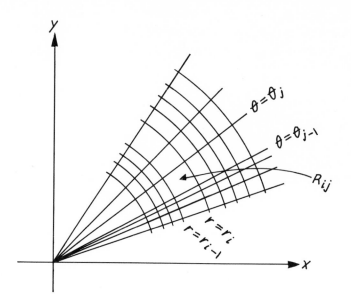

FIGURE 15.4.3

(We are assuming as usual that f is continuous). The volume V that we seek is the only number that can be counted upon to satisfy the inequality

$$\sum_{i=1}^{m}\sum_{j=1}^{n} m_{ij}(\text{area of } R_{ij}) \leq V \leq \sum_{i=1}^{m}\sum_{j=1}^{n} M_{ij}(\text{area of } R_{ij}). \qquad \text{(Explain)}$$

We now argue that the number

$$V = \iint_{R} f(r, \theta)r \, dr d\theta$$

has this property. In the first place, it can be shown that the integral is additive over the R_{ij} and therefore

$$\iint_{R} f(r, \theta)r \, dr d\theta = \sum_{i=1}^{m}\sum_{j=1}^{n} \iint_{R_{ij}} f(r, \theta)r \, dr d\theta.$$

All we have to show therefore is that

$$m_{ij}(\text{area of } R_{ij}) \leq \iint_{R_{ij}} f(r, \theta)r \, dr d\theta \leq M_{ij}(\text{area of } R_{ij}).$$

Observe now that

$$\iint_{R_{ij}} r \, dr d\theta \underset{\substack{\uparrow \\ \text{from last section}}}{=} \int_{\theta_{j-1}}^{\theta_{j}} \left(\int_{r_{i-1}}^{r_{i}} r \, dr \right) d\theta = \frac{1}{2}(r_i^2 - r_{i-1}^2)(\theta_j - \theta_{j-1}) \underset{\substack{\uparrow \\ \text{from section 9.4}}}{=} \text{area of } R_{ij}.$$

From this it follows that

$$\iint\limits_{R_{ij}} f(r, \theta)r \, dr \, d\theta \leq \iint\limits_{R_{ij}} M_{ij}r \, dr \, d\theta = M_{ij} \iint\limits_{R_{ij}} r \, dr \, d\theta = M_{ij}(\text{area of } R_{ij})$$

and that

$$\iint\limits_{R_{ij}} f(r, \theta)r \, dr \, d\theta \geq \iint\limits_{R_{ij}} m_{ij}r \, dr \, d\theta = m_{ij} \iint\limits_{R_{ij}} r \, dr \, d\theta = m_{ij}(\text{area of } R_{ij}). \quad \square$$

The volume formula we just verified for "polar rectangles" holds for more general regions. In particular, it holds for regions Ω of the type depicted in Figure 15.4.4. For such Ω we have

(15.4.1)

$$V = \iint\limits_{\Omega} f(r, \theta)r \, dr \, d\theta = \int_{\theta_1}^{\theta_2} \left(\int_{r_1(\theta)}^{r_2(\theta)} f(r, \theta)r \, dr \right) d\theta.$$

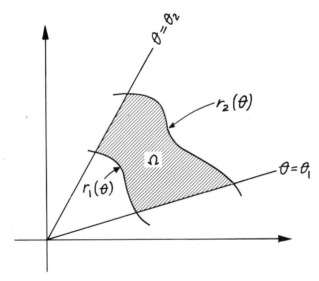

FIGURE 15.4.4

If $f(r, \theta) \equiv 1$, the double integral takes the form

$$\iint\limits_{\Omega} r \, dr \, d\theta.$$

In cubic units it gives the volume of a solid with base Ω and constant height 1. In square units, it gives the area of Ω.

Problem.   Derive the formula for the volume of a sphere using the methods of this section.

SOLUTION.   We take the sphere to have radius R and center at the origin. The upper spherical surface is given by

$$z = \sqrt{R^2 - r^2}.$$ (Check this out)

As a base region we can take

$$\Omega : 0 \leq r \leq R, \ 0 \leq \theta \leq 2\pi.$$

Consequently,

$$V = 2 \iint_{\Omega} \sqrt{R^2 - r^2} \, r \, dr d\theta$$

$$= \int_0^{2\pi} \left(\int_0^R \sqrt{R^2 - r^2} \, (2r) dr \right) d\theta$$

$$= \int_0^{2\pi} \left[-\frac{2}{3} (R^2 - r^2)^{3/2} \right]_0^R d\theta$$

$$= \int_0^{2\pi} \frac{2}{3} R^3 \, d\theta$$

$$= \frac{4\pi}{3} R^3. \quad \square$$

Problem.   Calculate by double integration the area of the region Ω that is enclosed by the cardioid

$$r = 1 - \cos \theta.$$

SOLUTION.   We can express Ω by the inequalities

$$0 \leq r \leq 1 - \cos \theta, \ 0 \leq \theta \leq 2\pi.$$

Consequently,

$$\text{area of } \Omega = \iint_{\Omega} r \, dr d\theta$$

$$= \int_0^{2\pi} \left(\int_0^{1-\cos\theta} r \, dr \right) d\theta$$

$$= \int_0^{2\pi} \left[\frac{r^2}{2} \right]_0^{1-\cos\theta} d\theta$$

$$= \int_0^{2\pi} \frac{(1 - \cos \theta)^2}{2} \, d\theta$$

$$= \frac{1}{2} \int_0^{2\pi} (1 - 2 \cos \theta + \cos^2\theta) d\theta.$$

Since

$$\frac{1}{2}\int_0^{2\pi}(1-2\cos\theta)d\theta = \pi$$

and

$$\frac{1}{2}\int_0^{2\pi}\cos^2\theta d\theta = \frac{1}{4}\int_0^{2\pi}(1+\cos 2\theta)d\theta = \frac{\pi}{2},$$

we have

$$\text{area of }\Omega = \frac{3\pi}{2}. \quad \square$$

Problem. Calculate the volume of the solid bounded above by $z = 2 - \sqrt{x^2 + y^2}$ and below by

$$\Omega: 0 \le r \le 2\cos\theta, \quad -\frac{\pi}{2} \le \theta \le \frac{\pi}{2}.$$

SOLUTION. We can rewrite the upper boundary as

$$z = 2 - r.$$

Therefore

$$
\begin{aligned}
V &= \int_{-\pi/2}^{\pi/2}\left(\int_0^{2\cos\theta}(2r - r^2)dr\right)d\theta \\
&= \int_{-\pi/2}^{\pi/2}\left[r^2 - \frac{r^3}{3}\right]_0^{2\cos\theta}d\theta \\
&= \int_{-\pi/2}^{\pi/2}\left(4\cos^2\theta - \frac{8}{3}\cos^3\theta\right)d\theta \\
&= 2\int_0^{\pi/2}\left[2(1+\cos 2\theta) - \frac{8}{3}(1-\sin^2\theta)\cos\theta\right]d\theta \\
&= 2\left[2\theta + \sin 2\theta - \frac{8}{3}\sin\theta + \frac{8}{9}\sin^3\theta\right]_0^{\pi/2} \\
&= 2\left(\pi - \frac{8}{3} + \frac{8}{9}\right) \\
&= \frac{2}{9}(9\pi - 16). \quad \square
\end{aligned}
$$

Change of Variables Formula

It is possible to change a double integral

$$\iint_\Omega g(x, y)\,dxdy$$

from rectangular coordinates to polar coordinates. The change of variables rule is easy to state:

(15.4.2)
$$\iint_\Omega g(x, y)\, dxdy = \iint_\Omega g(r \cos \theta, r \sin \theta) r\, drd\theta.$$

We shall verify this rule in the case that g is non-negative.

VERIFICATION.   The surface given in rectangular coordinates by

$$z = g(x, y)$$

is given in polar coordinates by

$$z = g(r \cos \theta, r \sin \theta) = f(r, \theta).$$

The double integral

$$\iint_\Omega g(x, y)\, dxdy$$

gives the volume of the solid trapped between Ω and the given surface. By (15.4.1), the double integral

$$\iint_\Omega g(r \cos \theta, r \sin \theta) r\, drd\theta = \iint_\Omega f(r, \theta) r\, drd\theta$$

gives the volume of the same solid.   □

Problem.   Evaluate the double integral

$$\iint_\Omega e^{-(x^2+y^2)}\, dxdy$$

where Ω is the unit disc

$$\{(x, y) : x^2 + y^2 \leq 1\}.$$

SOLUTION.   If you try to compute this integral by the usual methods, you will run into integrals that cannot be evaluated in closed form. By changing to polar coordinates, the calculations become simple. In polar coordinates we have

$$\Omega : 0 \leq r \leq 1,\ 0 \leq \theta \leq 2\pi.$$

The change of variables formula gives

$$\int\int_\Omega e^{-(x^2+y^2)}\,dx\,dy = \int\int_\Omega e^{-r^2}\,r\,dr\,d\theta$$

$$= \int_0^{2\pi}\left[\int_0^1 e^{-r^2}\,r\,dr\right]d\theta$$

$$= \int_0^{2\pi}\left[-\frac{1}{2}e^{-r^2}\right]_0^1 d\theta$$

$$= \int_0^{2\pi}\frac{1}{2}\left(1-\frac{1}{e}\right)d\theta$$

$$= \pi\left(1-\frac{1}{e}\right). \quad \square$$

Problem. Evaluate

$$I = \int\int_\Omega \frac{1}{(1+x^2+y^2)^{3/2}}\,dx\,dy$$

where Ω is the triangle of Figure 15.4.5.

SOLUTION.   By the change of variables formula,

$$\int\int_\Omega \frac{1}{(1+x^2+y^2)^{3/2}}\,dx\,dy = \int\int_\Omega \frac{r}{(1+r^2)^{3/2}}\,dr\,d\theta.$$

In terms of polar coordinates, Ω is given by

$$0 \leq \theta \leq \pi/4,\ 0 \leq r \leq \sec\theta. \qquad \text{(See Figure 15.4.6)}$$

Therefore

$$I = \int_0^{\pi/4}\left(\int_0^{\sec\theta}\frac{r\,dr}{(1+r^2)^{3/2}}\right)d\theta$$

$$= -\int_0^{\pi/4}\left[(1+r^2)^{-1/2}\right]_0^{\sec\theta} d\theta$$

$$= \int_0^{\pi/4}[1-(1+\sec^2\theta)^{-1/2}]\,d\theta$$

$$= \int_0^{\pi/4}\left(1-\frac{\cos\theta}{\sqrt{2-\sin^2\theta}}\right)d\theta$$

$$= \left[\theta-\arcsin\left(\frac{1}{\sqrt{2}}\sin\theta\right)\right]_0^{\pi/4}$$

$$= \frac{\pi}{4}-\frac{\pi}{6} = \frac{\pi}{12}. \quad \square$$

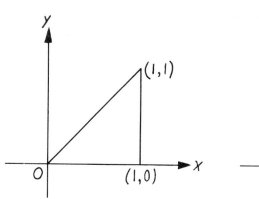

FIGURE 15.4.5   FIGURE 15.4.6

Exercises

1.* Find the area of the region which lies inside the circle $r = \frac{3}{2}$ and to the right of the line $4r \cos \theta = 3$.

2. Find the area of the region which lies inside the circle $r = 3 \cos \theta$ and outside the circle $r = \frac{3}{2}$.

3.* Find the area of the region which lies inside the circle $r = 3 \cos \theta$ and outside the circle $r = \cos \theta$.

4. Find the area of the region which lies inside the cardioid $r = 1 + \cos \theta$ and to the right of the line $4r \cos \theta = 3$.

5.* Find the area of the region which lies inside the cardioid $r = 1 + \cos \theta$ and outside the circle $r = 1$.

6. Find the area of the region which lies inside the circle $r = 1$ and outside the cardioid $r = 1 + \cos \theta$.

7.* Find the area of the region which lies inside the circle $r = 1$ and outside the parabola $r(1 + \cos \theta) = 1$.

8. Calculate the volume of the solid bounded above by $z = 1 - (x^2 + y^2)$ and below by

$$\Omega : 0 \le r \le \cos \theta, \quad -\frac{\pi}{2} \le \theta \le \frac{\pi}{2}.$$

9.* Calculate the volume of the solid bounded above by the spherical surface $x^2 + y^2 + z^2 = 4$ and below by the circular disc

$$\Omega : 0 \le r \le 1, \ 0 \le \theta \le 2\pi.$$

10. A spherical wedge is cut from a ball of radius a by two planes which meet at a diameter of the ball. Find the volume of the wedge if the angle between the planes is α radians.

11.* Find the volume of the solid bounded above by the cone $z^2 = x^2 + y^2$ and below by the region Ω which lies inside the curve $x^2 + y^2 = 2ax$.

12. Find the volume of the solid bounded above by the plane $z = x$ and bounded below by the paraboloid $z = x^2 + y^2$.

15.5 Triple integrals

Now that you are familiar with double integrals

$$\int \int_\Omega f(x, y)\, dxdy,$$

you will find it easy to understand triple integrals

$$\int \int \int_S f(x, y, z)\, dxdydz.$$

Basically the only difference is this: instead of dealing with functions of two variables continuous on a plane region Ω, we will be dealing with functions of three variables continuous on some portion S of space.

Instead of beginning with a rectangle

$$R = \{(x, y) : a_1 \leq x \leq a_2,\ b_1 \leq y \leq b_2\}$$

we begin with a *box* (a rectangular solid)

$$\Pi = \{(x, y, z) : a_1 \leq x \leq a_2,\ b_1 \leq y \leq b_2,\ c_1 \leq z \leq c_2\}. \text{ (Figure 15.5.1)}$$

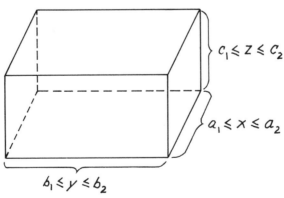

FIGURE 15.5.1

To partition this box, we first partition the edges. Taking

$$P_1 = \{x_0, \ldots, x_m\} \quad \text{as a partition of } [a_1, a_2]$$
$$P_2 = \{y_0, \ldots, y_n\} \quad \text{as a partition of } [b_1, b_2]$$
$$P_3 = \{z_0, \ldots, z_q\} \quad \text{as a partition of } [c_1, c_2],$$

we form the set

$$P = P_1 \times P_2 \times P_3 = \{(x_i, y_j, z_k) : x_i \in P_1, y_j \in P_2, z_k \in P_3\}$$

and call this a *partition of* Π. P breaks up Π into $m \times n \times q$ non-overlapping boxes

$$\Pi_{ijk} = \{(x, y, z) : x_{i-1} \leq x \leq x_i, \; y_{j-1} \leq y \leq y_j, \; z_{k-1} \leq z \leq z_k\}.$$

A typical such box is pictured in Figure 15.5.2.

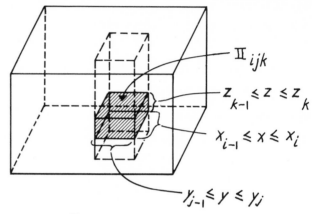

FIGURE 15.5.2

Taking

$$M_{ijk} \text{ as the maximum value of } f \text{ on } \Pi_{ijk}$$

and

$$m_{ijk} \text{ as the minimum value of } f \text{ on } \Pi_{ijk},$$

we form the *upper sum*

$$U_f(P) = \sum_{i=1}^{m} \sum_{j=1}^{n} \sum_{k=1}^{q} M_{ijk}(\text{volume of } \Pi_{ijk})$$

$$= \sum_{i=1}^{m} \sum_{j=1}^{n} \sum_{k=1}^{q} M_{ijk}(x_i - x_{i-1})(y_j - y_{j-1})(z_k - z_{k-1})$$

and the *lower sum*

$$L_f(P) = \sum_{i=1}^{m} \sum_{j=1}^{n} \sum_{k=1}^{q} m_{ijk}(\text{volume of } \Pi_{ijk})$$

$$= \sum_{i=1}^{m} \sum_{j=1}^{n} \sum_{k=1}^{q} m_{ijk}(x_i - x_{i-1})(y_j - y_{j-1})(z_k - z_{k-1}).$$

As in the case of functions of one and two variables, it turns out that, with f continuous on Π, there is one, and only one, number I which satisfies the inequality

$$L_f(P) \le I \le U_f(P) \quad \text{for all partitions } P \text{ of } \Pi.$$

This number I is called the triple integral of f over Π and is denoted by

$$\iiint_\Pi f(x, y, z)\, dx dy dz.$$

To obtain the integral over a more general solid S we first encase S in a rectangular box Π. We then extend f to all of Π by defining f to be 0 outside of S. The triple integral over S is then defined as the triple integral of f over Π:

$$\iiint_S f(x, y, z)\, dx dy dz = \iiint_\Pi f(x, y, z)\, dx dy dz.$$

Interpretation of the Triple Integral as a Mass

The density of a solid S is by definition its mass per unit volume. If the density ρ is constant throughout S, then we can get the total mass of S simply by multiplying the density by the volume:

$$\text{mass of } S = (\text{density of } S) \cdot (\text{volume of } S)$$

$$M = \rho V.$$

Suppose now that the density varies continuously from point to point; say

$$\rho = f(x, y, z).$$

What is the total mass of S then? The answer is simple:

$$\text{mass of } S = \iiint_S f(x, y, z)\, dx dy dz.$$

To justify this assertion we first enlarge S to a box Π assigning density 0 to points outside of S. The mass of S will then be the mass of Π. We now take P as a partition of Π, and use it to break up Π into little sub-boxes Π_{ijk} in the manner previously discussed. For each little box

$$\begin{pmatrix} \text{min density} \\ \text{on } \Pi_{ijk} \end{pmatrix} \cdot (\text{volume of } \Pi_{ijk}) \le \text{mass of } \Pi_{ijk} \le \begin{pmatrix} \text{max density} \\ \text{on } \Pi_{ijk} \end{pmatrix} \cdot \begin{pmatrix} \text{volume} \\ \text{of } \Pi_{ijk} \end{pmatrix}.$$

In our previous notation,

$$m_{ijk} (\text{volume of } \Pi_{ijk}) \le \text{mass of } \Pi_{ijk} \le M_{ijk} (\text{volume of } \Pi_{ijk}).$$

Adding up these inequalities, we see that the total mass of Π must satisfy the condition

$$L_f(P) \le \text{mass of } \Pi \le U_f(P).$$

Since P was chosen arbitrarily, this inequality must hold for all partitions P; consequently we must have

$$\text{mass of } \Pi = \iiint_{\Pi} f(x, y, z)\,dx\,dy\,dz.$$

Since the density outside of S was defined to be 0, we have

$$\iiint_{S} f(x, y, z)\,dx\,dy\,dz = \iiint_{\Pi} f(x, y, z)\,dx\,dy\,dz$$

and, since

$$\text{mass of } S = \text{mass of } \Pi,$$

we have

$$\text{mass of } S = \iiint_{S} f(x, y, z)\,dx\,dy\,dz. \quad \square$$

The triple integral

$$\iiint_{S} 1\,dx\,dy\,dz = \iiint_{S} dx\,dy\,dz$$

gives the mass of S when S has constant density 1. This is simply the volume of S:

$$\boxed{\text{volume of } S = \iiint_{S} dx\,dy\,dz.}$$

15.6   Reduction to repeated integrals

As with double integrals, we usually evaluate triple integrals by first reducing them to repeated integrals. If S is given by inequalities of the form

$$a_1 \leq x \leq a_2, \quad \phi_1(x) \leq y \leq \phi_2(x), \quad \psi_1(x, y) \leq z \leq \psi_2(x, y)$$

(see Figure 15.6.1), then

$$\boxed{\iiint_{S} f(x, y, z)\,dx\,dy\,dz = \int_{a_1}^{a_2} \left\{ \int_{\phi_1(x)}^{\phi_2(x)} \left[\int_{\psi_1(x,y)}^{\psi_2(x,y)} f(x, y, z)\,dz \right] dy \right\} dx,}$$

which, by omitting the parentheses, can be written

$$\boxed{\int_{a_1}^{a_2} \int_{\phi_1(x)}^{\phi_2(x)} \int_{\psi_1(x,y)}^{\psi_2(x,y)} f(x, y, z)\,dz\,dy\,dx.\dagger}$$

† In this section we give no proofs. All the functions in question, f, ϕ_1, ϕ_2, ψ_1, ψ_2 are assumed to be continuous.

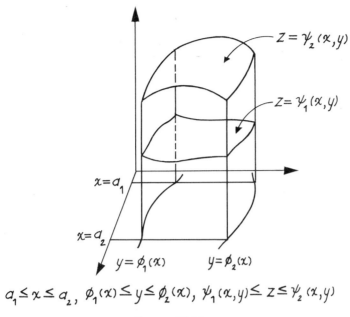

$$a_1 \leq x \leq a_2, \quad \phi_1(x) \leq y \leq \phi_2(x), \quad \psi_1(x,y) \leq z \leq \psi_2(x,y)$$

FIGURE 15.6.1

Here we integrate first with respect to z, then with respect to y, and then with respect to x. Other orders of integration are possible. If, for instance, S is of the form

$$b_1 \leq y \leq b_2, \quad \phi_1(y) \leq z \leq \phi_2(y), \quad \psi_1(y, z) \leq x \leq \psi_2(y, z),$$

then the triple integral over S leads to the repeated integral

$$\int_{b_1}^{b_2} \left\{ \int_{\phi_1(y)}^{\phi_2(y)} \left[\int_{\psi_1(y,z)}^{\psi_2(y,z)} f(x, y, z)\, dx \right] dz \right\} dy = \int_{b_1}^{b} \int_{\phi_1(y)}^{\phi_2(y)} \int_{\psi_1(y,z)}^{\psi_2(y,z)} f(x, y, z)\, dx\,dz\,dy.$$

In this case we integrate first with respect to x, then with respect to z, and then with respect to y. Still other orders of integration are of course possible.

We illustrate the technique in some problems.

Problem 1. Use triple integration to find the volume of the tetrahedron S depicted in Figure 15.6.2.

SOLUTION. We begin by referring to Figure 15.6.3. The inclined face of S has equation

$$x + y + z = 1.$$

It intersects the xy-plane in a line which has equation

$$x + y = 1.$$

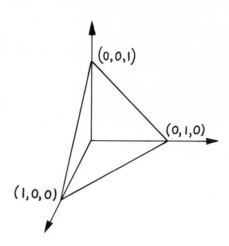

FIGURE 15.6.2

As x ranges from 0 to 1 (see Figure 15.6.4), y ranges from 0 to $1 - x$, and z ranges from 0 to $1 - x - y$. In short S is given by the inequalities

$$0 \le x \le 1, \quad 0 \le y \le 1 - x, \quad 0 \le z \le 1 - x - y.$$

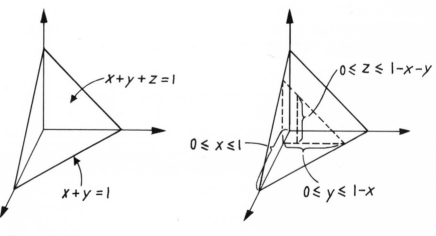

FIGURE 15.6.3   FIGURE 15.6.4

The volume of S is therefore

$$V = \iiint\limits_S dx\,dy\,dz$$

$$= \int_0^1 \int_0^{1-x} \int_0^{1-x-y} dz\,dy\,dx$$

$$= \int_0^1 \int_0^{1-x} (1 - x - y)\,dy\,dx$$

$$= \int_0^1 \left[(1 - x)y - \frac{1}{2} y^2 \right]_0^{1-x} dx$$

$$= \int_0^1 \frac{1}{2} (1 - x)^2\,dx$$

$$= \left[-\frac{1}{6} (1 - x)^3 \right]_0^1$$

$$= \frac{1}{6}. \quad \square$$

REMARK.   In the last problem we integrated first with respect to z, then with respect to y, and then with respect to x. This came from expressing the tetrahedron by the inequalities

$$0 \le x \le 1, \quad 0 \le y \le 1 - x, \quad 0 \le z \le 1 - x - y.$$

Other characterizations are also possible. If we use the inequalities

$$0 \le z \le 1, \quad 0 \le x \le 1 - z, \quad 0 \le y \le 1 - z - x,$$

then we obtain

$$V = \int_0^1 \int_0^{1-z} \int_0^{1-z-x} dy\,dx\,dz.$$

This formulation of the problem calls for us to integrate first with respect to y, then with respect to x, and then with respect to z. As you can check, this procedure leads to the same result. $\square$

Problem 2.   Find the total mass of the tetrahedron of problem 1 if the density at (x, y, z) is xy.

SOLUTION.   Using the first characterization of S, we have

$$\text{mass} = \iiint\limits_S xy\,dx\,dy\,dz = \int_0^1 \int_0^{1-x} \int_0^{1-x-y} xy\,dz\,dy\,dx.$$

Since

$$\int_0^{1-x-y} xy\,dz = xy(1 - x - y) = x(1 - x)y - xy^2,$$

we have

$$\int_0^{1-x} \int_0^{1-x-y} xy \, dz dy = \int_0^{1-x} [x(1-x)y - xy^2] \, dy$$

$$= \left[\frac{1}{2} x(1-x)y^2 - \frac{1}{3} xy^3 \right]_0^{1-x}$$

$$= \frac{1}{6} x(1-x)^3$$

$$= \frac{1}{6} (x - 3x^2 + 3x^3 - x^4).$$

Consequently,

$$M = \int_0^1 \frac{1}{6} (x - 3x^2 + 3x^3 - x^4) \, dx$$

$$= \frac{1}{6} \left[\frac{1}{2} x^2 - x^3 + \frac{3}{4} x^4 - \frac{1}{5} x^5 \right]_0^1$$

$$= \frac{1}{6} \left(\frac{1}{2} - 1 + \frac{3}{4} - \frac{1}{5} \right) = \frac{1}{120}. \quad \square$$

Problem 3. Find the mass of a cylindrical solid of base radius r and height h if the density is proportional to the distance from one of the bases.

SOLUTION.   For convenience we place the cylinder as in Figure 15.6.5. The cylindrical solid, call it S, is then given by the three inequalities

$$-r \leq x \leq r, \quad -\sqrt{r^2 - x^2} \leq y \leq \sqrt{r^2 - x^2}, \quad 0 \leq z \leq h.$$

FIGURE 15.6.5

Taking k as the constant of proportionality, we have

$$M = \iiint\limits_S kz\,dxdydz$$

$$= \int_{-r}^{r}\int_{-\sqrt{r^2-x^2}}^{\sqrt{r^2-x^2}}\int_{0}^{h} kz\,dzdydx$$

$$= 4k\int_{0}^{r}\int_{0}^{\sqrt{r^2-x^2}}\int_{0}^{h} z\,dzdydx \qquad\qquad\text{(Explain)}$$

$$= 4k\int_{0}^{r}\int_{0}^{\sqrt{r^2-x^2}}\frac{1}{2}h^2\,dydx$$

$$= 2kh^2\int_{0}^{r}\sqrt{r^2-x^2}\,dx = 2kh^2\cdot\frac{1}{4}\pi r^2 = \frac{1}{2}kh^2r^2\pi. \quad\square$$

Problem 4. Integrate

$$f(x, y, z) = xy + yz + zx$$

over that portion of the first octant $x \geq 0$, $y \geq 0$, $z \geq 0$ which is cut off by the ellipsoid

$$\frac{x^2}{a^2} + \frac{y^2}{b^2} + \frac{z^2}{c^2} = 1.$$

SOLUTION. See Figure 15.6.6. Call the solid S. The upper boundary of S has equation

$$z = \psi(x, y) = c\left(1 - \frac{x^2}{a^2} - \frac{y^2}{b^2}\right)^{1/2}.$$

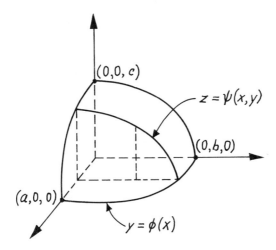

FIGURE 15.6.6

This surface intersects the xy-plane in the curve

$$y = \phi(x) = b\left(1 - \frac{x^2}{a^2}\right)^{1/2}.$$

As x ranges from 0 to a, y ranges from 0 to $\phi(x)$, and z ranges from 0 to $\psi(x, y)$. We are therefore led to the repeated integral

$$\begin{aligned}
I &= \int_0^a \int_0^{\phi(x)} \int_0^{\psi(x,y)} (xy + yz + zx)\, dz\, dy\, dx \\
&= \int_0^a \int_0^{\phi(x)} \left\{ xy\, \psi(x, y) + \frac{1}{2}(x + y)[\psi(x, y)]^2 \right\} dy\, dx \\
&= \int_0^a \int_0^{\phi(x)} \left[cxy\left(1 - \frac{x^2}{a^2} - \frac{y^2}{b^2}\right)^{1/2} + \frac{1}{2} c^2(x + y)\left(1 - \frac{x^2}{a^2} - \frac{y^2}{b^2}\right) \right] dy\, dx.
\end{aligned}$$

Here

$$\begin{aligned}
\int_0^{\phi(x)} \cdots\, dy &= \left[-\frac{1}{3} b^2 cx\left(1 - \frac{x^2}{a^2} - \frac{y^2}{b^2}\right)^{3/2} + \frac{1}{2} c^2 x\left(1 - \frac{x^2}{a^2}\right) y \right. \\
&\quad \left. + \frac{1}{4} c^2\left(1 - \frac{x^2}{a^2}\right) y^2 - \frac{c^2}{6b^2} xy^3 - \frac{c^2}{8b^2} y^4 \right]_0^{\phi(x)} \\
&= \frac{1}{3}(b + c)bcx\left(1 - \frac{x^2}{a^2}\right)^{3/2} + \frac{1}{8} b^2 c^2\left(1 - \frac{x^2}{a^2}\right)^2.
\end{aligned}$$

We now integrate this with respect to x from $x = 0$ to $x = a$, and obtain

$$I = \frac{1}{15} abc(ab + bc + ca). \quad \square$$

Exercises

Evaluate

1.* $\int_0^a \int_0^b \int_0^c dx\, dy\, dz.$

2. $\int_0^1 \int_0^x \int_0^y y\, dz\, dy\, dx.$

3.* $\int_0^1 \int_1^{2y} \int_0^x (x + 2z)\, dz\, dx\, dy.$

4. $\int_0^1 \int_{1-x}^{1+x} \int_0^{xy} 4z\, dz\, dy\, dx.$

5.* Use triple integration to find the volume of the tetrahedron S depicted in Figure 15.6.7.

6. Find the mass of the tetrahedron of exercise 5 if the density at (x, y, z) is

   (a) $x^2 + y^2$.   (b) $\frac{1}{2}(x + y + z)$.

7.* Find the mass of a block in the shape of a unit cube if its density is proportional
    (a) to the distance from one of the faces.
    (b) to the square of the distance from one of the vertices.

8. Find the mass of a cylindrical solid of base radius r and height h if the density is proportional to the n'th power of the distance from one of the bases.

9.* Find the volume of the solid bounded above by the surface $x^2 + z = 4$, below by the plane $x + z = 2$, and on the sides by the planes $y = 0$ and $y = 2$.

10. Find the mass of the solid of exercise 9 if the density at (x, y, z) is

   (a) y.　　　　　　　　　　(b) x^2.　　　　　　　　　　(c) $x^2 y^2$.

11.* Use triple integration to find the volume of the solid bounded above by $z = 4 - x^2$ and below by $z = 3x^2 + y^2$.

12. Find the mass of the solid in exercise 11 if the density function is $f(x, y, z) = |y|$.

13. Use triple integration to show that a ball of radius r has volume $\frac{4}{3}\pi r^3$.

14.* Use triple integration to find the volume of the solid which is bounded above by the plane $z - x = 0$ and below by the surface $z = x^2 + y^2$.

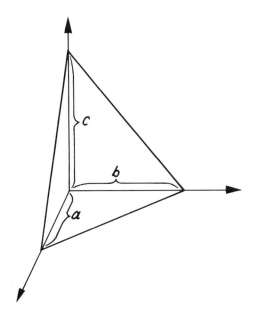

FIGURE 15.6.7

15.7　Averages and centroids

In Chapter 9 we defined the average of a continuous function by setting

$$\text{average of } f \text{ on } [a, b] = \frac{1}{b - a} \int_a^b f(x)\, dx = \frac{1}{\text{length of } [a, b]} \int_a^b f(x)\, dx.$$

Averages for functions of several variables are defined in a similar manner. If f is continuous on a plane region Ω, its average on Ω is defined by setting

$$\text{average of } f \text{ on } \Omega = \frac{1}{\text{area of } \Omega} \iint\limits_{\Omega} f(x, y)\, dx dy.$$

If f is continuous on a portion S of space, its average on S is defined by setting

$$\text{average of } f \text{ on } S = \frac{1}{\text{volume of } S} \iiint_S f(x, y, z) \, dx\,dy\,dz.$$

Problem. Calculate the average height (average z-coordinate) of that portion of the plane

$$\frac{x}{2} + \frac{y}{3} + \frac{z}{4} = 1$$

which lies in the first octant: $x \geq 0, \quad y \geq 0, \quad z \geq 0.$

SOLUTION. That portion of the plane which lies in the first octant is sketched in Figure 15.7.1. What we want to do here is average the function

$$z = 4\left(1 - \frac{1}{2}x - \frac{1}{3}y\right)$$

over the triangular region

$$\Omega : 0 \leq x \leq 2, \quad 0 \leq y \leq 3\left(1 - \frac{1}{2}x\right).$$

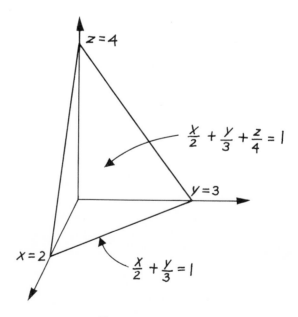

FIGURE 15.7.1

As you can verify,

$$\iint_{\Omega} 4\left(1 - \frac{1}{2}x - \frac{1}{3}y\right) dx\, dy = 4 \qquad \text{and} \qquad \text{area of } \Omega = 3.$$

The average height is therefore

$$\frac{1}{\text{area of } \Omega} \iint_{\Omega} 4\left(1 - \frac{1}{2}x - \frac{1}{3}y\right) dx\, dy = \frac{4}{3}. \quad \square$$

Problem.   Find the average density of the cylindrical solid

$$S: -r \le x \le r, \ -\sqrt{r^2 - x^2} \le y \le \sqrt{r^2 - x^2}, \ 0 \le z \le h$$

if the density at each point (x, y, z) is $\rho = y^2\sqrt{r^2 - x^2}$.

SOLUTION.   The average we want is the quotient

$$\frac{\text{mass of } S}{\text{volume of } S} = \frac{1}{V} \iiint_{S} y^2\sqrt{r^2 - x^2}\, dx\, dy\, dz.$$

In the first place,

$$\iiint_{\Omega} y^2\sqrt{r^2 - x^2}\, dx\, dy\, dz = \int_{-r}^{r}\int_{-\sqrt{r^2-x^2}}^{\sqrt{r^2-x^2}}\int_{0}^{h} y^2\sqrt{r^2 - x^2}\, dz\, dy\, dx$$

$$= 4\int_{0}^{r}\int_{0}^{\sqrt{r^2-x^2}}\int_{0}^{h} y^2\sqrt{r^2 - x^2}\, dz\, dy\, dx$$

$$= 4\int_{0}^{r}\int_{0}^{\sqrt{r^2-x^2}} hy^2\sqrt{r^2 - x^2}\, dy\, dx$$

$$= 4h\int_{0}^{r} \frac{1}{3}(r^2 - x^2)^2\, dx$$

$$= \frac{4}{3}h\int_{0}^{r} (r^4 - 2r^2x^2 + x^4)\, dx$$

$$= \frac{4}{3}h\left[r^4 x - \frac{2}{3}r^2 x^3 + \frac{1}{5}x^5\right]_{0}^{r}$$

$$= \frac{4}{3}h\left[r^5\left(1 - \frac{2}{3} + \frac{1}{5}\right)\right]$$

$$= \frac{4}{3}hr^5\left(\frac{8}{15}\right)$$

$$= \frac{32}{45}hr^5.$$

Since the volume of the cylindrical solid is $\pi r^2 h$, the average density is

$$\frac{1}{V} M = \frac{1}{\pi r^2 h} \cdot \frac{32}{45} hr^5 = \frac{32}{45\pi} r^3. \quad \square$$

Centroids

The *centroid* of a plane region Ω is the point $(\bar{x}, \bar{y})$ where $\bar{x}$ is the average x-coordinate of points in Ω and $\bar{y}$ is the average y-coordinate of points in Ω:

$$\bar{x} = \frac{1}{\text{area of } \Omega} \iint\limits_{\Omega} x \, dxdy \quad , \quad \bar{y} = \frac{1}{\text{area of } \Omega} \iint\limits_{\Omega} y \, dxdy.$$

If you think of Ω as a thin distribution of matter of constant density, then the centroid of Ω becomes the center of gravity, the balance point.

For regions that have a geometric center, the center and the centroid coincide. For example, in the case of a rectangle

$$R : a \leq x \leq b, \ c \leq y \leq d$$

we have

$$(\bar{x}, \bar{y}) = \left(\frac{a+b}{2}, \frac{c+d}{2} \right).$$

This follows from observing that

$$\iint\limits_{R} x \, dxdy = \int_a^b \int_c^d x \, dydx = \frac{b^2 - a^2}{2} (d-c) = \frac{a+b}{2} (b-a)(d-c)$$

$$= \frac{a+b}{2} \ (\text{area of } R)$$

and

$$\iint\limits_{R} y \, dxdy = \int_a^b \int_c^d y \, dydx = \frac{d^2 - c^2}{2} (b-a) = \frac{c+d}{2} (b-a)(d-c)$$

$$= \frac{c+d}{2} \ (\text{area of } R). \quad \square$$

A region may fail to have a center and yet be symmetric with respect to some line l. The centroid will then lie on l.

Problem. Find the centroid of the semi-circular region bounded above by $y = \sqrt{r^2 - x^2}$ and below by the x-axis.

SOLUTION.   Here

$$\Omega : -r \leq x \leq r, \ 0 \leq y \leq \sqrt{r^2 - x^2}.$$

Since Ω is symmetric with respect to the y-axis, we can expect $\bar{x} = 0$. You can verify this by showing that

$$\iint_{\Omega} x \, dxdy = 0.$$

Since

$$\iint_{\Omega} y \, dxdy = \int_{-r}^{r}\int_{0}^{\sqrt{r^2-x^2}} y \, dydx = \int_{-r}^{r} \frac{r^2 - x^2}{2} \, dx = \left[\frac{r^2 x}{2} - \frac{x^3}{6}\right]_{-r}^{r} = \frac{2}{3}r^3$$

and

$$\text{area of } \Omega = \frac{1}{2}\pi r^2,$$

we have

$$\bar{y} = \frac{1}{\text{area of } \Omega} \iint_{\Omega} y \, dxdy = \frac{4r}{3\pi}. \quad \square$$

Problem.   Find the centroid of the quarter disc depicted in Figure 15.7.3.

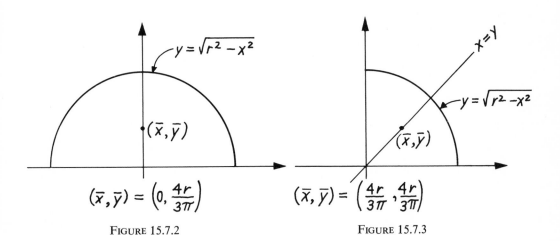

$$(\bar{x}, \bar{y}) = \left(0, \frac{4r}{3\pi}\right)$$

FIGURE 15.7.2

$$(\bar{x}, \bar{y}) = \left(\frac{4r}{3\pi}, \frac{4r}{3\pi}\right)$$

FIGURE 15.7.3

SOLUTION.   Here we have symmetry with respect to the line $x = y$. We can therefore expect $\bar{x} = \bar{y}$. As in the last problem

$$\bar{y} = \frac{1}{\text{area of } \Omega} \iint_{\Omega} y \, dxdy = \frac{4r}{3\pi}.$$

The centroid is the point

$$(\bar{x}, \bar{y}) = \left(\frac{4r}{3\pi}, \frac{4r}{3\pi}\right). \quad \square$$

Problem. Find the centroid of the region bounded above by the line $y = 2x$ and below by the parabola $y = x^2$.

SOLUTION. The line intersects the parabola at the origin and at the point $(2, 4)$. The region Ω can be characterized by the inequalities

$$0 \le x \le 2, \quad x^2 \le y \le 2x.$$

Here

$$\text{area of } \Omega = \iint_{\Omega} dxdy = \int_0^2 \int_{x^2}^{2x} dydx = \int_0^2 (2x - x^2)\, dx = \left[x^2 - \frac{1}{3}x^3\right]_0^2 = \frac{4}{3}$$

$$\iint_{\Omega} x\, dxdy = \int_0^2 \int_{x^2}^{2x} x\, dydx = \int_0^2 (2x^2 - x^3)\, dx = \left[\frac{2}{3}x^3 - \frac{1}{4}x^4\right]_0^2 = \frac{4}{3}$$

$$\iint_{\Omega} y\, dxdy = \int_0^2 \int_{x^2}^{2x} y\, dydx = \frac{1}{2}\int_0^2 (4x^2 - x^4)\, dx = \frac{1}{2}\left[\frac{4}{3}x^3 - \frac{1}{5}x^5\right]_0^2 = \frac{32}{15}$$

$$\bar{x} = \frac{1}{\text{area of } \Omega} \iint_{\Omega} x\, dxdy = 1, \quad \bar{y} = \frac{1}{\text{area of } \Omega} \iint_{\Omega} y\, dxdy = \frac{8}{5}.$$

The centroid is the point $\left(1, \dfrac{8}{5}\right). \quad \square$

There is a simple relation between centroids and volumes of revolution, a relation which was first pointed out by Pappus of Alexandria (born about 340 A.D.).

Theorem of Pappus

When a plane region Ω is revolved about an axis which lies in its plane but does not cross it, the volume of the resulting solid of revolution is the area of Ω multiplied by the circumference of the circle described by the centroid of Ω.

To confirm the theorem, we take Ω as in Figure 15.7.4 and see what happens when we revolve Ω about each of the coordinate axes.

The coordinates of the centroid are

$$\bar{x} = \frac{1}{\text{area of } \Omega} \iint_{\Omega} x\, dxdy, \qquad \bar{y} = \frac{1}{\text{area of } \Omega} \iint_{\Omega} y\, dxdy.$$

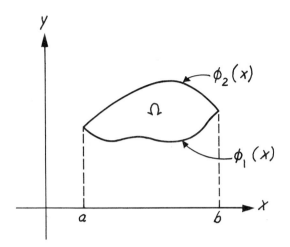

$$\Omega: \quad a \leq x \leq b, \quad \phi_1(x) \leq y \leq \phi_2(x)$$

FIGURE 15.7.4

When Ω is revolved about the x-axis, the resulting solid has volume

$$V_x = \int_a^b \pi[\phi_2(x)]^2 \, dx - \int_a^b \pi[\phi_1(x)]^2 \, dx \qquad \text{(By 9.3.2)}$$
$$= \pi \int_a^b \left([\phi_2(x)]^2 - [\phi_1(x)]^2\right) dx.$$

When Ω is revolved about the y-axis, the resulting solid has volume

$$V_y = \int_a^b 2\pi x \phi_2(x) \, dx - \int_a^b 2\pi x \phi_1(x) \, dx \qquad \text{(By 9.3.3)}$$
$$= 2\pi \int_a^b x[\phi_2(x) - \phi_1(x)] \, dx.$$

According to Pappus we must have

$$V_x = 2\pi \bar{y} \text{ (area of } \Omega) \qquad \text{and} \qquad V_y = 2\pi \bar{x} \text{ (area of } \Omega).$$

Since

$$2\pi \bar{y} \cdot \text{area of } \Omega = 2\pi \iint_\Omega y \, dx dy$$
$$= 2\pi \int_a^b \int_{\phi_1(x)}^{\phi_2(x)} y \, dy dx$$
$$= 2\pi \int_a^b \left[\frac{1}{2} y^2\right]_{\phi_1(x)}^{\phi_2(x)} dx$$
$$= 2\pi \int_a^b \frac{1}{2} \left([\phi_2(x)]^2 - [\phi_1(x)]^2\right) dx$$
$$= \pi \int_a^b \left([\phi_2(x)]^2 - [\phi_1(x)]^2\right) dx$$
$$= V_x,$$

the first relation is confirmed. We now confirm the second relation:

$$2\pi\bar{x}\cdot\text{area of }\Omega = 2\pi\iint_{\Omega} x\,dxdy$$

$$= 2\pi\int_a^b\int_{\phi_1(x)}^{\phi_2(x)} x\,dydx$$

$$= 2\pi\int_a^b x\,[\phi_2(x) - \phi_1(x)]\,dx$$

$$= V_y. \quad \square$$

The *centroid* of a solid S is the point $(\bar{x}, \bar{y}, \bar{z})$ where $\bar{x}$ is the average x-coordinate of points in S, $\bar{y}$ the average y-coordinate, and $\bar{z}$ the average z-coordinate. The defining formulas are:

$$\boxed{\bar{x} = \frac{1}{\text{volume of }S}\iiint_S x\,dxdydz} \quad , \quad \boxed{\bar{y} = \frac{1}{\text{volume of }S}\iiint_S y\,dxdydz}$$

$$\boxed{\bar{z} = \frac{1}{\text{volume of }S}\iiint_S z\,dxdydz.}$$

For a solid of constant density the centroid is the center of mass. Centers of mass are important in physics. The reason is roughly this. When a complicated object (or collection of objects) S of total mass M is subjected to an outside force **F**, not every part of S reacts with the same acceleration. What happens then to Newton's famous $\mathbf{F} = M\mathbf{a}$? It still holds, not for every part of S, but for the center of mass. In short, Newton's $\mathbf{F} = M\mathbf{a}$ should be read

$$\begin{pmatrix}\text{total outside force}\\ \text{applied to }S\end{pmatrix} = \begin{pmatrix}\text{total mass}\\ \text{of }S\end{pmatrix}\cdot\begin{pmatrix}\text{acceleration of the}\\ \text{center of mass of }S\end{pmatrix}.$$

As in the two dimensional case, if S has a geometric center, the center and centroid coincide. If S fails to have a center but has an axis or plane of symmetry, then the centroid will lie on that axis or on that plane.

Problem. Find the centroid of the tetrahedron with vertices $(0, 0, 0)$, $(1, 0, 0)$, $(0, 1, 0)$, $(0, 0, 1)$.

SOLUTION. Call the tetrahedron S. S is characterized by the inequalities

$$0 \leq x \leq 1, \quad 0 \leq y \leq 1 - x, \quad 0 \leq z \leq 1 - x - y.$$

As you have seen before,

$$V = \frac{1}{6}\cdot$$

Consequently,

$$\bar{x} = \frac{1}{V} \int \int_S \int x \, dxdydz$$

$$= 6 \int_0^1 \int_0^{1-x} \int_0^{1-x-y} x \, dzdydx$$

$$= 6 \int_0^1 \int_0^{1-x} [x(1-x) - xy] \, dydx$$

$$= 6 \int_0^1 \left[x(1-x)y - \frac{1}{2} xy^2 \right]_0^{1-x} dx$$

$$= 6 \int_0^1 \frac{1}{2} x(1-x)^2 \, dx$$

$$= 3 \int_0^1 (x - 2x^2 + x^3) \, dx$$

$$= 3 \left[\frac{1}{2} x^2 - \frac{2}{3} x^3 + \frac{1}{4} x^4 \right]_0^1$$

$$= 3 \left(\frac{1}{2} - \frac{2}{3} + \frac{1}{4} \right) = 3 \left(\frac{1}{12} \right) = \frac{1}{4}.$$

In a similar manner (or by symmetry), you can verify that $\bar{y}$ and $\bar{z}$ are also $1/4$. The centroid is the point

$$\left(\frac{1}{4}, \frac{1}{4}, \frac{1}{4} \right). \quad \square$$

Exercises

Find the centroid of the bounded region determined by the following curves.

1.* $y = 6x - x^2$, $y = x$.

2. $y = 4x - x^2$, $y = 2x - 3$.

3.* $x^2 = 4y$, $x - 2y + 4 = 0$.

4. $y = x^2$, $2x - y + 3 = 0$.

5.* $y^3 = x^2$, $2y = x$.

6. $y^2 = 2x$, $y = x - x^2$.

7.* $y = x^2 - 2x - 3$, $y = 6x - x^2 - 3$.

8. $y = 6x - x^2$, $x + y = 6$.

9.* $\sqrt{x} + \sqrt{y} = \sqrt{a}$, $x = 0$, $y = 0$.

10. $x + 1 = 0$, $x + y^2 = 0$.

11.* Find the centroid of the triangle with vertices (a_1, a_2), (b_1, b_2), (c_1, c_2).

12.* Use the theorem of Pappus to find the volume of the torus generated by revolving the circle

$$(x - b)^2 + y^2 = a^2, \quad b > a$$

about the y-axis.

13.* Taking a, b, c as positive, find the centroid of the tetrahedron with vertices $(0, 0, 0)$, $(a, 0, 0)$, $(0, b, 0)$, and $(0, 0, c)$.

14. Find the centroid of the solid bounded above by $x^2 + z = 4$, below by $x + z = 2$, to the left by $y = 0$, and to the right by $y = 3$.

15. The rectangle of Figure 15.7.5 is revolved about the line marked l. Find the volume of the resulting solid.

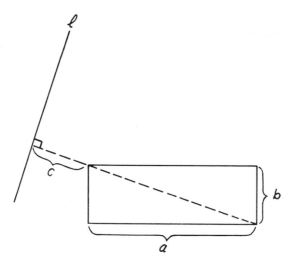

FIGURE 15.7.5

For a solid of varying density, $\rho = f(x, y, z)$, the center of mass is given by the equations

$$x_M = \frac{1}{M} \iiint_S xf(x, y, z)\, dxdydz, \qquad y_M = \frac{1}{M} \iiint_S yf(x, y, z)\, dxdydz$$

$$z_M = \frac{1}{M} \iiint_S zf(x, y, z)\, dxdydz.$$

16.* Find the center of mass of a unit cube

$$0 \le x \le 1, \quad 0 \le y \le 1, \quad 0 \le z \le 1$$

if the density is proportional to

(a) the square of the distance from the origin
(b) the distance from the xy-plane
(c) the square of the distance from the diagonal which joins $(0, 0, 0)$ to $(1, 1, 1)$.

17. Find the center of mass of the tetrahedron of exercise 13 if the density at (x, y, z) is

(a) yz.   (b) xyz.   (c) $y^2 + z^2$.

18. Find the center of mass of the solid of exercise 14 if the density at (x, y, z) is $1 + y$.

19.   Show that in polar coordinates the formulas for the centroid become

$$\bar{x} = \frac{1}{\text{area of } \Omega} \iint\limits_{\Omega} r^2 \cos\theta \, dr d\theta, \quad \bar{y} = \frac{1}{\text{area of } \Omega} \iint\limits_{\Omega} r^2 \sin\theta \, dr d\theta.$$

20.* Find the centroid of the region enclosed by the cardioid $r = a(1 + \cos\theta)$.

15.8   Cylindrical coordinates

The cylindrical coordinates (r, θ, z) of a point P in space are illustrated in Figure 15.8.1. The first two coordinates r and θ are the usual polar coordinates, taking $r \geq 0$. The third coordinate is the third rectangular coordinate z.

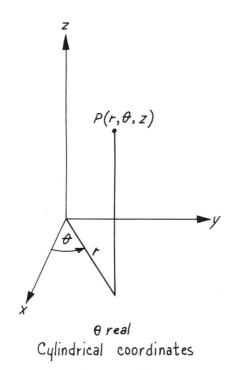

θ real

Cylindrical coordinates

FIGURE 15.8.1

The fundamental solid in cylindrical coordinates is a set of the form

$$\Pi : \quad a_1 \leq r \leq a_2, \quad b_1 \leq \theta \leq b_2, \quad d_1 \leq z \leq d_2.$$

Geometrically this is a *cylindrical wedge*.   (See Figure 15.8.2.)
    Suppose now that S is a solid given in cylindrical coordinates and suppose that $f(r, \theta, z)$ gives the density at each point (r, θ, z). We will sketch informally how the mass of S can be found. We begin by encasing S in a cylindrical wedge Π. We then extend the density function f to all of Π by defining f to be zero outside of S. The mass of S, whatever it is,

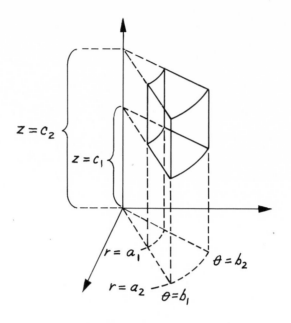

A cylindrical wedge

FIGURE 15.8.2

must be the same as the mass of Π. The advantage of dealing with Π rather than with S is that we can break up Π in an obvious manner into little solids

$$\Pi_{ijk}: \quad r_{i-1} \leq r \leq r_i, \quad \theta_{j-1} \leq \theta \leq \theta_j, \quad z_{k-1} \leq z \leq z_k$$

which are again cylindrical wedges. If M_{ijk} and m_{ijk} are respectively the maximum and minimum densities on Π_{ijk}, then obviously

$$m_{ijk}(\text{volume of } \Pi_{ijk}) \leq \text{mass of } \Pi_{ijk} \leq M_{ijk}(\text{volume of } \Pi_{ijk}).$$

Adding up all these inequalities we have an estimate for the total mass:

$$\sum\sum\sum m_{ijk}(\text{volume of } \Pi_{ijk}) \leq \text{mass } \Pi \leq \sum\sum\sum M_{ijk}(\text{volume of } \Pi_{ijk}).$$

Since

$$\text{volume of } \Pi_{ijk} = \frac{1}{2}(r_i^2 - r_{i-1}^2)(\theta_j - \theta_{j-1})(z_k - z_{k-1})$$

$$= \int_{z_{k-1}}^{z_k}\int_{\theta_{j-1}}^{\theta_j}\int_{r_{i-1}}^{r_i} r \, dr d\theta dz$$

$$= \iiint_{\Pi_{ijk}} r \, dr d\theta dz,$$

we can rewrite this estimate as

$$\sum\sum\sum m_{ijk}\iiint_{\Pi_{ijk}} r \, dr d\theta dz \leq \text{mass of } \Pi \leq \sum\sum\sum M_{ijk}\iiint_{\Pi_{ijk}} r \, dr d\theta dz.$$

Much in the manner of Section 15.4, we can show that the triple integral

$$\iiint\limits_{\Pi} f(r, \theta, z)r\,dr d\theta dz \qquad\qquad \text{(if it exists)}$$

does satisfy this estimate for every choice of the Π_{ijk}. As a consequence we set

$$\text{mass of } \Pi = \iiint\limits_{\Pi} f(r, \theta, z)r\,dr d\theta dz,$$

and, since Π has density 0 outside of S, we set

$$\boxed{\text{mass of } S = \iiint\limits_{S} f(r, \theta, z)r\,dr d\theta dz.}$$

The triple integral

$$\iiint\limits_{S} 1r\,dr d\theta dz = \iiint\limits_{S} r\,dr d\theta dz$$

gives the mass of S when S has constant density 1. This is of course the volume of S:

$$\boxed{\text{volume of } S = \iiint\limits_{S} r\,dr d\theta dz.}$$

We illustrate the use of these formulas in some simple problems.

Problem. Find the mass of a cylindrical solid of radius R and height h if the density at each point is proportional to its distance from the axis of the cylinder.

SOLUTION. We call the solid S and express it by the inequalities

$$0 \le r \le R, \quad 0 \le \theta \le 2\pi, \quad 0 \le z \le h.$$

The density function is of the form

$$f(r, \theta, z) = kr.$$

According to our formula,

$$\begin{aligned}
\text{mass of } S &= \iiint\limits_{S} kr^2\,dr d\theta dz \\
&= \int_0^h \int_0^{2\pi} \int_0^R kr^2\,dr d\theta dz \\
&= \int_0^h \int_0^{2\pi} \frac{1}{3} kR^3\,d\theta dz \\
&= \int_0^h \frac{2\pi}{3} kR^3\,dz \\
&= \frac{2\pi}{3} kR^3 h. \quad \square
\end{aligned}$$

Problem. Find the volume of the solid S given in cylindrical coordinates by the inequalities

$$-\frac{\pi}{2} \le \theta \le \frac{\pi}{2}, \quad 0 \le r \le \cos\theta, \quad r^2 \le z \le r\cos\theta.$$

SOLUTION

$$V = \iiint_S r\,dr\,d\theta\,dz$$

$$= \int_{-\pi/2}^{\pi/2}\int_0^{\cos\theta}\int_{r^2}^{r\cos\theta} r\,dz\,dr\,d\theta$$

$$= \int_{-\pi/2}^{\pi/2}\int_0^{\cos\theta} (r^2\cos\theta - r^3)\,dr\,d\theta$$

$$= \int_{-\pi/2}^{\pi/2}\left[\frac{1}{3}r^3\cos\theta - \frac{1}{4}r^4\right]_0^{\cos\theta} d\theta$$

$$= \int_{-\pi/2}^{\pi/2}\frac{1}{12}\cos^4\theta\,d\theta$$

$$= \frac{\pi}{32}. \quad \square$$

Problem. Find the total mass of the solid S of the last problem if the density at each point is proportional to the square of its distance from the z-axis.

SOLUTION. The density function here is of the form

$$f(r, \theta, z) = kr^2.$$

According to the mass formula,

$$\text{mass of } S = \iiint_S kr^3\,dr\,d\theta\,dz$$

$$= \int_{-\pi/2}^{\pi/2}\int_0^{\cos\theta}\int_{r^2}^{r\cos\theta} kr^3\,dz\,dr\,d\theta$$

$$= \int_{-\pi/2}^{\pi/2}\int_0^{\cos\theta} k(r^4\cos\theta - r^5)\,dr\,d\theta$$

$$= k\int_{-\pi/2}^{\pi/2}\left[\frac{1}{5}r^5\cos\theta - \frac{1}{6}r^6\right]_0^{\cos\theta} d\theta$$

$$= k\int_{-\pi/2}^{\pi/2}\frac{1}{30}\cos^6\theta\,d\theta$$

$$= \frac{1}{96}k\pi. \quad \square$$

Exercises

1.* Find the mass of a cylindrical solid of radius R and height h if the density at each point is proportional to
    (a) the distance from one of the bases.
    (b) the square root of the distance from the axis of the cylinder.
    (c) the square of the distance from the curved boundary.

2.* Use cylindrical coordinates to show that a cone of base radius R and height h has volume

$$V = \frac{1}{3}\pi R^2 h.$$

3. Find the mass of the cone of exercise 2 if the density is proportional to the distance (a) from the axis. (b) from the base.

4. Use cylindrical coordinates to find the volume of the solid S which is bounded above by the paraboloid $z = 1 - (x^2 + y^2)$ and below by the xy-plane.

5. Find the mass of the solid of exercise 4 if the density is proportional to
    (a) the distance from the xy-plane.
    (b) the square of the distance from the origin.

6.* Find the volume of the solid bounded by the paraboloid of revolution $x^2 + y^2 = az$, the xy-plane, and the cylinder $x^2 + y^2 = 2ax$.

7.* Find the volume of the solid bounded above by the cone $z^2 = x^2 + y^2$, below by the xy-plane, and on the sides by the cylinder $x^2 + y^2 = 2ax$.

8.* Find the volume of the solid bounded above by the plane $2z = 4 + r\cos\theta$, below by the xy-plane, and on the sides by the cylinder $r = 2\cos\theta$.

9.* Find the volume of the solid bounded by the hyperboloid $z^2 = a^2 + r^2$ and the upper nappe of the cone $z^2 = 2r^2$.

10. Find the volume of the solid bounded above by $r^2 + z^2 = 25$ and below by $z = r + 1$.

11*. Find the volume of the solid bounded above by the cone $z = a - r$, below by the xy-plane, and on the sides by $r = a\cos\theta$.

15.9   Spherical coordinates

The spherical coordinates of a point P in space are illustrated in Figure 15.9.1. Rectangular coordinates (x, y, z) are related to spherical coordinates by the equations

$$x = r\sin\phi\cos\theta, \quad y = r\sin\phi\sin\theta, \quad z = r\cos\phi.$$

You can check out these formulas in terms of Figure 15.9.1. In spherical coordinates the fundamental solids are sets of the form

$$\Pi: \quad a_1 \le r \le a_2, \quad b_1 \le \theta \le b_2, \quad c_1 \le \phi \le c_2.$$

Such solids are called *spherical wedges*. A typical one is pictured in Figure 15.9.2.

Spherical coordinates

FIGURE 15.9.1

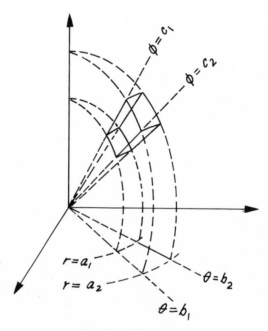

A spherical wedge

FIGURE 15.9.2

The volume of a spherical wedge Π is given by the formula

$$V = \iiint\limits_{\Pi} r^2 \sin \phi \, dr d\theta d\phi.$$

To see this, note first that Π is a solid of revolution. One way to obtain Π is to rotate the face

$$\Omega: \quad a_1 \le r \le a_2, \quad \theta = b_1, \quad c_1 \le \phi \le c_2$$

about the z-axis for $b_2 - b_1$ radians.

As you can verify (using exercise 19 of Section 15.7) the centroid of Ω is at a distance

$$\frac{1}{\text{area of } \Omega} \iint\limits_{\Omega} r^2 \sin \phi \, dr d\theta$$

from the z-axis. As the face Ω is rotated from $\theta = b_1$ to $\theta = b_2$ the centroid travels through a circular arc of length

$$l = (b_2 - b_1) \cdot \frac{1}{\text{area of } \Omega} \iint\limits_{\Omega} r^2 \sin \phi \, dr d\phi.$$

From the Theorem of Pappus we know that the volume of a solid of revolution is the length of the path traveled by Ω multiplied by the area of Ω. In this case we have

$$\text{volume of } \Pi = l \cdot \text{area of } \Omega = (b_2 - b_1) \iint\limits_{\Omega} r^2 \sin \phi \, dr d\phi.$$

Since

$$(b_2 - b_1) \iint\limits_{\Omega} r^2 \sin \phi \, dr d\phi = (b_2 - b_1) \int_{a_1}^{a_2} \int_{c_1}^{c_2} r^2 \sin \phi \, d\phi dr$$

$$= \int_{b_1}^{b_2} \int_{a_1}^{a_2} \int_{c_1}^{c_2} r^2 \sin \phi \, d\phi dr d\theta$$

$$= \iiint\limits_{\Pi} r^2 \sin \phi \, dr d\theta d\phi,$$

we have the desired formula

$$V = \iiint\limits_{\Pi} r^2 \sin \phi \, dr d\theta d\phi. \quad \square$$

From the fact that a spherical wedge Π has volume

$$\iiint\limits_{\Pi} r^2 \sin \phi \, dr d\theta d\phi$$

one can argue that the mass of II is given by the integral

$$\iint\int_{\Pi} f(r, \theta, \phi)\, r^2 \sin\phi\, dr d\theta d\phi$$

where, as usual, f is the density function. This formula for mass is then extended to a more general solid S in the usual manner. Encase S in a spherical wedge II and define the density outside of S to be 0. Obviously then

$$\text{mass of II} = \text{mass of } S$$

and, since

$$\iint\int_{\Pi} f(r, \theta, \phi)\, r^2 \sin\phi\, dr d\theta d\phi = \iint\int_{S} f(r, \theta, \phi)\, r^2 \sin\phi\, dr d\theta d\phi,$$

we have

$$\boxed{\text{mass of } S = \iint\int_{S} f(r, \theta, \phi)\, r^2 \sin\phi\, dr d\theta d\phi.}$$

If $f(r, \theta, \phi) = 1$, the integral on the right becomes simply

$$\iint\int_{S} 1 \cdot r^2 \sin\phi\, dr d\theta d\phi = \iint\int_{S} r^2 \sin\phi\, dr d\theta d\phi.$$

This is the volume of S:

$$\boxed{\text{volume of } S = \iint\int_{S} r^2 \sin\phi\, dr d\theta d\phi.}$$

We illustrate the application of these formulas in some problems.

Problem. Find the mass of a solid ball of radius 1 if the density at each point d units from the center is

$$\frac{1}{1 + d^2}.$$

SOLUTION.   In spherical coordinates the unit ball is the solid

$$S: \ 0 \le r \le 1, \ \ 0 \le \theta \le 2\pi, \ \ 0 \le \phi \le \pi.$$

The density function is

$$f(r, \theta, \phi) = \frac{1}{1 + r^2}.$$

We therefore have

$$\text{mass of } S = \iiint\limits_{S} \frac{r^2}{1+r^2} \sin \phi \, dr d\theta d\phi$$

$$= \int_0^\pi \int_0^{2\pi} \int_0^1 \frac{r^2}{1+r^2} \sin \phi \, dr d\theta d\phi$$

$$= \int_0^\pi \int_0^{2\pi} \int_0^1 \left(1 - \frac{1}{1+r^2}\right) \sin \phi \, dr d\theta d\phi$$

$$= \int_0^\pi \int_0^{2\pi} \left(1 - \frac{\pi}{4}\right) \sin \phi \, d\theta d\phi$$

$$= \left(1 - \frac{\pi}{4}\right) \int_0^\pi 2\pi \sin \phi \, d\phi$$

$$= 4\pi - \pi^2. \quad \square$$

Problem. Find the volume of the solid enclosed by the surface

$$(x^2 + y^2 + z^2)^2 = 2z(x^2 + y^2).$$

SOLUTION. We begin by expressing the surface in spherical coordinates. Since z remains nonnegative, ϕ must remain less than or equal to $\pi/2$. Using the relations $x = r \sin \phi \cos \theta$, $y = r \sin \phi \sin \theta$, $z = r \cos \phi$, we find that the bounding surface becomes

$$r = 2 \sin^2 \phi \cos \phi.$$

We can express the solid inside this surface by

$$S: \quad 0 \le \theta \le 2\pi, \quad 0 \le \phi \le \frac{\pi}{2}, \quad 0 \le r \le 2 \sin^2 \phi \cos \phi.$$

Consequently,

$$V = \iiint\limits_{S} r^2 \sin \phi \, dr d\theta d\phi$$

$$= \int_0^{2\pi} \int_0^{\pi/2} \int_0^{2 \sin^2 \phi \cos \phi} r^2 \sin \phi \, dr d\phi d\theta$$

$$= \int_0^{2\pi} \int_0^{\pi/2} \frac{8}{3} \sin^7 \phi \cos^3 \phi \, d\phi d\theta$$

$$= \frac{8}{3} \int_0^{2\pi} \int_0^{\pi/2} (\sin^7 \phi \cos \phi - \sin^9 \phi \cos \phi) \, d\phi d\theta$$

$$= \frac{8}{3} \int_0^{2\pi} \frac{1}{40} \, d\theta$$

$$= \frac{2}{15} \pi. \quad \square$$

Exercises

1. Obtain the formula for the volume of a ball of radius R using spherical coordinates.

2. Do exercise 10 of Section 15.4 using spherical coordinates.

3.* Interpret the surface

$$\phi = \alpha$$

geometrically.

4. Find the volume of the solid common to the sphere $r = a$ and the cone $\phi = \alpha$, $\alpha \in \left(0, \dfrac{\pi}{2}\right)$.

5.* Find the volume of the solid enclosed by the surface

$$r = 1 - \cos \phi.$$

6.* Find an equation for the sphere

$$x^2 + y^2 + (z - b)^2 = b^2$$

in spherical coordinates.

7. Find the mass of the ball

$$r \leq 2b \cos \phi$$

if the density at (r, θ, ϕ) is

(a) r.   (b) $r \sin \phi$.   (c) $r \cos^2 \theta \sin \phi$.

8.* Find the volume of the solid enclosed by the surface

$$z^2 = (x^2 + y^2)(x^2 + y^2 + z^2)^3.$$

9. Find the volume of the solid common to the two spheres

$$r = 2 \quad \text{and} \quad r = 2\sqrt{2} \cos \phi.$$

APPENDIX

A.1 Sets

By a *set* we mean a collection of objects. We are not particular about the nature of the objects. However, we do require that a set be *well defined*; namely, given any object x, the statement "x is in the set" must be either true or false. The question "Is x in the set?" must be answerable in terms of an unqualified yes or an unqualified no. This excludes collections that involve highly subjective judgments, such as "all men of good will" and "all pleasant days."

The objects which are in the set are known as the *elements* or *members* of the set. To indicate "x is a member of the set A," we write

$$x \in A.$$

This is also read "x is an element of A" or "x belongs to A" or "x is in A." The notation $x \notin A$ is used to indicate that x is not an element of A. For example,

$$-1 \notin \text{set of positive numbers.}$$

A set B is called a *subset* of a set A if and only if

$$x \in B \qquad \text{implies} \qquad x \in A.$$

Thus, for B to fail to be a subset of A, there must be an object in B which is not in A. To indicate that B is a subset of A, we write $B \subseteq A$ or $A \supseteq B$. (See Figure A.1.1.) These expressions are also read "B is contained in A" or "A contains B."

Example. The set of equilateral triangles $\subseteq$ the set of triangles.

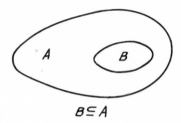

$$B \subseteq A$$

FIGURE A.1.1

Example.   The set of integers $\supseteq$ the set of even integers.

Example.   The set of college freshmen $\subseteq$ the set of college students.

Equality between sets is reserved for identity. That is, $A = B$ if and only if A and B have exactly the same membership. More formally, $A = B$ if and only if $A \subseteq B$ and $B \subseteq A$.

We distinguish between the element a of A and the subset $\{a\}$ of A which has a as the only element. Thus $a \in \{a\}$ is valid, but $a = \{a\}$ is not. The set consisting of the elements a and b is denoted by $\{a, b\}$. That consisting of a, b, and c is denoted by $\{a, b, c\}$, and so on.

The set of elements common to two sets A and B is called the *intersection* of A and B, and is denoted by $A \cap B$. (See Figure A.1.2.) Thus,

$$x \in A \cap B \qquad \text{if and only if} \qquad x \in A \quad \text{and} \quad x \in B.$$

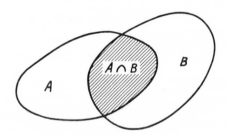

FIGURE A.1.2

Example.   If A is the set of nonnegative numbers and B is the set of nonpositive numbers, then $A \cap B = \{0\}$.

Example.   If A is the set of all multiples of 3 and B is the set of all multiples of 4, then $A \cap B$ is the set of all multiples of 12.

If the sets A and B have no elements in common, we say that A and B are disjoint and write $A \cap B = \emptyset$. We regard $\emptyset$ as a set having no elements and refer to it as an *empty*, *vacuous*, or *void* set.

Example. The set of all real numbers whose square is negative is an empty set.

The *union* of sets A and B, written $A \cup B$, is the set of elements which are either in A or in B. (See Figure A.1.3.) This does not exclude objects which are elements of both A and B. In symbols,

$$x \in A \cup B \qquad \text{if and only if} \qquad x \in A \quad \text{or} \quad x \in B.$$

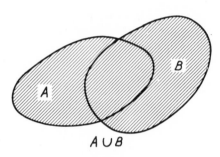

$$A \cup B$$

FIGURE A.1.3

Example. If A is the set of all even numbers between 1 and 9 and B is the set of all even numbers greater than 5, then $A \cup B$ is the set of all positive even numbers.

Example. If A is the set of all college students and B is the set of all college freshmen, then $A \cup B$ is the set of all college students.

Set theory is now a highly developed discipline, but it is not our intention to develop it here. The notions just introduced are enough for our purposes.

A.2 Induction

Suppose that one were asked to verify that a certain set S contains the set of positive integers. One could in sequence start to verify that

$$1 \in S, \quad 2 \in S, \quad 3 \in S, \quad 4 \in S, \quad 5 \in S, \quad \text{etc.}$$

Even if for each positive integer n it required only one second to verify that $n \in S$, such a procedure could not in any finite amount of time yield a verification that S contains the entire set of positive integers. To avoid such difficulties, mathematicians have invented a special procedure. That this procedure works is an *assumption* we make. We therefore state the result as an axiom.

Axiom of Induction

Let S be a set of integers. If

(A) $1 \in S$ and   (B) $k \in S$ implies $k + 1 \in S$,

then all the positive integers are in S.

To show the *plausibility* of this axiom, we suppose that S satisfies conditions (A) and (B). Let's choose a positive integer m and "argue" that $m \in S$.

From (A) we know that $1 \in S$. Thus from (B) we know that $1 + 1 \in S$, and thus that $(1 + 1) + 1 \in S$, and so on. Since m can be obtained from 1 by adding 1, $(m - 1)$ successive times, it "seems obvious" that $m \in S$.

As an example of the above procedure, we note that

$$5 = \left(\left[(1 + 1) + 1 \right] + 1 \right) + 1$$

and thus $5 \in S$.

As an application of the axiom of induction, we prove that, if $x \geq -1$, then

$$(1 + x)^n \geq (1 + nx) \qquad \text{for all positive integers } n.$$

Let S be the set of integers for which the inequality holds. We have to show that S contains the set of positive integers. Since

$$(1 + x)^1 \geq (1 + 1x),$$

we see that $1 \in S$. If $k \in S$, then

$$(1 + x)^k \geq (1 + kx).$$

Thus

$$(1 + x)^{k+1} = (1 + x)^k (1 + x) \geq (1 + kx)(1 + x),$$

the inequality holding since $1 + x \geq 0$. Since

$$(1 + kx)(1 + x) = 1 + (k + 1)x + kx^2 \geq 1 + (k + 1)x,$$

it follows that

$$(1 + x)^{k+1} \geq 1 + (k + 1)x,$$

and thus $k + 1 \in S$. Having shown that $1 \in S$ and that

$$k \in S \qquad \text{implies} \qquad k + 1 \in S,$$

we conclude that S contains the set of positive integers. $\square$

Exercises

1. Show that the following statements hold for each positive integer n:
   (a) $n(n + 1)$ is divisible by 2. [HINT: $(k + 1)(k + 2) = k(k + 1) + 2(k + 1)$]
   (b) $n(n + 1)(n + 2)$ is divisible by 6.
   (c) $1 + 2 + 3 + \cdots + n = \frac{1}{2}n(n + 1)$.
   (d) $1 + 3 + 5 + \cdots + (2n - 1) = n^2$.
   (e) $1^2 + 2^2 + 3^2 + \cdots + n^2 = \frac{1}{6}n(n + 1)(2n + 1)$.
   (f) $1^3 + 2^3 + 3^3 + \cdots + n^3 = (1 + 2 + 3 + \cdots + n)^2$. [HINT: Use part (c)]
   (g) $3^{2n+1} + 2^{n+2}$ is divisible by 7.

2. For what integers n is $9^n - 8n - 1$ divisible by 64? Prove that your answer is correct.

In the rest of the Appendix we prove three important results that we did not prove in the main body of the text: the intermediate-value theorem, the maximum-minimum theorem, and the integrability of continuous functions. Many details are omitted. These are left as exercises.

A.3   The intermediate-value theorem (Bernard Bolzano, 1781–1848)

Lemma

Let f be continuous on $[a, b]$. If

$$f(a) < 0 < f(b) \qquad \text{or} \qquad f(b) < 0 < f(a),$$

then there is a number c between a and b such that

$$f(c) = 0.$$

PROOF. Suppose that $f(a) < 0 < f(b)$. (The other case can be treated in a similar manner.) Since $f(a) < 0$, we know from the continuity of f that there exists a number ξ such that f is negative on $[a, \xi)$. Let

$$c = \text{lub } \{\xi : f \text{ is negative on } [a, \xi)\}.$$

Clearly, $c \le b$. We cannot have $f(c) > 0$, for then f would be positive on some interval extending to the left of c, and we know that, to the left of c, f is negative. Incidentally this argument excludes the possibility $c = b$ and means that $c < b$. We cannot have $f(c) < 0$, for then there would be an interval $[a, t)$, with $t > c$, on which f is negative, and this would contradict the definition of c. It follows that $f(c) = 0$. $\square$

The Intermediate-value Theorem

If f is continuous on $[a, b]$ and C is a number between $f(a)$ and $f(b)$, then there is at least one number c between a and b such that

$$f(c) = C.$$

PROOF. Suppose for example that

$$f(a) < C < f(b).$$

(The other possibility can be handled in a similar manner). The function

$$g(x) = f(x) - C$$

is continuous on $[a, b]$. Since

$$g(a) = f(a) - C < 0 \quad \text{and} \quad g(b) = f(b) - C > 0,$$

we know from the lemma that there is a number c between a and b such that

$$g(c) = 0.$$

Obviously then

$$f(c) = C. \quad \square$$

A.4   The maximum-minimum theorem (Karl Weierstrass, 1815–1897)

Lemma

If f is continuous on $[a, b]$, then f is bounded on $[a, b]$.

PROOF.   Consider

$$\{x: x \in [a, b] \text{ and } f \text{ is bounded on } [a, x]\}.$$

It is easy to see that this set is nonempty and bounded above by b. Thus we can set

$$c = \text{lub } \{x : f \text{ is bounded on } [a, x]\}.$$

Now we argue that $c = b$. To do so, we suppose that

$$c < b.$$

From the continuity of f at c, it is easy to see that f is bounded on $[c - \epsilon, c + \epsilon]$ for some $\epsilon > 0$. Being bounded on $[a, c - \epsilon]$ and on $[c - \epsilon, c + \epsilon]$, it is obviously bounded on $[a, c + \epsilon]$. This contradicts our choice of c. We can therefore conclude that $c = b$. This tells us that

$$f \text{ is bounded on } [a, x] \text{ for all } x < b.$$

We are now almost through. From the continuity of f, we know that f is bounded on some interval of the form $[b - \epsilon, b]$. Since $b - \epsilon < b$, we know from what we just proved that f is bounded on $[a, b - \epsilon]$. Being bounded on $[a, b - \epsilon]$ and on $[b - \epsilon, b]$, it is bounded on $[a, b]$. $\square$

The Maximum-minimum Value Theorem

If f is continuous on $[a, b]$, then f takes on both a maximum value and a minimum value on $[a, b]$.

PROOF.   By the lemma, f is bounded on $[a, b]$, and thus we can set

$$M = \text{lub } \{f(x): x \in [a, b]\}.$$

We must show that there exists c in $[a, b]$ such that

$$f(c) = M.$$

To do this, we set

$$g(x) = \frac{1}{M - f(x)}.$$

If f does not take on the value M, then g is continuous on $[a, b]$ and thus, by the lemma, bounded on $[a, b]$. A look at the definition of g makes it clear that g cannot be bounded on $[a, b]$. The assumption that f does not take on the value M has led to a contradiction. (That f takes on a minimum value can be proved in a similar manner.) $\square$

A.5   The integrability of continuous functions   (G. F. B. Riemann, 1826–1866)

The aim here is to prove that, if f is continuous on $[a, b]$, then there is one and only one number I which satisfies the inequality

$$L_f(P) \leq I \leq U_f(P) \quad \text{for all partitions } P \text{ of } [a, b].$$

> **Definition**
>
> A function f is said to be *uniformly continuous* on $[a, b]$ iff for each $\epsilon > 0$ there exists $\delta > 0$ such that, if
>
> $$x, y \in [a, b] \quad \text{and} \quad |x - y| < \delta,$$
>
> then
>
> $$|f(x) - f(y)| < \epsilon.$$

For convenience, let's agree to say that *the interval* $[a, b]$ *has the property* P_ϵ iff there exist sequences $\{x_n\}$, $\{y_n\}$ satisfying

$$x_n, y_n \in [a, b], \quad |x_n - y_n| < \frac{1}{n}, \quad |f(x_n) - f(y_n)| \geq \epsilon.$$

> **Lemma**
>
> If f is not uniformly continuous on $[a, b]$, then $[a, b]$ has the property P_ϵ for some $\epsilon > 0$.

The proof is easy. $\square$

> **Lemma**
>
> Let f be continuous on $[a, b]$. If $[a, b]$ has the property P_ϵ, then at least one of the subintervals $[a, (a + b)/2]$, $[(a + b)/2, b]$ has the property P_ϵ.

PROOF.   Let's suppose that the lemma is false. For convenience, we let

$$c = \frac{a+b}{2},$$

so that the halves become

$$[a, c] \quad \text{and} \quad [c, b].$$

Since $[a, c]$ fails to have the property P_ϵ, there exists an integer p such that, if

$$x, y \in [a, c] \quad \text{and} \quad |x - y| < 1/p,$$

then

$$|f(x) - f(y)| < \epsilon.$$

Since $[c, b]$ fails to have the property P_ϵ, there exists an integer q such that, if

$$x, y \in [c, b] \quad \text{and} \quad |x - y| < 1/q,$$

then

$$|f(x) - f(y)| < \epsilon.$$

Since f is continuous at c, there exists an integer r such that if $|x - c| < 1/r$, then $|f(x) - f(c)| < \epsilon/2$. Set

$$s = \max \{p, q, r\}$$

and suppose that

$$x, y \in [a, b], \quad |x - y| < 1/s.$$

If x, y are both in $[a, c]$ or both in $[c, b]$, then

$$|f(x) - f(y)| < \epsilon.$$

The only other possibility is that

$$x \in [a, c] \quad \text{and} \quad y \in [c, b].$$

In this case we have

$$|x - c| < 1/r, \quad |y - c| < 1/r,$$

and thus

$$|f(x) - f(c)| < \epsilon/2, \quad |f(y) - f(c)| < \epsilon/2.$$

By the triangle inequality, we again have

$$|f(x) - f(y)| < \epsilon.$$

In summary, we have obtained the existence of an integer s with the property that

$$x, y \in [a, b], \quad |x - y| < 1/s \quad \text{implies} \quad |f(x) - f(y)| < \epsilon.$$

Hence $[a, b]$ does not have the property P_ϵ. This is a contradiction and proves the lemma. □

Theorem

If f is continuous on $[a, b]$, then f is uniformly continuous on $[a, b]$.

PROOF.   We suppose that f is not uniformly continuous on $[a, b]$ and base our argument on a mathematical version of the classical maxim "Divide and conquer."

By the first lemma of this section, we know that $[a, b]$ has the property P_ϵ for some $\epsilon > 0$. We bisect $[a, b]$ and note by the second lemma, that one of the halves, say $[a_1, b_1]$, has the property P_ϵ. We then bisect $[a_1, b_1]$ and note that one of the halves, say $[a_2, b_2]$, has the property P_ϵ. Continuing in this manner, we obtain a sequence of intervals $[a_n, b_n]$, each with the property P_ϵ. For each n, we can choose $x_n, y_n \in [a_n, b_n]$ such that

$$|x_n - y_n| < 1/n \quad \text{and} \quad |f(x_n) - f(y_n)| \geq \epsilon.$$

Since

$$a \leq a_n \leq a_{n+1} < b_{n+1} \leq b_n \leq b,$$

we see that the sequences

$$\{a_n\} \quad \text{and} \quad \{b_n\}$$

are both bounded and monotonic. Thus they are convergent. Since $b_n - a_n \to 0$, we see that $\{a_n\}$ and $\{b_n\}$ both converge to the same limit, say l. From the inequality

$$a_n \leq x_n \leq y_n \leq b_n,$$

we conclude that

$$x_n \to l \quad \text{and} \quad y_n \to l.$$

This tells us that

$$|f(x_n) - f(y_n)| \to |f(l) - f(l)| = 0,$$

which contradicts the statement that for all n

$$|f(x_n) - f(y_n)| \geq \epsilon. \quad \square$$

Lemma

If P and Q are partitions of $[a, b]$, then

$$L_f(P) \leq U_f(Q).$$

PROOF. $P \cup Q$ is a partition of $[a, b]$ which contains both P and Q. It's obvious then that

$$L_f(P) \leq L_f(P \cup Q) \leq U_f(P \cup Q) \leq U_f(Q). \quad \square$$

From the last lemma it follows that the set of all lower sums is bounded above and has a least upper bound L. The number L satisfies the inequality

$$L_f(P) \leq L \leq U_f(P) \quad \text{for all partitions} \quad P$$

and is clearly the least of such numbers. Similarly, we find that the set of all upper sums is bounded below and has a greatest lower bound U. The number U satisfies the inequality

$$L_f(P) \leq U \leq U_f(P) \quad \text{for all partitions} \quad P$$

and is clearly the greatest of such numbers.

We are now ready to prove the basic theorem.

The Integrability Theorem

If f is continuous on $[a, b]$, then there exists one and only one number I which satisfies

$$L_f(P) \leq I \leq U_f(P) \quad \text{for all partitions } P \text{ of } [a, b].$$

PROOF. We know that

$$L_f(P) \leq L \leq U \leq U_f(P) \qquad \text{for all} \quad P,$$

so that existence is no problem. We will have uniqueness if we can prove that

$$L = U.$$

To do this, we let $\epsilon > 0$ and note that f, being continuous on $[a, b]$, is uniformly continuous on $[a, b]$. Thus there exists $\delta > 0$ such that, if

$$x, y \in [a, b] \qquad \text{and} \qquad |x - y| < \delta,$$

then

$$|f(x) - f(y)| < \frac{\epsilon}{b - a} \cdot$$

We now choose a partition

$$P = \{x_0, x_1, \cdots, x_n\}$$

for which

$$\max{(x_i - x_{i-1})} < \delta.$$

For this partition P, we have

$$U_f(P) - L_f(P) = \sum_{i=1}^{n} M_i(x_i - x_{i-1}) - \sum_{i=1}^{n} m_i(x_i - x_{i-1})$$

$$= \sum_{i=1}^{n} (M_i - m_i)(x_i - x_{i-1})$$

$$< \sum_{i=1}^{n} \frac{\epsilon}{b - a}(x_i - x_{i-1})$$

$$= \frac{\epsilon}{b - a}\sum_{i=1}^{n}(x_i - x_{i-1})$$

$$= \frac{\epsilon}{b - a}(x_n - x_0)$$

$$= \frac{\epsilon}{b - a}(b - a)$$

$$= \epsilon.$$

Since $U_f(P) - L_f(P) < \epsilon$ and $0 \leq U - L \leq U_f(P) - L_f(P)$, we see that

$$0 \leq U - L < \epsilon.$$

Since ϵ was chosen arbitrarily, we must have

$$U - L = 0 \qquad \text{and} \qquad L = U. \quad \square$$

TABLE OF INTEGRALS

1. $\int \alpha \, dx = \alpha x + C$

2. $\int x^n \, dx = \dfrac{x^{n+1}}{n+1} + C, \quad n \neq -1$

3. $\int \dfrac{dx}{x} = \log |x| + C$

4. $\int e^x \, dx = e^x + C$

5. $\int p^x \, dx = \dfrac{p^x}{\log p} + C$

6. $\int \log x \, dx = x \log x - x + C$

7. $\int \cos x \, dx = \sin x + C$

8. $\int \sin x \, dx = -\cos x + C$

9. $\int \sec^2 x \, dx = \tan x + C$

10. $\int \operatorname{cosec}^2 x \, dx = -\cot x + C$

11. $\int \sec x \tan x \, dx = \sec x + C$

12. $\int \operatorname{cosec} x \cot x \, dx = -\operatorname{cosec} x + C$

13. $\int \tan x \, dx = \log |\sec x| + C$

14. $\int \cot x \, dx = \log |\sin x| + C$

15. $\int \sec x \, dx = \log |\sec x + \tan x| + C$

16. $\int \csc x \, dx = \log |\csc x - \cot x| + C$

17. $\int \dfrac{dx}{\sqrt{a^2 - x^2}} = \arcsin \left(\dfrac{x}{a}\right) + C$ [Throughout take $a > 0$]

18. $\int \dfrac{dx}{a^2 + x^2} = \dfrac{1}{a} \arctan \left(\dfrac{x}{a}\right) + C$

19. $\int \arcsin x \, dx = x \arcsin x + \sqrt{1 - x^2} + C$

20. $\int \arctan x \, dx = x \arctan x - \tfrac{1}{2} \log (1 + x^2) + C$

21. $\int \cosh x \, dx = \sinh x + C$

22. $\int \sinh x \, dx = \cosh x + C$

23. $\int \operatorname{sech}^2 x \, dx = \tanh x + C$

24. $\int \operatorname{cosech}^2 x \, dx = -\coth x + C$

25. $\int \operatorname{sech} x \tanh x \, dx = -\operatorname{sech} x + C$

26. $\int \operatorname{cosech} x \coth x \, dx = -\operatorname{cosech} x + C$

27. $\int \dfrac{dx}{x^2 - a^2} = \dfrac{1}{2a} \log \left| \dfrac{x - a}{x + a} \right| + C$

28. $\int \dfrac{dx}{\sqrt{x^2 + a^2}} = \sinh^{-1} \left(\dfrac{x}{a}\right) + C$

29. $\int \dfrac{dx}{\sqrt{x^2 - a^2}} = \cosh^{-1} \left(\dfrac{x}{a}\right) + C$

Alternate form of 28, 29:

$$\int \dfrac{dx}{\sqrt{x^2 \pm a^2}} = \log (x + \sqrt{x^2 \pm a^2}) + C$$

30. $\int \sqrt{a^2 - x^2} \, dx = \dfrac{x}{2} \sqrt{a^2 - x^2} + \dfrac{a^2}{2} \arcsin \left(\dfrac{x}{a}\right) + C$

31. $\int \sqrt{x^2 + a^2} \, dx = \dfrac{x}{2} \sqrt{x^2 + a^2} + \dfrac{a^2}{2} \sinh^{-1} \left(\dfrac{x}{a}\right) + C$

32. $\int \sqrt{x^2 - a^2} \, dx = \dfrac{x}{2} \sqrt{x^2 - a^2} - \dfrac{a^2}{2} \cosh^{-1} \left(\dfrac{x}{a}\right) + C$

Alternate form of 31, 32:

$$\int \sqrt{x^2 \pm a^2} \, dx = \dfrac{x}{2} \sqrt{x^2 \pm a^2} \pm \dfrac{a^2}{2} \log (x + \sqrt{x^2 \pm a^2}) + C$$

ANSWERS TO STARRED EXERCISES

Section 1.3

1. $x = 2$

3. $x = a$ and $x = b$

4. $(1, 3)$

6. $(-\infty, 1) \cup (3, \infty)$

7. $\left(-\infty, \dfrac{1}{3}\right)$

9. $(-1, 1)$

10. $(-\infty, \infty)$

12. $[0, \infty)$

13. $(-\infty, 0)$

15. $(1, \infty)$

16. $[-2, 2]$

18. $(0, \infty)$

19. $(-\infty, 0] \cup (5, \infty)$

21. $(-\infty, 1) \cup (2, \infty)$

Section 1.4

1. $\operatorname{dom}(f) = (-\infty, \infty)$; ran $(f) = [0, \infty)$
3. $\operatorname{dom}(F) = (-\infty, \infty)$; $\operatorname{ran}(F) = (-\infty, \infty)$
5. $\operatorname{dom}(f) = (-\infty, 0) \cup (0, \infty)$; $\operatorname{ran}(f) = (-\infty, 0) \cup (0, \infty)$
7. $\operatorname{dom}(F) = (-1, 1)$; $\operatorname{ran}(F) = [1, \infty)$

9. one-to-one

11. one-to-one

13. one-to-one

15. $\sqrt{x^2 + 5}$

17. $\dfrac{1}{x} - 1$

19. $\dfrac{1}{x^2 + 1}$

21. $y^{5/3}$

23. $(1 - y^{1/5})^{1/3}$

25. $\dfrac{1}{y}$

27. $\left(\dfrac{1 - y}{y}\right)^{1/3}$

29. odd

31. neither

33. even

35. even

36. even

37. odd

38. symmetric with respect to the y-axis
39. symmetric with respect to the origin

Section 2.2

1. 2	3. 7	5. −1
7. 0	9. 0	11. 1
13. 2	15. 0	16. 0
17. 1	18. 4	19. no limit
20. 0		

Section 2.3

1. (b) $\dfrac{1}{4}$ (c) 4   (e) no limit   (h) 1

2. (b) 2   (c) no limit

3. (a) 3   (d) 0   (e) no limit

4. (a) 27   (c) 0

Section 2.4

1. (a) 0   (c) 0   (e) 0   (h) no limit   (j) −1   (l) 1

3. (a) no limit   (b) 1

5. (b) $\min\{f(x), g(x)\} = \dfrac{1}{2}\left[[f(x) + g(x)] - |f(x) - g(x)| \right].$

Section 2.5

1. (a) 1   (c) −1   (e) no limit   (g) 0   (i) 1   (k) −1   (m) does not exist

2. (b) (i) 0   (ii) 1   (iii) 1   (iv) 1   (v) no limit   (vi) 1

5. (a) 0   (c) 1

Section 2.6

1. (a) continuous at 2   (b) continuous at 2

(c) continuous at 2   (d) not defined at 2

(e) continuous at 2   (f) discontinuous at 2

(g) continuous at 2   (h) continuous at 2

(i) discontinuous at 2   (j) discontinuous at 2

2. ·(a) no discontinuities   (b) no discontinuities

(c) no discontinuities   (d) no discontinuities

(e) no discontinuities   (f) discontinuous at 2, not defined at 3

4. (a) nowhere continuous   (b) continuous only at 0

Section 3.1

1. $f'(x) = 0$ 3. $f'(x) = 3$ 5. $f'(x) = -\dfrac{1}{x^2}$

7. $f'(x) = x$ 9. $f'(x) = 6x^2$ 11. $f'(x) = 2(x - 1)$

13. $f'(x) = -\dfrac{1}{2}x^{-3/2}$ 15. $f'(x) = -\dfrac{1}{2}(x - 1)^{-3/2}$

16. not differentiable at $x = 1$
17. not differentiable at $x = \pm 2$
18. not differentiable at $x = 0$
19. not differentiable at $x = 5/2$

Section 3.2

1. $f'(x) = -1$

3. $f'(x) = 55x^4 - 18x^2$

5. $f'(x) = 2ax + b$

7. $f'(x) = \dfrac{2}{x^3}$

9. $f'(x) = \dfrac{x^2 - 2x - 1}{(x - 1)^2}$

11. $f'(x) = -\dfrac{x^2(12x^3 - 15x^2 + 4x - 6)}{(x - 1)^2}$

13. $f'(x) = 3x^2 - 6x - 1$

15. $f'(x) = 3x^2 - 12x + 11$

17. $f'(x) = -\dfrac{2(3x^2 - x + 1)}{x^2(x - 2)^2}$

19. $f'(x) = (9x^8 - 8x^9)\left(1 - \dfrac{1}{x^2}\right) + \left(x + \dfrac{1}{x}\right)(72x^7 - 72x^8) = -80x^9 + 81x^8 - 64x^7 + 63x^6$

21. $f'(0) = -\dfrac{1}{4}$ $f'(1) = -1$

23. $f'(0) = 0$ $f'(1) = -1$

25. $f'(0) = \dfrac{ad - bc}{d^2}$ $f'(1) = \dfrac{ad - bc}{(c + d)^2}$

27. $f'(0) = 2$

29. $f'(0) = -\dfrac{1}{4}$

Section 3.3

1. $\dfrac{dy}{dx} = 12x^3 - 2x$

3. $\dfrac{dy}{dx} = 1 + \dfrac{1}{x^2}$

5. $\dfrac{dy}{dx} = \dfrac{1 - x^2}{(1 + x^2)^2}$

7. $\dfrac{dy}{dx} = \dfrac{2x - x^2}{(1 - x)^2}$

9. $\dfrac{dy}{dx} = \dfrac{-6x^2}{(x^3 - 1)^2}$

11. $\dfrac{d}{dx}(2x - 5) = 2$

13. $\dfrac{d}{dx}(7x^3 - 1) = 21x^2$

15. $\dfrac{d}{dt}\left(\dfrac{t^2 + 1}{t^2 - 1}\right) = \dfrac{-4t}{(t^2 - 1)^2}$

17. $\dfrac{d}{dt}\left(\dfrac{t^4}{2t^3 - 1}\right) = \dfrac{2t^3(t^3 - 2)}{(2t^3 - 1)^2}$

19. $\dfrac{d}{du}\left(\dfrac{2u}{1 - 2u}\right) = \dfrac{2}{(1 - 2u)^2}$

21. $\dfrac{d}{du}\left(\dfrac{u}{u - 1} - \dfrac{u}{u + 1}\right) = -\left[\dfrac{1}{(u - 1)^2} + \dfrac{1}{(u + 1)^2}\right] = -2\left[\dfrac{u^2 + 1}{(u^2 - 1)^2}\right]$

23. $\dfrac{d}{dx}\left(\dfrac{x^2}{1 - x^2} - \dfrac{1 - x^2}{x^2}\right) = 2x\left[\dfrac{1}{(1 - x^2)^2} + \dfrac{1}{x^4}\right]$

25. $\dfrac{d}{dx}\left(\dfrac{x^3 + x^2 + x + 1}{x^3 - x^2 + x - 1}\right) = \dfrac{-2}{(x - 1)^2}$

27. 47

29. $\dfrac{1}{4}$

Section 3.4

1. 8

3. 4

5. $-\dfrac{5}{36}$

7. $\dfrac{dA}{dr} = 8\pi r,\; 8\pi r_0,\; r_0 = \dfrac{1}{8\pi}$

9. $-\dfrac{h}{b}$

11. -4

Section 3.5

1. $f'(x) = 2(1 - 2x)^{-2}$

3. $f'(x) = 100(x^5 - x^{10})^{19}(x^4 - 2x^9)$

5. $f'(x) = 1 + \dfrac{1}{x^2}$

7. $f'(x) = 4(x - x^3 - x^5)^3(1 - 3x^2 - 5x^4)$

9. $f'(t) = 200t(t^2 - 1)^{99}$

11. $f'(t) = -4(t^{-1} + t^{-2})^3(t^{-2} + 2t^{-3})$

13. $f'(x) = 324x^3 \dfrac{1 - x^2}{(x^2 + 1)^5}$

15. $f'(x) = 2(x^4 + x^2 + x)(4x^3 + 2x + 1)$

17. $f'(x) = -\left(\dfrac{x^3}{3} + \dfrac{x^2}{2} + \dfrac{x}{1}\right)^{-2}(x^2 + x + 1)$

19. $f'(x) = 3\left(\dfrac{1}{x + 2} - \dfrac{1}{x - 2}\right)^2\left[\dfrac{-1}{(x + 2)^2} + \dfrac{1}{(x - 2)^2}\right] = \dfrac{384x}{(x + 2)^4(x - 2)^4}$

21. $\dfrac{dy}{dx} = -\dfrac{2x + 1}{(2x^2 + 2x + 1)^2}$

23. $\dfrac{dy}{dx} = 80x\dfrac{(5x^2 + 1)^3}{[1 - 4(5x^2 + 1)^4]^2}$

27. 1

29. 1

31. 1

33. 2

35. 2

37. 0

Section 3.6

1. $f''(x) = 42x - 120x^3$

3. $\dfrac{d^2y}{dx^2} = 2 - \dfrac{6}{x^4}$

5. $\dfrac{d^3y}{dx^3} = 48$

7. $\dfrac{d^2}{dx^2}\left(\dfrac{1 - x}{1 + x}\right) = \dfrac{4}{(1 + x)^3}$

9. $\dfrac{d^2}{dx^2}\left(\dfrac{ax + b}{cx + d}\right) = \dfrac{2c(bc - ad)}{(cx + d)^3}$

11. $\dfrac{d}{dx}\left[x\dfrac{d^2}{dx^2}\left(\dfrac{1}{1 + x}\right)\right] = 2\dfrac{1 - 2x}{(1 + x)^4}$

13. $\dfrac{d^{100}}{dx^{100}}(x^9 - 2x^7 + x^5 + 1) = 0$

15. $f'''(x) = 2$

17. $\dfrac{d^2}{dx^2}\left[\left(\dfrac{6 - x}{x^2 - 1}\right)^2\right] = 2\left[\dfrac{(x^2 - 1)(-3x^2 + 36x - 73) + 6x(x - 6)(x^2 - 12x + 1)}{(x^2 - 1)^4}\right]$

19. $n!$

Section 3.7

1. $\dfrac{dy}{dx} = \dfrac{3}{2}x^2(x^3 + 1)^{-1/2}$

3. $\dfrac{dy}{dx} = \dfrac{2x^2 + 1}{\sqrt{x^2 + 1}}$

5. $\dfrac{dy}{dx} = (x^2 + 1)^{-1/2} - x^2(x^2 + 1)^{-3/2}$

7. $\dfrac{dy}{dx} = x(2x^2 + 1)^{-3/4}$

9. $\dfrac{dy}{dx} = \dfrac{1}{3}x^{-2/3} - \dfrac{1}{3}x^{-4/3}$

11. $\dfrac{dy}{dx} = \dfrac{2}{3}(2x^3 - x + 1)^{-1/3}(6x^2 - 1)$

13. $\dfrac{dy}{dx} = \dfrac{x(2x^2 - 5)}{\sqrt{3 - x^2}\sqrt{2 - x^2}}$

15. $\dfrac{dy}{dx} = \dfrac{(2x + 3)(6x^2 + 3x + 4)}{\sqrt{x^2 + 1}}$

17. $f'(x) = \dfrac{2x(x^2 - 1)}{|x^2 - 1|}$

19. $\dfrac{d}{dx}[f(x^2 + 1)] = 2xf'(x^2 + 1)$

21. $\dfrac{d}{dx}\sqrt{f(x^2 + 1)} = \dfrac{xf'(x^2 + 1)}{\sqrt{f(x^2 + 1)}}$

Section 3.8

1. (a) $y = 11x + 16$ (c) $y = -4x$
2. (a) $(-2, -10)$ (c) $(1, 1)$ and $(-1, -1)$ (e) $(15/16, -1/4)$
4. (a) there are none   (c) $(0, 0)$ (e) $(1, 0)$ (f) $(0, 1), (1, 0)$, and $(-1, 0)$

Section 3.9

1. $f'(x) = 4x(x^2 - 1)$

3. $f'(x) = \dfrac{(3x - 1)(x - 3)}{(1 - x^2)^2}$

5. $f'(x) = \dfrac{2(3x - 5)(3x - 1)(x - 3)}{(1 - x^2)^3}$

7. $f'(x) = -2x^3$ for $x \neq 1, -1$

9. $f'(x) = 3x^2 + 6x + 2$

11. $\left(\dfrac{1}{4}, \dfrac{1}{2}\right)$

13. $\left(\dfrac{3 + \sqrt{3}}{3}, \dfrac{\sqrt{3}}{9}\right)$ and $\left(\dfrac{3 - \sqrt{3}}{3}, -\dfrac{\sqrt{3}}{9}\right)$

15. $(0, 2)$ and $(-2, 4)$

17. $c = \dfrac{\sqrt{3}\sqrt{13}}{3}$

Section 3.10

1. increasing on $(-\infty, -1]$ and $[1, \infty)$, decreasing on $[-1, 1]$
3. increasing on $(-\infty, -1]$ and $[1, \infty)$, decreasing on $[-1, 0)$ and $(0, 1]$

5. increasing on $\left(-\infty, \dfrac{-3 - \sqrt{3}}{3}\right]$ and $\left[\dfrac{-3 + \sqrt{3}}{3}, \infty\right)$,

   decreasing on $\left[\dfrac{-3 - \sqrt{3}}{3}, \dfrac{-3 + \sqrt{3}}{3}\right]$

7. increasing on $(-\infty, 2)$, decreasing on $(2, \infty)$
9. increasing on $(-\infty, -1)$ and $(-1, 0]$, decreasing on $[0, 1)$ and $(1, \infty)$
11. increasing on $[-\sqrt{5}, 0]$ and $[\sqrt{5}, \infty)$, decreasing on $(-\infty, -\sqrt{5}]$ and $[0, \sqrt{5}]$
13. increasing on $(-\infty, -1)$ and $(-1, \infty)$
15. decreasing on $[0, \infty)$
17. increasing on $[0, \infty)$, decreasing on $(-\infty, 0]$

19. $f(x) = \dfrac{x^3}{3} - x + 1$

21. $f(x) = x^2 - 5x + 10$

23. $f(x) = -\dfrac{2}{x^2} + 2$

25. $f(x) = \dfrac{1}{5}(x^3 - 1)^5$

Section 3.11

1. no critical pts; no local extreme values
3. critical pts ± 1; local max $f(-1) = -2$, local min $f(1) = 2$
5. critical pts $\dfrac{-3 \pm \sqrt{3}}{3}$; local max $f\left(\dfrac{-3 - \sqrt{3}}{3}\right) = \dfrac{2\sqrt{3}}{9}$, local min $f\left(\dfrac{-3 + \sqrt{3}}{3}\right) =$

   $-\dfrac{2\sqrt{3}}{9}$

7. no critical pts; no local extreme values
9. no critical pts; no local extreme values

11. critical pts $-4, 0, 4$; local max $f(0) = 16$, local min $f(-4) = f(4) = 0$
13. critical pt 2; no local extreme values
15. critical pts $-1, \frac{1}{2}$; local max $f(\frac{1}{2}) = \frac{27}{16}$
17. critical pt 0; local min $f(0) = 0$
19. critical pts $-2, -\frac{1}{2}, 1$; local max $f(-\frac{1}{2}) = \frac{9}{4}$, local min $f(-2) = f(1) = 0$
21. critical pts $0, -\frac{3}{2}$; local max $f(-\frac{3}{2}) = -6\frac{3}{4}$
23. critical pt $-\frac{3}{2}$; local max $f(-\frac{3}{2}) = 4$

Section 3.12

1. critical pt -2; $f(-2) = 0$ end-pt min and absolute min
3. critical pts $0, 2, 3$; $f(0) = 1$ end-pt max and absolute max, $f(2) = -3$ local min and absolute min, $f(3) = -2$ end-pt max
5. critical pt $1/\sqrt[3]{2}$; $f(1/\sqrt[3]{2}) = 3/\sqrt[3]{4}$ local min
7. critical pts $1/10, 1/\sqrt[3]{2}, 2$; $f(1/10) = 10\,1/100$ end-pt max and absolute max; $f(1/\sqrt[3]{2}) = 3/\sqrt[3]{4}$ local min and absolute min, $f(2) = 4\,1/2$ end-pt max
9. critical pts $0, 3/2, 2$; $f(0) = 2$ end-pt max and absolute max, $f(3/2) = -1/4$ local min and absolute min, $f(2) = 0$ end-pt max
11. critical pt 0; $f(0) = 1/3$ end-pt and absolute max
13. critical pts $0, 1/4, 1$; $f(0) = 0$ end-pt min and absolute min, $f(1/4) = 1/16$ local max, $f(1) = 0$ local min and absolute min
15. critical pts $2, 3$; $f(2) = 2$ local max and absolute max, $f(3) = 0$ end-pt min
17. critical pt 1; no extreme values
19. critical pts $1, 4$; $f(1) = -2$ local min, $f(4) = 1$ local max

Section 3.13

1. $20, 20$
3. 20 by 10
5. $\left(\frac{3}{2}, \sqrt{\frac{3}{2}}\right)$
7. $2r^2$
9. the equilateral triangle
11. half of the area of the given triangle
13. length of side $\frac{1}{6}(a + b - \sqrt{a^2 - ab + b^2})$
15. (a) use it all for the circle   (b) use $\dfrac{9l}{\sqrt{3}\pi + 9}$ for the triangle
16. (a) base radius $\dfrac{2r}{3}$ and height $\dfrac{h}{3}$
17. (a) base radius $\sqrt{\dfrac{2}{3}}R$ (c) base radius $\dfrac{2\sqrt{2}}{3}R$
18. $\dfrac{2a^3\pi}{9\sqrt{3}}$

Section 3.14

1. concave down on $(-\infty, 0)$, concave up on $(0, \infty)$
3. concave down on $(-\infty, 0]$, concave up on $[0, \infty)$; pt of inflection $(0, 2)$
5. concave up on $(-\infty, -1/\sqrt{3}]$, concave down on $[-1/\sqrt{3}, 1/\sqrt{3}]$, concave up on $[1/\sqrt{3}, \infty)$; pts of inflection $(-1/\sqrt{3}, -5/36)$, $(1/\sqrt{3}, -5/36)$

7. concave down on $(-\infty, -1)$ and on $(-1, 0]$, concave up on $[0, 1)$ and on $(1, \infty)$; pt of inflection $(0, 0)$

9. concave up on $(-\infty, -1/\sqrt{3}]$, concave down on $[-1/\sqrt{3}, 1/\sqrt{3}]$, concave up on $[1/\sqrt{3}, \infty)$; pts of inflection $(-1/\sqrt{3}, 4/9)$, $(1/\sqrt{3}, 4/9)$

11. concave up on $(0, \infty)$

13. $d = \dfrac{1}{3}(a + b + c)$

15. $a = -\dfrac{1}{2}, b = \dfrac{1}{2}$

Section 3.15

1. critical pt 2; $f(2) = 0$ local min and absolute min; decreasing on $(-\infty, 2]$, increasing on $[2, \infty)$; concave up everywhere; no pts of inflection

3. critical pts $\frac{1}{3}, 1$; $f(\frac{1}{3}) = 1\frac{4}{27}$ local max, $f(1) = 1$ local min; increasing on $(-\infty, \frac{1}{3}]$, decreasing on $[\frac{1}{3}, 1]$, increasing on $[1, \infty)$; concave down on $(-\infty, \frac{2}{3}]$, concave up on $[\frac{2}{3}, \infty)$; pt of inflection $(\frac{2}{3}, 1\frac{2}{27})$

5. no critical pts; no extreme values; decreasing on $(-\infty, \frac{1}{3})$ and on $(\frac{1}{3}, \infty)$; concave down on $(-\infty, \frac{1}{3})$, concave up on $(\frac{1}{3}, \infty)$; no pts of inflection

7. critical pts $-\frac{2}{3}, 0$; $f(-\frac{2}{3}) = -\frac{4}{9}$ local max, $f(0) = 0$ local min; increasing on $(-\infty, -\frac{2}{3}]$, decreasing on $[-\frac{2}{3}, -\frac{1}{3})$, decreasing on $(-\frac{1}{3}, 0]$, increasing on $[0, \infty)$; concave down on $(-\infty, -\frac{1}{3})$, concave up on $(-\frac{1}{3}, \infty)$; no pts of inflection

9. critical pt $\frac{1}{3}$; $f(\frac{1}{3}) = \frac{1}{12}$ local max and absolute max; decreasing on $(-\infty, -\frac{1}{3})$, increasing on $(-\frac{1}{3}, \frac{1}{3}]$, decreasing on $[\frac{1}{3}, \infty)$; concave down on $(-\infty, -\frac{1}{3})$ and on $(-\frac{1}{3}, \frac{2}{3}]$, concave up on $[\frac{2}{3}, \infty)$; pt of inflection $(\frac{2}{3}, \frac{2}{27})$

11. critical pt 0; no extreme values; increasing everywhere; concave down on $(-\infty, 0]$, concave up on $[0, \infty)$; pt of inflection $(0, 0)$

13. critical pt 2; $f(2) = 1$ local min and absolute min; decreasing on $(-\infty, 2]$, increasing on $[2, \infty)$; concave up everywhere; no pts of inflection

15. critical pts $-1, -\frac{1}{2}, 0$; $f(-1) = f(0) = 0$ local and absolute min, $f(-\frac{1}{2}) = \frac{1}{16}$ local max; decreasing on $(-\infty, -1]$, increasing on $[-1, -\frac{1}{2}]$, decreasing on $[-\frac{1}{2}, 0]$, increasing on $[0, \infty)$; concave up on $\left(-\infty, \dfrac{-3 - \sqrt{3}}{6}\right]$, concave down on $\left[\dfrac{-3 - \sqrt{3}}{6}, \dfrac{-3 + \sqrt{3}}{6}\right]$, concave up on $\left[\dfrac{-3 + \sqrt{3}}{6}, \infty\right)$; pts of inflection $\left(\dfrac{-3 - \sqrt{3}}{6}, \dfrac{1}{36}\right)$, $\left(\dfrac{-3 + \sqrt{3}}{6}, \dfrac{1}{36}\right)$

17. critical pts $2/3, 1$; $f(2/3) = 2/3\sqrt{3}$ local max and absolute max, $f(1) = 0$ end-pt min; increasing on $(-\infty, 2/3]$, decreasing on $[2/3, 1]$; concave down on $(-\infty, 1]$; no pts of inflection

19. critical pts $\pm\sqrt{2}$; $f(-\sqrt{2}) = -\sqrt{2}/2$ local min and absolute min, $f(\sqrt{2}) = \sqrt{2}/2$ local max and absolute max; decreasing on $(-\infty, -\sqrt{2}]$, increasing on $[-\sqrt{2}, \sqrt{2}]$, decreasing on $[\sqrt{2}, \infty)$; concave down on $(-\infty, -\sqrt{6}]$, concave up on $[-\sqrt{6}, 0]$, concave down on $[0, \sqrt{6}]$, concave up on $[\sqrt{6}, \infty)$; pts of inflection $(-\sqrt{6}, -\sqrt{6}/4)$, $(0, 0)$, $(\sqrt{6}, \sqrt{6}/4)$

21. critical pt -1; $f(-1) = 2$ local min and absolute min; decreasing on $(-\infty, -1]$, increasing on $[-1, \infty)$; concave up everywhere; no pts of inflection

Section 3.16

1. (a) -2 units per second

(b) 4 units per second

3. increasing $8/3$ units per second

5. (a) $-\dfrac{5}{2\sqrt{2}}$ (b) $-\dfrac{7}{8\sqrt{2}}$ (c) $\dfrac{5}{2\sqrt{2}}$ (d) $\dfrac{7}{8\sqrt{2}}$

    (e) max velocity at $t = 0$ (f) no max speed

6. $\dfrac{2r}{h}$ in. per minute

8. (a) $\dfrac{1}{\pi}$ in. per minute   (b) $\dfrac{1}{2\sqrt[3]{2\pi}}$ in. per minute

10. (a) 2 seconds   (b) 16 ft   (c) 48 ft per second

12. (a) $\dfrac{1625}{16}$ ft   (b) $\dfrac{6475}{64}$ ft   (c) 100 ft

Section 3.17

1. $10\frac{1}{30}$ taking $x = 1000$ 3. 0.212 taking $x = 25$

5. 1.975 taking $x = 32$ 7. 8.15 taking $x = 32$

9. area $\cong 2\pi rh$,   area $= (2r + h)h\pi$

13. $2\pi rht$ 14. error ≤ 0.01 ft

15. (a) $x > 2500$

16. (a) 3.26 ft   (b) 0.00153 seconds

    (c) lose 2 minutes 12 seconds

Section 3.18

1. $\dfrac{dy}{dx} = -\dfrac{x}{y}$ 3. $\dfrac{dy}{dx} = -\dfrac{b^2 x}{a^2 y}$ 5. $\dfrac{dy}{dx} = -\left(\dfrac{y}{x}\right)^{1/3}$

7. $\dfrac{dy}{dx} = -\dfrac{x^3 + 3x^2 y}{x^3 + y^3}$ 9. $\dfrac{dy}{dx} = -\dfrac{2y + 1}{2x + 1}$

11. $m = -\frac{2}{3}$ 13. $m = -\dfrac{1}{2}$ 15. at right angles

18. $\dfrac{d^2 y}{dx^2} = -\dfrac{b^4}{a^2 y^3}$ 20. $\dfrac{d^2 y}{dx^2} = \dfrac{1 - ab}{(x + by)^3}$

22. $\dfrac{dy}{dx} = \dfrac{5}{8}, \dfrac{d^2 y}{dx^2} = -\dfrac{9}{128}$ 23. $\dfrac{dy}{dx} = 0, \dfrac{d^2 y}{dx^2} = -\dfrac{1}{3}$

Section 3.19

1. $A = 1, B = -3, C = 5$ 3. $A = 9, B = 1$

5. max of $\dfrac{3}{2}$ at $x = -2$; min of $\dfrac{5}{6}$ at $x = 2$

7. max of $\dfrac{1}{8}$ at $x = \dfrac{4}{3}$ 9. 20 in.   11. (3, 6)

13. 120 ft per min.   15. base $= 2a\sqrt{3}$, altitude $= 3b$

17. decreasing 4 in. per min.   21. (a) 1   (b) $\dfrac{4}{3}$

24. $\dfrac{3}{2} ka^2$ 25. decreasing 4 units per sec.

27. \$5400   28. $x = \dfrac{a^{1/3} l}{a^{1/3} + b^{1/3}}$

Section 4.2

1. $L_f(P) = \dfrac{5}{8}, U_f(P) = 1\dfrac{3}{8}$

3. $L_f(P) = \dfrac{9}{64}, U_f(P) = \dfrac{37}{64}$

5. $L_f(P) = 1\dfrac{1}{16}, U_f(P) = 1\dfrac{9}{16}$

7. (a) $L_f(P) = -3x_1(x_1 - x_0) - 3x_2(x_2 - x_1) - \cdots - 3x_n(x_n - x_{n-1})$
   $U_f(P) = -3x_0(x_1 - x_0) - 3x_1(x_2 - x_1) - \cdots - 3x_{n-1}(x_n - x_{n-1})$

   (b) $-3\left(\dfrac{b^2 - a^2}{2}\right)$

Section 4.4

1. -2 3. 1 5. $4\dfrac{2}{3}$ 7. $\dfrac{32}{3}$ 9. $8\dfrac{5}{8}$ 11. $-\dfrac{4}{15}$

13. $\dfrac{2^{18} - 1}{18}$ 15. $1\dfrac{3}{4}$ 17. $\dfrac{14\sqrt{2}}{3}$ 19. $-\dfrac{1}{12}$ 21. $\dfrac{7}{9}$ 23. $\dfrac{1}{10}$

Section 4.5

1. part of the motion is in the negative direction

3. $\dfrac{2}{3}$ 5. 2 7. $\dfrac{2}{9}$ 9. $\dfrac{1}{3}$ 11. $21\dfrac{1}{3}$ 13. $\dfrac{1}{2}$

15. (a) $-285\dfrac{1}{3}$ (b) $283\dfrac{2}{3}$ 17. $\left(x_0 + \dfrac{1}{4}, y_0 + \dfrac{2}{3}\right)$

Section 4.6

1. 1 3. 65 5. $\dfrac{4}{5}(2\sqrt{2} - 1)$ 7. 2

9. 2 11. -2 13. $\dfrac{9}{800}$ 15. $\dfrac{x^3}{2}$

17. $\alpha = \dfrac{3}{2}$ 19. $\dfrac{2}{x}$ 21. $\dfrac{1}{2x}$ 23. $-f(x)$

25. $f(x) + xf'(x)$

Section 4.7

1. $-\dfrac{1}{3x^3} + C$

3. $\dfrac{2}{3}(\sqrt{1 + x})^3 + C$

5. $2\sqrt{1 + x} + C$

7. $-\dfrac{1}{2(1 + x^2)} + C$

9. $2\sqrt{x}\left(\dfrac{x}{3} - 1\right) + C$

11. $2\sqrt{x}\left(\dfrac{x^2}{5} - \dfrac{x}{3}\right) + C$

13. $\dfrac{x^3 + 2}{2x} + C$

15. $x\left(\dfrac{x^2}{3} - \dfrac{(a + b)x}{2} + ab\right) + C$

17. $f(x)g(x) + C$

19. $(1 + [f(x)]^2)^{1/2} + C$

Section 5.1

2. (a) domain $(0, \infty), f'(x) = \dfrac{1}{x}$

 (c) domain $(-1, \infty), f'(x) = \dfrac{1}{x+1}$

 (d) domain $(0, \infty), f'(x) = \dfrac{3}{x}$

 (f) domain $(0, 1) \cup (1, \infty), f'(x) = -\dfrac{1}{x(\log x)^2}$

 (g) domain $(0, \infty), f'(x) = \dfrac{3(\log x)^2}{}$

 (i) domain $(1, \infty), f'(x) = \dfrac{1}{x \log x}$

3. (a) 1   (c) 1   (d) $\log 7$

 (f) $\dfrac{1}{2}$ (g) $\dfrac{3}{8}$ (i) $\dfrac{1}{2}(\log 2)(\log 2c^2)$

4. (a) -1 (c) $\log \dfrac{2}{3}$ (d) $\dfrac{1}{2}\log \dfrac{8}{15}$ (f) $\log \dfrac{4}{3}$

5. (a) $-\dfrac{1}{2}\log |3 - x^2| + C$ (c) $\dfrac{2}{3}\log (1 + x\sqrt{x}) + C$

 (d) $\log \left|\dfrac{x - a}{x - b}\right| + C$ (f) $\log |x(x - 1)| + C$

6. (a) 3.0   (c) 4.4   (d) -2.3 (f) 0.9

7. (a) 1620   (c) $\dfrac{51}{4}$

8. (a) 1   (c) $\dfrac{1}{e}$ (e) 1 and e^2

 (g) no such x (i) $e - 1$ (k) a^2

9. (a) $\dfrac{15}{8} - \log 4$ 10. (a) $\log 5$

12. (a) domain $(0, \infty)$; increasing everywhere; no extreme values; concave down everywhere; no pts of inflection

 (c) domain $(-\infty, 0) \cup (0, \infty)$; increasing on $(0, \infty)$, decreasing on $(-\infty, 0)$; no extreme values; concave down everywhere; no pts of inflection

 (d) domain $(0, \infty)$; decreasing on $(0, 1]$, increasing on $[1, \infty)$; $f(1) = 1$ local min and absolute min; concave up everywhere; no pts of inflection

 (f) domain $(0, \infty)$; increasing on $(0, 1]$, decreasing on $[1, \infty)$; $f(1) = -\log 2$ local max and absolute max; concave down on $(0, \sqrt{2 + \sqrt{5}}]$, concave up on $[\sqrt{2 + \sqrt{5}}, \infty)$; pt of inflection at $x = \sqrt{2 + \sqrt{5}}$

Section 5.2

1. (a) $-2e^{-2x}$ (c) $\dfrac{e^x - e^{-x}}{2}$

 (d) $\dfrac{e^x + e^{-x}}{2}$ (f) $2(x + \log x)\left(x + \dfrac{1}{x}\right)$

(g) $(x + 1)e^{x-1} + xe^x$

(i) $\dfrac{3}{(x + 2)^2} e^{(x-1)/(x+2)}$

(j) $\dfrac{3}{x^2 + x - 2}$

(l) $e^{x \log x} (1 + \log x)$

(m) $\dfrac{4e^{2x}}{(e^{2x} + 1)^2}$

(o) $-\log (x + 1)$

(p) e^{x^2}

(r) $-\dfrac{1}{(1 - x)^2} e^{-1/(1-x)}$

2.   (a) $\dfrac{1}{2} e^{2x} + C$

(c) $\dfrac{1}{k} e^{kx} + C$

(d) $\dfrac{1}{2} e^{x^2} + C$

(f) $-e^{1/x} + C$

(g) $e^{2\sqrt{x}} + C$

(i) $-\dfrac{1}{2} e^{-2x} + 2e^{-x} + x + C$

3.   (a) $e - 1$

(c) $\dfrac{e + e^{-1}}{2} - 1$

(d) $\dfrac{1}{6} \left(1 - \dfrac{1}{\pi^6} \right)$

(f) $\dfrac{e - e^{-1}}{2}$

(g) $3 \log \left(\dfrac{e + 2}{2} \right)$

(i) $2(e^2 - e^{\sqrt{\log 2}})$

(j) $3e + 2e^{-1} - 5$

(l) $2(e^{-1} - e^{-\sqrt{\log 2}})$

4.   (a)   .67   (c)   16

5.   (a) $e + \dfrac{1}{e} - 2$ (c) $e^2 - e + \log 2$

6.   (a) $P(1, e)$

7.   (a) $y(x) = e^{2x}$ (c) $y(x) = \pi e^x$ (e) $y(x) = 0$

8.   (a) $y(x) = 2e^{3x}$ (c) $y(x) = e^{3x-5}$

9.   (a)   (i) domain $(-\infty, \infty)$ (ii) increasing on $[0, \infty)$, decreasing on $(-\infty, 0]$
     (iii) $f(0) = 1$ local min and absolute min   (iv) concave up everywhere
    (c)   (i) domain $(-\infty, \infty)$ (ii) increasing on $[0, \infty)$, decreasing on $(-\infty, 0]$
     (iii) $f(0) = 1$ local min and absolute min   (iv) concave up everywhere
    (e)   (i) domain $(-\infty, \infty)$ (ii) increasing on $[-1, \infty)$, decreasing on $(-\infty, -1]$

     (iii) $f(-1) = -\dfrac{1}{e}$ local min and absolute min

     (iv) concave up on $[-2, \infty)$, concave down on $(-\infty, -2]$, point of inflection at
     $x = -2$
    (g)   (i) domain $(-\infty, 0) \cup (0, \infty)$ (ii) increasing on $(-\infty, 0)$, decreasing on $(0, \infty)$
     (iii) no extreme values   (iv) concave up on $(-\infty, 0)$ and on $(0, \infty)$

11.   (a)   (i) $\dfrac{4 \log 2}{\log 4 - \log 3}$ years

(b)   (i) $\dfrac{16}{3}$ lbs.   (iii) $4 \left(\dfrac{3}{4} \right)^{11}$ lbs.

Section 5.3

1.   (a)   6   (c) -6 (d) $\dfrac{1}{6}$ (f) -2 (g) $-\dfrac{1}{2}$ (i) -1

2.   (a) $\dfrac{3^x}{\log 3} + C$ (c) $-\dfrac{2^{-x}}{\log 2} + C$ (d) $\dfrac{10^{x^2}}{2 \log 10} + C$

(f) $\dfrac{2^x - 2^{-x}}{\log 2} + C$ (g) $\log_5 x + C$ (i) $\dfrac{2^x + 2^{-x}}{\log 2} + C$

3. (a) $\dfrac{1}{e \log 3}$ (c) $\dfrac{1}{e}$ (e) $\dfrac{e^{1/\log 3}}{e \log 3}$

4. (a) $x^x[1 + \log x]$ (c) $[(x^2 + 2)^{\log x}]\left[\dfrac{2x \log x}{x^2 + 2} + \dfrac{\log(x^2 + 2)}{x}\right]$

   (d) $-\left(\dfrac{1}{x}\right)^x (1 + \log x)$ (f) $[(\log x)^{\log x}]\left[\dfrac{1 + \log(\log x)}{x}\right]$

8. (a) 0   (c) $e^{\pm \sqrt{\log 2 \cdot \log 3}}$ (e) 2

9. (i) $t_1 < \log a < t_2$ (ii) $x_1 < e^b < x_2$

10. (a) domain $(-\infty, \infty)$; decreasing on $(-\infty, 0]$, increasing on $[0, \infty)$; $f(0) = \dfrac{1}{10}$ local min and absolute min

    (c) domain all $x \ne \pm 1$; decreasing on $(-\infty, -1)$ and on $(-1, 0]$, increasing on $[0, 1)$ and on $(1, \infty)$; $f(0) = 10$ local min

    (e) domain $[-1, 1]$; increasing on $[-1, 0]$, decreasing on $[0, 1]$; $f(0) = 10$ local max and absolute max, $f(-1) = f(1) = 1$ end-pt min and absolute min

    (g) domain $(0, \infty)$; decreasing on $(0, \infty)$; no extreme values

11. (a) $\dfrac{4}{3}\left(\sqrt[4]{8} - 1\right)$ (c) $\dfrac{14}{11}\left(2^{11/7} - 1\right)$ (d) $\dfrac{1}{3} \log 2$ (f) $1 - \sqrt{1 - t^2}$

    (g) $\dfrac{2^\pi}{\pi \log 2}(2^\pi - 1) + \dfrac{2^{2\pi+1} - 1}{2\pi + 1}$ (i) 2

13. $n_0\left(\dfrac{n_1}{n_0}\right)^t$

Section 5.4

1. $-xe^{-x} - e^{-x} + C$

3. $\dfrac{x^2 - 1}{2} \log(x + 1) - \dfrac{x^2}{4} + \dfrac{x}{2} + C$

4. $-e^{-x}(x^2 + 2x + 2) + C$

6. $x \log(-x) - x + C$

7. $\dfrac{2}{3}x^{3/2}\left(\log x - \dfrac{2}{3}\right) + C$

9. $-\left(\dfrac{x^2 + 1}{2}\right)e^{-x^2} + C$

10. $e^x(x^2 - 2x + 2) - \dfrac{x^3}{3} + C$

12. $-2x^2(1 - x)^{1/2} - \dfrac{8}{3}x(1 - x)^{3/2} - \dfrac{16}{15}(1 - x)^{5/2} + C$

13. $\dfrac{2}{3}x(x + 1)^{3/2} - \dfrac{4}{15}(x + 1)^{5/2} + C$

15. $x(\log x)^2 - 2x \log x + 2x + C$

16. $\dfrac{x2^x}{\log 2} - \dfrac{2^x}{(\log 2)^2} + C$

18. $\dfrac{x^3}{3}(\log x)^2 - \dfrac{2}{9}x^3 \log x + \dfrac{2}{27}x^3 + C$

20. (a) 1 (c) $\dfrac{8 \log 2 - 3}{(\log 2)^2}$

Section 5.5

1. $y(x) = -e^{2-x}$

3. $y(x) = -1 + 3e^{(x-1/3)}$

6. $y(x) = 2e^{-x} + x - 1$

7. $y(x) = (2 + x)e^x$

9. $y(x) = \dfrac{3}{2x} + \dfrac{2x^2}{3} - \dfrac{18}{x}$

11. $y(x) = e^{-x}\left[e + \log\left(\dfrac{1 + e^x}{2}\right)\right]$

13. (i) $200\left(\dfrac{4}{5}\right)^{t/5}$ (ii) $200\left(\dfrac{4}{5}\right)^{t^2/25}$

15. $20 + 5e^{-0.03t}$

Section 5.6

1. $2\sqrt{ab}$

3. $\left(\pm\dfrac{1}{\sqrt{2}},\dfrac{1}{\sqrt{e}}\right)$

5. $x=\dfrac{1}{\sqrt{e}}$

7. 1

9. (a) $y=\dfrac{1}{2}(e^{\alpha x}-e^{-\alpha x})$ (c) $y=e^{\alpha x}$

10. (a) $x(1)=\dfrac{1}{2}(e^2-e^{-2})$

Section 6.1

1. $3\cos 3x$

3. $x\sec^2 x+\tan x$

4. $\cos x-\sin x$

6. $\dfrac{1}{2\sqrt{x}}\cos x$

7. $\pi[\cos^2\pi x-\sin^2\pi x]$

9. $\pi x^2\cos\pi x+2x\sin\pi x$

10. $\sin x\cos x$

12. $\dfrac{3}{2}\tan^2\dfrac{x}{2}\sec^2\dfrac{x}{2}$

13. $e^x\cos x+e^x\sin x$

15. $-\dfrac{x\sin x^2}{\sqrt{\cos x^2}}$

16. $(\cos\pi x)^x[-\pi x\tan\pi x+\log(\cos\pi x)]$

18. $ke^{-kx}[\cos kx-\sin kx]$

19. $\pi 10^x\sec^2\pi x+10^x\log 10\tan\pi x$

21. $e^x\left[\dfrac{\pi}{2}\cos\dfrac{\pi x}{2}+\sin\dfrac{\pi x}{2}\right]$

22. $\dfrac{1}{2}\left(\dfrac{\sec^2 x}{\tan x}\right)=\operatorname{cosec}2x$

24. $4\tan^3 x\sec^2 x$

25. $(\cos x)e^{\sin x}$

27. $2\tan x\sec^2 x[\sec^2 x+\tan^2 x]$

28. $n\sin^{n-1}x[\sin nx\cos x+\sin x\cos nx]$ 30. $-\tan 2x$

32. increasing on $[0,2\pi]$; $f(0)=0$ end-pt min and absolute min, $f(2\pi)=2\pi$ end-pt max and absolute max; concave down on $[0,\pi]$, concave up on $[\pi,2\pi]$; point of inflection (π,π)

34. decreasing on $\left(-\dfrac{\pi}{2},0\right]$, increasing on $\left[0,\dfrac{\pi}{2}\right)$; $f(0)=0$ local min and absolute min; concave up on $\left(-\dfrac{\pi}{2},\dfrac{\pi}{2}\right)$

36. increasing on $\left[0,\dfrac{\pi}{2}\right]$ and on $\left[\dfrac{3\pi}{2},2\pi\right]$, decreasing on $\left[\dfrac{\pi}{2},\dfrac{3\pi}{2}\right]$; $f(0)=1$ end-point min, $f\left(\dfrac{\pi}{2}\right)=e^{\pi/2}$ local max, $f\left(\dfrac{3\pi}{2}\right)=-e^{3\pi/2}$ local min and absolute min, $f(2\pi)=e^{2\pi}$ end-pt max and absolute max; concave up on $\left[0,\dfrac{\pi}{4}\right]$ and on $\left[\dfrac{5\pi}{4},2\pi\right]$, concave down on $\left[\dfrac{\pi}{4},\dfrac{5\pi}{4}\right]$; pts of inflection $\left(\dfrac{\pi}{4},\sqrt{2}e^{\pi/4}\right),\left(\dfrac{5\pi}{4},-\sqrt{2}e^{5\pi/4}\right)$

39. 3

41. $\dfrac{2}{3}$

42. 0

44. doesn't exist

Section 6.2

1. $\dfrac{1}{3}\sin(3x-1)+C$

3. $\sin^3 x+C$

4. $\dfrac{1}{2}\sec 2x+C$

6. $-\dfrac{2}{3}(1+\cos x)^{3/2}+C$

7. $-e^{-\sin x}+C$

9. $-2\cos(\sqrt{x})+C$

10. $-2\sqrt{1-\sin x}+C$

12. $-\log(1+\cos x)+C$

13. $-\dfrac{1}{3\pi}\cos^3(\pi x)+C$

15. $\dfrac{1}{\pi}\log|\sin(\pi x)|+C$

16. $-\tan(\pi-x)+C$

18. $-\dfrac{1}{2}\log(2-\sin 2x)+C$

19. $\tan x+C$

21. $\dfrac{2}{3}(1+\tan x)^{3/2}+C$

22. $\dfrac{1}{2}(x+\sin x)+C$

23. $\dfrac{1}{2}\left(x+\dfrac{1}{2}\sin 2x\right)+C$

25. $\dfrac{1}{2}\left(x+\dfrac{1}{2\pi}\sin 2\pi x\right)+C$

26. $x\sin x+\cos x+C$

28. $\dfrac{e^x}{2}(\sin x-\cos x)+C$

Section 6.3

1. $\dfrac{\pi}{2}$

3. 0

4. $\dfrac{\pi}{2}$

6. $\dfrac{\pi}{4}$

7. $\dfrac{\pi}{4}$

9. $\dfrac{\pi}{3}$

10. $-\dfrac{\pi}{6}$

12. 0

13. $\dfrac{1}{x^2+2x+2}$

15. $\dfrac{2x}{\sqrt{1-x^4}}$

17. $\dfrac{2x}{\sqrt{1-4x^2}}+\text{arc}\sin 2x$

19. $\dfrac{2\,\text{arc}\sin x}{\sqrt{1-x^2}}$

21. $\dfrac{x-(1+x^2)\,\text{arc}\tan x}{x^2(1+x^2)}$

23. $\dfrac{1}{(1+4x^2)\sqrt{\text{arc}\tan 2x}}$

25. $\dfrac{1}{x[1+(\log x)^2]}$

27. $-\dfrac{r}{|r|\sqrt{1-r^2}}$

29. $\dfrac{1}{1+r^2}$

31. $\sqrt{\dfrac{c-x}{c+x}}\quad(c>0)$

33. $\dfrac{x^2}{(c^2-x^2)^{3/2}}\quad(c>0)$

38. $\dfrac{\pi}{4}$

40. $\dfrac{\pi}{4}$

41. $\dfrac{\pi}{6}$

42. doesn't exist

43. $\dfrac{\pi}{20}$

44. $\dfrac{\pi}{10}$

47. (ii) $\dfrac{d}{dx}[\text{arc}\cos x]=-\dfrac{1}{\sqrt{1-x^2}}$

(iii) $\dfrac{d}{dx}[\text{arc}\cot x]=-\dfrac{1}{1+x^2}$

(iv) $\dfrac{d}{dx}[\text{arc}\,\text{cosec}\,x]=-\dfrac{1}{x\sqrt{x^2-1}}$

Section 6.4

1. $\dfrac{1}{2}\log 2$

3. $\dfrac{\pi}{6}$

5. $\dfrac{\pi\sqrt{3}-3}{6}$

7. $\sqrt{a^2+b^2}$

9. (a) $\dfrac{\pi}{4}$

(c) $1-\dfrac{\pi^2}{32}$

(e) $-\dfrac{1}{2}$

11. decreasing .04 radians per minute
12. increasing .06 radians per minute
13. 5π miles per minute
14. 12 ft
15. $r = 2\sqrt{6}$ in. $h = 4\sqrt{3}$ in.
17. $\theta = $ arc tan m
18. $\theta = \dfrac{\pi}{4} + \dfrac{\alpha}{2}$ radians

Section 6.5

1. $2x \cosh x^2$

3. $\dfrac{a \sinh ax}{2\sqrt{\cosh ax}}$

5. $\dfrac{1}{1 - \cosh x}$

7. $ab(\cosh bx - \sinh ax)$

9. $\dfrac{a \cosh ax}{\sinh ax}$

16. minimum value of 3

18. no extreme values

21. $y = 2 \cosh 3x + \dfrac{1}{3} \sinh 3x$

Section 6.6

1. $2 \tanh x \,\mathrm{sech}^2\, x$

3. $\dfrac{\mathrm{sech}^2\, x}{\tanh x}$

5. $\dfrac{2e^{2x} \cosh (\text{arc tan } e^{2x})}{1 + e^{4x}}$

7. $\dfrac{-x \,\mathrm{cosech}^2\,(\sqrt{x^2 + 1})}{\sqrt{x^2 + 1}}$

9. $\dfrac{-\mathrm{sech}\, x \,(\tanh x + 2 \sinh x)}{(1 + \cosh x)^2}$

15. (i) $\dfrac{3}{5}$ (ii) $\dfrac{5}{3}$ (iii) $\dfrac{4}{3}$ (iv) $\dfrac{5}{4}$ (v) $\dfrac{3}{4}$

Section 7.1

1. (a) $\dfrac{8}{\sqrt{13}}$ (c) $\dfrac{1}{\sqrt{5}}$

3. (a) $\dfrac{17}{2}$

4. decreasing $\dfrac{8b^2}{5} \pi$ units per minute

Section 7.3

1. (b) $y^2 = -8x$ (d) $(y - 2)^2 = 8(x - 1)$ (f) $(x - 1)^2 = 4y$
   (h) $y^2 + 4y + 6x - 17 = 0$
2. (a) focus $(\tfrac{1}{2}, 0)$, vertex $(0, 0)$, axis $y = 0$, directrix $x = -\tfrac{1}{2}$
   (c) focus $(\tfrac{3}{2}, 0)$, vertex $(1, 0)$, axis $y = 0$, directrix $x = \tfrac{1}{2}$
   (e) focus $(-2, \tfrac{7}{2})$, vertex $(-2, \tfrac{3}{2})$, axis $x = -2$, directrix $y = -\tfrac{1}{2}$
   (g) focus $(-\tfrac{1}{2}, 1)$, vertex $(-\tfrac{1}{2}, \tfrac{3}{4})$, axis $x = -\tfrac{1}{2}$, directrix $y = \tfrac{1}{2}$
3. (a) $(x - y)^2 = 6x + 10y - 9$ (c) $(x + y)^2 = -12x + 20y + 28$
8. $v_{0x} = v_0 \cos \theta$, $v_{0y} = v_0 \sin \theta$
9. $v_{0x} = v_0 \cos \theta$, $v_{0y} = v_0 \sin \theta$
10. $y = -\dfrac{16}{v_0^2} \sec^2 \theta \, x^2 + \tan \theta \, x$
12. $\dfrac{v_0^2}{16} \cos \theta \sin \theta$
14. $\dfrac{\pi}{4}$

Section 7.4

1. foci $(\pm\sqrt{5}, 0)$, major axis has length 6, minor axis has length 4
3. foci $(0, \pm\sqrt{2})$, major axis has length $2\sqrt{6}$, minor axis has length 4
5. foci $(\pm 1, 0)$, major axis has length 4, minor axis has length $2\sqrt{3}$
7. foci $(1, \pm 4\sqrt{3})$, major axis has length 16, minor axis has length 8
9. $\dfrac{x^2}{9} + \dfrac{y^2}{8} = 1$ 11. $\dfrac{(x-6)^2}{25} + \dfrac{(y-1)^2}{16} = 1$ 13. $\dfrac{(x-1)^2}{21} + \dfrac{(y-3)^2}{25} = 1$
15. The ellipse approaches a circle of radius a.
17. $\dfrac{x^2}{25} + \dfrac{4y^2}{75} = 1$

Section 7.5

1. foci $(\pm\sqrt{2}, 0)$; asymptotes $y = x, y = -x$
3. foci $(\pm 5, 0)$; asymptotes $y = \dfrac{4}{3}x, y = -\dfrac{4}{3}x$
5. foci $(0, \pm 5)$; asymptotes $y = \dfrac{4}{3}x, y = -\dfrac{4}{3}x$
7. foci $(-4, 3), (6, 3)$; asymptotes $y = \dfrac{4}{3}(x-1) + 3, y = -\dfrac{4}{3}(x-1) + 3$
9. foci $(1, 0), (-3, 0)$; asymptotes $y = \sqrt{3}(x+1), y = -\sqrt{3}(x+1)$
11. $\dfrac{x^2}{9} - \dfrac{y^2}{16} = 1$ 13. $\dfrac{y^2}{25} - \dfrac{x^2}{144} = 1$
15. $\dfrac{x^2}{9} - \dfrac{(y-1)^2}{16} = 1$ 17. $xy = \dfrac{1}{2}$
18. foci $(\sqrt{2}, \sqrt{2}), (-\sqrt{2}, -\sqrt{2})$; asymptotes $x = 0, y = 0$

Section 7.6

9. $\left[1, \dfrac{\pi}{2} + 2n\pi\right], \left[-1, \dfrac{3\pi}{2} + 2n\pi\right]$ 11. $[3, \pi + 2n\pi], [-3, 2n\pi]$
13. $\left[\sqrt{8}, \dfrac{7\pi}{4} + 2n\pi\right], \left[-\sqrt{8}, \dfrac{3\pi}{4} + 2n\pi\right]$ 15. $\left[8, \dfrac{\pi}{6} + 2n\pi\right], \left[-8, \dfrac{7\pi}{6} + 2n\pi\right]$
17. yes; $[1, \pi] = [-1, 0]$ and the pair $r = -1, \theta = 0$ satisfies the equation
19. yes; the pair $r = 1/2, \theta = \pi/2$ satisfies the equation
21. $[2, \pi] = [-2, 0]$. The coordinates of $[-2, 0]$ satisfy $r^2 = 4\cos\theta$ and the coordinates of $[2, \pi]$ satisfy $r = 3 + \cos\theta$
22. $(0, 0), (1, 1)$ 24. $(0, 1)$
25. symmetry about the x-axis
27. symmetry with respect to both axes and the origin
29. symmetry about the origin
31. circle of radius 1 centered at the origin
33. the x-axis
35. the line $y = 1$ in rectangular coordinates
37. circle of radius $\frac{1}{2}$ with center at $(0, \frac{1}{2})$ in rectangular coordinates
39. hyperbola $xy = 1$ in rectangular coordinates
41. parabola with focus at the origin and directrix $x = -1$
43. ellipse with foci $(0, 0), (2/3, 0)$; major axis $4/3$, minor axis $2/\sqrt{3}$

Section 7.7

1. $x(t) = t, y(t) = t, t$ real
3. $x(t) = -5t + 8, y(t) = 2t - 3, t$ real
4. $x(t) = -2, y(t) = t, t$ real
6. $x(t) = 5 \cos t, y(t) = 2 \sin t, t$ real
7. $x(t) = 5 \cosh t, y(t) = 2 \sinh t, t$ real
9. $x(t) = -t^2 + 1, y(t) = t, t$ real
10. $x(t) = t, y(t) = t^2 - 1, t$ real
12. $x(\theta) = e^\theta \cos \theta, y(\theta) = e^\theta \sin \theta, \theta$ real
13. $y = 3x - 3$
15. $y = 1$
17. $y = -3x + 3$
19. $y = -x + 1 + \sqrt{2}$
21. $y = \dfrac{1}{5}x + \dfrac{4}{5}$
23. $x = -\dfrac{1}{2}$
25. $y = \dfrac{1}{3}x + 1$
27. no horizontal tangent; vertical tangent at $(2, 2), (-2, 0)$
29. horizontal tangents at $(0, 1), (0, -1)$; vertical tangents at $(1, 1/\sqrt{2}), (-1, 1/\sqrt{2}),$ $(1, -1/\sqrt{2}), (-1, -1/\sqrt{2})$
31. (i) the paths intersect at $(2, 10)$ and $(5, 3)$
    (ii) the particles collide at $(5, 3)$

Section 7.8

1. $\alpha = \dfrac{\pi}{4}, \dfrac{X^2}{2} - \dfrac{Y^2}{2} = 1$
3. $\alpha = \dfrac{\pi}{6}, 4X^2 - Y^2 = 1$
5. $\alpha = \dfrac{\pi}{4}, 2Y^2 + \sqrt{2}X = 0$
7. $\alpha = -\dfrac{\pi}{6}, Y^2 + X = 0$
9. $\alpha = \dfrac{\pi}{8}, \cos \dfrac{\pi}{8} = \dfrac{\sqrt{2 + \sqrt{2}}}{2}, \sin \dfrac{\pi}{8} = \dfrac{\sqrt{2 - \sqrt{2}}}{2}$

Section 8.1

1. $-e^{2-x} + C$
3. $\dfrac{3}{2} \sin \dfrac{2}{3}x + C$
4. $\dfrac{\pi}{4c}$
6. $e - \sqrt{e}$
7. $\left(\dfrac{x^2 - 1}{2}\right) \log (x + 1) - \dfrac{x^2}{4} + \dfrac{x}{2} + C$
9. $-\dfrac{1}{5^x \log 5} + C$
10. $-\log (2\sqrt{3} - 3)$
12. 2
13. $-\tan (1 - x) + C$
15. $\dfrac{x5^x}{\log 5} - \dfrac{5^x}{(\log 5)^2} + C$
16. $\dfrac{1}{4} \log 2$
18. $\dfrac{1}{2} \log 3$
19. $-\dfrac{e^{-x}}{5} (\sin 2x + 2 \cos 2x) + C$
21. $\dfrac{1}{2} \arcsin x^2 + C$
22. $\left(\dfrac{x^2}{2} - \dfrac{1}{16}\right) \arcsin 2x + \dfrac{x}{8} \sqrt{1 - 4x^2} + C$
24. $-\dfrac{1}{2} \cot x + C$
25. $\dfrac{1}{a} \arctan \left(\dfrac{x + \alpha}{a}\right) + C$
27. $\dfrac{1}{4} \sinh 2x - \dfrac{1}{2}x + C$
28. $x \cosh x - \sinh x + C$

30. $\frac{1}{2}(\cos x \cosh x + \sin x \sinh x) + C$

31. $\log(\cosh x) - \frac{1}{2}\tanh^2 x + C$

33. $\frac{1}{4a}e^{2ax} + \frac{x}{2} + C$

Section 8.2

1. $\log\left|\dfrac{x-2}{x+5}\right| + C$

3. $\log\left|\dfrac{x^2-1}{x}\right| + C$

4. $5\log|x-1| - 3\log|x| + \dfrac{3}{x} + C$

6. $\dfrac{x^4}{4} + \dfrac{4x^3}{3} + 6x^2 + 32x - \dfrac{32}{x-2} + 80\log|x-2| + C$

7. $5\log|x-2| - 4\log|x-1| + C$

9. $\dfrac{-1}{2(x-1)^2} + C$

10. $\dfrac{3}{4}\log|x-1| - \dfrac{1}{2(x-1)} + \dfrac{1}{4}\log|x+1| + C$

12. $\dfrac{1}{3}\left(\dfrac{1}{x+1} - \dfrac{1}{x-2}\right) + C$

13. $\dfrac{1}{32}\log\left|\dfrac{x-2}{x+2}\right| - \dfrac{1}{16}\arctan\dfrac{x}{2} + C$

15. $\dfrac{1}{16}\log\left|\dfrac{x^2+2x+2}{x^2-2x+2}\right| + \dfrac{1}{8}[\arctan(x+1) + \arctan(x-1)] + C$

17. $\dfrac{\pi}{16}$

19. $\dfrac{12+3\pi}{16}$

21. $\log\dfrac{\sqrt{5}}{2}$

23. $\dfrac{\pi}{8}$

25. $\dfrac{1}{4}\log 3$

27. $\dfrac{2+\pi}{64}$

29. $\dfrac{\pi}{6}$

31. $\dfrac{\pi}{6}$

33. (a) $C(t) = 2A_0\left(\dfrac{t}{t+1}\right)$ (b) $C(t) = 4A_0\dfrac{3^t - 2^t}{2(3^t) - 2^t}$

(c) $C(t) = A_0(m+n)\left(\dfrac{m^t - n^t}{m^{t+1} - n^{t+1}}\right)$

Section 8.3

1. $-2(\sqrt{x} + \log|1 - \sqrt{x}|) + C$

3. $2\sqrt{x} - 2\arctan\sqrt{x} + C$

5. $2\log(\sqrt{1+e^x} - 1) - x + 2\sqrt{1+e^x} + C$

7. $\dfrac{17}{400}$

9. $x + 2\sqrt{x} + 2\log|\sqrt{x} - 1| + C$

11. $x + 4\sqrt{x-1} + 4\log|\sqrt{x-1} - 1| + C$

13. $\log\left|\dfrac{\sqrt{e^x+1}-1}{\sqrt{e^x+1}+1}\right| + C$

15. $\dfrac{2(x-8)\sqrt{x+4}}{3} + C$

17. $\dfrac{13\sqrt{5}-25}{150}$

19. $\dfrac{4b+2ax}{a^2\sqrt{ax+b}} + C$

Section 8.4

1. $\dfrac{\pi}{4}$

3. $\sqrt{3} - \dfrac{1}{2}\log(2 + \sqrt{3})$

5. $\dfrac{\pi}{6}$

7. $\dfrac{8}{3}$

9. $-\sqrt{4 - x^2} + C$

11. $2\arcsin\left(\dfrac{x}{2}\right) - \dfrac{x}{2}\sqrt{4 - x^2} + C$

13. $\arcsin\left(\dfrac{e^x}{3}\right) + C$

15. $\sinh^{-1}\left(\dfrac{x + 1}{2}\right) + C$

17. $\sqrt{(x + 1)^2 + 4} - \sinh^{-1}\left(\dfrac{x + 1}{2}\right) + C$

19. $\dfrac{x}{a^2\sqrt{a^2 - x^2}} + C$

21. $\dfrac{x}{\sqrt{a^2 - x^2}} - \arcsin\left(\dfrac{x}{a}\right) + C$

23. $\arcsin\dfrac{3}{4} - \arcsin\dfrac{2}{3}$

25. $\log\left(\dfrac{6 + 2\sqrt{10}}{5 + \sqrt{29}}\right)$

27. $-\dfrac{(1 - x^2)^{3/2}}{3x^3} + C$

29. $-\dfrac{1}{a}\cosh^{-1}\left(\dfrac{a}{x}\right) + C$

31. $-\dfrac{1}{a}\sinh^{-1}\left(\dfrac{a}{x}\right) + C$

33. $\dfrac{\sqrt{x^2 - a^2}}{a^2 x} + C$

Section 8.5

1. $\dfrac{1}{3}\cos^3 x - \cos x + C$

3. $\dfrac{\pi}{8} + \dfrac{1}{4}$

5. $\dfrac{3\pi}{8}$

7. $\dfrac{3\pi}{16}$

9. $\dfrac{1}{5}\cos^5 x - \dfrac{1}{3}\cos^3 x + C$

11. $\dfrac{1}{8}x - \dfrac{1}{8}\sin x \cos x + \dfrac{1}{4}\sin^3 x \cos x + C$

13. $\dfrac{1}{2}\sec x \tan x + \dfrac{1}{2}\log|\sec x + \tan x| + C$

15. $-\log|\sin x| - \dfrac{1}{2}\cot^2 x + C$

17. $-\dfrac{1}{2}\operatorname{cosec} x \cot x + \dfrac{1}{2}\log|\operatorname{cosec} x - \cot x| + C$

19. $\dfrac{1}{3}\tan^3 x - \tan x + x + C$

Section 8.6

1. $\tan\left(\dfrac{x}{2}\right) + C$

3. $-\cot\left(\dfrac{x}{2}\right) + C$

5. $\dfrac{1}{\sqrt{2}}\arctan\left(\dfrac{1}{\sqrt{2}}\right)$

7. $\dfrac{2}{3}\arctan\left[\dfrac{1}{3}\tan\left(\dfrac{x}{2}\right)\right] + C$

9. $-\dfrac{x}{3} + \dfrac{5}{6}\arctan\left[2\tan\left(\dfrac{x}{2}\right)\right] + C$

11. $-2\left[\tan\left(\dfrac{x}{2}\right)+1\right]^{-1} - \log\left(1+\sin x\right)+C$

13. $-\dfrac{4}{3}\left[\tan\left(\dfrac{x}{2}\right)+1\right]^{-3} - 2\left[\tan\left(\dfrac{x}{2}\right)+1\right]^{-2} - \left[\tan\left(\dfrac{x}{2}\right)+1\right]^{-1} - x + C$

Section 8.7

1. (a) 0.85   (b) 0.72   (c) 0.79   (d) 0.78   (e) 0.78

3. all

Section 9.1

1. α

3. $\dfrac{1}{3}$

5. $\dfrac{2\sqrt{2}}{3}$

7. $\dfrac{1}{2}\left[\sqrt{2}+\log\left(\sqrt{2}+1\right)\right]$

9. $\dfrac{\pi}{4}$

11. 0 for both

14. 0

16. $\alpha(b+a)+\beta$

18. $\dfrac{e^b - e^a}{b - a}$

20. (a) The terminal velocity is twice the average velocity.
    (b) The average velocity during the first $x/2$ seconds is one-third of the average velocity during the next $x/2$ seconds.

23. $\dfrac{\pi}{2}b$ and $\dfrac{\pi}{2}a$

Section 9.2

1. $10\dfrac{2}{3}$

3. $10\dfrac{2}{3}$

5. 10

7. $\dfrac{3}{16}$

9. $\dfrac{37}{12}$

11. πab

13. $2\dfrac{1}{2}$

Section 9.3

1. (i) $\dfrac{\pi}{5}$ (ii) $\dfrac{\pi}{2}$

3. (i) $\dfrac{1}{2}\pi(e^2-1)$ (ii) 2π

5. (i) $\dfrac{3}{10}\pi$ (ii) $\dfrac{3}{10}\pi$

7. (i) $\dfrac{4\pi ab^2}{3}$ (ii) $\dfrac{4\pi a^2 b}{3}$

9. (i) π (ii) $2\pi\left(1-\dfrac{2}{e}\right)$

11. $\dfrac{1}{3}\pi h(R^2 + Rr + r^2)$

13. (a) $\dfrac{4}{3}\sqrt{3}ab^2$ (b) $\dfrac{4}{3}ab^2$ (c) $\dfrac{16}{3}ab^2$ (d) πab

15. (a) 31.25%   (b) $14\dfrac{22}{27}\%$

17. (a) $\pi[f(x)]^2$ (b) $2\pi x f(x)$

19. (i) $\pi(e-2)$ (ii) $\dfrac{1}{2}\pi(e^2+1)$

21. $\dfrac{16}{3}r^2$

Section 9.4

1. $\dfrac{\pi a^2}{4}$

3. $\dfrac{a^2}{2}$

5. $\dfrac{\pi a^2}{2}$

7. $\dfrac{1}{4} - \dfrac{\pi}{16}$

9. $\dfrac{3\pi}{16} + \dfrac{3}{8}$

11. $\dfrac{5a^2}{2}$

13. $\dfrac{1}{12}(3e^{2\pi} - 3 - 2\pi^3)$

15. $\dfrac{1}{4}(e^{2\pi} + 1 - 2e^{\pi})$

Section 9.5

1. $\sqrt{m^2 + 1}\,(d - c)$

3. $2\sqrt{3}$

5. $2 \log(\sqrt{2} + 1)$

7. $2 - \sqrt{2} - \dfrac{1}{2} \log 3 + \log(\sqrt{2} + 1)$

9. $\dfrac{2}{3}[2\sqrt{2} - 1]$

11. $\dfrac{\pi}{3} + \dfrac{\sqrt{3}}{2}$

13. $\dfrac{1}{2}[\sqrt{2} + \log(1 + \sqrt{2})]$

15. $\sqrt{2}(e^{\pi} - 1)$

17. $\sqrt{2}(e^{4\pi} - 1)$

19. $\dfrac{\sqrt{5}}{2}(e^{4\pi} - 1)$

23. $\dfrac{\pi}{4}$

24. $f(x) = \cosh x$

Section 9.6

1. $2\pi r$

3. 4

5. $\dfrac{1}{9}\pi(17^{3/2} - 1)$

7. $\dfrac{61}{432}\pi$

9. $3\pi\sqrt{13}$

11. $2\pi r^2$

13. $\dfrac{1}{4}\pi\left(4 + e^2 - \dfrac{1}{e^2}\right)$

15. $\dfrac{6}{5}\pi a^2$

17. $\sqrt{2}\pi(e^{\pi} - 1)$

19. $\pi s(R + r)$ where s is the slant height

21. (i) $2\pi b^2 + \dfrac{2\pi ab}{e} \arcsin e$　(ii) $2\pi a^2 + \dfrac{\pi b^2}{e} \log\left|\dfrac{1 + e}{1 - e}\right|$

where e is the eccentricity $\dfrac{\sqrt{a^2 - b^2}}{a}$

Section 9.7

1. (a) $\dfrac{1}{4}$ ft-lbs   (b) $\dfrac{9}{16}$ ft-lbs

3. $\dfrac{3}{2}$ ft

5. (a) $(6480\pi + 8640)$ ft-lbs   (b) $(15{,}120\pi + 8640)$ ft-lbs

7. (a) $\dfrac{1}{2}\sigma l^2$ ft-lbs   (b) $\dfrac{3}{2}\sigma l^2$ ft-lbs

Section 9.8

1. 2

3. $\dfrac{9}{2}$

5. $\dfrac{5}{12}$

7. 3.6

9. 4

11. πa^2

13. $a^2 \log 2$

14. 36

15. 2.7

16. $\dfrac{3}{2}$

18. 5

20. $\dfrac{2}{\pi - 2}$

22. $\dfrac{1}{4}\pi a^3$

24. $\dfrac{1}{15}\pi a^3$

26. $\dfrac{32}{35}\pi ab^2$

28. $\dfrac{64}{5}\pi$

30. $\dfrac{4}{5}\pi a^2 b$

33. $\dfrac{2}{3}r^3 \tan\theta$

34. $\dfrac{1}{2}$

35. $\dfrac{19}{27}$

37. $\dfrac{335\,a}{27}$

39. $6a$

41. $\dfrac{a^2 + ab + b^2}{a + b}$

42. $\dfrac{52}{3}\pi p^2$

44. $\dfrac{47}{16}\pi a^2$

46. $\dfrac{208\pi}{9}$

47. $\dfrac{10}{3}\pi$

Section 10.1

1. decreasing; bounded below by 0 and above by 2
3. increasing; bounded below by 1 but not bounded above
5. nonincreasing; bounded below by 0 and above by 1/2
7. increasing; bounded below by 1/2 but not bounded above
9. increasing; bounded below by $(4/5)\sqrt{5}$ and above by 2
11. decreasing; bounded below by 0 and above 2/5
13. not monotonic; not bounded below and not bounded above
15. increasing; bounded below by 0 and above by $\log 2$
17. decreasing; bounded below by 1 and above by 4
19. increasing; bounded below by 1/2 and above by 1
21. decreasing; bounded below by 0 and above by 1/2
23. decreasing; bounded below by 0 and above by $\log 2$
25. decreasing on $\{2, 3, \cdots\}$; bounded below by 0 and above by 4/9
27. decreasing; bounded below by 0 and above by $\sinh 1$

Section 10.2

1. converges to 0
7. diverges
13. diverges
19. converges to 1
25. converges to 0
30. converges to e^2

3. diverges
9. converges to 4
15. converges to $\log 2$
21. converges to 1
27. converges to 0

5. converges to 1
11. converges to 0
17. converges to 1
23. converges to 0
28. converges to 1/2

Section 10.3

1. converges to 1
5. converges to 0
9. converges to 0
15. converges to 1
21. converges to 2

2. converges to 1
7. converges to 0
11. converges to 1
17. converges to 0
22. converges to $1/e$

3. converges to 0
8. converges to 1
13. converges to 0
19. converges to π
24. diverges

27. $\lim\limits_{n \to \infty} 2n \sin \dfrac{\pi}{n} = 2\pi.$

The number

$$2\,n \sin \frac{\pi}{n}$$

is the perimeter of a regular polygon of n sides inscribed in the unit circle. As n tends to ∞, the perimeter of the polygon tends to the circumference of the circle.

28. $\dfrac{1}{2}$ 30. $\dfrac{1}{8}$ 33. converges to $\dfrac{1}{e}$ 35. converges to 1

37. converges to 0 if $t < 1$, converges to e^z if $t = 1$, diverges if $t > 1$

Section 10.5

1. $\dfrac{1}{4}$ 3. $\dfrac{1}{2}$ 5. $\dfrac{400}{33}$

7. $\dfrac{5}{6}$ 9. $\dfrac{15}{2}$ 11. $\dfrac{2150}{99}$

13. $\dfrac{1}{4}$ 15. $\displaystyle\sum_{k=1}^{\infty} \dfrac{7}{10^k} = \dfrac{7}{9}$ 17. $\displaystyle\sum_{k=1}^{\infty} \dfrac{24}{100^k} = \dfrac{8}{33}$

19. $\displaystyle\sum_{k=1}^{\infty} \dfrac{112}{1000^k} = \dfrac{112}{999}$ 21. $\dfrac{62}{100} + \displaystyle\sum_{k=2}^{\infty} \dfrac{45}{100^k} = \dfrac{687}{1100}$

27. (a) $\displaystyle\sum_{k=0}^{\infty} (-1)^k x^{k+1}$ (c) $\displaystyle\sum_{k=0}^{\infty} x^{2k}$

29. $100 \displaystyle\sum_{k=1}^{\infty} \left(\dfrac{1}{1.05}\right)^k = 2{,}000.$

Section 10.6

1. converges, comparison with $\sum(1/k^2)$
3. converges, root test
7. converges, comparison with $\sum(1/k^2)$
11. diverges, ratio test
15. converges, root test
19. converges, root test
23. converges, integral test
27. converges, ratio test
31. diverges, integral test

5. converges, ratio test
9. diverges, comparison with $\sum(1/\sqrt{k})$
13. diverges, comparison with $\sum(1/3k)$
17. diverges, ratio test
21. converges, ratio test
25. converges, comparison with $\sum 1/k^{3/2}$
29. diverges, k'th term does not tend to zero

Section 10.7

1. diverges
5. converges but not absolutely
9. converges but not absolutely
13. converges absolutely
17. converges absolutely

3. diverges
7. diverges
11. diverges
15. converges but not absolutely
19. diverges

Section 10.8

1. $1 - x + \dfrac{x^2}{2!} - \dfrac{x^3}{3!} + \dfrac{x^4}{4!} - \dfrac{x^5}{5!}$

3. $x + \dfrac{x^3}{3!} + \dfrac{x^5}{5!}$

5. $x + \dfrac{1}{6}x^3 + \dfrac{3}{40}x^5$

7. $x + \dfrac{1}{3}x^3 + \dfrac{2}{15}x^5$

9. $1 + \dfrac{x^2}{2!} + \dfrac{x^4}{4!}$

11. $x - \dfrac{1}{2}x^2 + \dfrac{1}{3}x^3 - \dfrac{1}{4}x^4$

13. $x - \dfrac{1}{2}x^2 + \dfrac{1}{3}x^3 - \dfrac{1}{4}x^4$

15. $-\dfrac{x^2}{2} - \dfrac{x^4}{12}$

17. 1.65

19. 0.54

21. 1.12

23. 7.39

29. $\sin x = \sin a + (x - a)\cos a - \dfrac{(x - a)^2}{2!}\sin a - \dfrac{(x - a)^3}{3!}\cos a + \cdots$

31. $\sinh x = \sinh a + (x - a)\cosh a + \dfrac{(x - a)^2}{2!}\sinh a + \dfrac{(x - a)^3}{3!}\cosh a + \cdots$

33. $\log x = \log a + \dfrac{1}{a}(x - a) - \dfrac{1}{2a^2}(x - a)^2 + \dfrac{1}{3a^2}(x - a)^3 - \cdots$

Section 10.9

1. $0.09 \le N \le 0.10$

3. $-0.11 \le N \le -0.10$

5. $0.38 \le N \le 0.39$

7. $\log x = \log a + \dfrac{x}{a} - \dfrac{x^2}{2a^2} + \dfrac{x^3}{3a^3} - \cdots + (-1)^{n-1}\dfrac{x^n}{na^n} + \cdots$

9. $\dfrac{1}{4}$

11. $\dfrac{120}{119}$

Section 10.10

1. 1

3. ∞

5. 0

7. 2

9. 1

11. $\dfrac{1}{2}$

13. 1

15. 10

17. $1/|a|$

19. $\dfrac{1}{\pi}$

21. $0.80 \le I \le 0.81$

23. $0.60 \le I \le 0.61$

24. $0.294 \le I \le 0.301$

26. $0.60 \le I \le 0.61$

Section 10.11

6. (a) $1 + \dfrac{1}{2}x - \dfrac{1}{8}x^2 + \dfrac{1}{16}x^3 - \dfrac{5}{128}x^4$

   (c) $1 + \dfrac{1}{2}x^2 - \dfrac{1}{8}x^4$

7. (a) 9.90   (c) 4.99

Section 10.12

1. 1

3. 0

5. 1

7. 0

9. diverges

11. 0

13. 0

15. 0

17. $\dfrac{4}{3}$

19. $\dfrac{2}{3}$

21. 1

23. $\dfrac{e + e^{-1}}{2}$

25. diverges

27. converges absolutely

29. converges but not absolutely

31. converges absolutely

33. converges but not absolutely

35. $r = 1$, series converges for $-1 \le x < 1$

37. $r = 1$, series converges for $-1 < x < 1$

39. $1 + (\log a)\, x + \dfrac{(\log a)^2}{2!}\, x^2 + \cdots + \dfrac{(\log a)^n}{n!}\, x^n + \cdots$

41. $x^2 - \dfrac{1}{2} x^4 + \dfrac{1}{3} x^6 - \cdots + \dfrac{(-1)^{n-1}}{n}\, x^{2n} + \cdots$

45. $\tanh^{-1} x = x + \dfrac{1}{3} x^3 + \dfrac{1}{5} x^5 + \cdots + \dfrac{x^{2n-1}}{2n-1} + \cdots$

46. (a) 1   (b) 0

47. $0.49 \le I \le 0.50$

49. 3.92

Section 11.1

1. 0

3. 1

4. 0

6. 1

7. 0

9. a^2

10. 0

12. 1

13. $\dfrac{\pi}{2}$

15. 0

Section 11.2

1. 0

3. 1

4. $\dfrac{1}{n} a^{1-n}$

6. 1

7. 0

9. 2

10. $\log \dfrac{a}{a+1}$

12. $\dfrac{1+\pi}{1-\pi}$

13. $\dfrac{1}{\sqrt{a}}$

15. -2

16. $\dfrac{1}{2}$

18. 0

19. $-\dfrac{1}{2}$

21. e^2

22. $\dfrac{1}{2}$

24. $\dfrac{2}{n}$

25. $-\dfrac{1}{6}$

27. $\dfrac{1}{3}$

Section 11.3

1. ∞

3. $-\infty$

4. -1

6. 0

7. 5

9. 1

10. 0

12. 0

13. 1

15. 1

16. 1

18. $\dfrac{1}{2}$

19. e

21. 1

22. $\dfrac{1}{3}$

24. ∞

Section 11.4

1. 1

3. $\dfrac{1}{p}$

4. $\dfrac{\pi}{2}$

6. 2

7. 6

9. $\dfrac{\pi}{2}$

10. 2

12. $\dfrac{\pi}{2}$

13. diverges

15. 1

16. $-\dfrac{1}{4}$

18. $\dfrac{1}{2}\log 3$

19. -1

21. $\dfrac{3}{2}$

22. $\log 2$

24. $\dfrac{1}{4}$

25. (b) 1   (c) $\dfrac{\pi}{2}$ (d) 2π (e) 2π

27. (b) $\dfrac{4}{3}$ (c) 2π (d) $\dfrac{8}{7}\pi$

29. converges by comparison with $\displaystyle\int_{1}^{\infty}\dfrac{dx}{x^{3/2}}$

31. diverges since for x large the integrand is greater than $\dfrac{1}{x}$ and $\displaystyle\int_{1}^{\infty}\dfrac{1}{x}\,dx$ diverges

32. converges by comparison with $\displaystyle\int_{\pi}^{\infty}\dfrac{1}{x^2}\,dx$

34. diverges by comparison with $\displaystyle\int_{e}^{\infty}\dfrac{dx}{(x+1)\log(x+1)}$

Section 12.1

2. (a) $\sqrt{2}$ (c) 7   (e) $\sqrt{(y_1-x_1)^2+(y_2-x_2)^2}$
3. (a) $x^2+y^2+z^2=r^2$ (b) $(x-a_1)^2+(y-a_2)^2+(z-a_3)^2=r^2$
4. (a) $z=a_3$ (c) $x=a_1$
5. (i) $(-1,1,-2)$ (iii) $(1,1,2)$ (v) $(1,3,2)$

Section 12.3

1. V_1, V_6, V_8 3. V_8 5. V_2, V_7

7. (a) $(4,-3,-4)$ (c) $i-\dfrac{17}{2}k$

8. (a) $\sqrt{2}$ (c) $\sqrt{41}$ (e) $\sqrt{2}$

9. (i) $a+b$ (ii) $-(a+b)$ (iii) $a-b$ (iv) $b-a$

11. (a) $6i+3j+12k$ (b) $A=\dfrac{26}{7}, B=-\dfrac{11}{7}, C=\dfrac{3}{7}$

13. $\alpha=\pm3$

15. (a) $\dfrac{2}{\sqrt{6}}(i+2j-k)$ (b) $-\dfrac{2}{\sqrt{13}}(3j+2k)$

Section 12.4

1. $a\cdot b=5, a\cdot c=8, b\cdot c=18$

3. $\text{comp}_b\,a=\dfrac{5}{\sqrt{14}}, \text{comp}_c\,a=\dfrac{8}{5}$

5. (a) $a\perp b$ (b) $a\perp b$

7. $\mathbf{a} \cdot \mathbf{b} = \mathbf{a} \cdot \mathbf{c}$ iff $\mathbf{a} \cdot (\mathbf{b} - \mathbf{c}) = 0$ iff $\mathbf{a} \perp \mathbf{b} - \mathbf{c}$

12. $W = \mathbf{F} \cdot \mathbf{r}$ 14. (a) $W_1 = W_2$ (c) $W_2 = \sqrt{3}\,W_1$

16. (a) $x = 3, x = \dfrac{5}{2}$ 17. (a) $\theta = \arccos\left(\dfrac{1}{\sqrt{3}}\right)$

Section 12.5

1. P and Q 2. l_1, l_3, l_4 are parallel   3. all nonzero scalar multiples of $\mathbf{b}$

5. $P(6, \sqrt{3}, 0), \dfrac{\pi}{3}$ 7. $P(1, 3, 1)$, $\arccos\left(\dfrac{1}{2\sqrt{3}}\right)$

8. (a) $\mathbf{r}(t) = (3\mathbf{i} + \mathbf{j}) + t\mathbf{k}$

   (d) $\mathbf{r}(t) = \mathbf{a} + t(\mathbf{b} - \mathbf{a})$ where $\mathbf{a} = a_1\mathbf{i} + a_2\mathbf{j} + a_3\mathbf{k}$ and $\mathbf{b} = b_1\mathbf{i} + b_2\mathbf{j} + b_3\mathbf{k}$

9. (a) $t_0 = -\dfrac{\mathbf{a} \cdot \mathbf{b}}{\|\mathbf{b}\|^2}$ (b) $\mathbf{R}(t) = \mathbf{a} - \left(\dfrac{\mathbf{a} \cdot \mathbf{b}}{\|\mathbf{b}\|^2}\right)\mathbf{b} \pm t\dfrac{\mathbf{b}}{\|\mathbf{b}\|}$

10. (a) $\dfrac{1}{\sqrt{2}}$ (b) $\sqrt{2}$

Section 12.6

1. Q 2. R, S 3. $\dfrac{\pi}{2}$ 5. $\arccos\left(\dfrac{4}{\sqrt{42}}\right)$

7. $\pm\,\mathbf{k}$ 9. $\pm\dfrac{2}{\sqrt{53}}\left(\dfrac{1}{2}\mathbf{i} + 2\mathbf{j} + 3\mathbf{k}\right)$

10. $\pm\dfrac{1}{\sqrt{A^2 + B^2 + C^2}}(A\mathbf{i} + B\mathbf{j} + C\mathbf{k})$ 11. $(5, 0, 0), \left(0, \dfrac{5}{2}, 0\right), (0, 0, -\sqrt{5})$

13. $(0, 0, 0)$ 15. $(0, 0, 0)$

17. $(A, 0, 0), (0, B, 0), (0, 0, C)$ 21. coplanar   23. not coplanar

Section 12.7

1. $-2\mathbf{k}$ 3. $\mathbf{i} + \mathbf{j} + \mathbf{k}$ 5. $-3\mathbf{i} - \mathbf{j} - 2\mathbf{k}$

7. -1 9. $\mathbf{0}$ 11. $\mathbf{i} + \mathbf{j} - 2\mathbf{k}$

13. -3 15. $5\mathbf{i} - 4\mathbf{j} - \mathbf{k}$ 22. (a) $3/2$ (b) $2\sqrt{3}$

23. (a) 1 (b) 2 25. (a) $x + z = 2$ (b) $x + y - z = 1$

Section 13.1

1. $\mathbf{f}'(t) = 2\mathbf{i} - \mathbf{j} + 3\mathbf{k}$

3. $\mathbf{f}'(t) = -\dfrac{1}{2\sqrt{1 - t}}\mathbf{i} + \dfrac{1}{2\sqrt{1 + t}}\mathbf{j} - \dfrac{2}{(1 + t)^2}\mathbf{k}$

5. $\mathbf{f}'(t) = \cos t\,\mathbf{i} - \sin t\,\mathbf{j} + \sec^2 t\,\mathbf{k}$ 7. $\mathbf{f}'(t) = \dfrac{1}{\sqrt{1 - t^2}}\mathbf{i} + \dfrac{2}{1 + 2t}\mathbf{j} + 2t\mathbf{k}$

9. $\mathbf{i} + 3\mathbf{j}$ 11. $2\mathbf{i} + \dfrac{1}{2}\pi^2\mathbf{k}$

13. $\dfrac{1}{e}\left\{(2e - 5)\mathbf{i} + \sqrt{2}(e - 2)\mathbf{j} + (e - 1)\mathbf{k}\right\}$

17. $\mathbf{f}(t) = (\sinh t + 1)\mathbf{i} + \left(\cosh t - \dfrac{1}{2}\right)\mathbf{j} + (t + 1)\mathbf{k}$

19. $\mathbf{f}(t) = e^{2t}(\mathbf{i} - \mathbf{k})$

Section 13.2

1. $\mathbf{f}'(t) = \mathbf{b}, \mathbf{f}''(t) = \mathbf{0}$
3. $\mathbf{f}'(t) = 2e^{2t}\mathbf{i} - \cos t\,\mathbf{j}, \mathbf{f}''(t) = 4e^{2t}\mathbf{i} + \sin t\,\mathbf{j}$
5. $\mathbf{f}'(t) = 2t\,\mathbf{g}'(t^2)$
7. $\mathbf{f}'(t) = \dfrac{\sqrt{t}}{2}\mathbf{g}'(\sqrt{t}) + \mathbf{g}(\sqrt{t})$
9. $(-\sin t)e^{\cos t}\mathbf{i} + (\cos t)e^{\sin t}\mathbf{j}$
11. $\sinh t\,\mathbf{i} + \cosh t\,\mathbf{j}$
13. $2(\mathbf{b} \times \mathbf{d})$
17. $\mathbf{f}(t) = \mathbf{a} + t\mathbf{b} + \dfrac{1}{2}t^2\mathbf{c}$

Section 13.3

1. (a) $\mathbf{R}(t) = (\mathbf{i} + 2\mathbf{k}) + t(\pi\mathbf{j} + \mathbf{k})$ (c) $\mathbf{r}(t) = \mathbf{a} + t\mathbf{b}$
   (e) $\mathbf{R}(t) = (2\mathbf{i} + 5\mathbf{k}) + t(4\mathbf{i} - \mathbf{j} + 4\mathbf{k})$
2. (a) ellipse, $\dfrac{x^2}{a^2} + \dfrac{y^2}{b^2} = 1$ (c) parabola, $y = \dfrac{b}{a^2}x^2$
3. $\mathbf{r}(t) = e^{\alpha t}[\mathbf{i} + 2\mathbf{j} + 3\mathbf{k}]$
5. $P(1, 2, -2)$, arc $\cos\left(\dfrac{1}{\sqrt{5}}\right)$

Section 13.4

1. (a) $\mathbf{v}(t) = \omega[a\sinh\omega t\,\mathbf{i} + b\cosh\omega t\,\mathbf{j}]$
   (b) $\|\mathbf{v}(t)\| = |\omega|\sqrt{a^2\sinh^2\omega t + b^2\cosh^2\omega t}$
   (c) $\mathbf{a}(t) = \omega^2[a\cosh\omega t\,\mathbf{i} + b\sinh\omega t\,\mathbf{j}] = \omega^2\mathbf{r}(t)$
   (d) $\mathbf{P}(t) = m\mathbf{v}(t) = m\omega[a\sinh\omega t\,\mathbf{i} + b\cosh\omega t\,\mathbf{j}]$
   (e) $\mathbf{F}(t) = m\mathbf{a}(t) = m\omega^2[a\cosh\omega t\,\mathbf{i} + b\sinh\omega t\,\mathbf{j}] = m\omega^2\mathbf{r}(t)$
   (f) power $= \mathbf{F}(t)\cdot\mathbf{v}(t) = m\omega^3(a^2 + b^2)\sinh\omega t\cosh\omega t$
   (g) K.E. $= \dfrac{1}{2}m\|\mathbf{v}(t)\|^2 = \dfrac{1}{2}m\omega^2[a^2\sinh^2\omega t + b^2\cosh^2\omega t]$
   (h) $\mathbf{L}(t) = \mathbf{r}(t) \times m\mathbf{v}(t) = ab\omega m\mathbf{k}$
   (i) $\boldsymbol{\tau}(t) = \mathbf{r}(t) \times \mathbf{F}(t) = \mathbf{0}$
2. $\mathbf{F}(t) = 2m\mathbf{k}$

Section 13.5

1. $2\pi\sqrt{a^2 + b^2}$
3. $\log(1 + \sqrt{2})$
5. $\dfrac{14}{3}$
7. $26 + \dfrac{25}{6}\log 5$
9. $\mathbf{R}(s) = \mathbf{a} + s\dfrac{\mathbf{b}}{\|\mathbf{b}\|}$
11. $k(t) = \dfrac{1}{2}(1 + t^2)^{-3/2}$
13. $k(t) = |3a\sin t\cos t|^{-1}$
15. $k(t) = \dfrac{1}{4}\sqrt{1 + \sin^2(\tfrac{1}{2}t)}$
17. $k(t) = \dfrac{\sinh t}{\sqrt{2}\cosh^2 t}$
19. $k = \dfrac{|f''(x)|}{(1 + [f'(x)]^2)^{3/2}}$
20. $k = \operatorname{sech}^2 x$
22. $k = \dfrac{2}{3}$
24. max. curvature 1, min. curvature 0
25. $(-a, 0)$ and $(a, 0)$
27. $k(\theta) = \dfrac{[f(\theta)]^2 + 2[f'(\theta)]^2 - f(\theta)f''(\theta)}{([f(\theta)]^2 + [f'(\theta)]^2)^{3/2}}$
29. $k(\theta) = \dfrac{\theta^2 + 2}{a[\theta^2 + 1]^{3/2}}$

Section 14.1

1. dom (f) = the set of all points (x, y) except those that lie on the line $y = -x$
   ran $(f) = (-\infty, 0) \cup (0, \infty)$
3. dom (f) = the set of all points (x, y) such that $xy \leq 1$; this region includes the two branches of the hyperbola $xy = 1$ and all the points in between
   ran $(f) = [0, \infty)$
5. dom (f) = the entire plane
   ran $(f) = (-1, 1)$
7. dom (f) = the set of all points (x, y) except for those on the coordinate axes
   ran $(f) = (-\infty, \infty)$
9. dom (f) = all of space
   ran $(f) = [0, \infty)$
11. dom (f) = the set of all points (x, y) such that $x^2 > y^2$; in other words, all the points of the plane which lie between the graph of $y = |x|$ and the graph of $y = -|x|$
    ran $(f) = (0, \infty)$
13. dom (f) = the set of all points (x, y, z) such that $x^2 \neq y^2$; that is, all points of space except those which lie on the planes $x + y = 0$ and $x - y = 0$
    ran $(f) = (-\infty, \infty)$

Section 14.3

1. $\dfrac{\partial f}{\partial x} = 6x - y, \dfrac{\partial f}{\partial y} = 1 - x$

3. $\dfrac{\partial z}{\partial x} = 2Ax + By + D, \dfrac{\partial z}{\partial y} = Bx + 2Cy + E$

5. $\dfrac{\partial f}{\partial x} = e^{x-y} - 2xy, \dfrac{\partial f}{\partial y} = -e^{x-y} - x^2$

7. $\dfrac{\partial g}{\partial x} = \dfrac{(AD - BC)y}{(Cx + Dy)^2}, \dfrac{\partial g}{\partial y} = \dfrac{(BC - AD)x}{(Cx + Dy)^2}$

9. $\dfrac{\partial u}{\partial x} = y^2 e^{-z}, \dfrac{\partial u}{\partial y} = 2xye^{-z}, \dfrac{\partial u}{\partial z} = -xy^2 e^{-z}$

11. $\dfrac{\partial \rho}{\partial \theta} = \sin\left(\phi - \dfrac{\pi}{2}\right), \dfrac{\partial \rho}{\partial \phi} = \left(\theta - \dfrac{\pi}{2}\right)\cos\left(\phi - \dfrac{\pi}{2}\right)$

13. $\dfrac{\partial \rho}{\partial \theta} = e^{\theta + \phi} [\cos(\theta - \phi) - \sin(\theta - \phi)]$

    $\dfrac{\partial \rho}{\partial \phi} = e^{\theta + \phi} [\cos(\theta - \phi) + \sin(\theta - \phi)]$

15. $f'_x(0, e) = 1, f'_y(0, e) = e^{-1}$

17. $g'_x\left(0, \dfrac{\pi}{4}\right) = -1, g'_y\left(0, \dfrac{\pi}{4}\right) = 0$

21. (a) $50\sqrt{3}$ sq. in.   (b) $5\sqrt{3}$ (c) 50 (d) $\dfrac{5}{18}\pi$ sq. in.   (e) -2

Section 14.4

1. interior $= \{(x, y): 2 < x < 4, 1 < y < 3\}$ (the inside of the rectangle)
   boundary = the union of the four line segments that bound the rectangle
   set is closed

3. interior = the entire set (region between two concentric circles)
   boundary = $\{(x, y): x^2 + y^2 = 1 \text{ or } x^2 + y^2 = 4\}$ (the two circles)
   set is open

5. interior = $\{(x, y): 1 < x^2 < 4\}$
   $= \{(x, y): -2 < x < 1\} \cup \{(x, y): 1 < x < 2\}$
   (two vertical strips without the boundary lines)
   boundary = $\{(x, y): x = -2, x = -1, x = 1, \text{ or } x = 2\}$
   (four vertical lines)
   set is neither open nor closed

7. interior = $\{(x, y): y < x^2\}$ (region below the parabola)
   boundary = $\{(x, y): y = x^2\}$ (the parabola)
   set is closed

9. interior = the entire set [the inside of the ball of radius $\frac{1}{2}$ centered at $(1, 1, 1)$]

   boundary = $\left\{(x, y, z): (x - 1)^2 + (y - 1)^2 + (z - 1)^2 = \frac{1}{4}\right\}$ (the spherical surface)

   set is open

Section 14.5

1. $\dfrac{\partial^2 f}{\partial x^2} = 2A,\ \dfrac{\partial^2 f}{\partial y \partial x} = \dfrac{\partial^2 f}{\partial x \partial y} = 2B,\ \dfrac{\partial^2 f}{\partial y^2} = 2C$

3. $\dfrac{\partial^2 f}{\partial x^2} = Cy^2 e^{xy},\ \dfrac{\partial^2 f}{\partial y \partial x} = \dfrac{\partial^2 f}{\partial x \partial y} = Ce^{xy}(xy + 1),\ \dfrac{\partial^2 f}{\partial y^2} = Cx^2 e^{xy}$

5. $\dfrac{\partial^2 f}{\partial x^2} = 2\cos y - y^2 \sin x,\ \dfrac{\partial^2 f}{\partial y \partial x} = \dfrac{\partial^2 f}{\partial x \partial y} = 2(y\cos x - x\sin y),\ \dfrac{\partial^2 f}{\partial y^2} = 2\sin x - x^2\cos y$

7. $\dfrac{\partial^2 f}{\partial x^2} = 2,\ \dfrac{\partial^2 f}{\partial y^2} = 4(x + 3y^2 + z^3),\ \dfrac{\partial^2 f}{\partial z^2} = 6z(2x + 2y + 5z^3)$

   $\dfrac{\partial^2 f}{\partial y \partial x} = \dfrac{\partial^2 f}{\partial x \partial y} = 4y,\ \dfrac{\partial^2 f}{\partial z \partial x} = \dfrac{\partial^2 f}{\partial x \partial z} = 6z^2$

   $\dfrac{\partial^2 f}{\partial z \partial y} = \dfrac{\partial^2 f}{\partial y \partial z} = 12yz^2$

9. $\dfrac{\partial^2 f}{\partial x^2} = 2(y + z),\ \dfrac{\partial^2 f}{\partial y^2} = 2(x + z),\ \dfrac{\partial^2 f}{\partial z^2} = 2(x + y)$
   All the second mixed partials are $2(x + y + z)$.

Section 14.6

1. $\nabla f = e^{xy}[(xy + 1)\mathbf{i} + x^2\mathbf{j}]$
3. $\nabla f = (6x - y)\mathbf{i} + (1 - x)\mathbf{j}$
5. $\nabla f = (e^{x-y} - 2xy)\mathbf{i} - (e^{x-y} + x^2)\mathbf{j}$
7. $\nabla f = e^{-z}[y^2\mathbf{i} + 2xy\mathbf{j} - xy^2\mathbf{k}]$
9. $\nabla f = (y + z)\mathbf{i} + (x + z)\mathbf{j} + (x + y)\mathbf{k}$
11. $\nabla f = e^{x-y}[(1 + x + y)\mathbf{i} + (1 - x - y)\mathbf{j}]$
13. $\nabla f = e^x\left[\log y\,\mathbf{i} + \dfrac{1}{y}\,\mathbf{j}\right]$
15. $\nabla f = (z^2 + 2xy)\mathbf{i} + (x^2 + 2yz)\mathbf{j} + (y^2 + 2xz)\mathbf{k}$
17. $\nabla f = -\mathbf{i} + 18\mathbf{j}$
19. $\nabla f = -\mathbf{i}$

Section 14.7

1. $-2\sqrt{2}$
3. $\dfrac{1}{5}(7 - 4e)$
5. $\dfrac{\sqrt{2}}{4}(a - b)$

7. $\dfrac{4}{\sqrt{6}}$
9. $-3\sqrt{2}$
11. $-\dfrac{1}{\sqrt{x^2 + y^2}}$

13. (i) $\sqrt{2}[a(B - A) + b(C - B)]$ (ii) $\sqrt{2}[a(A - B) + b(B - C)]$

15. $-\dfrac{7}{\sqrt{5}}$
17. $y = x^3$ from $(1, 1)$ to $(0, 0)$

19. $(b^2)^{a^2}x^{b^2} = (a^2)^{b^2}y^{a^2}$ from (a^2, b^2) to $(0, 0)$

Section 14.8

1. $\dfrac{du}{dt} = \sin 2t - 3\cos 2t$

2. $\dfrac{du}{dt} = 3t^2 + 4 + 3t^{-2}$

3. $\dfrac{du}{dt} = e^{(1/2)t}\left(\dfrac{1}{2}\sin 2t + 2\cos 2t\right) + e^{2t}\left(2\sin\dfrac{1}{2}t + \dfrac{1}{2}\cos\dfrac{1}{2}t\right)$

7. $(2 + 3t^2)\cos^2 t \cos(2t + t^3) - 2\cos t \sin t \sin(2t + t^3)$

9. $\dfrac{\partial f}{\partial g}\dfrac{dg}{dx}\dfrac{dx}{dt} + \dfrac{\partial f}{\partial h}\dfrac{dh}{dy}\dfrac{dy}{dt}$

11. $\dfrac{\partial u}{\partial r} = \dfrac{\partial u}{\partial x}\dfrac{\partial x}{\partial r} + \dfrac{\partial u}{\partial y}\dfrac{\partial y}{\partial r}$

 $\dfrac{\partial u}{\partial s} = \dfrac{\partial u}{\partial x}\dfrac{\partial x}{\partial s} + \dfrac{\partial u}{\partial y}\dfrac{\partial y}{\partial s}$

12. $f(x, y, z) = a_1 x + a_2 y + a_3 z + C$

14. (a) ± 8 units per second   (b) $4\sqrt{5}$ units per second

15. (a) 2 units per second·   (b) $\pm 24/7$ units per second
    (c) about 4.44 units per second

16. temperature 375/96 degrees; increasing 11/96 degrees per second

17. (a) increasing about 0.91 in. per second
    (b) increasing about 8.88 sq. in. per second

Section 14.9

1. tangent $x + y + 2 = 0$; normal $x - y = 0$
3. tangent $\sqrt{2}x - 5y + 3 = 0$; normal $5x + \sqrt{2}y - 6\sqrt{2} = 0$
5. tangent $7x - 17y + 6 = 0$; normal $17x + 7y - 82 = 0$
7. tangent $x - y - 3 = 0$; normal $x + y + 1 = 0$
9. 0
11. $4x - 5y + 4z = 0$
13. $2x + y + 2z - 8 = 0$
15. $z = 2(x + y)$

17. $b^2c^2x_0 x - a^2c^2y_0 y - a^2b^2z_0 z = a^2b^2c^2$
19. $\left(\dfrac{1}{3}, \dfrac{11}{6}, -\dfrac{1}{12}\right)$

21. $(0, 0, 0)$ and (a, a, a^3)

23. The tangent planes meet at right angles and therefore the normals ∇F and ∇G must meet at right angles:

$$\frac{\partial F}{\partial x}\frac{\partial G}{\partial x} + \frac{\partial F}{\partial y}\frac{\partial G}{\partial y} + \frac{\partial F}{\partial z}\frac{\partial G}{\partial z} = 0$$

25. $\dfrac{9}{2}a^3 \left(V = \dfrac{1}{3}Bh\right)$

Section 14.10

1. $(1, 0)$ gives max of 1

3. $(1, -1)$ is a saddle point

5. $(-2, 1)$ gives min of -2

7. no stationary points and no extreme values

9. $(1, 1)$ gives min of -3

11. no stationary points but 0 is min

13. $(-2, 2)$ is a saddle point

15. $\left(\dfrac{x_1 + x_2 + x_3}{2}, \dfrac{y_1 + y_2 + y_3}{3}\right)$

16. $x = (a^2b)^{1/3}, y = (ab^2)^{1/3}$

Section 14.11

1. $(4, -2)$ gives min of -10

3. $\left(\dfrac{10}{3}, \dfrac{8}{3}\right)$ gives max of $\dfrac{28}{3}$

5. $(0, 0)$ is a saddle point; $(2, 2)$ gives a local min of -8

7. $\left(1, \dfrac{3}{2}\right)$ is a saddle point; $\left(5, \dfrac{27}{2}\right)$ gives a local min of $-\dfrac{117}{4}$

9. no extreme values

11. no extreme values

13. no extreme values

15. $\left(\dfrac{1}{2}, 4\right)$ gives a local min of 6

17. $(0, 0)$ gives min of 0; $(0, \pm 1)$ give local max of $\dfrac{2}{e}$; $(\pm 1, 0)$ are saddle points

19. $\dfrac{1}{27}$

21. $\dfrac{8abc}{3\sqrt{3}}$

22. $\theta = \dfrac{\pi}{6}, x = \dfrac{P}{2 + 2\sec\theta - \tan\theta}$

$y = \dfrac{1}{2}[P - x(1 + \sec\theta)]$

23. $a^2 + b^2 + c^2$

Section 14.12

1. 2

3. $-\dfrac{ab}{2}$

5. $\dfrac{2ab^2}{3\sqrt{3}}$

7. $-\dfrac{1}{3\sqrt{3}}$

9. no maximum exists

11. $19\sqrt{2}$

13. $\dfrac{abc}{27}$

15. 1

17. a^3

19. $\left(\dfrac{x_1 + x_2 + x_3}{2}, \dfrac{y_1 + y_2 + y_3}{2}\right)$ if the vertices are at $(x_1, y_1), (x_2, y_2), (x_3, y_3)$

Section 14.13

1. $du = (3x^2y - 2xy^2)\triangle x + (x^3 - 2x^2y)\triangle y$
3. $du = (\cos y + y \sin x)\triangle x - (x \sin y + \cos x)\triangle y$
5. $du = \triangle x - (\tan z)\triangle y - (y \sec^2 z)\triangle z$
7. $\triangle u = -7.15, du = -7.5$ 8. $du = 1$

9. $22\dfrac{249}{352}$ taking $u = x^{1/2}y^{1/4}, x = 121, y = 16, \triangle x = 4, \triangle y = 1$

11. $\dfrac{\pi}{7\sqrt{2}}$ taking $u = \sin x \cos y, x = \pi, y = \dfrac{\pi}{4}, \triangle x = -\dfrac{\pi}{7}, \triangle y = -\dfrac{\pi}{20}$

13. $-\dfrac{1}{90}$ 15. (a) 0.3   (b) 0.5   (c) $6\dfrac{1}{4}\%$

16. (a) $\dfrac{37\sqrt{15}\pi}{18} \cong 25$ cu. in.   (b) $3\pi \cong 9.42$ sq. in.

Section 14.14

1. $f(x, y) = \dfrac{1}{2}x^2y^2 + C$ 3. $f(x, y) = xy + C$

5. no such function exists
7. $f(x, y) = \sin x + y \cos x + C$
9. $f(x,y) = \sinh x + x \sinh y + C$
11. $f(x, y) = xe^xy + e^{-y} + C$

13. $f(x, y) = \dfrac{x^3}{3} \text{arc } \sin y + y - y \log y + C$

Section 14.15

1. 1   3. 0   5. $-\dfrac{17}{6}$ 7. 0

9. $\log\dfrac{8}{5}$ 11. $-\pi$ 13. $\dfrac{23}{21}$ 15. $|W| = A$

Section 14.16

1. 0   3. -1 5. 0   7. -4 9. 0

10. (a) $f(\mathbf{r}) = K \log \|\mathbf{r}\| + C$ (b) $f(\mathbf{r}) = -\left(\dfrac{K}{n-2}\right)\dfrac{1}{\|\mathbf{r}\|^{n-2}} + C$

Section 15.1

1. $L_f(P) = 1$ 2. $U_f(P) = 7$ 5. $L_f(P) = 2\dfrac{1}{4}$ 6. $U_f(P) = 5\dfrac{3}{4}$

9. $I = 4$; the volume of the prism bounded above by the plane $z = x + 2y$ and below by R

10. $L_f(P) = -\dfrac{7}{16}$ 11. $U_f(P) = \dfrac{7}{16}$ 14. $I = 0$ 15. $I = 2\dfrac{2}{3}$

Section 15.3

1. $\dfrac{4}{3}$

3. $\dfrac{8}{\pi}$

5. $\dfrac{1}{6} + \dfrac{1}{\pi}$

7. 2

9. π

11. $\dfrac{e}{2} - 1$

13. $\dfrac{e^4 - 1}{4}$

15. $\dfrac{9}{2}$

17. $\dfrac{1}{2}(16 - 3\pi)$

19. 4

21. $\dfrac{2}{15}$

23. $\dfrac{\pi}{2}$

Section 15.4

1. $\dfrac{3(4\pi - 3\sqrt{3})}{16}$

3. 2π

5. $\dfrac{\pi}{4} + 2$

7. $\dfrac{\pi}{2} - \dfrac{2}{3}$

9. $\dfrac{2}{3}(8 - 3\sqrt{3})\pi$

11. $\dfrac{32}{9}a^3$

Section 15.6

1. abc

3. $\dfrac{2}{3}$

5. $V = \dfrac{1}{6}abc$

7. (a) $M = \dfrac{1}{2}k$ (b) $M = k$ ($k =$ the constant of proportionality)

9. $V = 9$

11. $V = 4\pi$

14. $V = \dfrac{1}{32}\pi$

Section 15.7

1. $\left(\dfrac{5}{2}, 5\right)$

3. $\left(1, \dfrac{8}{5}\right)$

5. $\left(\dfrac{10}{3}, \dfrac{40}{21}\right)$

7. $(2, 1)$

9. $\left(\dfrac{a}{5}, \dfrac{a}{5}\right)$

11. $\left(\dfrac{a_1 + b_1 + c_1}{3}, \dfrac{a_2 + b_2 + c_2}{3}\right)$

12. $2\pi^2 a^2 b$

13. $\left(\dfrac{a}{4}, \dfrac{b}{4}, \dfrac{c}{4}\right)$

16. (a) $\left(\dfrac{7}{12}, \dfrac{7}{12}, \dfrac{7}{12}\right)$ (b) $\left(\dfrac{1}{2}, \dfrac{1}{2}, \dfrac{2}{3}\right)$ (c) $\left(\dfrac{1}{2}, \dfrac{1}{2}, \dfrac{1}{2}\right)$

20. $\bar{x} = \dfrac{5a}{6}, \bar{y} = 0$

Section 15.8

1. (a) $\dfrac{kR^2h^2\pi}{2}$ (b) $\dfrac{4kR^2\sqrt{R}h\pi}{5}$ (c) $\dfrac{kR^4h\pi}{6}$

2. Here

$$S: 0 \leq \theta \leq 2\pi, \quad 0 \leq r \leq R, \quad 0 \leq z \leq \dfrac{h}{R}(R - r)$$

and

$$V = \int_0^{2\pi} \int_0^R \int_0^{(h/R)(R-r)} r\,dz\,dr\,d\theta = \dfrac{1}{3}\pi R^2 h.$$

6. $V = \displaystyle\int_{-\pi/2}^{\pi/2} \int_0^{2a \cos \theta} \int_0^{(1/a)r^2} r \, dz \, dr \, d\theta = \frac{3}{2} \pi a^3.$

7. $\dfrac{32}{9} a^3$ 8. $\dfrac{5}{2} \pi$ 9. $\dfrac{2}{3} \pi a^3 (\sqrt{2} - 1)$ 11. $\dfrac{1}{36} a^3 (9\pi - 16)$

Section 15.9

3. for $0 < \alpha < \pi/2$, an infinite cone with vertex at the origin and the non-negative z-axis as its axis; for $\pi/2 < \alpha < \pi$, an infinite cone with vertex at the origin and the non-positive z-axis as its axis; for $\alpha = \pi/2$, the xy-plane;
    for $\alpha = 0$ and $\alpha = \pi$, the surface degenerates: in the first case, to the non-negative z-axis, and in the second case, to the non-positive z-axis.

5. $\dfrac{8\pi}{3}$ 6. $r = 2b \cos \phi$ 8. $\dfrac{2\pi}{3}$

INDEX

C D E F G H I J   9 8 7 6 5 4 3 2